Functions Modeling Change
Custom Version

Precalculus / MAC1140

Santa Fe College—Gainesville ,with material from
Finite Mathematics: An Applied Approach, 11th Edition
by Michael Sullivan, Technical Mathematics with Calculus,
6th Edition by Paul A. Calter and Michael A. Calter, and
Calculus Early Transcendentals Combined 9th Edition
by Howard Anton, Irl C. Bivens, and Stephen Davis

WILEY *Custom*
LEARNING SOLUTIONS

To order books or for customer service, please call 1(800)-CALL-WILEY (225-5945).

Printed in the United States of America.

ISBN 978-1-118-12956-2

Printed and Bound by EPAC Technologies, Inc.

10 9 8 7 6 5 4 3 2 1

Contents

List of Titles

Functions Modeling Change: A Preparation for Calculus, Fourth Edition

    by Eric Connally, Deborah Hughes-Hallett, Andrew M. Gleason, *et al*

    Copyright © 2011, ISBN 978-0-470-48474-6

Finite Mathematics, An Applied Approach, Eleventh Edition

    by Michael Sullivan

    Copyright © 2011, ISBN 978-0-470-47827-3

Technical Mathematics, Sixth Edition

    by Paul A. Calter, MSME, MFA and Michael A. Calter, Ph.D.

    Copyright © 2011, ISBN 978-0-470-46472-4

Calculus, Early Trancendentals, 9th Edition

    by Howard Anton, Irl Bivens, Stephen Davis

    Copyright © 2009, ISBN 978-0-470-18345-8

Functions Modeling Change:
A Preparation for Calculus

Fourth Edition

PREFACE

Mathematics has the extraordinary power to reduce complicated problems to simple rules and procedures. Therein lies the danger in teaching mathematics: it is possible to teach the subject as nothing but the rules and procedures—thereby losing sight of both the mathematics and its practical value. The fourth edition of *Functions Modeling Change: A Preparation for Calculus* continues our effort to refocus the teaching of mathematics on concepts as well as procedures.

Fourth Edition: Focus

The focus of this edition remains the same as in previous editions: a balance of understanding and skills. We stress conceptual understanding and multiple ways of representing mathematical ideas. Our goal is to provide students with a clear understanding of functions as a solid foundation for subsequent courses in mathematics and other disciplines. When we designed this curriculum under an NSF grant, we started with a clean slate. We focused on the key concepts, emphasizing depth of understanding.

Skills are developed in the context of problems and reinforced in a variety of settings, thereby encouraging retention. This balance of skills and understanding enables students to realize the power of mathematics in modeling.

Fourth Edition: Flexibility

Precalculus courses are taken by a wide range of students and are taught in a wide variety of styles. As instructors ourselves, we know that the balance we choose depends on the students we have: sometimes a focus on conceptual understanding is best; sometimes more skill-building is needed.

To enable instructors to select the balance appropriate for their students, we have increased the options available in the fourth edition. Instructors will find that by selecting sections and exercises that reflect their goals, they can tailor the materials to their students and their institution.

Origin of Text: The Calculus Consortium for Higher Education

This book is the work of faculty at a diverse consortium of institutions, and was originally generously supported by the National Science Foundation. It represents the first consensus among such a diverse group of faculty to have shaped a mainstream precalculus text. Bringing together the results of research and experience with the views of many users, this text is designed to be used in a wide range of institutions.

Guiding Principles: Varied Problems and the Rule of Four

Since students usually learn most when they are active, the exercises in a text are of central importance. In addition, we have found that multiple representations encourage students to reflect on the meaning of the material. Consequently, we have been guided by the following principles.

- Problems should be varied and some should be challenging. Many of our problems cannot be done by following a template in the text.
- The Rule of Four: each concept and function should be represented symbolically, numerically, graphically, and verbally. This principle, originally introduced by the consortium, promotes multiple representations.

- Students and instructors should have a quick way to pinpoint misunderstandings before moving on. To this end, we include Check Your Understanding true-false problems at the end of each chapter.
- The components of a precalculus curriculum should be tied together by clearly defined themes. Functions as models of change is our central theme, and algebra is integrated where appropriate.
- Topics should be fewer in number than is customary so that they can be treated in greater depth. The core syllabus of precalculus should include only those topics that are essential to the study of calculus.
- Problems involving real data should be included to prepare students to use mathematics in other fields.
- To use mathematics effectively, students should develop skill in both symbolic manipulation and the use of technology. The exact proportions of each may vary widely, depending on the preparation of the student and the wishes of the instructor.
- Materials for precalculus should allow for a broad range of teaching styles. They should be flexible enough to use in large lecture halls, small classes, or in group or lab settings.

Changes in the Fourth Edition

The fourth edition retains the hallmarks of earlier editions and reflects the many helpful suggestions from users in the following changes.

- **Algebraic Skills Refreshers** are introduced in two formats, both integrated with the text:
  - **Skills Refresher exercises** are included at the start of many exercise sets, identified by **S1, S2**, etc.
  - **Skills Refresher sections** are included at the end of some chapters.
- A new **Chapter 3** on **Quadratic Functions** brings together and expands the material on quadratics in the former Sections 2.6 and 5.5.
- **Section 4.4** on **Compound Interest** and **Section 4.5** on **the Number** e have been reorganized to give instructors more flexibility in deciding how to introduce e.
- **Limit Notation** has been moved to the end of **Section 5.3** to provide additional flexibility in how, or whether, limit notation is introduced.
- A new **Section 6.5** on **Combining Transformations** investigates the effect of varying the order in which transformations are applied to functions and their graphs.
- The material on **trigonometry** in the former Chapters 6 and 7 has been expanded and reorganized into three chapters, allowing instructors to tailor their approach to the needs of their students.
  - **Chapter 7 defines the trigonometric functions** in circles and triangles.
  - **Chapter 8 studies the behavior of the trigonometric functions** and their graphs, and introduces trigonometric identities, polar coordinates, and complex numbers.
  - **Chapter 9 investigates trigonometric identities** and their applications to modeling.
- **Data and problems** have been updated and revised as appropriate. Many new problems have been added.
- **ConcepTests** for precalculus are available for instructors looking for innovative ways to promote active learning in the classroom. Further information is provided under Supplementary Materials on page ix.

What Student Background is Expected?

Students using this book should have successfully completed a course in intermediate algebra or high school algebra II. The book is thought-provoking for well-prepared students while still accessible to students with weaker backgrounds. Providing numerical and graphical approaches as well as algebraic gives students various ways to master the material. This encourages students to persist, thereby lowering failure rates.

Our Experiences

Previous editions of this book were used by hundreds of schools around the country. In this diverse group of schools, the first three editions were successfully used with many different types of students in semester and quarter systems, in large lectures and small classes, as well as in full-year courses in secondary schools. They were used in computer labs, small groups, and traditional settings, and with a number of different technologies.

Content

The central theme of this course is functions as models of change. We emphasize that functions can be grouped into families and that functions can be used as models for real-world behavior. Because linear, quadratic, exponential, power, and periodic functions are more frequently used to model physical phenomena, they are introduced before polynomial and rational functions. Once introduced, a family of functions is compared and contrasted with other families of functions.

A large number of the examples and problems that students see in this precalculus course are given in the context of real-world problems. Indeed, we hope that students will be able to create mathematical models that help them understand the world in which they live. The inclusion of non-routine problems is intended to establish the idea that such problems are not only part of mathematics, but in some sense are the point of mathematics.

The book does not require any specific software or technology. Instructors have used the material with graphing calculators and graphing software. Any technology with the ability to graph functions will suffice.

Chapter 1: Linear Functions and Change

This chapter introduces the concept of a function and graphical, tabular, symbolic, and verbal representations of functions, discussing the advantages and disadvantages of each representation. It introduces rates of change and uses them to characterize linear functions. A section on fitting a linear function to data is included.

The **Skills Refresher** section for Chapter 1 reviews linear equations and the coordinate plane.

Chapter 2: Functions

This chapter studies function notation in more detail, after its introduction in Chapter 1. It introduces domain, range, and the concepts of composite and inverse functions and investigates the idea of concavity using rates of change. A section on piecewise functions is included.

Chapter 3: Quadratic Functions

This chapter introduces the standard, factored, and vertex forms of a quadratic function and explores their relationship to graphs. The family of quadratic functions provides an opportunity to see the effect of parameters on functional behavior.

The **Skills Refresher** section for Chapter 3 reviews factoring, completing the square, and quadratic equations.

Chapter 4: Exponential Functions

This chapter introduces the family of exponential functions and the number e. It compares exponential and linear functions, solves exponential equations graphically, and gives applications to compound interest.

The **Skills Refresher** section for Chapter 4 reviews the properties of exponents.

Chapter 5: Logarithmic Functions

This chapter introduces logarithmic functions with base 10 and base e, both in order to solve exponential equations and as inverses of exponential functions. After discussing manipulations with logarithms, the chapter focuses on modeling with exponential functions and logarithms. Logarithmic scales and a section on linearizing data conclude the chapter.

The **Skills Refresher** section for Chapter 5 reviews the properties of logarithms.

Chapter 6: Transformations of Functions and Their Graphs

This chapter investigates transformations—shifting, reflecting, and stretching. The last section investigates the effect of changing the order of transformations and suggests a standard way of writing transformations.

Chapter 7: Trigonometry in Circles and Triangles

This chapter, which opens with modeling periodic phenomena, introduces the trigonometric functions of an angle measured in degrees: sine, cosine, tangent, and, briefly, secant, cosecant, and cotangent. Definitions of these functions use the unit circle and are related to definitions using right triangles. The graphs of sine, cosine, and tangent are introduced. The treatment of triangles includes both right and non-right triangles and the inverse trigonometric functions for angles in a right triangle.

The **Skills Refresher** section for Chapter 7 reviews the special angles in $30°$-$60°$-$90°$ and $45°$-$45°$-$90°$ triangles.

Chapter 8: The Trigonometric Functions

This chapter opens with the definition of radians and then studies sinusoidal behavior. It introduces basic identities and revisits inverse trigonometric functions. It also introduces polar coordinates and complex numbers, including Euler's and de Moivre's formulas.

Chapter 9: Trigonometric Identities and Their Applications

The first two sections of this chapter provide a thorough treatment of identities, including double-angle identities and identities involving the sum and difference of angles. The third section shows the uses of trigonometry in mathematical modeling.

Chapter 10: Compositions, Inverses, and Combinations of Functions

This chapter discusses combinations of functions. It investigates composite and inverse functions, which were introduced in Chapter 2, in more detail.

Chapter 11: Polynomial and Rational Functions

This chapter discusses power functions, polynomials, and rational functions. The chapter concludes by comparing several families of functions, including polynomial and exponential functions, and by fitting functions to data.

The **Skills Refresher** section for Chapter 11 reviews algebraic fractions.

Chapter 12: Vectors

This chapter contains material on vectors and operations involving vectors. An introduction to matrices is included in the last section.

Chapter 13: Sequences and Series

This chapter introduces arithmetic and geometric sequences and series and their applications.

Chapter 14: Parametric Equations and Conic Sections

The concluding chapter looks at parametric equations, implicit functions, hyperbolic functions, and conic sections: circles, ellipses, and hyperbolas. The chapter includes a section on the geometrical properties of the conic sections and their applications to orbits.

Supplementary Materials

The following supplementary materials are available for the Fourth Edition:
- **The Instructor's Manual** contains teaching tips, lesson plans, syllabi, and worksheets. It has been expanded and revised to include worksheets, identification of technology-oriented problems, and new syllabi. (ISBN 978-0-470-93904-8)
- **The Printed Test Bank** contains test questions arranged by section. (ISBN 978-0-470-54738-0)
- **The Instructor's Solution Manual** has complete solutions to all problems. (ISBN 978-0-470-54736-6)
- **The Student Solution Manual** has complete solutions to half the odd-numbered problems. (ISBN 978-0-470-54735-9)
- **The Student Study Guide** includes study tips, learning objectives, practice problems, and solutions. The topics are tied directly to the book.
- **The Getting Started Graphing Calculator Manual** instructs students on how to use their TI-83 and TI-84 series calculators with the text. It contains samples, tips, and trouble-shooting sections to answer students' questions.
- **The Computerized Test Bank**, available in both PC and Macintosh formats, allows instructors to create, customize, and print a test containing any combinations of questions from a large bank of questions. Instructors can also customize the questions or create their own.
- **Classroom Activities** are posted at the book companion website. These activities were developed to facilitate in-class group work as well as to introduce new concepts and to practice skills. In addition to the blank copies for each activity that can be handed out to the students, a copy of the activity with fully worked out solutions is also available.
- **The Book Companion Site** contains all instructor supplements.
- **WileyPLUS** is a powerful and highly integrated suite of online teaching and learning resources providing course management options to instructors and students. Instructors can automate the process of assigning, delivering, and grading algorithmically generated homework exercises, and giving hints and solutions, while providing students with immediate feedback. In addition, WileyPLUS provides student tutorials, an instructor gradebook, integrated links to the electronic version of the text, and all of the text supplemental materials. For more information, visit www.wiley.com/college/wileyplus or contact your local Wiley representative for more details.
- **The Faculty Resource Network** is a peer network of academic faculty dedicated to the effective use of technology in the classroom. This group can help you apply innovative classroom techniques, implement specific software packages, and tailor the technology experience to the specific needs of each individual class. Ask your Wiley representative for more details.

ConcepTests

ConcepTests, modeled on the pioneering work of Harvard physicist Eric Mazur, are questions designed to promote active learning during class, particularly (but not exclusively) in large lectures. Our evaluation data show students taught with ConcepTests outperformed students taught by traditional lecture methods 73% versus 17% on conceptual questions, and 63% versus 54% on computational problems. ConcepTests arranged by section are available in print, PowerPoint, and Classroom Response System-ready formats from your Wiley representative. (ISBN 978-0-470-93902-4)

Acknowledgments

We would like to thank the many people who made this book possible. First, we would like to thank the National Science Foundation for their trust and their support; we are particularly grateful to Jim Lightbourne and Spud Bradley.

We are also grateful to our Advisory Board for their guidance: Benita Albert, Lida Barrett, Simon Bernau, Robert Davis, Lovenia Deconge-Watson, John Dossey, Ronald Douglas, Eli Fromm, Bill Haver, Don Lewis, Seymour Parter, John Prados, and Stephen Rodi.

Working with Laurie Rosatone, Anne Scanlan-Rohrer, Ken Santor, Shannon Corliss, Joanna Dingle, Jonathan Cottrell, Beth Pearson, and Maureen Eide at John Wiley is a pleasure. We appreciate their patience and imagination.

Many people have contributed significantly to this text. They include: Lauren Akers, Fahd Alshammari, David Arias, Tim Bean, Charlotte Bonner, Bill Bossert, Brian Bradie, Noah S. Brannen, Mike Brilleslyper, Donna Brouillette, Jo Cannon, Ray Cannon, Kenny Ching, Anna Chung, Pierre Cressant, Laurie Delitsky, Bob Dobrow, Helen M. Doerr, Ian Dowker, Carolyn Edmond, Maryann Faller, Aidan Flanagan, Brendan Fry, Brad Garner, Carrie Garner, John Gerke, Christie Gilliland, Wynne Guy, Donnie Hallstone, David Halstead, Larry Henly, Dean Hickerson, Jo Ellen Hillyer, Bob Hoburg, Phil Hotchkiss, Mike Huffman, Mac Hyman, Rajini Jesudason, Loren Johnson, Scott Kaplowitch, Thomas Kershaw, Mary Kilbride, Steve Kinholt, Kandace Kling, Rob LaQuaglia, Barbara Leasher, Richard Little, David Lovelock, Guadalupe Lozano Terán, Nicholas Lyktey, Chaimaa Makoudi, Len Malinowski, Nancy Marcus, Kate McGivney, Gowri Meda, Bob Megginson, Deborah Moore, Eric Motylinski, Bill Mueller, Kyle Niedzwiecki, Kathryn Oswald, Igor Padure, Bridget Neale Paris, Janet Ray, Ritam Ray, Ken Richardson, Halip Saifi, Sharon Sanders, Mary Schumacher, Mike Seery, Mike Sherman, Donna Sherrill, Max Shuchman, Fred Shure, Kanwal Singh, Myra Snell, Natasha Speer, Sonya Stanley, Michael Steuer, Jim Stone, Peggy Tibbs, Jeff Taft, Elias Toubassi, Jerry Uhl, Pat Wagener, Benjamin West, Dale Winter, and Xianbao Xu.

Reports from the following reviewers were most helpful in shaping the second, third, and fourth editions: Victor Akatsa, Jeffrey Anderson, Beth Borel, Linda Braddy, Michael Brassington, Ingrid Brown-Scott, Linda Casper, Kim Chudnick, Ted Coe, Ray Collings, Joe Coyle, Pam Crawford, Monica Davis, Phyllis Desormeaux, Helen Doerr, Diane Downie, Peter Dragnev, Patricia Dueck, Julie Fisher, Jennifer Fowler, Alyne Fulte, David Gillette, Jack Green, Zdenka Guadarrama, Donnie Hallstone, Jeff Hoherz, Majid Hosseini, Rick Hough, Ann Humes, Pallavi Ketkar, William Kiele, Mile Krajcevski, John LaMaster, Phyllis Leonard, Daphne MacLean, Diane Mathios, Vince McGarry, Maria Miles, Laura Moore-Mueller, Ellen Musen, Dave Nolan, Linda O'Brien, Chris Parks, Scott Perry, Jeffrey S. Powell, Mary Rack, Emily Roth, Barbara Shabell Deirdre Smith, Ernie Solheid, Sandy Spears, Diana Staats, John Stadler, Mary Jane Sterling, Allison Sutton, John Thomason, Diane Van Nostrand, Jim Vicich, Linda Wagner, Nicole Williams, Jim Winston, Vauhn Wittman-Grahler, and Bruce Yoshiwara.

Special thanks are owed to Faye Riddle for administering the project and to Alex Kasman for his software support.

Eric Connally	Deborah Hughes-Hallett	Andrew M. Gleason	Philip Cheifetz
Ann Davidian	Dan Flath	Selin Kalaycıoğlu	Brigitte Lahme
Patti Frazer Lock	Elliot Marks	William G. McCallum	Jerry Morris
Karen Rhea	Ellen Schmierer	Pat Shure	Adam H. Spiegler
Carl Swenson			

To Students: How to Learn from this Book

- This book may be different from other math textbooks that you have used, so it may be helpful to know about some of the differences in advance. At every stage, this book emphasizes the *meaning* (in practical, graphical or numerical terms) of the symbols you are using. There is much less emphasis on "plug-and-chug" and using formulas, and much more emphasis on the interpretation of these formulas than you may expect. You will often be asked to explain your ideas in words or to explain an answer using graphs.

- The book contains the main ideas of precalculus in plain English. Success in using this book will depend on reading, questioning, and thinking hard about the ideas presented. It will be helpful to read the text in detail, not just the worked examples.

- There are few examples in the text that are exactly like the homework problems, so homework problems can't be done by searching for similar–looking "worked out" examples. Success with the homework will come by grappling with the ideas of precalculus.

- Many of the problems in the book are open-ended. This means that there is more than one correct approach and more than one correct solution. Sometimes, solving a problem relies on common-sense ideas that are not stated in the problem explicitly but which you know from everyday life.

- This book assumes that you have access to a calculator or computer that can graph functions and find (approximate) roots of equations. There are many situations where you may not be able to find an exact solution to a problem, but can use a calculator or computer to get a reasonable approximation. An answer obtained this way can be as useful as an exact one. However, the problem does not always state that a calculator is required, so use your own judgment.

- This book attempts to give equal weight to four methods for describing functions: graphical (a picture), numerical (a table of values), algebraic (a formula) and verbal (words). Sometimes it's easier to translate a problem given in one form into another. For example, you might replace the graph of a parabola with its equation, or plot a table of values to see its behavior. It is important to be flexible about your approach: if one way of looking at a problem doesn't work, try another.

- Students using this book have found discussing these problems in small groups helpful. There are a great many problems that are not cut-and-dried; it can help to attack them with the other perspectives your colleagues can provide. If group work is not feasible, see if your instructor can organize a discussion session in which additional problems can be worked on.

- You are probably wondering what you'll get from the book. The answer is, if you put in a solid effort, you will get a real understanding of functions as well as a real sense of how mathematics is used in the age of technology.

Table of Contents

4 EXPONENTIAL FUNCTIONS   129

5 LOGARITHMIC FUNCTIONS   179

6 TRANSFORMATIONS OF FUNCTIONS AND THEIR GRAPHS   223

Chapter One

LINEAR FUNCTIONS AND CHANGE

Contents

1.1 FUNCTIONS AND FUNCTION NOTATION

In everyday language, the word *function* expresses the notion of dependence. For example, a person might say that election results are a function of the economy, meaning that the winner of an election is determined by how the economy is doing. Someone else might claim that car sales are a function of the weather, meaning that the number of cars sold on a given day is affected by the weather.

In mathematics, the meaning of the word *function* is more precise, but the basic idea is the same. A function is a relationship between two quantities. If the value of the first quantity determines exactly one value of the second quantity, we say the second quantity is a function of the first. We make the following definition:

A **function** is a rule that takes certain numbers as inputs and assigns to each input number exactly one output number. The output is a function of the input.

The inputs and outputs are also called *variables*.

Representing Functions: Words, Tables, Graphs, and Formulas

A function can be described using words, data in a table, points on a graph, or a formula.

Example 1 It is a surprising biological fact that most crickets chirp at a rate that increases as the temperature increases. For the snowy tree cricket (*Oecanthus fultoni*), the relationship between temperature and chirp rate is so reliable that this type of cricket is called the thermometer cricket. We can estimate the temperature (in degrees Fahrenheit) by counting the number of times a snowy tree cricket chirps in 15 seconds and adding 40. For instance, if we count 20 chirps in 15 seconds, then a good estimate of the temperature is $20 + 40 = 60°F$.

The rule used to find the temperature T (in °F) from the chirp rate R (in chirps per minute) is an example of a function. The input is chirp rate and the output is temperature. Describe this function using words, a table, a graph, and a formula.

Solution
- **Words**: To estimate the temperature, we count the number of chirps in fifteen seconds and add forty. Alternatively, we can count R chirps per minute, divide R by four and add forty. This is because there are one-fourth as many chirps in fifteen seconds as there are in sixty seconds. For instance, 80 chirps per minute works out to $\frac{1}{4} \cdot 80 = 20$ chirps every 15 seconds, giving an estimated temperature of $20 + 40 = 60°F$.
- **Table**: Table 1.1 gives the estimated temperature, T, as a function of R, the number of chirps per minute. Notice the pattern in Table 1.1: each time the chirp rate, R, goes up by 20 chirps per minute, the temperature, T, goes up by $5°F$.
- **Graph**: The data from Table 1.1 are plotted in Figure 1.1. For instance, the pair of values $R = 80, T = 60$ is plotted as the point P, which is 80 units along the horizontal axis and 60 units up the vertical axis. Data represented in this way are said to be plotted on the *Cartesian plane*. The precise position of P is shown by its coordinates, written $P = (80, 60)$.

Table 1.1   *Chirp rate and temperature*

R, chirp rate (chirps/minute)	T, predicted temperature (°F)
20	45
40	50
60	55
80	60
100	65
120	70
140	75
160	80

Figure 1.1: Chirp rate and temperature

- **Formula**: A formula is an equation giving T in terms of R. Dividing the chirp rate by four and adding forty gives the estimated temperature, so:

$$\underbrace{\text{Estimated temperature (in °F)}}_{T} = \frac{1}{4} \cdot \underbrace{\text{Chirp rate (in chirps/min)}}_{R} + 40.$$

Rewriting this using the variables T and R gives the formula:

$$T = \frac{1}{4}R + 40.$$

Let's check the formula. Substituting $R = 80$, we have

$$T = \frac{1}{4} \cdot 80 + 40 = 60,$$

which agrees with point $P = (80, 60)$ in Figure 1.1. The formula $T = \frac{1}{4}R + 40$ also tells us that if $R = 0$, then $T = 40$. Thus, the dashed line in Figure 1.1 crosses (or intersects) the T-axis at $T = 40$; we say the T-*intercept* is 40.

All the descriptions given in Example 1 provide the same information, but each description has a different emphasis. A relationship between variables is often given in words, as at the beginning of Example 1. Table 1.1 is useful because it shows the predicted temperature for various chirp rates. Figure 1.1 is more suggestive of a trend than the table, although it is harder to read exact values of the function. For example, you might have noticed that every point in Figure 1.1 falls on a straight line that slopes up from left to right. In general, a graph can reveal a pattern that might otherwise go unnoticed. Finally, the formula has the advantage of being both compact and precise. However, this compactness can also be a disadvantage since it may be harder to gain as much insight from a formula as from a table or a graph.

Mathematical Models

When we use a function to describe an actual situation, the function is referred to as a **mathematical model**. The formula $T = \frac{1}{4}R + 40$ is a mathematical model of the relationship between the temperature and the cricket's chirp rate. Such models can be powerful tools for understanding phenomena and making predictions. For example, this model predicts that when the chirp rate is 80 chirps per

3

minute, the temperature is 60°F. In addition, since $T = 40$ when $R = 0$, the model predicts that the chirp rate is 0 at 40°F. Whether the model's predictions are accurate for chirp rates down to 0 and temperatures as low as 40°F is a question that mathematics alone cannot answer; an understanding of the biology of crickets is needed. However, we can safely say that the model does not apply for temperatures below 40°F, because the chirp rate would then be negative. For the range of chirp rates and temperatures in Table 1.1, the model is remarkably accurate.

In everyday language, saying that T is a function of R suggests that making the cricket chirp faster would somehow make the temperature change. Clearly, the cricket's chirping does not cause the temperature to be what it is. In mathematics, saying that the temperature "depends" on the chirp rate means only that knowing the chirp rate is sufficient to tell us the temperature.

Function Notation

To indicate that a quantity Q is a function of a quantity t, we abbreviate

$$Q \text{ is a function of } t \quad \text{to} \quad Q \text{ equals "} f \text{ of } t\text{"}$$

and, using function notation, to

$$Q = f(t).$$

Thus, applying the rule f to the input value, t, gives the output value, $f(t)$. In other words, $f(t)$ represents a value of Q. Here Q is called the *dependent variable* and t is called the *independent variable*. Symbolically,

$$\text{Output} = f(\text{Input})$$

or

$$\text{Dependent} = f(\text{Independent}).$$

We could have used any letter, not just f, to represent the rule.

Example 2 The number of gallons of paint needed to paint a house depends on the size of the house. A gallon of paint typically covers 250 square feet. Thus, the number of gallons of paint, n, is a function of the area to be painted, A ft^2. We write $n = f(A)$.

(a) Find a formula for f.
(b) Explain in words what the statement $f(10,000) = 40$ tells us about painting houses.

Solution (a) If $A = 5000$ ft^2, then $n = 5000/250 = 20$ gallons of paint. In general, n and A are related by the formula

$$n = \frac{A}{250}.$$

(b) The input of the function $n = f(A)$ is an area and the output is an amount of paint. The statement $f(10,000) = 40$ tells us that an area of $A = 10,000$ ft^2 requires $n = 40$ gallons of paint.

The expressions "Q depends on t" or "Q is a function of t" do *not* imply a cause-and-effect relationship, as the snowy tree cricket example illustrates.

Example 3 Example 1 gives the following formula for estimating air temperature based on the chirp rate of the snowy tree cricket:

$$T = \frac{1}{4}R + 40.$$

In this formula, T depends on R. Writing $T = f(R)$ indicates that the relationship is a function. ,

---

Functions Don't Have to Be Defined by Formulas

People sometimes think that functions are always represented by formulas. However, the next example shows a function that is not given by a formula.

Example 4 The average monthly rainfall, R, at Chicago's O'Hare airport is given in Table 1.2, where time, t, is in months and $t = 1$ is January, $t = 2$ is February, and so on. The rainfall is a function of the month, so we write $R = f(t)$. However, there is no equation that gives R when t is known. Evaluate $f(1)$ and $f(11)$. Explain what your answers mean.

Table 1.2   *Average monthly rainfall at Chicago's O'Hare airport*

Month, t	1	2	3	4	5	6	7	8	9	10	11	12
Rainfall, R (inches)	1.8	1.8	2.7	3.1	3.5	3.7	3.5	3.4	3.2	2.5	2.4	2.1

Solution The value of $f(1)$ is the average rainfall in inches at Chicago's O'Hare airport in a typical January. From the table, $f(1) = 1.8$ inches. Similarly, $f(11) = 2.4$ means that in a typical November, there are 2.4 inches of rain at O'Hare.

When Is a Relationship Not a Function?

It is possible for two quantities to be related and yet for neither quantity to be a function of the other.

Example 5 A national park contains foxes that prey on rabbits. Table 1.3 gives the two populations, F and R, over a 12-month period, where $t = 0$ means January 1, $t = 1$ means February 1, and so on.

Table 1.3   *Number of foxes and rabbits in a national park, by month*

t, month	0	1	2	3	4	5	6	7	8	9	10	11
R, rabbits	1000	750	567	500	567	750	1000	1250	1433	1500	1433	1250
F, foxes	150	143	125	100	75	57	50	57	75	100	125	143

(a) Is F a function of t? Is R a function of t?
(b) Is F a function of R? Is R a function of F?

Solution (a) Both F and R are functions of t. For each value of t, there is exactly one value of F and exactly one value of R. For example, Table 1.3 shows that if $t = 5$, then $R = 750$ and $F = 57$. This means that on June 1 there are 750 rabbits and 57 foxes in the park. If we write $R = f(t)$ and $F = g(t)$, then $f(5) = 750$ and $g(5) = 57$.

(b) No, F is not a function of R. For example, suppose $R = 750$, meaning there are 750 rabbits. This happens both at $t = 1$ (February 1) and at $t = 5$ (June 1). In the first instance, there are 143 foxes; in the second instance, there are 57 foxes. Since there are R-values which correspond to more than one F-value, F is not a function of R.

Similarly, R is not a function of F. At time $t = 5$, we have $R = 750$ when $F = 57$, while at time $t = 7$, we have $R = 1250$ when $F = 57$ again. Thus, the value of F does not uniquely determine the value of R.

5

How to Tell if a Graph Represents a Function: Vertical Line Test

What does it mean graphically for y to be a function of x? Look at the graph of y against x. For a function, each x-value corresponds to exactly one y-value. This means that the graph intersects any vertical line at most once. If a vertical line cuts the graph twice, the graph would contain two points with different y-values but the same x-value; this would violate the definition of a function. Thus, we have the following criterion:

Vertical Line Test: If there is a vertical line that intersects a graph in more than one point, then the graph does not represent a function.

Example 6 In which of the graphs in Figures 1.2 and 1.3 could y be a function of x?

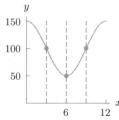

Figure 1.2: Since no vertical line intersects this curve at more than one point, y could be a function of x

Figure 1.3: Since one vertical line intersects this curve at more than one point, y is not a function of x

Solution The graph in Figure 1.2 could represent y as a function of x because no vertical line intersects this curve in more than one point. The graph in Figure 1.3 does not represent a function because the vertical line shown intersects the curve at two points.

A graph fails the vertical line test if at least one vertical line cuts the graph more than once, as in Figure 1.3. However, if a graph represents a function, then *every* vertical line must intersect the graph at no more than one point.

Exercises and Problems for Section 1.1

Skill Refresher

In Exercises S1–S4, simplify each expression.

S1. $c + \frac{1}{2}c$

S3. $2\pi r^2 + 2\pi r \cdot 2r$

S2. $P + 0.07P + 0.02P$

S4. $\dfrac{12\pi - 2\pi}{6\pi}$

In Exercises S5–S8, find the value of the expressions for the given value of x and y.

S5. $x - 5y$ for $x = \frac{1}{2}, y = -5$.

S6. $1 - 12x + x^2$ for $x = 3$.

S7. $\dfrac{3}{2 - x^3}$ for $x = -1$.

S8. $\dfrac{4}{1 + 1/x}$ for $x = -\frac{3}{4}$.

The figures in Exercises S9–S10 are parallelograms. Find the coordinates of the labeled point(s).

S9.

S10.

Exercises

1. Figure 1.4 gives the depth of the water at Montauk Point, New York, for a day in November.

   (a) How many high tides took place on this day?

   (b) How many low tides took place on this day?

   (c) How much time elapsed in between high tides?

depth of water (feet)

time (hours)

4   8 12 16 20 24

Figure 1.4

In Exercises 2–3, write the relationship using function notation (that is, y is a function of x is written $y = f(x)$).

2. Number of molecules, m, in a gas, is a function of the volume of the gas, v.

3. Weight, w, is a function of caloric intake, c.

In Exercises 4–7, label the axes for a sketch to illustrate the given statement.

4. "Over the past century we have seen changes in the population, P (in millions), of the city. . ."

5. "Sketch a graph of the cost of manufacturing q items. . ."

6. "Graph the pressure, p, of a gas as a function of its volume, v, where p is in pounds per square inch and v is in cubic inches."

7. "Graph D in terms of y. . ."

8. Using Table 1.4, graph $n = f(A)$, the number of gallons of paint needed to cover a house of area A. Identify the independent and dependent variables.

Table 1.4

A	0	250	500	750	1000	1250	1500
n	0	1	2	3	4	5	6

9. Use Table 1.5 to fill in the missing values. (There may be more than one answer.)

   (a) $f(0) = ?$ **(b)** $f(?) = 0$

   (c) $f(1) = ?$ **(d)** $f(?) = 1$

Table 1.5

x	0	1	2	3	4
$f(x)$	4	2	1	0	1

10. Use Figure 1.5 to fill in the missing values:

   (a) $f(0) = ?$ **(b)** $f(?) = 0$

Figure 1.5

Exercises 11–14 use Figure 1.6.

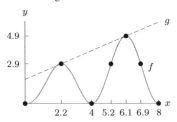

Figure 1.6

11. Find $f(6.9)$.

12. Give the coordinates of two points on the graph of g.

13. Solve $f(x) = 0$ for x.

14. Solve $f(x) = g(x)$ for x.

15. (a) You are going to graph $p = f(w)$. Which variable goes on the horizontal axis?
   (b) If $10 = f(-4)$, give the coordinates of a point on the graph of f.
   (c) If 6 is a solution of the equation $f(w) = 1$, give a point on the graph of f.

16. (a) Suppose x and y are the coordinates of a point on the circle $x^2 + y^2 = 1$. Is y a function of x? Why or why not?
   (b) Suppose x and y are the coordinates of a point on the part of the circle $x^2 + y^2 = 1$ that is above the x-axis. Is y a function of x? Why or why not?

17. (a) Is the area, A, of a square a function of the length of one of its sides, s?
   (b) Is the area, A, of a rectangle a function of the length of one of its sides, s?

18. Which of the following graphs represent functions?

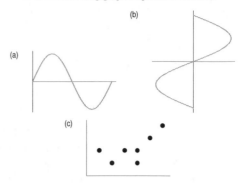

Figure 1.7

19. A buzzard is circling high overhead when it spies some road kill. It swoops down, lands, and eats. Later it takes off sluggishly, and resumes circling overhead, but at a lower altitude. Sketch a possible graph of the height of the buzzard as a function of time.

20. A person's blood sugar level at a particular time of the day is partially determined by the time of the most recent meal. After a meal, blood sugar level increases rapidly, then slowly comes back down to a normal level. Sketch a person's blood sugar level as a function of time over the course of a day. Label the axes to indicate normal blood sugar level and the time of each meal.

21. Let $f(t)$ be the number of people, in millions, who own cell phones t years after 1990. Explain the meaning of the following statements.

   (a) $f(10) = 100.3$ **(b)** $f(a) = 20$
   (c) $f(20) = b$ **(d)** $n = f(t)$

22. At the end of a semester, students' math grades are listed in a table which gives each student's ID number in the left column and the student's grade in the right column. Let N represent the ID number and the G represent the grade. Which quantity, N or G, must necessarily be a function of the other?

23. Table 1.6 gives the ranking r for three different names—Hannah, Alexis, and Madison. Of the three names, which was most popular and which was least popular in

   (a) 1995?   **(b)** 2004?

Table 1.6 *Ranking of names—Hannah (r_h), Alexis (r_a), and Madison (r_m)—for girls born between 1995 (t = 0) and 2004 (t = 9)[1]*

t	0	1	2	3	4	5	6	7	8	9
r_h	7	7	5	2	2	2	3	3	4	5
r_a	14	8	8	6	3	6	5	5	7	11
r_m	29	15	10	9	7	3	2	2	3	3

24. Table 1.6 gives information about the popularity of the names Hannah, Madison, and Alexis. Describe in words what your answers to parts (a)–(c) tell you about these names.

   (a) Evaluate $r_m(0) - r_h(0)$.
   (b) Evaluate $r_m(9) - r_h(9)$.
   (c) Solve $r_m(t) < r_a(t)$.

25. Figure 1.8 shows the fuel consumption (in miles per gallon, mpg) of a car traveling at various speeds.

   (a) How much gas is used on a 300-mile trip at 40 mph?
   (b) How much gas is saved by traveling 60 mph instead of 70 mph on a 200-mile trip?
   (c) According to this graph, what is the most fuel-efficient speed to travel? Explain.

Figure 1.8

---

[1] Data from the SSA website at www.ssa.gov, accessed January 12, 2006.

26. **(a)** Ten inches of snow is equivalent to about one inch of rain.[2] Write an equation for the amount of precipitation, measured in inches of rain, $r = f(s)$, as a function of the number of inches of snow, s.
    (b) Evaluate and interpret $f(5)$.
    (c) Find s such that $f(s) = 5$ and interpret your result.

27. An 8-foot-tall cylindrical water tank has a base of diameter 6 feet.

    (a) How much water can the tank hold?
    (b) How much water is in the tank if the water is 5 feet deep?
    (c) Write a formula for the volume of water as a function of its depth in the tank.

28. Match each story about a bike ride to one of the graphs (i)–(v), where d represents distance from home and t is time in hours since the start of the ride. (A graph may be used more than once.)

    (a) Starts 5 miles from home and rides 5 miles per hour away from home.
    (b) Starts 5 miles from home and rides 10 miles per hour away from home.
    (c) Starts 10 miles from home and arrives home one hour later.
    (d) Starts 10 miles from home and is halfway home after one hour.
    (e) Starts 5 miles from home and is 10 miles from home after one hour.

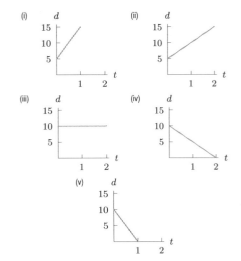

29. Table 1.7 shows the daily low temperature for a one-week period in New York City during July.

    (a) What was the low temperature on July 19?
    (b) When was the low temperature 73°F?
    (c) Is the daily low temperature a function of the date?
    (d) Is the date a function of the daily low temperature?

Table 1.7

Date	17	18	19	20	21	22	23
Low temp (°F)	73	77	69	73	75	75	70

30. Use the data from Table 1.3 on page 5.

    (a) Plot R on the vertical axis and t on the horizontal axis. Use this graph to explain why you believe that R is a function of t.
    (b) Plot F on the vertical axis and t on the horizontal axis. Use this graph to explain why you believe that F is a function of t.
    (c) Plot F on the vertical axis and R on the horizontal axis. From this graph show that F is not a function of R.
    (d) Plot R on the vertical axis and F on the horizontal axis. From this graph show that R is not a function of F.

31. Since Roger Bannister broke the 4-minute mile on May 6, 1954, the record has been lowered by over sixteen seconds. Table 1.8 shows the year and times (as min:sec) of new world records for the one-mile run.[3] The last time the record was broken was in 1999.

    (a) Is the time a function of the year? Explain.
    (b) Is the year a function of the time? Explain.
    (c) Let $y(r)$ be the year in which the world record, r, was set. Explain what is meant by the statement $y(3{:}47.33) = 1981$.
    (d) Evaluate and interpret $y(3{:}51.1)$.

Table 1.8

Year	Time	Year	Time	Year	Time
1954	3:59.4	1966	3:51.3	1981	3:48.53
1954	3:58.0	1967	3:51.1	1981	3:48.40
1957	3:57.2	1975	3:51.0	1981	3:47.33
1958	3:54.5	1975	3:49.4	1985	3:46.32
1962	3:54.4	1979	3:49.0	1993	3:44.39
1964	3:54.1	1980	3:48.8	1999	3:43.13
1965	3:53.6				

[2]http://mo.water.usgs.gov/outreach/rain, accessed May 7, 2006.
[3]www.infoplease.com/ipsa/A0112924.html, accessed January 15, 2006.

32. Table 1.9 gives $A = f(d)$, the amount of money in bills of denomination d circulating in US currency in 2008.[4] For example, there were $64.7 billion worth of $50 bills in circulation.

   (a) Find $f(100)$. What does this tell you about money?
   (b) Are there more $1 bills or $5 bills in circulation?

Table 1.9

Denomination ($)	1	2	5	10	20	50	100
Circulation ($bn)	9.5	1.7	11	16.3	125.1	64.7	625

33. There are x male job-applicants at a certain company and y female applicants. Suppose that 15% of the men are accepted and 18% of the women are accepted. Write an expression in terms of x and y representing each of the following quantities:

   (a) The total number of applicants to the company.
   (b) The total number of applicants accepted.
   (c) The percentage of all applicants accepted.

34. The sales tax on an item is 6%. Express the total cost, C, in terms of the price of the item, P.

35. Write a formula for the area of a circle as a function of its radius and determine the percent increase in the area if the radius is increased by 10%.

36. A price increases 5% due to inflation and is then reduced 10% for a sale. Express the final price as a function of the original price, P.

37. A chemical company spends $2 million to buy machinery before it starts producing chemicals. Then it spends $0.5 million on raw materials for each million liters of chemical produced.

   (a) The number of liters produced ranges from 0 to 5 million. Make a table showing the relationship between the number of million liters produced, l, and the total cost, C, in millions of dollars, to produce that number of million liters.
   (b) Find a formula that expresses C as a function of l.

38. A person leaves home and walks due west for a time and then walks due north.

   (a) The person walks 10 miles in total. If w represents the (variable) distance west she walks, and D represents her (variable) distance from home at the end of her walk, is D a function of w? Why or why not?
   (b) Suppose now that x is the distance that she walks in total. Is D a function of x? Why or why not?

1.2   RATE OF CHANGE

Sales of digital video disc (DVD) players have been increasing since they were introduced in early 1998. To measure how fast sales were increasing, we calculate a *rate of change* of the form

$$\frac{\text{Change in sales}}{\text{Change in time}}.$$

At the same time, sales of video cassette recorders (VCRs) have been decreasing. See Table 1.10.

Let us calculate the rate of change of DVD player and VCR sales between 1998 and 2003. Table 1.10 gives

$$\begin{array}{c}\text{Average rate of change of DVD} \\ \text{player sales from 1998 to 2003}\end{array} = \frac{\text{Change in DVD player sales}}{\text{Change in time}} = \frac{3050 - 421}{2003 - 1998} \approx 525.8\frac{\text{mn \$/}}{\text{year}}.$$

Thus, DVD player sales increased on average by $525.8 million per year between 1998 and 2003. See Figure 1.9. Similarly, Table 1.10 gives

$$\begin{array}{c}\text{Average rate of change of VCR sales} \\ \text{from 1998 to 2003}\end{array} = \frac{\text{Change in VCR sales}}{\text{Change in time}} = \frac{407 - 2409}{2003 - 1998} \approx -400.4\frac{\text{mn \$/}}{\text{year}}.$$

---

[4]www.visualeconomics.com/the-value-of-united-states-currency-in-circulation, The Value of United States Currency in Circulation, 2008, accessed November 16, 2009.

Thus, VCR sales decreased on average by \$400.4 million per year between 1998 and 2003. See Figure 1.10.

Figure 1.9: DVD player sales

Figure 1.10: VCR sales

Table 1.10 *Annual sales of VCRs and DVD players in millions of dollars*[5]

Year	1998	1999	2000	2001	2002	2003
VCR sales (million \$)	2409	2333	1869	1058	826	407
DVD player sales (million \$)	421	1099	1717	2097	2427	3050

Rate of Change of a Function

The rate of change of sales is an example of the rate of change of a function. In general, if $Q = f(t)$, we write ΔQ for a change in Q and Δt for a change in t. We define:[6]

> The **average rate of change**, or **rate of change**, of Q with respect to t over an interval is
>
> $$\text{Average rate of change over an interval} = \frac{\text{Change in } Q}{\text{Change in } t} = \frac{\Delta Q}{\Delta t}.$$

The average rate of change of the function $Q = f(t)$ over an interval tells us how much Q changes, on average, for each unit change in t within that interval. On some parts of the interval, Q may be changing rapidly, while on other parts Q may be changing slowly. The average rate of change evens out these variations.

Increasing and Decreasing Functions

In the previous example, the average rate of change of DVD player sales is positive on the interval from 1998 to 2003 since sales of DVD players increased over this interval. Similarly, the average rate of change of VCR sales is negative on the same interval since sales of VCRs decreased over this interval. The annual sales of DVD players is an example of an *increasing function* and the annual sales of VCRs is an example of a *decreasing function*. In general we say the following:

> If $Q = f(t)$ for t in the interval $a \le t \le b$,
> - f is an **increasing function** if the values of f increase as t increases in this interval.
> - f is a **decreasing function** if the values of f decrease as t increases in this interval.

---

[5]www.census.gov/prod/2005pubs/06statab/manufact.pdf, accessed January 16, 2006.

[6]The Greek letter Δ, delta, is often used in mathematics to represent change. In this book, we use rate of change to mean average rate of change across an interval. In calculus, rate of change means something called instantaneous rate of change.

Looking at DVD player sales, we see that an increasing function has a positive rate of change. From the VCR sales, we see that a decreasing function has a negative rate of change. In general:

If $Q = f(t)$,
- If f is an increasing function, then the average rate of change of Q with respect to t is positive on every interval.
- If f is a decreasing function, then the average rate of change of Q with respect to t is negative on every interval.

Example 1   The function $A = q(r) = \pi r^2$ gives the area, A, of a circle as a function of its radius, r. Graph q. Explain how the fact that q is an increasing function can be seen on the graph.

Solution   The area increases as the radius increases, so $A = q(r)$ is an increasing function. We can see this in Figure 1.11 because the graph climbs as we move from left to right and the average rate of change, $\Delta A / \Delta r$, is positive on every interval.

Figure 1.11: The graph of an increasing function, $A = q(r)$, rises when read from left to right

Example 2   Carbon-14 is a radioactive element that exists naturally in the atmosphere and is absorbed by living organisms. When an organism dies, the carbon-14 present at death begins to decay. Let $L = g(t)$ represent the quantity of carbon-14 (in micrograms, μg) in a tree t years after its death. See Table 1.11. Explain why we expect g to be a decreasing function of t. How is this represented on a graph?

Table 1.11   *Quantity of carbon-14 as a function of time*

t, time (years)	0	1000	2000	3000	4000	5000
L, quantity of carbon-14 (μg)	200	177	157	139	123	109

Solution   Since the amount of carbon-14 is decaying over time, g is a decreasing function. In Figure 1.12, the graph falls as we move from left to right and the average rate of change in the level of carbon-14 with respect to time, $\Delta L / \Delta t$, is negative on every interval.

Figure 1.12: The graph of a decreasing function, $L = g(t)$, falls when read from left to right

In general, we can identify an increasing or decreasing function from its graph as follows:

- The graph of an increasing function rises when read from left to right.
- The graph of a decreasing function falls when read from left to right.

Many functions have some intervals on which they are increasing and other intervals on which they are decreasing. These intervals can often be identified from the graph.

Example 3   On what intervals is the function graphed in Figure 1.13 increasing? Decreasing?

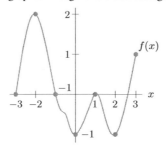

Figure 1.13: Graph of a function that is increasing on some intervals and decreasing on others

Solution   The function appears to be increasing for values of x between -3 and -2, for x between 0 and 1, and for x between 2 and 3. The function appears to be decreasing for x between -2 and 0 and for x between 1 and 2. Using inequalities, we say that f is increasing for $-3 < x < -2$, for $0 < x < 1$, and for $2 < x < 3$. Similarly, f is decreasing for $-2 < x < 0$ and $1 < x < 2$.

Function Notation for the Average Rate of Change

Suppose we want to find the average rate of change of a function $Q = f(t)$ over the interval $a \leq t \leq b$. On this interval, the change in t is given by

$$\Delta t = b - a.$$

At $t = a$, the value of Q is $f(a)$, and at $t = b$, the value of Q is $f(b)$. Therefore, the change in Q is given by

$$\Delta Q = f(b) - f(a).$$

13

Using function notation, we express the average rate of change as follows:

$$\text{Average rate of change of } Q = f(t) \atop \text{over the interval } a \le t \le b = \frac{\text{Change in } Q}{\text{Change in } t} = \frac{\Delta Q}{\Delta t} = \frac{f(b) - f(a)}{b - a}.$$

In Figure 1.14, notice that the average rate of change is given by the ratio of the rise, $f(b) - f(a)$, to the run, $b - a$. This ratio is also called the *slope* of the dashed line segment.[7]

In the future, we may drop the word "average" and talk about the rate of change over an interval.

Figure 1.14: The average rate of change is the ratio Rise/Run

In previous examples we calculated the average rate of change from data. We now calculate average rates of change for functions given by formulas.

Example 4 Calculate the average rates of change of the function $f(x) = x^2$ between $x = 1$ and $x = 3$ and between $x = -2$ and $x = 1$. Show your results on a graph.

Solution Between $x = 1$ and $x = 3$, we have

$$\text{Average rate of change of } f(x) \atop \text{over the interval } 1 \le x \le 3 = \frac{\text{Change in } f(x)}{\text{Change in } x} = \frac{f(3) - f(1)}{3 - 1}$$

$$= \frac{3^2 - 1^2}{3 - 1} = \frac{9 - 1}{2} = 4.$$

Between $x = -2$ and $x = 1$, we have

$$\text{Average rate of change of } f(x) \atop \text{over the interval } -2 \le x \le 1 = \frac{\text{Change in } f(x)}{\text{Change in } x} = \frac{f(1) - f(-2)}{1 - (-2)}$$

$$= \frac{1^2 - (-2)^2}{1 - (-2)} = \frac{1 - 4}{3} = -1.$$

The average rate of change between $x = 1$ and $x = 3$ is positive because $f(x)$ is increasing on this interval. See Figure 1.15. However, on the interval from $x = -2$ and $x = 1$, the function is partly decreasing and partly increasing. The average rate of change on this interval is negative because the decrease on the interval is larger than the increase.

---

[7] See Section 1.3 for further discussion of slope.

Figure 1.15: Average rate of change of $f(x)$ on an interval is the slope of the dashed line on that interval

Exercises and Problems for Section 1.2

Skill Refresher

In Exercises S1–S10, simplify each expression.

S1. $\dfrac{4-6}{3-2}$

S2. $\dfrac{1-3}{2^2-(-3)^2}$

S3. $\dfrac{-3-(-9)}{-1-2}$

S4. $\dfrac{(1-3^2)-(1-4^2)}{3-4}$

S5. $\dfrac{\left(\frac{1}{2}-(-4)\right)^2-\left(\frac{1}{2}-(5^2)\right)}{-4-5}$

S6. $2(x+a)-3(x-b)$

S7. $x^2-(2x+a)^2$

S8. $4x^2-(x-b)^2$

S9. $\dfrac{x^2-\frac{3}{4}-\left(y^2-\frac{3}{4}\right)}{x-y}$

S10. $\dfrac{2(x+h)^2-2x^2}{(x+h)-x}$

Exercises

1. In 2005, you have 40 CDs in your collection. In 2008, you have 120 CDs. In 2012, you have 40. What is the average rate of change in your CD collection's size between

   (a) 2005 and 2008?   (b) 2008 and 2012?

   (c) 2005 and 2012?

2. Table 1.10 on page 11 gives the annual sales (in millions) of VCRs and DVD players. What was the average rate of change of annual sales of each of them between

   (a) 1998 and 2000?   (b) 2000 and 2003?

   (c) Interpret these results in terms of sales.

3. Table 1.10 on page 11 shows that VCR sales are a function of DVD player sales. Is it an increasing or decreasing function?

4. Table 1.12 shows data for two populations (in hundreds) for five different years. Find the average rate of change of each population over the following intervals.

   (a) 1990 to 2000   (b) 1995 to 2007

   (c) 1990 to 2007

   Table 1.12

Year	1990	1992	1995	2000	2007
P_1	53	63	73	83	93
P_2	85	80	75	70	65

Exercises 5–9 use Figure 1.16.

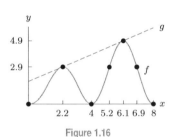

Figure 1.16

5. Find the average rate of change of f for $2.2 \le x \le 6.1$.

6. Give two different intervals on which $\Delta f(x)/\Delta x = 0$.

7. What is the average rate of change of g between $x = 2.2$ and $x = 6.1$?

8. What is the relation between the average rate of change of f and the average rate of change of g between $x = 2.2$ and $x = 6.1$?

9. Is the rate of change of f positive or negative on the following intervals?

   (a) $2.2 \le x \le 4$ (b) $5 \le x \le 6$

10. If G is an increasing function, what can you say about $G(3) - G(-1)$?

11. If F is a decreasing function, what can you say about $F(-2)$ compared to $F(2)$?

12. Figure 1.17 shows distance traveled as a function of time.

    (a) Find ΔD and Δt between:

        (i) $t = 2$ and $t = 5$ (ii) $t = 0.5$ and $t = 2.5$
        (iii) $t = 1.5$ and $t = 3$

    (b) Compute the rate of change, $\Delta D/\Delta t$, over each of the intervals in part (a), and interpret its meaning.

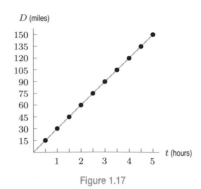

Figure 1.17

Problems

13. Figure 1.18 shows the percent of the side of the moon toward the earth illuminated by the sun at different times during the year 2008. Use the figure to answer the following questions.

    (a) Give the coordinates of the points A, B, C, D, E.
    (b) Plot the point $F = (15, 60)$ and $G = (60, 15)$. Which point is on the graph?
    (c) During which time intervals is the function increasing?
    (d) During which time intervals is the function decreasing?

Figure 1.18: Moon phases

14. Imagine you constructed a list of the world record times for a particular event—such as the mile footrace, or the 100-meter freestyle swimming race—in terms of when they were established. Is the world record time a function of the date when it was established? If so, is this function increasing or decreasing? Explain. Could a world record be established twice in the same year? Is the world record time a function of the year it was established?

15. (a) What is the average rate of change of $g(x) = 2x - 3$ between the points $(-2, -7)$ and $(3, 3)$?
    (b) Based on your answer to part (a), is g increasing or decreasing on the given interval? Explain.
    (c) Graph the function and determine over what intervals g is increasing and over what intervals g is decreasing.

16. (a) Let $f(x) = 16 - x^2$. Compute each of the following expressions, and interpret each as an average rate of change.

        (i) $\dfrac{f(2) - f(0)}{2 - 0}$ (ii) $\dfrac{f(4) - f(2)}{4 - 2}$
        (iii) $\dfrac{f(4) - f(0)}{4 - 0}$

    (b) Graph $f(x)$. Illustrate each ratio in part (a) by sketching the line segment with the given slope. Over which interval is the average rate of decrease the greatest?

17. Figure 1.19 gives the population of two different towns over a 50-year period of time.

    (a) Which town starts (in year $t = 0$) with the most people?
    (b) Which town is growing faster over these 50 years?

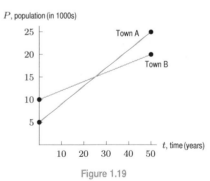

Figure 1.19

16

18. You have zero dollars now and the average rate of change in your net worth is $5000 per year. How much money will you have in forty years?

19. The most freakish change in temperature ever recorded was from $-4°F$ to $45°F$ between 7:30 am and 7:32 am on January 22, 1943 at Spearfish, South Dakota.[8] What was the average rate of change of the temperature for this time period?

20. The surface of the sun has dark areas known as sunspots, that are cooler than the rest of the sun's surface. The number of sunspots fluctuates with time, as shown in Figure 1.20.[9]

    (a) Explain how you know the number of sunspots, s, in year t is a function of t.

    (b) Approximate the time intervals on which s is an increasing function of t.

Figure 1.20

21. Table 1.13 shows the number of calories used per minute as a function of body weight for three sports.[10]

    (a) Determine the number of calories that a 200-lb person uses in one half-hour of walking.

    (b) Who uses more calories, a 120-lb person swimming for one hour or a 220-lb person bicycling for a half-hour?

    (c) Does the number of calories used by a person walking increase or decrease as weight increases?

Table 1.13

Activity	100 lb	120 lb	150 lb	170 lb	200 lb	220 lb
Walking	2.7	3.2	4.0	4.6	5.4	5.9
Bicycling	5.4	6.5	8.1	9.2	10.8	11.9
Swimming	5.8	6.9	8.7	9.8	11.6	12.7

22. Because scientists know how much carbon-14 a living organism should have in its tissues, they can measure the amount of carbon-14 present in the tissue of a fossil and then calculate how long it took for the original amount to decay to the current level, thus determining the time of the organism's death. A tree fossil is found to contain 130 μg of carbon-14, and scientists determine from the size of the tree that it would have contained 200 μg of carbon-14 at the time of its death. Using Table 1.11 on page 12, approximately how long ago did the tree die?

23. Find the average rate of change of $f(x) = 3x^2 + 1$ between the points

    (a) $(1, 4)$ and $(2, 13)$ **(b)** (j, k) and (m, n)

    (c) $(x, f(x))$ and $(x+h, f(x+h))$

24. Figure 1.21 shows the graph of the function $g(x)$.

    (a) Estimate $\dfrac{g(4) - g(0)}{4 - 0}$.

    (b) The ratio in part (a) is the slope of a line segment joining two points on the graph. Sketch this line segment on the graph.

    (c) Estimate $\dfrac{g(b) - g(a)}{b - a}$ for $a = -9$ and $b = -1$.

    (d) On the graph, sketch the line segment whose slope is given by the ratio in part (c).

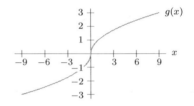

Figure 1.21

25. Table 1.14 gives the amount of garbage, G, in millions of tons, produced[11] in the US in year t.

    (a) What is the value of Δt for consecutive entries in this table?

    (b) Calculate the value of ΔG for each pair of consecutive entries in this table.

    (c) Are all the values of ΔG you found in part (b) the same? What does this tell you?

    (d) The function G changed from increasing to decreasing between 2007 and 2008. To what might this be attributed?

Table 1.14

t	1960	1970	1980	1990	2000	2007	2008
G	88.1	121.1	151.6	205.2	239.1	254.6	249.6

---

[8]*The Guinness Book of Records*. 1995.

[9]ftp://ftp.ngdc.noaa.gov/STP/SOLAR DATA/SUNSPOT NUMBERS/YEARLY.PLT, accessed November 30, 2009.

[10]From *1993 World Almanac*.

[11]http://www.epa.gov/osw/nonhaz/municipal/pubs/msw2008rpt.pdf, accessed November 23, 2009.

26. Table 1.15 shows the times, t, in sec, achieved every 10 meters by Carl Lewis in the 100-meter final of the World Championship in Rome in 1987.[12] Distance, d, is in meters.

(a) For each successive time interval, calculate the average rate of change of distance. What is a common name for the average rate of change of distance?

(b) Where did Carl Lewis attain his maximum speed during this race? Some runners are running their fastest as they cross the finish line. Does that seem to be true in this case?

Table 1.15

t	0.00	1.94	2.96	3.91	4.78	5.64
d	0	10	20	30	40	50
t	6.50	7.36	8.22	9.07	9.93	
d	60	70	80	90	100	

1.3 LINEAR FUNCTIONS

Constant Rate of Change

In the previous section, we introduced the average rate of change of a function on an interval. For many functions, the average rate of change is different on different intervals. For the remainder of this chapter, we consider functions that have the same average rate of change on every interval. Such a function has a graph that is a line and is called *linear*.

Population Growth

Mathematical models of population growth are used by city planners to project the growth of towns and states. Biologists model the growth of animal populations and physicians model the spread of an infection in the bloodstream. One possible model, a linear model, assumes that the population changes at the same average rate on every time interval.

Example 1 A town of 30,000 people grows by 2000 people every year. Since the population, P, is growing at the constant rate of 2000 people per year, P is a linear function of time, t, in years.

(a) What is the average rate of change of P over every time interval?

(b) Make a table that gives the town's population every five years over a 20-year period. Graph the population.

(c) Find a formula for P as a function of t.

Solution

(a) The average rate of change of population with respect to time is 2000 people per year.

(b) The initial population in year $t = 0$ is $P = 30,000$ people. Since the town grows by 2000 people every year, after five years it has grown by

$$\frac{2000 \text{ people}}{\text{year}} \cdot 5 \text{ years} = 10,000 \text{ people}.$$

Thus, in year $t = 5$ the population is given by

$$P = \text{Initial population} + \text{New population} = 30,000 + 10,000 = 40,000.$$

In year $t = 10$ the population is given by

$$P = 30,000 + \underbrace{2000 \text{ people/year} \cdot 10 \text{ years}}_{20,000 \text{ new people}} = 50,000.$$

[12]W. G. Pritchard, "Mathematical Models of Running", *SIAM Review.* 35, 1993, pp. 359–379.

Similar calculations for year $t = 15$ and year $t = 20$ give the values in Table 1.16. See Figure 1.22; the dashed line shows the trend in the data.

Table 1.16 *Population over 20 years*

t, years	P, population
0	30,000
5	40,000
10	50,000
15	60,000
20	70,000

Figure 1.22: Town's population over 20 years

(c) From part (b), we see that the size of the population is given by

$$P = \text{Initial population} + \text{Number of new people}$$
$$= 30,000 + 2000 \text{ people/year} \cdot \text{Number of years,}$$

so a formula for P in terms of t is

$$P = 30,000 + 2000t.$$

The graph of the population data in Figure 1.22 is a straight line. The average rate of change of the population over every interval is the same, namely 2000 people per year. Any linear function has the same average rate of change over every interval. Thus, we talk about *the* rate of change of a linear function. In general:

- A **linear function** has a constant rate of change.
- The graph of any linear function is a straight line.

Financial Models

Economists and accountants use linear functions for *straight-line depreciation*. For tax purposes, the value of certain equipment is considered to decrease, or depreciate, over time. For example, computer equipment may be state-of-the-art today, but after several years it is outdated. Straight-line depreciation assumes that the rate of change of value with respect to time is constant.

Example 2 A small business spends $20,000 on new computer equipment and, for tax purposes, chooses to depreciate it to $0 at a constant rate over a five-year period.

(a) Make a table and a graph showing the value of the equipment over the five-year period.
(b) Give a formula for value as a function of time.

Solution (a) After five years, the equipment is valued at $0. If V is the value in dollars and t is the number of years, we see that

$$\frac{\text{Rate of change of value}}{\text{from } t = 0 \text{ to } t = 5} = \frac{\text{Change in value}}{\text{Change in time}} = \frac{\Delta V}{\Delta t} = \frac{-\$20,000}{5 \text{ years}} = -\$4000 \text{ per year.}$$

Thus, the value drops at the constant rate of $4000 per year. (Notice that ΔV is negative because the value of the equipment decreases.) See Table 1.17 and Figure 1.23. Since V changes at a constant rate, $V = f(t)$ is a linear function and its graph is a straight line. The rate of change, $-\$4000$ per year, is negative because the function is decreasing and the graph slopes down.

Table 1.17 *Value of equipment depreciated over a 5-year period*

t, year	V, value ($)
0	20,000
1	16,000
2	12,000
3	8,000
4	4,000
5	0

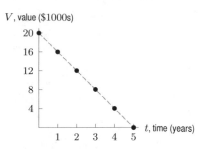

Figure 1.23: Value of equipment depreciated over a 5-year period

(b) After t years have elapsed,

$$\text{Decrease in value of equipment} = \$4000 \cdot \text{Number of years} = \$4000t.$$

The initial value of the equipment is $20,000, so at time t,

$$V = 20,000 - 4000t.$$

The total cost of production is another application of linear functions in economics.

A General Formula for the Family of Linear Functions

Example 1 involved a town whose population is growing at a constant rate with formula

$$\underbrace{\text{Current population}}_{} = \underbrace{\text{Initial population}}_{30,000 \text{ people}} + \underbrace{\text{Growth rate}}_{2000 \text{ people per year}} \times \underbrace{\text{Number of years}}_{t}$$

so

$$P = 30,000 + 2000t.$$

In Example 2, the value, V, as a function of t is given by

$$\underbrace{\text{Total cost}}_{} = \underbrace{\text{Initial value}}_{\$20,000} + \underbrace{\text{Change per year}}_{-\$4000 \text{ per year}} \times \underbrace{\text{Number of years}}_{t}$$

so

$$V = 20,000 + (-4000)t.$$

Using the symbols x, y, b, m, we see formulas for both of these linear functions follow the same pattern:

$$\underbrace{\text{Output}}_{y} = \underbrace{\text{Initial value}}_{b} + \underbrace{\text{Rate of change}}_{m} \times \underbrace{\text{Input}}_{x}.$$

Summarizing, we get the following results:

If $y = f(x)$ is a linear function, then for some constants b and m:

$$y = b + mx.$$

- m is called the **slope**, and gives the rate of change of y with respect to x. Thus,

$$m = \frac{\Delta y}{\Delta x}.$$

If (x_0, y_0) and (x_1, y_1) are any two distinct points on the graph of f, then

$$m = \frac{\Delta y}{\Delta x} = \frac{y_1 - y_0}{x_1 - x_0}.$$

- b is called the **vertical intercept**, or **y-intercept**, and gives the value of y for $x = 0$. In mathematical models, b typically represents an initial, or starting, value of the output.

Every linear function can be written in the form $y = b + mx$. Different linear functions have different values for m and b. These constants are known as *parameters*.

Example 3
In Example 1, the population function, $P = 30{,}000 + 2000t$, has slope $m = 2000$ and vertical intercept $b = 30{,}000$. In Example 2, the value of the computer equipment, $V = 20{,}000 - 4000t$, has slope $m = -4000$ and vertical intercept $b = 20{,}000$.

Tables for Linear Functions

A table of values could represent a linear function if the rate of change is constant, for all pairs of points in the table; that is,

$$\text{Rate of change of linear function} = \frac{\text{Change in output}}{\text{Change in input}} = \text{Constant}.$$

Thus, if the value of x goes up by equal steps in a table for a linear function, then the value of y goes up (or down) by equal steps as well. We say that changes in the value of y are *proportional* to changes in the value of x.

Example 4
Table 1.18 gives values of two functions, p and q. Could either of these functions be linear?

Table 1.18 *Values of two functions p and q*

x	50	55	60	65	70
$p(x)$	0.10	0.11	0.12	0.13	0.14
$q(x)$	0.01	0.03	0.06	0.14	0.15

Solution   The value of x goes up by equal steps of $\Delta x = 5$. The value of $p(x)$ also goes up by equal steps of $\Delta p = 0.01$, so $\Delta p / \Delta x$ is a constant. See Table 1.19. Thus, p could be a linear function.

Table 1.19   *Values of $\Delta p / \Delta x$*

x	$p(x)$	Δp	$\Delta p / \Delta x$
50	0.10		
		0.01	0.002
55	0.11		
		0.01	0.002
60	0.12		
		0.01	0.002
65	0.13		
		0.01	0.002
70	0.14		

Table 1.20   *Values of $\Delta q / \Delta x$*

x	$q(x)$	Δq	$\Delta q / \Delta x$
50	0.01		
		0.02	0.004
55	0.03		
		0.03	0.006
60	0.06		
		0.08	0.016
65	0.14		
		0.01	0.002
70	0.15		

In contrast, the value of $q(x)$ does not go up by equal steps. The value climbs by 0.02, then by 0.03, and so on. See Table 1.20. This means that $\Delta q / \Delta x$ is not constant. Thus, q could not be a linear function.

It is possible to have data from a linear function in which neither the x-values nor the y-values go up by equal steps. However the rate of change must be constant, as in the following example.

Example 5   The former Republic of Yugoslavia exported cars called Yugos to the US between 1985 and 1989. The car is now a collector's item.[13] Table 1.21 gives the quantity of Yugos sold, Q, and the price, p, for each year from 1985 to 1988.

(a) Using Table 1.21, explain why Q could be a linear function of p.
(b) What does the rate of change of this function tell you about Yugos?

Table 1.21   *Price and sales of Yugos in the US*

Year	Price in \$, p	Number sold, Q
1985	3990	49,000
1986	4110	43,000
1987	4200	38,500
1988	4330	32,000

Solution   (a) We are interested in Q as a function of p, so we plot Q on the vertical axis and p on the horizontal axis. The data points in Figure 1.24 appear to lie on a straight line, suggesting a linear function.

[13] www.inet.hr/˜pauric/epov.htm, accessed January 16, 2006.

Figure 1.24: Since the data from Table 1.21 falls on a straight line, the table could represent a linear function

To provide further evidence that Q is a linear function, we check that the rate of change of Q with respect to p is constant for the points given. When the price of a Yugo rose from $3990 to $4110, sales fell from 49,000 to 43,000. Thus,

$$\Delta p = 4110 - 3990 = 120,$$

$$\Delta Q = 43,000 - 49,000 = -6000.$$

Since the number of Yugos sold decreased, ΔQ is negative. Thus, as the price increased from $3990 to $4110,

$$\text{Rate of change of quantity as price increases} = \frac{\Delta Q}{\Delta p} = \frac{-6000}{120} = -50 \text{ cars per dollar.}$$

Next, we calculate the rate of change as the price increased from $4110 to $4200 to see if the rate remains constant:

$$\text{Rate of change} = \frac{\Delta Q}{\Delta p} = \frac{38,500 - 43,000}{4200 - 4110} = \frac{-4500}{90} = -50 \text{ cars per dollar,}$$

and as the price increased from $4200 to $4330:

$$\text{Rate of change} = \frac{\Delta Q}{\Delta p} = \frac{32,000 - 38,500}{4330 - 4200} = \frac{-6500}{130} = -50 \text{ cars per dollar.}$$

Since the rate of change, -50, is constant, Q could be a linear function of p. Given additional data, $\Delta Q / \Delta p$ might not remain constant. However, based on the table, it appears that the function is linear.

(b) Since ΔQ is the change in the number of cars sold and Δp is the change in price, the rate of change is -50 cars per dollar. Thus the number of Yugos sold decreased by 50 each time the price increased by $1.

Warning: Not All Graphs That Look Like Lines Represent Linear Functions

The graph of any linear function is a line. However, a function's graph can look like a line without actually being one. Consider the following example.

23

Example 6   The function $P = 100(1.02)^t$ approximates the population of Mexico in the early 2000s. Here P is the population (in millions) and t is the number of years since 2000. Table 1.22 and Figure 1.25 show values of P over a 5-year period. Is P a linear function of t?

Table 1.22   *Population of Mexico t years after 2000*

t (years)	P (millions)
0	100
1	102
2	104.04
3	106.12
4	108.24
5	110.41

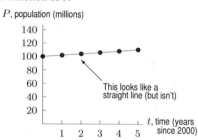

Figure 1.25: Graph of $P = 100(1.02)^t$ over 5-year period: Looks linear (but is not)

Solution   The formula $P = 100(1.02)^t$ is not of the form $P = b + mt$, so P is not a linear function of t. However, the graph of P in Figure 1.25 appears to be a straight line. We check P's rate of change in Table 1.22. When $t = 0$, $P = 100$ and when $t = 1$, $P = 102$. Thus, between 2000 and 2001,

$$\text{Rate of change of population} = \frac{\Delta P}{\Delta t} = \frac{102 - 100}{1 - 0} = 2.$$

For the interval from 2001 to 2002, we have

$$\text{Rate of change} = \frac{\Delta P}{\Delta t} = \frac{104.04 - 102}{2 - 1} = 2.04,$$

and for the interval from 2004 to 2005, we have

$$\text{Rate of change} = \frac{\Delta P}{\Delta t} = \frac{110.41 - 108.24}{5 - 4} = 2.17.$$

Thus, P's rate of change is not constant. In fact, P appears to be increasing at a faster and faster rate. Table 1.23 and Figure 1.26 show values of P over a longer (60-year) period. On this scale, these points do not appear to fall on a straight line. However, the graph of P curves upward so gradually at first that over the short interval shown in Figure 1.25, it barely curves at all. The graphs of many nonlinear functions, when viewed on a small scale, appear to be linear.

Table 1.23   *Population over 60 years*

t (years since 2000)	P (millions)
0	100
10	121.90
20	148.59
30	181.14
40	220.80
50	269.16
60	328.10

Figure 1.26: Graph of $P = 100(1.02)^t$ over 60 years: Not linear

Exercises and Problems for Section 1.3

Skill Refresher

In Exercises S1–S2, find $f(0)$ and $f(3)$.

S1. $f(x) = \frac{2}{3}x + 5$

S2. $f(t) = 17 - 4t$

In Exercises S3–S4, find $f(2) - f(0)$.

S3.

x	0	1	2	3
$f(x)$	-2	0	3	4

S4.

t	-1	0	1	2
$f(t)$	0	2	7	-1

In Exercises S5–S6, find the coordinates of the x and y intercepts.

S5. $y = -4x + 3$

S6. $5x - 2y = 4$

For each of the linear expressions in x in Exercises S7–S10, give the constant term and the coefficient of x.

S7. $3 - 2x + \frac{1}{2}$

S8. $4 - 3(x + 2) + 6(2x - 1)$

S9. $ax - ab - 3x + a + 3$

S10. $5(x - 1) + 3$

Exercises

Which of the tables in Exercises 1–6 could represent a linear function?

1.

x	0	100	300	600
$g(x)$	50	100	150	200

2.

x	0	10	20	30
$h(x)$	20	40	50	55

3.

t	1	2	3	4	5
$g(t)$	5	4	5	4	5

4.

x	0	5	10	15
$f(x)$	10	20	30	40

5.

γ	9	8	7	6	5
$p(\gamma)$	42	52	62	72	82

6.

x	-3	-1	0	3
$j(x)$	5	1	-1	-7

In Exercises 7–8, which line has the greater

(a) Slope?   (b) y-intercept?

7. $y = 7 + 2x$, $\quad y = 8 - 15x$

8. $y = 5 - 2x$, $\quad y = 7 - 3x$

In Exercises 9–12, identify the vertical intercept and the slope, and explain their meanings in practical terms.

9. The population of a town can be represented by the formula $P(t) = 54.25 - \frac{2}{7}t$, where $P(t)$ represents the population, in thousands, and t represents the time, in years, since 1970.

10. A stalactite grows according to the formula $L(t) = 17.75 + \frac{1}{250}t$, where $L(t)$ represents the length of the stalactite, in inches, and t represents the time, in years, since the stalactite was first measured.

11. The profit, in dollars, of selling n items is given by $P(n) = 0.98n - 3000$.

12. A phone company charges according to the formula $C(n) = 29.99 + 0.05n$, where n is the number of minutes, and $C(n)$ is the monthly phone charge, in dollars.

Problems

13. Table 1.24 gives the proposed fine $r = f(v)$ to be imposed on a motorist for speeding, where v is the motorist's speed and 55 mph is the speed limit.

(a) Decide whether f appears to be linear.
(b) What would the rate of change represent in practical terms for the motorist?
(c) Plot the data points.

Table 1.24

v (mph)	60	65	70	75	80	85
r (dollars)	75	100	125	150	175	200

14. In 2006, the population of a town was 18,310 and growing by 58 people per year. Find a formula for P, the town's population, in terms of t, the number of years since 2006.

15. A new Toyota RAV4 costs \$21,500. The car's value depreciates linearly to \$11,900 in three years time. Write a formula which expresses its value, V, in terms of its age, t, in years.

16. In 2003, the number, N, of cases of SARS (Severe Acute Respiratory Syndrome) reported in Hong Kong[14] was initially approximated by $N = 78.9 + 30.1t$, where t is the number of days since March 17. Interpret the constants 78.9 and 30.1.

17. Table 1.25 shows the cost C, in dollars, of selling x cups of coffee per day from a cart.

(a) Using the table, show that the relationship appears to be linear.

(b) Plot the data in the table.

(c) Find the slope of the line. Explain what this means in the context of the given situation.

(d) Why should it cost \$50 to serve zero cups of coffee?

Table 1.25

x	0	5	10	50	100	200
C	50.00	51.25	52.50	62.50	75.00	100.00

18. In each case, graph a linear function with the given rate of change. Label and put scales on the axes.

(a) Increasing at 2.1 inches/day

(b) Decreasing at 1.3 gallons/mile

19. A flight costs \$10,000 to operate, regardless of the number of passengers. Each ticket costs \$127. Express profit, π, as a linear function of the number of passengers, n, on the flight.

20. A small café sells drip coffee for \$0.95 per cup. On average, it costs the café \$0.25 to make a cup of coffee (for grounds, hot water, filters). The café also has a fixed daily cost of \$200 (for rent, wages, utilities).

(a) Let R, C, and P be the café's daily revenue, costs, and profit, respectively, for selling x cups of coffee in a day. Find formulas for R, C, and P as functions of x. [Hint: The revenue, R, is the total amount of money that the café brings in. The cost, C, includes the fixed daily cost as well as the cost for all x cups of coffee sold. P is the café's profit after costs have been accounted for.]

(b) Plot P against x. For what x-values is the graph of P below the x-axis? Above the x-axis? Interpret your results.

(c) Interpret the slope and both intercepts of your graph in practical terms.

21. Owners of an inactive quarry in Australia have decided to resume production. They estimate that it will cost them \$1000 per month to maintain and insure their equipment and that monthly salaries will be \$3000. It costs \$80 to mine a ton of rocks. Write a formula that expresses the total cost each month, c, as a function of r, the number of tons of rock mined per month.

22. Table 1.26 gives the area and perimeter of a square as a function of the length of its side.

(a) From the table, decide if either area or perimeter could be a linear function of side length.

(b) From the data make two graphs, one showing area as a function of side length, the other showing perimeter as a function of side length. Connect the points.

(c) If you find a linear relationship, give its corresponding rate of change and interpret its significance.

Table 1.26

Length of side	0	1	2	3	4	5	6
Area of square	0	1	4	9	16	25	36
Perimeter of square	0	4	8	12	16	20	24

23. Make two tables, one comparing the radius of a circle to its area, the other comparing the radius of a circle to its circumference. Repeat parts (a), (b), and (c) from Problem 22, this time comparing radius with circumference, and radius with area.

24. Sri Lanka is an island that experienced approximately linear population growth from 1950 to 2000. On the other hand, Afghanistan was torn by warfare in the 1980s and did not experience linear nor near-linear growth.[15]

(a) Table 1.27 gives the population of these two countries, in millions. Which of these two countries is A and which is B? Explain.

(b) What is the approximate rate of change of the linear function? What does the rate of change represent in practical terms?

(c) Estimate the population of Sri Lanka in 1988.

Table 1.27

Year	1950	1960	1970	1980	1990	2000
Population of country A	8.2	9.8	12.4	15.1	14.7	23.9
Population of country B	7.5	9.9	12.5	14.9	17.2	19.2

[14] World Health Organization, www.who.int/csr/sars/country/en.

[15] www.census.gov/ipc/www/idbsusum.html, accessed January 12, 2006.

25. Table 1.44 on page 54 gives the temperature-depth profile, $T = f(d)$, in a borehole in Belleterre, Quebec, where T is the average temperature at a depth d.

   (a) Could f be linear?

   (b) Graph f. What do you notice about the graph for $d \geq 150$?

   (c) What can you say about the average rate of change of f for $d \geq 150$?

26. The summit of Africa's largest peak, Mt. Kilimanjaro, consists of the northern and southern ice fields and the Furtwanger glacier. An article in the Proceedings of the National Academy of Sciences[16] indicates that in 2000 ($t = 0$) the area of the ice cover at the peak of Mt. Kilimanjaro was approximately 1951 m². By 2007, the area had shrunk to approximately 1555 m².

   (a) If this decline is modeled by a linear function, find $A = f(t)$, the equation of the ice-cover area as a function of time. Explain what the slope and A-intercept mean in terms of the ice cover.

   (b) Evaluate $f(11)$.

   (c) If this model is correct, when would you expect the ice cover to disappear?

27. Tuition cost T (in dollars) for part-time students at Stonewall College is given by $T = 300 + 200C$, where C represents the number of credits taken.

   (a) Find the tuition cost for eight credits.

   (b) How many credits were taken if the tuition was $1700?

   (c) Make a table showing costs for taking from one to twelve credits. For each value of C, give both the tuition cost, T, and the cost per credit, T/C. Round to the nearest dollar.

   (d) Which of these values of C has the smallest cost per credit?

   (e) What does the 300 represent in the formula for T?

   (f) What does the 200 represent in the formula for T?

28. A company finds that there is a linear relationship between the amount of money that it spends on advertising and the number of units it sells. If it spends no money on advertising, it sells 300 units. For each additional $5000 spent, an additional 20 units are sold.

   (a) If x is the amount of money that the company spends on advertising, find a formula for y, the number of units sold as a function of x.

   (b) How many units does the firm sell if it spends $25,000 on advertising? $50,000?

   (c) How much advertising money must be spent to sell 700 units?

   (d) What is the slope of the line you found in part (a)? Give an interpretation of the slope that relates units sold and advertising costs.

29. When each of the following equations are written in the form $y = b + mx$, the result is $y = 5 + 4x$. Find the constants r, s, k, j in these equations.

   (a) $y = 2r + x\sqrt{s}$

   (b) $y = \dfrac{1}{k} - (j - 1)x$.

30. Graph the following function in the window $-10 \leq x \leq 10, -10 \leq y \leq 10$. Is this graph a line? Explain.

$$y = -x \left(\frac{x - 1000}{900} \right)$$

31. Graph $y = 2x + 400$ using the window $-10 \leq x \leq 10, -10 \leq y \leq 10$. Describe what happens, and how you can fix it by using a better window.

32. Graph $y = 200x + 4$ using the window $-10 \leq x \leq 10, -10 \leq y \leq 10$. Describe what happens and how you can fix it by using a better window.

33. Figure 1.27 shows the graph of $y = x^2/1000 + 5$ in the window $-10 \leq x \leq 10, -10 \leq y \leq 10$. Discuss whether this is a linear function.

Figure 1.27

34. The cost of a cab ride is given by the function $C = 2.50 + 2d$, where d is the number of miles traveled and C is in dollars. Choose an appropriate window and graph the cost of a ride for a cab that travels no farther than a 10-mile radius from the center of the city.

---

[16]http://www.pnas.org/content/early/2009/10/30/0906029106.full.pdf+html, accessed November 27, 2009.

1.4   FORMULAS FOR LINEAR FUNCTIONS

To find a formula for a linear function we find values for the slope, m, and the vertical intercept, b, in the formula $y = b + mx$.

Finding a Formula for a Linear Function from a Table of Data

If a table of data represents a linear function, we first calculate m and then determine b.

Example 1   A grapefruit is thrown into the air. Its velocity, v, is a linear function of t, the time since it was thrown. A positive velocity indicates the grapefruit is rising and a negative velocity indicates it is falling. Check that the data in Table 1.28 corresponds to a linear function. Find a formula for v in terms of t.

Table 1.28   *Velocity of a grapefruit t seconds after being thrown into the air*

t, time (sec)	1	2	3	4
v, velocity (ft/sec)	48	16	−16	−48

Solution   Figure 1.28 shows the data in Table 1.28. The points appear to fall on a line. To check that the velocity function is linear, calculate the rates of change of v and see that they are constant. From time $t = 1$ to $t = 2$, we have

$$\text{Rate of change of velocity with time} = \frac{\Delta v}{\Delta t} = \frac{16 - 48}{2 - 1} = -32.$$

For the next second, from $t = 2$ to $t = 3$, we have

$$\text{Rate of change} = \frac{\Delta v}{\Delta t} = \frac{-16 - 16}{3 - 2} = -32.$$

You can check that the rate of change from $t = 3$ to $t = 4$ is also -32.

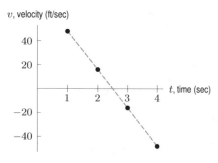

Figure 1.28: Velocity of a grapefruit is a linear function of time

A formula for v is of the form $v = b + mt$. Since m is the rate of change, we have $m = -32$ so $v = b - 32t$. The initial velocity (at $t = 0$) is represented by b. We are not given the value of v when $t = 0$, but we can use any data point to calculate b. For example, $v = 48$ when $t = 1$, so

$$48 = b - 32 \cdot 1,$$

which gives
$$b = 80.$$
Thus, a formula for the velocity is $v = 80 - 32t$.

What does the rate of change, m, in Example 1 tell us about the grapefruit? Think about the units:
$$m = \frac{\Delta v}{\Delta t} = \frac{\text{Change in velocity}}{\text{Change in time}} = \frac{-32 \text{ ft/sec}}{1 \text{ sec}} = -32 \text{ ft/sec per second.}$$

The value of m, -32 ft/sec per second, tells us that the grapefruit's velocity is decreasing by 32 ft/sec for every second that goes by. We say the grapefruit is accelerating at -32 ft/sec per second. (The units ft/sec per second are often written ft/sec². Negative acceleration is also called deceleration.)[17]

Finding a Formula for a Linear Function from a Graph

We can calculate the slope, m, of a linear function using two points on its graph. Having found m, we can use either of the points to calculate b, the vertical intercept.

Example 2   Figure 1.29 shows oxygen consumption as a function of heart rate for two people.

(a) Assuming linearity, find formulas for these two functions.
(b) Interpret the slope of each graph in terms of oxygen consumption.

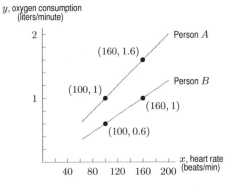

Figure 1.29: Oxygen consumption of two people running on treadmills

Solution   (a) Let x be heart rate and let y be oxygen consumption. Since we are assuming linearity, $y = b + mx$. The two points on person A's line, $(100, 1)$ and $(160, 1.6)$, give

$$\text{Slope of A's line} = m = \frac{\Delta y}{\Delta x} = \frac{1.6 - 1}{160 - 100} = 0.01.$$

Thus $y = b + 0.01x$. To find b, use the fact that $y = 1$ when $x = 100$:

$$1 = b + 0.01(100)$$
$$1 = b + 1$$
$$b = 0.$$

[17]The notation ft/sec² is shorthand for ft/sec per second; it does not mean a "square second" in the same way that areas are measured square feet or square meters.

Alternatively, b can be found using the fact that $x = 160$ if $y = 1.6$. Either way leads to the formula $y = 0.01x$.

For person B, we again begin with the formula $y = b + mx$. In Figure 1.29, two points on B's line are $(100, 0.6)$ and $(160, 1)$, so

$$\text{Slope of B's line } = m = \frac{\Delta y}{\Delta x} = \frac{1 - 0.6}{160 - 100} = \frac{0.4}{60} \approx 0.0067.$$

To find b, use the fact that $y = 1$ when $x = 160$:

$$1 = b + (0.4/60) \cdot 160$$
$$1 = b + 1.067$$
$$b = -0.067.$$

Thus, for person B, we have $y = -0.067 + 0.0067x$.

(b) The slope for person A is $m = 0.01$, so

$$m = \frac{\text{Change in oxygen consumption}}{\text{Change in heart rate}} = \frac{\text{Change in liters/min}}{\text{Change in beats/min}} = 0.01 \frac{\text{liters}}{\text{heartbeat}}.$$

Every additional heartbeat (per minute) for person A translates to an additional 0.01 liters (per minute) of oxygen consumed.

The slope for person B is $m = 0.0067$. Thus, for every additional beat (per minute), person B consumes an additional 0.0067 liter of oxygen (per minute). Since the slope for person B is smaller than for person A, person B consumes less additional oxygen than person A for the same increase in pulse.

What do the y-intercepts of the functions in Example 2 say about oxygen consumption? Often the y-intercept of a function is a starting value. In this case, the y-intercept would be the oxygen consumption of a person whose pulse is zero (i.e. $x = 0$). Since a person running on a treadmill must have a pulse, in this case it makes no sense to interpret the y-intercept this way. The formula for oxygen consumption is useful only for realistic values of the pulse.

Finding a Formula for a Linear Function from a Verbal Description

Sometimes the verbal description of a linear function is less straightforward than those we saw in Section 1.3. Consider the following example.

Example 3   We have $24 to spend on soda and chips for a party. A six-pack of soda costs $3 and a bag of chips costs $2. The number of six-packs we can afford, y, is a function of the number of bags of chips we decide to buy, x.

(a) Find an equation relating x and y.
(b) Graph the equation. Interpret the intercepts and the slope in the context of the party.

Solution   (a) If we spend all $24 on soda and chips, then we have the following equation:

$$\text{Amount spent on chips } + \text{ Amount spent on soda } = \$24.$$

If we buy x bags of chips at $2 per bag, then the amount spent on chips is $2x$. Similarly, if we buy y six-packs of soda at $3 per six-pack, then the amount spent on soda is $3y$. Thus,

$$2x + 3y = 24.$$

We can solve for y, giving

$$3y = 24 - 2x$$
$$y = 8 - \frac{2}{3}x.$$

This is a linear function with slope $m = -2/3$ and y-intercept $b = 8$.

(b) The graph of this function is a discrete set of points, since the number of bags of chips and the number of six-packs of soda must be (nonnegative) integers.

To find the y-intercept, we set $x = 0$, giving

$$2 \cdot 0 + 3y = 24.$$

So $3y = 24$, giving $y = 8$.

Substituting $y = 0$ gives the x-intercept,

$$2x + 3 \cdot 0 = 24.$$

So $2x = 24$, giving $x = 12$. Thus the points $(0, 8)$ and $(12, 0)$ are on the graph.

The point $(0, 8)$ indicates that we can buy 8 six-packs of soda if we buy no chips. The point $(12, 0)$ indicates that we can buy 12 bags of chips if we buy no soda. The other points on the line describe affordable options between these two extremes. For example, the point $(6, 4)$ is on the line, because

$$2 \cdot 6 + 3 \cdot 4 = 24.$$

This means that if we buy 6 bags of chips, we can afford 4 six-packs of soda.

Figure 1.30: Relation between the number of six-packs, y, and the number of bags of chips, x

The points marked in Figure 1.30 represent affordable options. All affordable options lie on or below the line $2x + 3y = 24$. Not all points on the line are affordable options. For example, suppose we purchase one six-pack of soda for $3.00. That leaves $21.00 to spend on chips, meaning we would have to buy 10.5 bags of chips, which is not possible. Therefore, the point $(10.5, 1)$ is not an option, although it is a point on the line $2x + 3y = 24$.

To interpret the slope, notice that

$$m = \frac{\Delta y}{\Delta x} = \frac{\text{Change in number of six-packs}}{\text{Change in number of bags of chips}},$$

so the units of m are six-packs of soda per bags of chips. The fact that $m = -2/3$ means that for each additional 3 bags of chips purchased, we can purchase 2 fewer six-packs of soda. This occurs because 2 six-packs cost $6, the same as 3 bags of chips. Thus, $m = -2/3$ is the rate at which the amount of soda we can buy decreases as we buy more chips.

Alternative Forms for the Equation of a Line

In Example 3, the equation $2x + 3y = 24$ represents a linear relationship between x and y even though the equation is not in the form $y = b + mx$. The following equations represent lines.

- The *slope-intercept form* is
$$y = b + mx \qquad \text{where } m \text{ is the slope and } b \text{ is the } y\text{-intercept.}$$
- The *point-slope form* is
$$y - y_0 = m(x - x_0) \quad \text{where } m \text{ is the slope and } (x_0, y_0) \text{ is a point on the line.}$$
- The *standard form* is
$$Ax + By + C = 0 \qquad \text{where } A, B, \text{ and } C \text{ are constants.}$$

If we know the slope of a line and the coordinates of a point on the line, it is often convenient to use the point-slope form of the equation.

Example 4   Use the point-slope form to find the equation of the line for the oxygen consumption of person A in Example 2.

Solution   In Example 2, we found the slope of person A's line to be $m = 0.01$. Since the point $(100, 1)$ lies on the line, the point-slope form gives the equation

$$y - 1 = 0.01(x - 100).$$

To check that this gives the same equation we got in Example 2, we multiply out and simplify:

$$y - 1 = 0.01x - 1$$
$$y = 0.01x.$$

Alternatively, we could have used the point $(160, 1.6)$ instead of $(100, 1)$, giving

$$y - 1.6 = 0.01(x - 160).$$

Multiplying out again gives $y = 0.01x$.

Exercises and Problems for Section 1.4

Skill Refresher

Solve the equations in Exercises S1–S5.

S1. $y - 5 = 21$

S2. $2x - 5 = 13$

S3. $2x - 5 = 4x - 9$

S4. $17 - 28y = 13y + 24$

S5. $\dfrac{5}{3}(y + 2) = \dfrac{1}{2} - y$

In Exercises S6–S10, solve for the indicated variable.

S6. $I = Prt$, for P.

S7. $C = \dfrac{5}{9}(F - 32)$, for F.

S8. $C = 2\pi r$, for r.

S9. $ab + ax = c - ax$, for x.

S10. $by - d = ay + c$, for y.

Exercises

If possible, rewrite the equations in Exercises 1–9 in slope-intercept form, $y = b + mx$.

1. $5(x + y) = 4$

2. $3x + 5y = 20$

3. $0.1y + x = 18$

4. $5x - 3y + 2 = 0$

5. $y - 0.7 = 5(x - 0.2)$

6. $y = 5$

7. $3x + 2y + 40 = x - y$

8. $x = 4$

9. $\dfrac{x + y}{7} = 3$

Is each function in Exercises 10–15 linear? If so, rewrite it the form $y = b + mx$.

10. $g(w) = -\dfrac{1 - 12w}{3}$

11. $F(P) = 13 - \dfrac{2^{-1}}{4}P$

12. $j(s) = 3s^{-1} + 7$

13. $C(r) = 2\pi r$

14. $h(x) = 3^x + 12$

15. $f(x) = m^2 x + n^2$

Find formulas for the linear functions in Exercises 16–23.

16. Slope -4 and x-intercept 7

17. Slope 3 and y-intercept 8

18. Passes through the points $(-1, 5)$ and $(2, -1)$

19. Slope $2/3$ and passes through the point $(5, 7)$

20. Has x-intercept 3 and y-intercept -5

21. Slope 0.1, passes through $(-0.1, 0.02)$

22. Function f has $f(0.3) = 0.8$ and $f(0.8) = -0.4$

23. Function f has $f(-2) = 7$ and $f(3) = -3$

Exercises 24–30 give data from a linear function. Find a formula for the function.

24.

Year, t	0	1	2
Value of computer, $\$V = f(t)$	2000	1500	1000

25.

Price per bottle, p (\$)	0.50	0.75	1.00
Number of bottles sold, $q = f(p)$	1500	1000	500

26.

Temperature, $y = f(x)$ (°C)	0	5	20
Temperature, x (°F)	32	41	68

27.

Temperature, $y = f(x)$, (°R)	459.7	469.7	489.7
Temperature, x (°F)	0	10	30

28.

29.

30.

Problems

Find formulas for the linear functions in Problems 31–34.

31. The graph of f contains $(-3, -8)$ and $(5, -20)$.

32. $g(100) = 2000$ and $g(400) = 3800$

33. $P = h(t)$ gives the size of a population that begins with 12,000 members and grows by 225 members each year.

34. The graph of h intersects the graph of $y = x^2$ at $x = -2$ and $x = 3$.

Table 1.29 gives the cost, $C(n)$, of producing a certain good as a linear function of n, the number of units produced. Use the table to answer Problems 35–37.

Table 1.29

n (units)	100	125	150	175
$C(n)$ (dollars)	11000	11125	11250	11375

35. Evaluate the following expressions. Give economic interpretations for each.

   (a) $C(175)$
   (b) $C(175) - C(150)$
   (c) $\dfrac{C(175) - C(150)}{175 - 150}$

36. Estimate $C(0)$. What is the economic significance of this value?

37. The *fixed cost* of production is the cost incurred before any goods are produced. The *unit cost* is the cost of producing an additional unit. Find a formula for $C(n)$ in terms of n, given that

   Total cost = Fixed cost + Unit cost · Number of units

38. In a college meal plan you pay a membership fee; then all your meals are at a fixed price per meal.

   (a) If 90 meals cost $1005 and 140 meals cost $1205, write a linear function that describes the cost of a meal plan, C, in terms of the number of meals, n.
   (b) What is the cost per meal and what is the membership fee?
   (c) Find the cost for 120 meals.
   (d) Find n in terms of C.
   (e) Use part (d) to determine the maximum number of meals you can buy on a budget of $1285.

39. An empty champagne bottle is tossed from a hot-air balloon. Its upward velocity is measured every second and recorded in Table 1.30.

   (a) Describe the motion of the bottle in words. What do negative values of v represent?
   (b) Find a formula for v in terms of t.
   (c) Explain the physical significance of the slope of your formula.
   (d) Explain the physical significance of the t-axis and v-axis intercepts.

Table 1.30

t (sec)	0	1	2	3	4	5
v (ft/sec)	40	8	−24	−56	−88	−120

40. John wants to buy a dozen rolls. The local bakery sells sesame and poppy-seed rolls for the same price.

   (a) Make a table of all the possible combinations of rolls if he buys a dozen, where s is the number of sesame seed rolls and p is the number of poppy-seed rolls.
   (b) Find a formula for p as a function of s.
   (c) Graph this function.

41. The demand for gasoline can be modeled as a linear function of price. If the price of gasoline is $p = \$3.10$ per gallon, the quantity demanded in a fixed period is $q = 65$ gallons. If the price rises to $3.50 per gallon, the quantity demanded falls to 45 gallons in that period.

   (a) Find a formula for q in terms of p.
   (b) Explain the economic significance of the slope of your formula.
   (c) Explain the economic significance of the q-axis and p-axis intercepts.

42. The solid waste generated each year in the cities of the US is increasing.[18] The solid waste generated, in millions of tons, was 88.1 in 1960 and 239.1 in 2000. The trend appears linear during this time.

   (a) Construct a formula for the amount of municipal solid waste generated in the US by finding the equation of the line through these two points.
   (b) Use this formula to predict the amount of municipal solid waste generated in the US, in millions of tons, in the year 2020.

43. Find the equation of the line l, shown in Figure 1.31, if its slope is $m = 4$.

Figure 1.31

44. Find a formula for the line intersecting the graph of $f(x)$ at $x = 1$ and $x = 3$, where

$$f(x) = \frac{10}{x^2 + 1}.$$

---

[18]http://www.epa.gov/osw/nonhaz/municipal/pubs/msw2008rpt.pdf, accessed November 23, 2009.

45. Find the equation of line l in Figure 1.32.

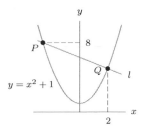

Figure 1.32

46. Find an equation for the line l in Figure 1.33 in terms of the constant A and values of the function f.

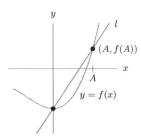

Figure 1.33

47. You can type four pages in 50 minutes and nine pages in an hour and forty minutes.

(a) Find a linear function for the number of pages typed, p, as a function of time, t. If time is measured in minutes, what values of t make sense in this example?

(b) How many pages can be typed in two hours?

(c) Interpret the slope of the function in practical terms.

(d) Use the result in part (a) to solve for time as a function of the number of pages typed.

(e) How long does it take to type a 15-page paper?

(f) Write a short paragraph explaining why it is useful to know both of the formulas obtained in part (a) and part (d).

48. Wire is sold by gauge size, where the diameter of the wire is a decreasing linear function of gauge. Gauge 2 wire has a diameter of 0.2656 inches and gauge 8 wire has a diameter of 0.1719 inches. Find the diameter for wires of gauge 12.5 and gauge 0. What values of the gauge do not make sense in this model?

49. A dose-response function can be used to describe the increase in risk associated with the increase in exposure to various hazards. For example, the risk of contracting lung cancer depends, among other things, on the number of cigarettes a person smokes per day. This risk can be described by a linear dose-response function. For example, it is known that smoking 10 cigarettes per day increases a person's probability of contracting lung cancer by a factor of 25, while smoking 20 cigarettes a day increases the probability by a factor of 50.

(a) Find a formula for $i(x)$, the increase in the probability of contracting lung cancer for a person who smokes x cigarettes per day as compared to a non-smoker.

(b) Evaluate $i(0)$.

(c) Interpret the slope of the function i.

In Problems 50–51, write the functions in slope-intercept form. Identify the values of b and m.

50. $v(s) = \pi x^2 - 3xr - 4rs - s\sqrt{x}$

51. $w(r) = \pi x^2 - 3xr - 4rs - s\sqrt{x}$

52. The development time, t, of an organism is the number of days required for the organism to mature, and the development rate is defined as $r = 1/t$. In cold-blooded organisms such as insects, the development rate depends on temperature: the colder it is, the longer the organism takes to develop. For such organisms, the degree-day model[19] assumes that the development rate r is a linear function of temperature H (in °C):

$$r = b + kH.$$

(a) According to the degree-day model, there is a minimum temperature H_{min} below which an organism never matures. Find a formula for H_{min} in terms of the constants b and k.

(b) Define S as $S = (H - H_{min})t$, where S is the number of degree-days. That is, S is the number of days t times the number of degrees between H and H_{min}. Use the formula for r to show that S is a constant. In other words, find a formula for S that does not involve H. Your formula will involve k.

(c) A certain organism requires $t = 25$ days to develop at a constant temperature of $H = 20°$C and has $H_{min} = 15°$C. Using the fact that S is a constant, how many days does it take for this organism to develop at a temperature of 25°C?

[19]Information drawn from a web site created by Dr. Alexei A. Sharov at the Virginia Polytechnic Institute, http://www.ento.vt.edu/ sharov/PopEcol/popecol.html.

(d) In part (c) we assumed that the temperature H is constant throughout development. If the temperature varies from day to day, the number of degree-days can be accumulated until they total S, at which point the organism completes development. For instance, suppose on the first day the temperature is $H = 20°C$ and that on the next day it is $H = 22°C$. Then for these first two days

Total number of degree days

$$= (20 - 15) \cdot 1 + (22 - 15) \cdot 1 = 12.$$

Based on Table 1.31, on what day does the organism reach maturity?

Table 1.31

Day	1	2	3	4	5	6	7	8	9	10	11	12
H (°C)	20	22	27	28	27	31	29	30	28	25	24	26

53. (Continuation of Problem 52.) Table 1.32 gives the development time t (in days) for an insect as a function of temperature H (in °C).

(a) Find a linear formula for r, the development rate, in terms of H.

(b) Find the value of S, the number of degree-days required for the organism to mature.

Table 1.32

H, °C	20	22	24	26	28	30
t, days	14.3	12.5	11.1	10.0	9.1	8.3

1.5 GEOMETRIC PROPERTIES OF LINEAR FUNCTIONS

Interpreting the Parameters of a Linear Function

The slope-intercept form for a linear function is $y = b + mx$, where b is the y-intercept and m is the slope. The parameters b and m can be used to compare linear functions.

Example 1 With time, t, in years, the populations of four towns, P_A, P_B, P_C and P_D, are given by the following formulas:

$$P_A = 20{,}000 + 1600t, \quad P_B = 50{,}000 - 300t, \quad P_C = 650t + 45{,}000, \quad P_D = 15{,}000(1.07)^t.$$

(a) Which populations are represented by linear functions?

(b) Describe in words what each linear model tells you about that town's population. Which town starts out with the most people? Which town is growing fastest?

Solution (a) The populations of towns A, B, and C are represented by linear functions because they are written in the form $P = b + mt$. Town D's population does not grow linearly since its formula, $P_D = 15{,}000(1.07)^t$, cannot be expressed in the form $P_D = b + mt$.

(b) For town A, we have

$$P_A = \underbrace{20{,}000}_{b} + \underbrace{1600}_{m} \cdot t,$$

so $b = 20{,}000$ and $m = 1600$. This means that in year $t = 0$, town A has 20,000 people. It grows by 1600 people per year.

For town B, we have

$$P_B = \underbrace{50{,}000}_{b} + \underbrace{(-300)}_{m} \cdot t,$$

so $b = 50{,}000$ and $m = -300$. This means that town B starts with 50,000 people. The negative slope indicates that the population is decreasing at the rate of 300 people per year.

For town C, we have

$$P_C = \underbrace{45,000}_{b} + \underbrace{650}_{m} \cdot t,$$

so $b = 45,000$ and $m = 650$. This means that town C begins with 45,000 people and grows by 650 people per year.

Town B starts out with the most people, 50,000, but town A, with a rate of change of 1600 people per year, grows the fastest of the three towns that grow linearly.

The Effect of the Parameters on the Graph of a Linear Function

The graph of a linear function is a line. Changing the values of b and m gives different members of the family of linear functions. In summary:

> Let $y = b + mx$. Then the graph of y against x is a line.
> - The y-intercept, b, tells us where the line crosses the y-axis.
> - If the slope, m, is positive, the line climbs from left to right. If the slope, m, is negative, the line falls from left to right.
> - The slope, m, tells us how fast the line is climbing or falling.
> - The larger the magnitude of m (either positive or negative), the steeper the graph of f.

Example 2   (a) Graph the three linear functions P_A, P_B, P_C from Example 1 and show how to identify the values of b and m from the graph.

(b) Graph P_D from Example 1 and explain how the graph shows P_D is not a linear function.

Solution   (a) Figure 1.34 gives graphs of the three functions:

$$P_A = 20,000 + 1600t, \qquad P_B = 50,000 - 300t, \quad \text{and} \quad P_C = 45,000 + 650t.$$

The values of b identified in Example 1 tell us the vertical intercepts. Figure 1.34 shows that the graph of P_A crosses the P-axis at $P = 20,000$, the graph of P_B crosses at $P = 50,000$, and the graph of P_C crosses at $P = 45,000$.

Figure 1.34: Graphs of three linear functions, P_A, P_B, and P_C, showing starting values and rates of climb

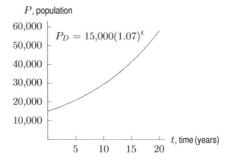

Figure 1.35: Graph of $P_D = 15,000(1.07)^t$ is not a line

37

Notice that the graphs of P_A and P_C are both climbing and that P_A climbs faster than P_C. This corresponds to the fact that the slopes of these two functions are positive ($m = 1600$ for P_A and $m = 650$ for P_C) and the slope of P_A is larger than the slope of P_C.

The graph of P_B falls when read from left to right, indicating that population decreases over time. This corresponds to the fact that the slope of P_C is negative ($m = -300$).

(b) Figure 1.35 gives a graph of P_D. Since it is not a line, P_D is not a linear function.

Intersection of Two Lines

To find the point at which two lines intersect, notice that the (x, y)-coordinates of such a point must satisfy the equations for both lines. Thus, in order to find the point of intersection algebraically, solve the equations simultaneously.[20]

If linear functions are modeling real quantities, their points of intersection often have practical significance. Consider the next example.

Example 3 The cost in dollars of renting a car for a day from three different rental agencies and driving it d miles is given by the following functions:

$$C_1 = 50 + 0.10d, \qquad C_2 = 30 + 0.20d, \qquad C_3 = 0.50d.$$

(a) Describe in words the daily rental arrangements made by each of these three agencies.
(b) Which agency is cheapest?

Solution (a) Agency 1 charges $50 plus $0.10 per mile driven. Agency 2 charges $30 plus $0.20 per mile. Agency 3 charges $0.50 per mile driven.
(b) The answer depends on how far we want to drive. If we are not driving far, agency 3 may be cheapest because it only charges for miles driven and has no other fees. If we want to drive a long way, agency 1 may be cheapest (even though it charges $50 up front) because it has the lowest per-mile rate.

The three functions are graphed in Figure 1.36. The graph shows that for d up to 100 miles, the value of C_3 is less than C_1 and C_2 because its graph is below the other two. For d between 100 and 200 miles, the value of C_2 is less than C_1 and C_3. For d more than 200 miles, the value of C_1 is less than C_2 and C_3.

By graphing these three functions on a calculator, we can estimate the coordinates of the points of intersection by tracing. To find the exact coordinates, we solve simultaneous equations. Starting with the intersection of lines C_1 and C_2, we set the costs equal, $C_1 = C_2$, and solve for d:

$$50 + 0.10d = 30 + 0.20d$$
$$20 = 0.10d$$
$$d = 200.$$

Thus, the cost of driving 200 miles is the same for agencies 1 and 2. Solving $C_2 = C_3$ gives

$$30 + 0.20d = 0.50d$$
$$0.30d = 30$$
$$d = 100,$$

[20]If you have questions about the algebra in this section, see the Skills Refresher on page 61.

which means the cost of driving 100 miles is the same for agencies 2 and 3.

Thus, agency 3 is cheapest up to 100 miles. Agency 1 is cheapest for more than 200 miles. Agency 2 is cheapest between 100 and 200 miles. See Figure 1.36. Notice that the point of intersection of C_1 and C_3, $(125, 62.5)$, does not influence our decision as to which agency is the cheapest.

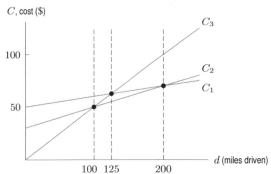

Figure 1.36: Cost of driving a car d miles when renting from three different agencies. Cheapest agency corresponds to the lowest graph for a given d value

Equations of Horizontal and Vertical Lines

An increasing linear function has positive slope and a decreasing linear function has negative slope. What about a line with slope $m = 0$? If the rate of change of a quantity is zero, then the quantity does not change. Thus, if the slope of a line is zero, the value of y must be constant. Such a line is horizontal.

Example 4 Explain why the equation $y = 4$ represents a horizontal line and the equation $x = 4$ represents a vertical line.

Solution The equation $y = 4$ represents a linear function with slope $m = 0$. To see this, notice that this equation can be rewritten as $y = 4 + 0 \cdot x$. Thus, the value of y is 4 no matter what the value of x is. See Figure 1.37. Similarly, the equation $x = 4$ means that x is 4 no matter what the value of y is. Every point on the line in Figure 1.38 has x equal to 4, so this line is the graph of $x = 4$.

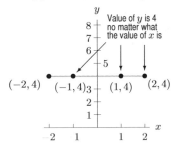

Figure 1.37: The horizontal line $y = 4$ has slope 0

Figure 1.38: The vertical line $x = 4$ has an undefined slope

39

What is the slope of a vertical line? Figure 1.38 shows three points, $(4, -1)$, $(4, 1)$, and $(4, 3)$ on a vertical line. Calculating the slope, gives

$$m = \frac{\Delta y}{\Delta x} = \frac{3 - 1}{4 - 4} = \frac{2}{0}.$$

The slope is undefined because the denominator, Δx, is 0. The slope of every vertical line is undefined for the same reason. All the x-values on such a line are equal, so Δx is 0, and the denominator of the expression for the slope is 0. A vertical line is not the graph of a function, since it fails the vertical line test. It does not have an equation of the form $y = b + mx$.

In summary,

For any constant k:
- The graph of the equation $y = k$ is a horizontal line and its slope is zero.
- The graph of the equation $x = k$ is a vertical line and its slope is undefined.

Slopes of Parallel and Perpendicular Lines

Figure 1.39 shows two parallel lines. These lines are parallel because they have equal slopes.

Figure 1.39: Parallel lines: l_1 and l_2 have equal slopes

Figure 1.40: Perpendicular lines: l_1 has a positive slope and l_2 has a negative slope

What about perpendicular lines? Two perpendicular lines are graphed in Figure 1.40. We can see that if one line has a positive slope, then any perpendicular line must have a negative slope. Perpendicular lines have slopes with opposite signs.

We show that if l_1 and l_2 are two perpendicular lines with slopes, m_1 and m_2, then m_1 is the negative reciprocal of m_2. If m_1 and m_2 are not zero, we have the following result:

Let l_1 and l_2 be two lines having slopes m_1 and m_2, respectively. Then:
- These lines are parallel if and only if $m_1 = m_2$.
- These lines are perpendicular if and only if $m_1 = -\dfrac{1}{m_2}$.

In addition, any two horizontal lines are parallel and $m_1 = m_2 = 0$. Any two vertical lines are parallel and m_1 and m_2 are undefined. A horizontal line is perpendicular to a vertical line. See Figures 1.41–1.43.

Figure 1.41: Any two horizontal lines are parallel

Figure 1.42: Any two vertical lines are parallel

Figure 1.43: A horizontal line and a vertical line are perpendicular

Justification of Formula for Slopes of Perpendicular Lines

Figure 1.44 shows l_1 and l_2, two perpendicular lines with slopes m_1 and m_2. Neither line is horizontal or vertical, so m_1 and m_2 are both defined and nonzero. We will show that

$$m_2 = -\frac{1}{m_1}.$$

Using right triangle $\triangle PQR$ with side lengths a and b we see that

$$m_1 = \frac{b}{a}.$$

Rotating $\triangle PQR$ by $90°$ about the point P produces triangle $\triangle PST$. Using $\triangle PST$ we see that

$$m_2 = -\frac{a}{b} = -\frac{1}{b/a} = -\frac{1}{m_1}.$$

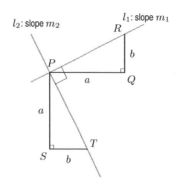

Figure 1.44

Exercises and Problems for Section 1.5

Skill Refresher

Solve the systems of equations in Exercises S1–S6, if possible.

Determine the points of intersection for Exercises S7–S8.

S1. $\begin{cases} x + y = 3 \\ y = 5 \end{cases}$

S2. $\begin{cases} x + y = 3 \\ x - y = 5 \end{cases}$

S3. $\begin{cases} x + y = 2 \\ 2x + 2y = 7 \end{cases}$

S4. $\begin{cases} y = x - 3 \\ 2y - 2x = -6 \end{cases}$

S5. $\begin{cases} 2x - y = 10 \\ x + 2y = 15 \end{cases}$

S6. $\begin{cases} 2(x + y) = 3 \\ x = y + 3(x - 5) \end{cases}$

S7.

S8.

Exercises

1. Without using a calculator, match the equations (a) – (f) to the graphs (I) – (VI).

(a) $y = -2.72x$
(b) $y = 0.01 + 0.001x$
(c) $y = 27.9 - 0.1x$
(d) $y = 0.1x - 27.9$
(e) $y = -5.7 - 200x$
(f) $y = x/3.14$

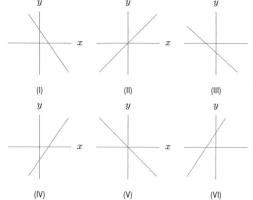

(I) (II) (III)

(IV) (V) (VI)

2. Without a calculator, match the equations (a)–(g) to the graphs (I)–(VII).

(a) $y = x - 5$
(b) $-3x + 4 = y$
(c) $5 = y$
(d) $y = -4x - 5$
(e) $y = x + 6$
(f) $y = x/2$
(g) $5 = x$

(I) (II) (III) (IV)

(V) (VI) (VII)

3. Figure 1.45 gives lines, A, B, C, D, and E. Without a calculator, match each line to f, g, h, u or v:

$$f(x) = 20 + 2x$$
$$g(x) = 20 + 4x$$
$$h(x) = 2x - 30$$
$$u(x) = 60 - x$$
$$v(x) = 60 - 2x$$

Figure 1.45

4. Without a calculator, match the following functions to the lines in Figure 1.46:

$$f(x) = 5 + 2x$$
$$g(x) = -5 + 2x$$
$$h(x) = 5 + 3x$$
$$j(x) = 5 - 2x$$
$$k(x) = 5 - 3x$$

Figure 1.46

5. (a) By hand, graph $y = 3$ and $x = 3$.
(b) Can the equations in part (a) be written in slope-intercept form?

Are the lines in Exercises 6–11 perpendicular? Parallel? Neither?

6. $y = 5x - 7; y = 5x + 8$

7. $y = 4x + 3; y = 13 - \frac{1}{4}x$

8. $y = 2x + 3; \quad y = 2x - 7$

9. $y = 4x + 7; \quad y = \frac{1}{4}x - 2$

10. $f(q) = 12q + 7; g(q) = \frac{1}{12}q + 96$

11. $2y = 16 - x; 4y = -8 - 2x$

Problems

12. Sketch a family of functions $y = -2 - ax$ for five different values of a with $a < 0$.

13. Find the equation of the line parallel to $3x + 5y = 6$ and passing through the point $(0, 6)$.

14. Find the equation of the line passing through the point $(2, 1)$ and perpendicular to the line $y = 5x - 3$.

15. Find the equations of the lines parallel to and perpendicular to the line $y + 4x = 7$, and through the point $(1, 5)$.

16. Estimate the slope of the line in Figure 1.47 and find an approximate equation for the line.

Figure 1.47

17. Line l in Figure 1.48 is parallel to the line $y = 2x + 1$. Find the coordinates of the point P.

Figure 1.48

18. Find the equation of the line l_2 in Figure 1.49.

Figure 1.49

19. The cost of a Frigbox refrigerator is $950, and it depreciates $50 each year. The cost of an Arctic Air refrigerator is $1200, and it depreciates $100 per year.

(a) If a Frigbox and an Arctic Air are bought at the same time, when do the two refrigerators have equal value?

(b) If both refrigerators continue to depreciate at the same rates, what happens to the values of the refrigerators in 20 years' time? What does this mean?

20. You need to rent a car and compare the charges of three different companies. Company A charges 20 cents per mile plus $20 per day. Company B charges 10 cents per mile plus $35 per day. Company C charges $70 per day with no mileage charge.

(a) Find formulas for the cost of driving cars rented from companies A, B, and C, in terms of x, the distance driven in miles in one day.

(b) Graph the costs for each company for $0 \le x \le 500$. Put all three graphs on the same set of axes.

(c) What do the slope and the vertical intercept tell you in this situation?

(d) Use the graph in part (b) to find under what circumstances company A is the cheapest. What about Company B? Company C? Explain why your results make sense.

21. Line l is given by $y = 3 - \frac{2}{3}x$ and point P has coordinates $(6, 5)$.

(a) Find the equation of the line containing P and parallel to l.

(b) Find the equation of the line containing P and perpendicular to l.

(c) Graph the equations in parts (a) and (b).

22. Assume A, B, C are constants with $A \ne 0$, $B \ne 0$. Consider the equation

$$Ax + By = C.$$

(a) Show that $y = f(x)$ is linear. State the slope and the x- and y-intercepts of $f(x)$.

(b) Graph $y = f(x)$, labeling the x- and y-intercepts in terms of A, B, and C, assuming

   (i) $A > 0, B > 0, C > 0$

  (ii) $A > 0, B > 0, C < 0$

  (iii) $A > 0, B < 0, C > 0$

23. Fill in the missing coordinates for the points in the following figures.

(a) The triangle in Figure 1.50.

(b) The parallelogram in Figure 1.51.

Figure 1.50

Figure 1.51

24. Using the window $-10 \leq x \leq 10, -10 \leq y \leq 10$, graph $y = x$, $y = 10x$, $y = 100x$, and $y = 1000x$.

    (a) Explain what happens to the graphs of the lines as the slopes become large.

    (b) Write an equation of a line that passes through the origin and is horizontal.

25. Graph $y = x + 1$, $y = x + 10$, and $y = x + 100$ in the window $-10 \leq x \leq 10, -10 \leq y \leq 10$.

    (a) Explain what happens to the graph of a line, $y = b + mx$, as b becomes large.

    (b) Write a linear equation whose graph cannot be seen in the window $-10 \leq x \leq 10, -10 \leq y \leq 10$ because all its y-values are less than the y-values shown.

26. The graphical interpretation of the slope is that it shows steepness. Using a calculator or a computer, graph the function $y = 2x - 3$ in the following windows:

    (a) $-10 \leq x \leq 10$ by $-10 \leq y \leq 10$
    (b) $-10 \leq x \leq 10$ by $-100 \leq y \leq 100$
    (c) $-10 \leq x \leq 10$ by $-1000 \leq y \leq 1000$
    (d) Write a sentence about how steepness is related to the window being used.

In Problems 27–28, what is true about the constant β in the following linear equation if its graph has the given property?

$$y = \frac{x}{\beta - 3} + \frac{1}{6 - \beta}.$$

27. Positive slope, positive y-intercept.

28. Perpendicular to the line $y = (\beta - 7)x - 3$.

29. A circle of radius 2 is centered at the origin and goes through the point $(-1, \sqrt{3})$.

    (a) Find an equation for the line through the origin and the point $(-1, \sqrt{3})$.

    (b) Find an equation for the tangent line to the circle at $(-1, \sqrt{3})$. [Hint: A tangent line is perpendicular to the radius at the point of tangency.]

30. Find an equation for the altitude through point A of the triangle ABC, where A is $(-4, 5)$, B is $(-3, 2)$, and C is $(9, 8)$. [Hint: The altitude of a triangle is perpendicular to the base.]

31. Fill in the missing coordinates in Figure 1.52. Write an equation for the line connecting the two points. Check your answer by solving the system of two equations.

Figure 1.52

32. Two lines are given by $y = b_1 + m_1 x$ and $y = b_2 + m_2 x$, where $b_1, b_2, m_1,$ and m_2 are constants.

    (a) What conditions are imposed on $b_1, b_2, m_1,$ and m_2 if the two lines have no points in common?

    (b) What conditions are imposed on $b_1, b_2, m_1,$ and m_2 if the two lines have all points in common?

    (c) What conditions are imposed on $b_1, b_2, m_1,$ and m_2 if the two lines have exactly one point in common?

    (d) What conditions are imposed on $b_1, b_2, m_1,$ and m_2 if the two lines have exactly two points in common?

1.6 FITTING LINEAR FUNCTIONS TO DATA

When real data are collected in the laboratory or the field, they are often subject to experimental error. Even if there is an underlying linear relationship between two quantities, real data may not fit this relationship perfectly. However, even if a data set does not perfectly conform to a linear function, we may still be able to use a linear function to help us analyze the data.

Laboratory Data: The Viscosity of Motor Oil

The viscosity of a liquid, or its resistance to flow, depends on the liquid's temperature. Pancake syrup is a familiar example: straight from the refrigerator, it pours very slowly. When warmed on the stove, its viscosity decreases and it becomes quite runny.

    The viscosity of motor oil is a measure of its effectiveness as a lubricant in the engine of a car. Thus, the effect of engine temperature is an important determinant of motor-oil performance. Table 1.33 gives the viscosity, v, of motor oil as measured in the lab at different temperatures, T.

Table 1.33 *The measured viscosity, v, of motor oil as a function of the temperature, T*

T, temperature (°F)	v, viscosity (lbs·sec/in^2)
160	28
170	26
180	24
190	21
200	16
210	13
220	11
230	9

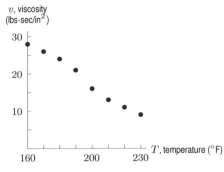

Figure 1.53: The viscosity data from Table 1.33

The *scatter plot* of the data in Figure 1.53 shows that the viscosity of motor oil decreases, approximately linearly, as its temperature rises. To find a formula relating viscosity and temperature, we fit a line to these data points.

Fitting the best line to a set of data is called *linear regression*. One way to fit a line is to draw a line "by eye." Alternatively, many computer programs and calculators compute regression lines. Figure 1.54 shows the data from Table 1.33 together with the computed regression line,

$$v = 75.6 - 0.293T.$$

Notice that none of the data points lie exactly on the regression line, although it fits the data well.

Figure 1.54: A graph of the viscosity data from Table 1.33, together with a regression line (provided by a calculator)

The Assumptions Involved In Finding a Regression Line

When we find a regression line for the data in Table 1.33, we are assuming that the value of v is related to the value of T. However, there may be experimental errors in our measurements. For example, if we measure viscosity twice at the same temperature, we may get two slightly different values. Alternatively, something besides engine temperature could be affecting the oil's viscosity (the oil pressure, for example). Thus, even if we assume that the temperature readings are exact, the viscosity readings include some degree of uncertainty.

Interpolation and Extrapolation

The formula for viscosity can be used to make predictions. Suppose we want to know the viscosity of motor oil at $T = 196°F$. The formula gives

$$v = 75.6 - 0.293 \cdot 196 \approx 18.2 \text{ lb} \cdot \text{sec/in}^2.$$

To see that this is a reasonable estimate, compare it to the entries in Table 1.33. At 190°F, the measured viscosity was 21, and at 200°F, it was 16; the predicted viscosity of 18.2 is between 16 and 21. See Figure 1.55. Of course, if we measured the viscosity at $T = 196°F$ in the lab, we might not get exactly 18.2.

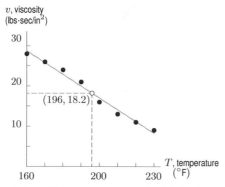

Figure 1.55: Regression line used to predict the viscosity at 196°F

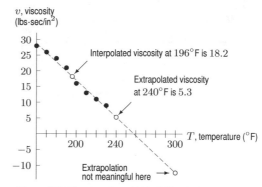

Figure 1.56: The data from Table 1.33 together with the predicted viscosity at $T = 196°F$, $T = 240°F$, and $T = 300°F$

Since the temperature $T = 196°F$ is between two temperatures for which v is known (190°F and 200°F), the estimate of 18.2 is said to be an *interpolation*. If instead we estimate the value of v at a temperature outside the values for T in Table 1.33, our estimate is called an *extrapolation*.

Example 1 Predict the viscosity of motor oil at 240°F and at 300°F.

Solution At $T = 240°F$, the formula for the regression line predicts that the viscosity of motor oil is

$$v = 75.6 - 0.293 \cdot 240 = 5.3 \text{ lb} \cdot \text{sec/in}^2.$$

This is reasonable. Figure 1.56 shows that the predicted point—represented by an open circle on the graph—is consistent with the trend in the data points from Table 1.33.

On the other hand, at $T = 300°F$ the regression-line formula gives

$$v = 75.6 - 0.293 \cdot 300 = -12.3 \text{ lb} \cdot \text{sec/in}^2.$$

This is unreasonable because viscosity cannot be negative. To understand what went wrong, notice that in Figure 1.56, the open circle representing the point $(300, -12.3)$ is far from the plotted data points. By making a prediction at 300°F, we have assumed—incorrectly—that the trend observed in laboratory data extended as far as 300°F.

In general, interpolation tends to be more reliable than extrapolation because we are making a prediction on an interval we already know something about instead of making a prediction beyond the limits of our knowledge.

How Regression Works

How does a calculator or computer decide which line fits the data best? We assume that the value of y is related to the value of x, although other factors could influence y as well. Thus, we assume that we can pick the value of x exactly but that the value of y may be only partially determined by this x-value.

Figure 1.57: A given set of data and the corresponding least-squares regression line

One way to fit a line to the data is shown in Figure 1.57. The line shown was chosen to minimize the sum of the squares of the vertical distances between the data points and the line. Such a line is called a *least-squares line*. There are formulas which a calculator or computer uses to calculate the slope, m, and the y-intercept, b, of the least-squares line.

Correlation

When a computer or calculator calculates a regression line, it also gives a *correlation coefficient*, r. This number lies between -1 and $+1$ and measures how well a particular regression line fits the data. If $r = 1$, the data lie exactly on a line of positive slope. If $r = -1$, the data lie exactly on a line of negative slope. If r is close to 0, the data may be completely scattered, or there may be a nonlinear relationship between the variables. (See Figure 1.58.)

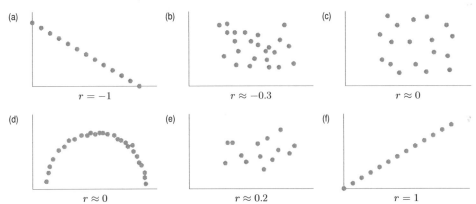

Figure 1.58: Various data sets and correlation coefficients

Example 2   The correlation coefficient for the viscosity data in Table 1.33 on page 45 is $r \approx -0.99$. The fact that r is negative tells us that the regression line has negative slope. The fact that r is close to -1 tells us that the regression line fits the data well.

The Difference Between Relation, Correlation, and Causation

It is important to understand that a high correlation (either positive or negative) between two quantities does *not* imply causation. For example, there is a high correlation between children's reading level and shoe size.[21] However, large feet do not cause a child to read better (or vice versa). Larger feet and improved reading ability are both a consequence of growing older.

Notice also that a correlation of 0 does not imply that there is no relationship between x and y. For example, in Figure 1.58(d) there is a relationship between x and y-values, while Figure 1.58(c) exhibits no apparent relationship. Both data sets have a correlation coefficient of $r \approx 0$. Thus a correlation of $r = 0$ usually implies there is no linear relationship between x and y, but this does not mean there is no relationship at all.

Exercises and Problems for Section 1.6

For data in Problems 1–6 is the given value of r reasonable? Give an explanation for your answer.

1. $r = 0.93$

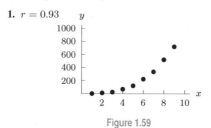

Figure 1.59

2. $r = -0.9$

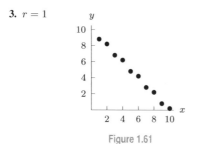

Figure 1.60

3. $r = 1$

Figure 1.61

4. $r = 0.92$

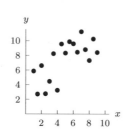

Figure 1.62

5. $r = 1$

Table 1.34

x	1	2	3	4	5
y	3.8	3.2	1.8	1.2	-0.2

6. $r = 0.343$

Table 1.35

x	1	2	3	4	5
y	3.477	5.531	14.88	5.924	8.049

---

[21]From *Statistics*, 2nd edition, by David Freedman. Robert Pisani, Roger Purves, Ani Adhikari, p. 142 (New York: W.W. Norton, 1991).

7. Match the r values with scatter plots in Figure 1.63.

$$r = -0.98, \quad r = -0.5, \quad r = -0.25,$$
$$r = 0, \quad r = 0.7, \quad r = 1.$$

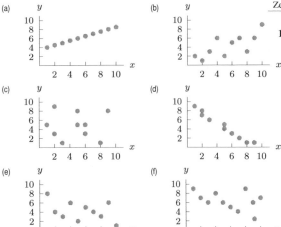

Figure 1.63

8. Table 1.36 shows the number of calories burned per minute by a person walking at 3 mph.

  (a) Make a scatter plot of this data.
  (b) Draw a regression line by eye.
  (c) Roughly estimate the correlation coefficient by eye.

Table 1.36

Body weight (lb)	100	120	150	170	200	220
Calories	2.7	3.2	4.0	4.6	5.4	5.9

9. An ecologist tracked 290 zebra that were born in 2000. The number of zebra, z, living each subsequent year is recorded in Table 1.37.

  (a) Make a scatter plot of this data. Let $t = 0$ represent 2000.
  (b) Draw by eye a line of good fit and estimate its equation. (Round the coefficients to integers.)
  (c) Use a calculator or computer to find the equation of the least squares line. (Round the coefficients to integers.)
  (d) Interpret the slope and each intercept of the line.

(e) Interpret the correlation between the year and the number of zebra born in 2000 that are still alive.

Table 1.37

Year	2000	2001	2002	2003	2004	2005	2006	2007	2008
Zebra	290	288	268	206	140	90	64	44	8

10. The rate of oxygen consumption for Colorado beetles increases with temperature. See Table 1.38.

  (a) Make a scatter plot of this data.
  (b) Draw an estimated regression line by eye.
  (c) Use a calculator or computer to find the equation of the regression line. (Alternatively, find the equation of your line in part (b).) Round constants in the equation to the nearest integer.
  (d) Interpret the slope and each intercept of the regression equation.
  (e) Interpret the correlation between temperature and oxygen rate.

Table 1.38

°C	10	15	20	25	30
Oxygen consumption rate	90	125	200	300	375

11. Table 1.39 gives the data on hand strength collected from college freshman using a grip meter.

  (a) Make a scatter plot of these data treating the strength of the preferred hand as the independent variable.
  (b) Draw a line on your scatter plot that is a good fit for these data and use it to find an approximate equation for the regression line.
  (c) Using a graphing calculator or computer, find the equation of the least squares line.
  (d) What would the predicted grip strength in the non-preferred hand be for a student with a preferred hand strength of 37?
  (e) Discuss interpolation and extrapolation using specific examples in relation to this regression line.
  (f) Discuss why r, the correlation coefficient, is both positive and close to 1.
  (g) Why do the points tend to cluster into two groups on your scatter plot?

Table 1.39 *Hand strength for 20 students in kilograms*

Preferred	28	27	45	20	40	47	28	54	52	21
Nonpreferred	24	26	43	22	40	45	26	46	46	22
Preferred	53	52	49	45	39	26	25	32	30	32
Nonpreferred	47	47	41	44	33	20	27	30	29	29

12. Table 1.40 shows men's and women's world records for swimming distances from 50 meters to 1500 meters.[22]

(a) What values would you add to Table 1.40 to represent the time taken by both men and women to swim 0 meters?

(b) Plot men's time against distance, with time t in seconds on the vertical axis and distance d in meters on the horizontal axis. It is claimed that a straight line models this behavior well. What is the equation for that line? What does its slope represent? On the same graph, plot women's time against distance and find the equation of the straight line that models this behavior well. Is this line steeper or flatter than the men's line? What does that mean in terms of swimming? What are the values of the vertical intercepts? Do these values have a practical interpretation?

(c) On another graph plot the women's times against the men's times, with women's times, w, on the vertical axis and men's times, m, on the horizontal axis. It should look linear. How could you have predicted this linearity from the equations you found in part (b)? What is the slope of this line and how can it be interpreted? A newspaper reporter claims that the women's records are about 8% slower than the men's. Do the facts support this statement? What is the value of the vertical intercept? Does this value have a practical interpretation?

Table 1.40 *Men's and women's world swimming records*

Distance (m)	50	100	200	400	800	1500
Men (sec)	21.64	47.84	104.06	220.08	458.65	874.56
Women (sec)	24.13	53.62	116.64	243.85	496.22	952.10

CHAPTER SUMMARY

- **Functions**
  Definition: a rule which takes certain numbers as inputs and assigns to each input exactly one output number.
  Function notation, $y = f(x)$.
  Use of vertical line test.

- **Average Rate of Change**
  Average rate of change of $Q = f(t)$ on $[a, b]$ is
  $$\frac{\Delta Q}{\Delta t} = \frac{f(b) - f(a)}{b - a}.$$
  Increasing, decreasing functions; identifying from average rate of change.

- **Linear Functions**
  Value of y changes at constant rate.
  Tables for linear functions.

- **Formulas for Linear Functions**
  Slope-intercept form: $y = b + mx$.
  Point-slope form: $y - y_0 = m(x - x_0)$.
  Standard form: $Ax + By + C = 0$.

- **Properties of Linear Functions**
  Interpretation of slope, vertical and horizontal intercepts.
  Intersection of lines: Solution of equations.
  Horizontal and vertical lines.
  Parallel lines: $m_1 = m_2$.
  Perpendicular lines: $m_1 = -\dfrac{1}{m_2}$.

- **Fitting Lines to Data**
  Linear regression; correlation. Interpolation, extrapolation; dangers of extrapolation.

REVIEW EXERCISES AND PROBLEMS FOR CHAPTER ONE

Exercises

In Exercises 1–5 a relationship is given between two quantities. Are both quantities functions of the other one, or is one or neither a function of the other? Explain.

1. $7w^2 + 5 = z^2$ **2.** $y = x^4 - 1$ **3.** $m = \sqrt{t}$

4. The number of gallons of gas, g, at \$2 per gallon and the number of pounds of coffee, c, at \$10 per pound that can be bought for a total of \$100.

5.

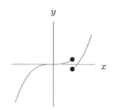

Figure 1.64

---

[22]Data from *The World Almanac and Book of Facts: 2006*, World Almanac Education Group, Inc., New York, 2006.

6. (a) Which of the graphs in Figure 1.65 represent y as a function of x? (Note that an open circle indicates a point that is not included in the graph; a solid dot indicates a point that is included in the graph.)

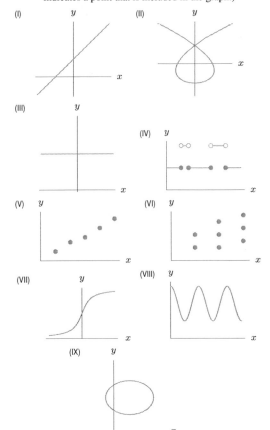

Figure 1.65

(b) Which of the graphs in Figure 1.65 could represent the following situations? Give reasons.

(i) SAT Math score versus SAT Verbal score for a small number of students.

(ii) Total number of daylight hours as a function of the day of the year, shown over a period of several years.

(c) Among graphs (I)–(IX) in Figure 1.65, find two which could give the cost of train fare as a function of the time of day. Explain the relationship between cost and time for both choices.

7. (a) Make a table of values for $f(x) = 10/(1 + x^2)$ for $x = 0, 1, 2, 3$.

(b) What x-value gives the largest $f(x)$ value in your table? How could you have predicted this before doing any calculations?

8. Table 1.41 gives the populations of two cities (in thousands) over a 17-year period.

(a) Find the average rate of change of each population on the following intervals:

(i) 1990 to 2000 (ii) 1990 to 2007

(iii) 1995 to 2007

(b) What do you notice about the average rate of change of each population? Explain what the average rate of change tells you about each population.

Table 1.41

Year	1990	1992	1995	2000	2007
P_1	42	46	52	62	76
P_2	82	80	77	72	65

9. The following tables represent the relationship between the button number, N, that you push, and the snack, S, delivered by three different vending machines.[23]

(a) One of these vending machines is not a good one to use, because S is not a function of N. Which one?

(b) For which vending machine(s) is S a function of N?

(c) For which of the vending machines is N not a function of S?

Vending Machine #1

N	S
1	M&Ms
2	pretzels
3	dried fruit
4	Hersheys
5	fat-free cookies
6	Snickers

Vending Machine #2

N	S
1	M&Ms or dried fruit
2	pretzels or Hersheys
3	Snickers or fat-free cookies

Vending Machine #3

N	S
1	M&Ms
2	M&Ms
3	pretzels
4	dried fruit
5	Hersheys
6	Hersheys
7	fat-free cookies
8	Snickers
9	Snickers

[23]For each N, vending machine #2 dispenses one or the other product at random.

10. Figure 1.66 shows the average monthly temperature in Albany, New York, over a twelve-month period. (January is month 1.)

(a) Make a table showing average temperature as a function of the month of the year.

(b) What is the warmest month in Albany?

(c) Over what interval of months is the temperature increasing? Decreasing?

average temperature (°F)

Figure 1.66

11. In 1947, Jesse Owens, the US gold medal track star of the 1930s and 1940s, ran a 100-yard race against a horse. The race, "staged" in Havana, Cuba, is filled with controversy; some say Owens received a head start, others claim the horse was drugged. Owens himself revealed some years later that the starting gun was placed next to the horse's ear, causing the animal to rear and remain at the gate for a few seconds. Figure 1.67 depicts speeds measured against time for the race.

(a) How fast were Owens and the horse going at the end of the race?

(b) When were the participants both traveling at the same speed?

speed (yds/secs)

Figure 1.67

In Exercises 12–13, could the table represent a linear function?

12.

λ	1	2	3	4	5
$q(\lambda)$	2	4	8	16	32

13.

t	3	6	9	12	15
$a(t)$	2	4	6	8	10

Problems 14–16 give data from a linear function. Find a formula for the function.

14.

x	200	230	300	320	400
$g(x)$	70	68.5	65	64	60

15.

t	1.2	1.3	1.4	1.5
$f(t)$	0.736	0.614	0.492	0.37

16.

t	5.2	5.3	5.4	5.5
$f(t)$	73.6	61.4	49.2	37

17. Without a calculator, match the functions (a)–(c) to the graphs (i)–(iii).

(a) $f(x) = 3x + 1$ (b) $g(x) = -2x + 1$

(c) $h(x) = 1$

In Exercises 18–20, which line has the greater

(a) Slope?   (b) y-intercept?

18. $y = -1 + 2x;$ $y = -2 + 3x$

19. $y = 3 + 4x;$ $y = 5 - 2x$

20. $y = \frac{1}{4}x;$ $y = 1 - 6x$

Are the lines in Exercises 21–24 perpendicular? Parallel? Neither?

21. $y = 5x + 2;$ $y = 2x + 5$

22. $y = 14x - 2;$ $y = -\frac{1}{14}x + 2$

23. $y = 3x + 3;$ $y = -\frac{1}{3}x + 3$

24. $7y = 8 + 21x; 9y = 77 - 3x$

Problems

In Problems 25–27, use Table 1.42, which gives values of $v = r(s)$, the eyewall wind profile of a typical hurricane.[24] The eyewall of a hurricane is the band of clouds that surrounds the eye of the storm. The eyewall wind speed v (in mph) is a function of the height above the ground s (in meters).

Table 1.42

s	0	100	200	300	400	500
v	90	110	116	120	121	122
s	600	700	800	900	1000	1100
v	121	119	118	117	116	115

25. Evaluate and interpret $r(300)$.

26. At what altitudes does the eyewall wind speed appear to equal or exceed 116 mph?

27. At what height is the eyewall wind speed greatest?

28. You are looking at the graph of y, a function of x.

  (a) What is the maximum number of times that the graph can intersect the y-axis? Explain.

  (b) Can the graph intersect the x-axis an infinite number of times? Explain.

29. A bug starts out ten feet from a light, flies closer to the light, then farther away, then closer than before, then farther away. Finally the bug hits the bulb and flies off. Sketch the distance of the bug from the light as a function of time.

30. Although there were 17 women in the Senate in 2009, the first woman elected to the Senate was Hattie Wyatt Caraway of Arkansas. She was appointed to fill the vacancy caused by the death of her husband, then won election in 1932, was reelected in 1938, and served until 1945. Table 1.43 shows the number of female senators at the beginning of the first session of each Congress.[25]

  (a) Is the number of female senators a function of the Congress's number, c? Explain.

  (b) Is the Congress's number a function of the number of female senators? Explain.

  (c) Let $S(c)$ represent the number of female senators serving in the cth Congress. What does the statement $S(104) = 8$ mean?

  (d) Evaluate and interpret $S(110)$.

Table 1.43 *Female senators, S, in Congress c*

c	96	98	100	102	104	106	108	110	111
S	1	2	2	2	8	9	14	16	17

31. A light is turned off for several hours. It is then turned on. After a few hours it is turned off again. Sketch the light bulb's temperature as a function of time.

32. According to Charles Osgood, CBS news commentator, it takes about one minute to read 15 double-spaced typewritten lines on the air.[26]

  (a) Construct a table showing the time Charles Osgood is reading on the air in seconds as a function of the number of double-spaced lines read for $0, 1, 2, \ldots, 10$ lines. From your table, how long does it take Charles Osgood to read 9 lines?

  (b) Plot this data on a graph with the number of lines on the horizontal axis.

  (c) From your graph, estimate how long it takes Charles Osgood to read 9 lines. Estimate how many lines Charles Osgood can read in 30 seconds.

  (d) Construct a formula which relates the time T to n, the number of lines read.

33. The distance between Cambridge and Wellesley is 10 miles. A person walks part of the way at 5 miles per hour, then jogs the rest of the way at 8 mph. Find a formula that expresses the total amount of time for the trip, $T(d)$, as a function of d, the distance walked.

34. A cylindrical can is closed at both ends and its height is twice its radius. Express its surface area, S, as a function of its radius, r. [Hint: The surface of a can consists of a rectangle plus two circular disks.]

35. A lawyer does nothing but sleep and work during a day. There are 1440 minutes in a day. Write a linear function relating minutes of sleep, s, to minutes of work, w.

For the functions in Problems 36–38:

  (a) Find the average rate of change between the points

    (i) $(-1, f(-1))$ and $(3, f(3))$

    (ii) $(a, f(a))$ and $(b, f(b))$

    (iii) $(x, f(x))$ and $(x + h, f(x + h))$

  (b) What pattern do you see in the average rate of change between the three pairs of points?

36. $f(x) = 5x - 4$ **37.** $f(x) = \frac{1}{2}x + \frac{5}{2}$

38. $f(x) = x^2 + 1$

---

[24]Data from the National Hurricane Center, www.nhc.noaa.gov/aboutwindprofile.shtml, accessed October 7, 2004.

[25]http://en.wikipedia.org/wiki/111th United States Congress Members.

[26]T. Parker, *Rules of Thumb* (Boston: Houghton Mifflin, 1983).

39. Table 1.44 gives the average temperature, T, at a depth d, in a borehole in Belleterre, Quebec.[27] Evaluate $\Delta T/\Delta d$ on the following intervals, and explain what your answers tell you about borehole temperature.

(a) $25 \leq d \leq 150$
(b) $25 \leq d \leq 75$
(c) $100 \leq d \leq 200$

Table 1.44

d, depth (m)	25	50	75	100
T, temp (°C)	5.50	5.20	5.10	5.10
d, depth (m)	125	150	175	200
T, temp (°C)	5.30	5.50	5.75	6.00
d, depth (m)	225	250	275	300
T, temp (°C)	6.25	6.50	6.75	7.00

40. The population, $P(t)$, in millions, of a country in year t, is given by the formula $P(t) = 22 + 0.3t$.

(a) Construct a table of values for $t = 0, 10, 20, \dots ,50$.
(b) Plot the points you found in part (a).
(c) What is the country's initial population?
(d) What is the average rate of change of the population, in millions of people/year?

41. A woodworker sells rocking horses. His start-up costs, including tools, plans, and advertising, total $5000. Labor and materials for each horse cost $350.

(a) Calculate the woodworker's total cost, C, to make 1, 2, 5, 10, and 20 rocking horses. Graph C against n, the number of rocking horses that he carves.
(b) Find a formula for C in terms of n.
(c) What is the rate of change of the function C? What does the rate of change tell us about the woodworker's expenses?

42. Outside the US, temperature readings are usually given in degrees Celsius; inside the US, they are often given in degrees Fahrenheit. The exact conversion from Celsius, C, to Fahrenheit, F, uses the formula

$$F = \frac{9}{5}C + 32.$$

An approximate conversion is obtained by doubling the temperature in Celsius and adding 30° to get the equivalent Fahrenheit temperature.

(a) Write a formula using C and F to express the approximate conversion.

(b) How far off is the approximation if the Celsius temperature is $-5°$, $0°$, $15°$, $30°$?
(c) For what temperature (in Celsius) does the approximation agree with the actual formula?

43. Find a formula for the linear function $h(t)$ whose graph intersects the graph of $j(t) = 30(0.2)^t$ at $t = -2$ and $t = 1$.

44. Find the equation of the line l in Figure 1.68. The shapes under the line are squares.

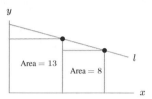

Figure 1.68

45. A bullet is shot straight up into the air from ground level. After t seconds, the velocity of the bullet, in meters per second, is approximated by the formula

$$v = f(t) = 1000 - 9.8t.$$

(a) Evaluate the following: $f(0)$, $f(1)$, $f(2)$, $f(3)$, $f(4)$. Compile your results in a table.
(b) Describe in words what is happening to the speed of the bullet. Discuss why you think this is happening.
(c) Evaluate and interpret the slope and both intercepts of $f(t)$.
(d) The gravitational field near the surface of Jupiter is stronger than that near the surface of the earth, which, in turn, is stronger than the field near the surface of the moon. How is the formula for $f(t)$ different for a bullet shot from Jupiter's surface? From the moon?

46. A theater manager graphed weekly profits as a function of the number of patrons and found that the relationship was linear. One week the profit was $11,328 when 1324 patrons attended. Another week 1529 patrons produced a profit of $13,275.50.

(a) Find a formula for weekly profit, y, as a function of the number of patrons, x.
(b) Interpret the slope and the y-intercept.
(c) What is the break-even point (the number of patrons for which there is zero profit)?

---

[27]Hugo Beltrami of St. Francis Xavier University and David Chapman of the University of Utah posted this data at http://geophysics.stfx.ca/public/borehole/borehole.html, accessed November 10, 2005.

(d) Find a formula for the number of patrons as a function of profit.

(e) If the weekly profit was $17,759.50, how many patrons attended the theater?

47. Describe a linear (or nearly linear) relationship that you have encountered outside the classroom. Determine the rate of change and interpret it in practical terms.

48. In economics, the *demand* for a product is the amount of that product that consumers are willing to buy at a given price. The quantity demanded of a product usually decreases if the price of that product increases. Suppose that a company believes there is a linear relationship between the demand for its product and its price. The company knows that when the price of its product was $3 per unit, the quantity demanded weekly was 500 units, and that when the unit price was raised to $4, the quantity demanded weekly dropped to 300 units. Let D represent the quantity demanded weekly at a unit price of p dollars.

(a) Calculate D when $p = 5$. Interpret your result.

(b) Find a formula for D in terms of p.

(c) The company raises the price of the good and that the new quantity demanded weekly is 50 units. What is the new price?

(d) Give an economic interpretation of the slope of the function you found in part (b).

(e) Find D when $p = 0$. Find p when $D = 0$. Give economic interpretations of both these results.

49. In economics, the *supply* of a product is the quantity of that product suppliers are willing to provide at a given price. In theory, the quantity supplied of a product increases if the price of that product increases. Suppose that there is a linear relationship between the quantity supplied, S, of the product described in Problem 48 and its price, p. The quantity supplied weekly is 100 when the price is $2 and the quantity supplied rises by 50 units when the price rises by $0.50.

(a) Find a formula for S in terms of p.

(b) Interpret the slope of your formula in economic terms.

(c) Is there a price below which suppliers will not provide this product?

(d) The *market clearing price* is the price at which supply equals demand. According to theory, the free-market price of a product is its market clearing price. Using the demand function from Problem 48, find the market clearing price for this product.

50. When economists graph demand or supply equations, they place quantity on the horizontal axis and price on the vertical axis.

(a) On the same set of axes, graph the demand and supply equations you found in Problems 48 and 49, with price on the vertical axis.

(b) Indicate how you could estimate the market clearing price from your graph.

51. The figure gives graphs of g, a linear function, and of $f(x) = 12 - 0.5(x + 4)^2$. Find a possible formula for g.

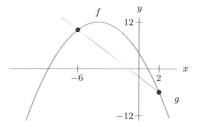

52. Write in slope-intercept form and identify the values of b and m:

$$f(r) = rx^3 + 3rx^2 + 2r + 4sx + 7s + 3.$$

53. Find an equation for the line intersecting the graph of f at $x = -2$ and $x = 5$ given that $f(x) = 2 + \dfrac{3}{x + 5}$.

54. A business consultant works 10 hours a day, 6 days a week. She divides her time between meetings with clients and meetings with co-workers. A client meeting requires 3 hours while a co-worker meeting requires 2 hours. Let x be the number of co-worker meetings the consultant holds during a given week. If y is the number of client meetings for which she has time remaining, then y is a function of x. Assume this relationship is linear and that meetings can be split up and continued on different days.

(a) Graph the relationship between y and x. [Hint: Consider the maximum number of client and co-worker meetings that can be held.]

(b) Find a formula for y as a function of x.

(c) Explain what the slope and the x- and y-intercepts represent in the context of the consultant's meeting schedule.

(d) A change is made so that co-worker meetings take 90 minutes instead of 2 hours. Graph this situation. Describe those features of this graph that have changed from the one sketched in part (a) and those that have remained the same.

55. You start 60 miles east of Pittsburgh and drive east at a constant speed of 50 miles per hour. (Assume that the road is straight and permits you to do this.) Find a formula for d, your distance from Pittsburgh as a function of t, the number of hours of travel.

56. Find a formula for the line parallel to the line $y = 20 - 4x$ and containing the point $(3, 12)$.

57. Find the equation of the linear function g whose graph is perpendicular to the line $5x - 3y = 6$; the two lines intersect at $x = 15$.

58. Find the coordinates of point P in Figure 1.69.

Figure 1.69

59. You want to choose one long-distance telephone company from the following options.

- Company A charges $0.37 per minute.
- Company B charges $13.95 per month plus $0.22 per minute.
- Company C charges a fixed rate of $50 per month.

Let Y_A, Y_B, Y_C represent the monthly charges using Company A, B, and C, respectively. Let x be the number of minutes per month spent on long-distance calls.

(a) Find formulas for Y_A, Y_B, Y_C as functions of x.
(b) Figure 1.70 gives the graphs of the functions in part (a). Which function corresponds to which graph?
(c) Find the x-values for which Company B is cheapest.

Figure 1.70

60. A commission is a payment made to an employee based on a percentage of sales made. For example, car salespeople earn commission on the selling price of a car. In parts (a)–(d), explain how to choose between the options for different levels of sales.

(a) A weekly salary of $100 or a weekly salary of $50 plus 10% commission.

(b) A weekly salary of $175 plus 7% commission or a weekly salary of $175 plus 8% commission.
(c) A weekly salary of $145 plus 7% commission or a weekly salary of $165 plus 7% commission.
(d) A weekly salary of $225 plus 3% commission or a weekly salary of $180 plus 6% commission.

61. Table 1.45 shows the IQ of ten students and the number of hours of TV each watches per week.

(a) Make a scatter plot of the data.
(b) By eye, make a rough estimate of the correlation coefficient.
(c) Use a calculator or computer to find the least squares regression line and the correlation coefficient. Your values should be correct to four decimal places.

Table 1.45

IQ	110	105	120	140	100	125	130	105	115	110
TV	10	12	8	2	12	10	5	6	13	3

62. For 35 years, major league baseball Hall of Fame member Henry Aaron held the record for the greatest number of career home runs. His record was broken by Barry Bonds in 2007. Table 1.46 shows Aaron's cumulative yearly record [28] from the start of his career, 1954, until 1973.

(a) Plot Aaron's cumulative number of home runs H on the vertical axis, and the time t in years along the horizontal axis, where $t = 1$ corresponds to 1954.
(b) By eye, draw a straight line that fits these data well and find its equation.
(c) Use a calculator or computer to find the equation of the regression line for these data. What is the correlation coefficient, r, to 4 decimal places? To 3 decimal places? What does this tell you?
(d) What does the slope of the regression line mean in terms of Henry Aaron's home-run record?
(e) From your answer to part (d), how many home runs do you estimate Henry Aaron hit in each of the years 1974, 1975, 1976, and 1977? If you were told that Henry Aaron retired at the end of the 1976 season, would this affect your answers?

Table 1.46 *Henry Aaron's cumulative home-run record, H, from 1954 to 1973, with t in years since 1953*

t	1	2	3	4	5	6	7	8	9	10
H	13	40	66	110	140	179	219	253	298	342
t	11	12	13	14	15	16	17	18	19	20
H	366	398	442	481	510	554	592	639	673	713

[28] Adapted from "Graphing Henry Aaron's home-run output" by H. Ringel, *The Physics Teacher*, January 1974, page 43.

63. The graph of a linear function $y = f(x)$ passes through the two points $(a, f(a))$ and $(b, f(b))$, where $a < b$ and $f(a) < f(b)$.

    (a) Graph the function labeling the two points.

    (b) Find the slope of the line in terms of f, a, and b.

64. Let $f(x) = 0.003 - (1.246x + 0.37)$.

    (a) Calculate the following average rates of change:

        (i) $\dfrac{f(2) - f(1)}{2 - 1}$ (ii) $\dfrac{f(1) - f(2)}{1 - 2}$

        (iii) $\dfrac{f(3) - f(4)}{3 - 4}$

    (b) Rewrite $f(x)$ in the form $f(x) = b + mx$.

Write the linear function $y = -3 - x/2$ in the forms given in Problems 65–66, assuming all constants are positive.

65. $y = \dfrac{p}{p - 1} - r^2 x$ **66.** $y = \dfrac{x + k}{z}$

67. You spend c dollars on x apples and y bananas. In Figure 1.71, line l gives y as a function of x.

    (a) If apples cost p dollars each and bananas cost q each, label the x- and y-intercepts of l. [Note: Your labels will involve the constants p, q or c.]

    (b) What is the slope of l?

Figure 1.71: Axes not necessarily to scale

68. The apples in Problem 67 cost more than bananas, so $p > q$. Which of the two lines, l_1 or l_2, in Figure 1.72 could represent $y = f(x)$?

Figure 1.72

69. Many people think that hair growth is stimulated by haircuts. In fact, there is no difference in the rate hair grows after a haircut, but there *is* a difference in the rate at which hair's ends break off. A haircut eliminates dead and split ends, thereby slowing the rate at which hair breaks. However, even with regular haircuts, hair will not grow to an indefinite length. The average life cycle of human scalp hair is 3-5 years, after which the hair is shed.[29]

    Judy trims her hair once a year, when its growth is slowed by split ends. She cuts off just enough to eliminate dead and split ends, and then lets it grow another year. After 5 years, she realizes her hair won't grow any longer. Graph the length of her hair as a function of time. Indicate when she receives her haircuts.

70. Academics have suggested that loss of worker productivity can result from sleep deprivation. An article in the September 26, 1993, *New York Times* quotes David Poltrack, the senior vice president for planning and research at CBS, as saying that seven million Americans are staying up an hour later than usual to watch talk show host David Letterman. The article goes on to quote Timothy Monk, a professor at the University of Pittsburgh School of Medicine, as saying, "... my hunch is that the effect [on productivity due to sleep deprivation among this group] would be in the area of a 10 percent decrement." The article next quotes Robert Solow, a Nobel prize-winning professor of economics at MIT, who suggests the following procedure to estimate the impact that this loss in productivity will have on the US economy— an impact he dubbed "the Letterman loss." First, Solow says, we find the percentage of the work force who watch the program. Next, we determine this group's contribution to the gross domestic product (GDP). Then we reduce the group's contribution by 10% to account for the loss in productivity due to sleep deprivation. The amount of this reduction is "the Letterman loss."

    (a) The article estimated that the GDP is $6.325 trillion, and that 7 million Americans watch the show. Assume that the nation's work force is 118 million

[29] *Britannica Micropaedia* vol. 5 (Chicago: Encyclopaedia Britannica, Inc., 1989).

people and that 75% of David Letterman's audience belongs to this group. What percentage of the work force is in Dave's audience?

(b) What percent of the GDP would be expected to come from David Letterman's audience? How much money would they have contributed if they had not watched the show?

(c) How big is "the Letterman loss"?

71. Judging from the graph of $y = f(x)$ in the figure, find a possible formula for the line intersecting it at $x = -2\pi$ and $x = 3\pi$.

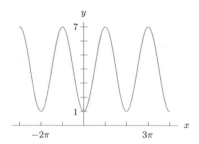

Problems 72–74 refer to Table 1.47, which describes a *boustrophedonic pairing function.* [30] We can use this table to list all the positive roots of the positive integers, such as $\sqrt{2}, \sqrt{3}, \sqrt[3]{2}, \sqrt[3]{3}, \sqrt[4]{2}, \sqrt[4]{3}, \ldots$, without omitting any. If n is an entry in the table, we let c stand for the column number and r the row number of the entry and define the function g by

$$g(n) = c^{1/r}.$$

For instance, if $n = 6$, then $c = 2$ and $r = 3$ so we have $g(6) = 2^{1/3}$, or $\sqrt[3]{2}$.

Table 1.47

	1	2	3	4	5	6	⋯
1	1	2	9	10	25	26	⋯
2	4	3	8	11	24	27	⋯
3	5	6	7	12	23	28	⋯
4	16	15	14	13	22	29	⋯
5	17	18	19	20	21	30	⋯
6	36	35	34	33	32	31	⋯
⋮	⋮	⋮	⋮	⋮	⋮	⋮	⋱

72. Evaluate $g(22)$. **73.** Evaluate $g(54)$.

74. Find a solution to $g(n) = \sqrt{3}$. Is this solution unique? Explain your reasoning.

Problems 75–76 ask about the A series of paper. Many countries use A4 paper, which is somewhat different from the 8.5 by 11 inch paper standard in the US.[31] A4 is part of a series of paper sizes specified in ISO 216, an international standard. Two sheets of A4 paper, if laid side by side (not end to end), are the same size as one sheet of A3 paper. Likewise, two sheets of A3 are the same as one sheet of A2, and so on. See Figure 1.73. Each sheet in the series has the same proportions, length to width, and the largest sheet, A0, has an area of exactly 1 m².

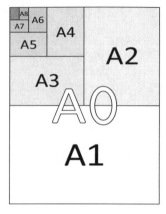

Figure 1.73

75. Let $f(n)$ be the area in cm² of the size n sheet in the A-series, so that $f(1)$ is the area of A1 paper, $f(2)$ of A2 paper, and so on. Since 1 m equals 100 cm, we know that $f(0) = (100 \text{ cm})^2 = 10,000 \text{ cm}^2$. Complete the table of values of f.

Table 1.48

n	0	1	2	3	4	5
$f(n)$	10,000					

---

[30]The term *boustrophedonic* means "ox-plowing": Notice how the entries in the table, $1, 2, 3, 4 \ldots$, turn back and forth, like an ox plowing a field.

[31]http://en.wikipedia.org/wiki/ISO_216, accessed January 30, 2008. Note that the actual sizes of A-series paper are rounded to the nearest millimeter.

76. We know that A1 paper has the same proportion (length over width) as A0. Further, the length of A1 paper is the same as the width W of A0, and the width of A1 is half the length L of A0. (See the figure.)

(a) Find a formula for L in terms of W. What does your formula tell you about the shape of A-series paper? How does the shape compare to US letter paper?

(b) Given that A4 paper has area 625 cm^2, find its width and height.

CHECK YOUR UNDERSTANDING

Are the statements in Problems 1–54 true or false? Give an explanation for your answer.

1. $Q = f(t)$ means Q is equal to f times t.

2. A function must be defined by a formula.

3. If $P = f(x)$ then P is called the dependent variable.

4. Independent variables are always denoted by the letter x or t.

5. It is possible for two quantities to be related and yet neither be a function of the other.

6. A function is a rule that takes certain values as inputs and assigns to each input value exactly one output value.

7. It is possible for a table of values to represent a function.

8. If Q is a function of P, then P is a function of Q.

9. The graph of a circle is not the graph of a function.

10. If $n = f(A)$ is the number of angels that can dance on the head of a pin whose area is A square millimeters, then $f(10) = 100$ tells us that 10 angels can dance on the head of a pin whose area is 100 square millimeters.

11. Average speed can be computed by dividing the distance traveled by the time elapsed.

12. The average rate of change of a function Q with respect to t over an interval can be symbolically represented as $\dfrac{\Delta t}{\Delta Q}$.

13. If $y = f(x)$ and as x increases, y increases, then f is an increasing function.

14. If f is a decreasing function, then the average rate of change of f on any interval is negative.

15. The average rate of change of a function over an interval is the slope of a line connecting two points of the graph of the function.

16. The average rate of change of $y = 3x - 4$ between $x = 2$ and $x = 6$ is 7.

17. The average rate of change of $f(x) = 10 - x^2$ between $x = 1$ and $x = 2$ is the ratio $\dfrac{10 - 2^2 - 10 - 1^2}{2 - 1}$.

18. If $y = x^2$ then the slope of the line connecting the point $(2, 4)$ to the point $(3, 9)$ is the same as the slope of the line connecting the point $(-2, 4)$ to the point $(-3, 9)$.

19. A linear function can have different rates of change over different intervals.

20. The graph of a linear function is a straight line.

21. If a line has the equation $3x + 2y = 7$, then the slope of the line is 3.

22. A table of values represents a linear function if $\dfrac{\text{Change in output}}{\text{Change in input}} = \text{constant}$.

23. If a linear function is decreasing, then its slope is negative.

24. If $y = f(x)$ is linear and its slope is negative, then in the expression $\dfrac{\Delta y}{\Delta x}$ either Δx or Δy is negative, but not both.

25. A linear function can have a slope that is zero.

26. If a line has slope 2 and y-intercept -3, then its equation may be written $y = -3x + 2$.

27. The line $3x + 5y = 7$ has slope $3/5$.

28. A line that goes through the point $(-2, 3)$ and whose slope is 4 has the equation $y = 4x + 5$.

29. The line $4x + 3y = 52$ intersects the x-axis at $x = 13$.

30. If $f(x) = -2x + 7$ then $f(2) = 3$.

31. The line that passes through the points $(1, 2)$ and $(4, -10)$ has slope 4.

32. The linear equation $y - 5 = 4(x + 1)$ is equivalent to the equation $y = 4x + 6$.

33. The line $y - 4 = -2(x + 3)$ goes through the point $(4, -3)$.

34. The line whose equation is $y = 3 - 7x$ has slope -7.

35. The line $y = -5x + 8$ intersects the y-axis at $y = 8$.

36. The equation $y = -2 - \frac{2}{3}x$ represents a linear function.

37. The lines $y = 8 - 3x$ and $-2x + 16y = 8$ both cross the y-axis at $y = 8$.

38. The graph of $f(x) = 6$ is a line whose slope is six.

39. The lines $y = -\frac{4}{5}x + 7$ and $4x - 5y = 8$ are parallel.

40. The lines $y = 7 + 9x$ and $y - 4 = -\frac{1}{9}(x + 5)$ are perpendicular.

41. The lines $y = -2x + 5$ and $y = 6x - 3$ intersect at the point $(1, 3)$.

42. If two lines never intersect then their slopes are equal.

43. The equation of a line parallel to the y-axis could be $y = -\frac{3}{4}$.

44. A line parallel to the x-axis has slope zero.

45. The slope of a vertical line is undefined.

46. Fitting the best line to a set of data is called linear regression.

47. The process of estimating a value within the range for which we have data is called interpolation.

48. Extrapolation tends to be more reliable than interpolation.

49. If two quantities have a high correlation then one quantity causes the other.

50. If the correlation coefficient is zero, there is not a relationship between the two quantities.

51. A correlation coefficient can have a value of $-\frac{3}{7}$.

52. A value of a correlation coefficient is always between negative and positive one.

53. A correlation coefficient of one indicates that all the data points lie on a straight line.

54. A regression line is also referred to as a least squares line.

SKILLS REFRESHER FOR CHAPTER ONE: LINEAR EQUATIONS AND THE COORDINATE PLANE

Solving Linear Equations

To solve a linear equation, we isolate the variable.

Example 1 Solve $22 + 1.3t = 31.1$ for t.

Solution We subtract 22 from both sides. Since $31.1 - 22 = 9.1$, we have

$$1.3t = 9.1.$$

We divide both sides by 1.3, so

$$t = \frac{9.1}{1.3} = 7.$$

Example 2 Solve $3 - [5.4 + 2(4.3 - x)] = 2 - (0.3x - 0.8)$ for x.

Solution We begin by clearing the innermost parentheses on each side. Using the distributive law, this gives

$$3 - [5.4 + 8.6 - 2x] = 2 - 0.3x + 0.8.$$

Then

$$3 - 14 + 2x = 2 - 0.3x + 0.8$$
$$2.3x = 13.8,$$
$$x = 6.$$

Example 3 Solve $ax = c + bx$ for x. Assume $a \neq b$.

Solution To solve for x, we first get all the terms involving x on the left side by subtracting bx from both sides

$$ax - bx = c.$$

Factoring on the left, $ax - bx = (a - b)x$, enables us to solve for x by dividing both sides by $(a - b)$:

$$x(a - b) = c$$
$$x = \frac{c}{(a - b)}.$$

Since $a \neq b$, division by $(a - b)$ is possible.

Example 4 Solve for q if $p^2 q + r(-q - 1) = 4(p + r)$.

Solution We first collect all the terms containing q on the left side of the equation.

$$p^2 q - rq - r = 4p + 4r$$
$$p^2 q - rq = 4p + 5r.$$

To solve for q, we factor and then divide by the coefficient of q.

$$q(p^2 - r) = 4p + 5r$$
$$q = \frac{4p + 5r}{p^2 - r}.$$

Solving Exactly Versus Solving Approximately

Some equations can be solved exactly, often by using algebra. For example, the equation $7x - 1 = 0$ has the exact solution $x = 1/7$. Other equations can be hard or even impossible to solve exactly. However, it is often possible, and sometimes easier, to find an approximate solution to an equation by using a graph or a numerical method on a calculator. The equation $7x - 1 = 0$ has the approximate solution $x \approx 0.14$ (since $1/7 = 0.142857\ldots$). We use the sign $\approx$, meaning approximately equal, when we want to emphasize that we are making an approximation.

Systems of Linear Equations

To solve for two unknowns, we must have two equations—that is, two relationships between the unknowns. Similarly, three unknowns require three equations, and n unknowns (n an integer) require n equations. The group of equations is known as a *system* of equations. To solve the system, we find the *simultaneous* solutions to all equations in the system.

We can solve these equations either by *substitution* (see Example 5) or by *elimination* (see Example 6).

Example 5　Solve for x and y in the following system of equations using substitution.

$$\begin{cases} y + \dfrac{x}{2} = 3 \\ 2(x + y) = 1 - y \end{cases}$$

Solution　Solving the first equation for y, we write $y = 3 - x/2$. Substituting for y in the second equation gives

$$2\left(x + \left(3 - \frac{x}{2}\right)\right) = 1 - \left(3 - \frac{x}{2}\right).$$

Then

$$2x + 6 - x = -2 + \frac{x}{2}$$
$$x + 6 = -2 + \frac{x}{2}$$
$$2x + 12 = -4 + x$$
$$x = -16.$$

Using $x = -16$ in the first equation to find the corresponding y, we have

$$y - \frac{16}{2} = 3$$
$$y = 3 + 8 = 11.$$

Thus, the solution that simultaneously solves both equations is $x = -16, y = 11$.

Example 6　Solve for x and y in the following system of equations using elimination.

$$\begin{cases} 8x - 5y = 11 \\ -2x + 10y = -1. \end{cases}$$

Solution   To eliminate y, we observe that if we multiply the first equation by 2, the coefficients of y are -10 and 10:

$$\begin{cases} 16x - 10y = 22 \\ -2x + 10y = -1. \end{cases}$$

Adding these two equations gives

$$14x = 21$$
$$x = 3/2.$$

We can substitute this value for x in either of the original equations to find y. For example,

$$8\left(\frac{3}{2}\right) - 5y = 11$$
$$12 - 5y = 11$$
$$-5y = -1$$
$$y = 1/5$$

Thus, the solution is $x = 3/2, y = 1/5$.

Intersection of Two Lines

The coordinates of the point of intersection of two lines satisfy the equations of both lines. Thus, the point can be found by solving the equations simultaneously.

Example 7   Find the point of intersection of the lines $y = 3 - \dfrac{2}{3}x$ and $y = -4 + \dfrac{3}{2}x$.

Solution   Since the y-values of the two lines are equal at the point of intersection, we have

$$-4 + \frac{3}{2}x = 3 - \frac{2}{3}x.$$

Notice that we have converted a pair of equations into a single equation by eliminating one of the two variables. This equation can be simplified by multiplying both sides by 6:

$$6\left(-4 + \frac{3}{2}x\right) = 6\left(3 - \frac{2}{3}x\right)$$
$$-24 + 9x = 18 - 4x$$
$$13x = 42$$
$$x = \frac{42}{13}.$$

We can evaluate either of the original equations at $x = \dfrac{42}{13}$ to find y. For example, $y = -4 + \dfrac{3}{2}x$ gives

$$y = -4 + \frac{3}{2}\left(\frac{42}{13}\right) = \frac{11}{13}.$$

Therefore, the point of intersection is $\left(\dfrac{42}{13}, \dfrac{11}{13}\right)$. You can check that this point also satisfies the other equation. The lines and their point of intersection are shown in Figure 1.74.

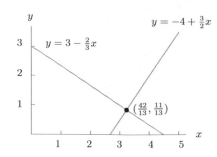

Figure 1.74: Intersection of lines is solution to simultaneous equations

Exercises Skills for Chapter 1

Solve the equations in Exercises 1–12.

1. $3x = 15$

2. $-2y = 12$

3. $4z = 22$

4. $x + 3 = 10$

5. $w - 23 = -34$

6. $7 - 3y = -14$

7. $13t + 2 = 47$

8. $0.5x - 3 = 7$

9. $3t - \dfrac{2(t-1)}{3} = 4$

10. $2(r + 5) - 3 = 3(r - 8) + 21$

11. $B - 4[B - 3(1 - B)] = 42$

12. $1.06s - 0.01(248.4 - s) = 22.67s$

In Exercises 13–22, solve for the indicated variable.

13. $A = l \cdot w$, for l.

14. $l = l_0 + \dfrac{k}{2}w$, for w.

15. $h = v_0 t + \dfrac{1}{2}at^2$, for a.

16. $3xy + 1 = 2y - 5x$, for y.

17. $u(v + 2) + w(v - 3) = z(v - 1)$, for v.

18. $S = \dfrac{rL - a}{r - 1}$, for r.

19. $\dfrac{a - cx}{b + dx} + a = 0$, for x.

20. $\dfrac{At - B}{C - B(1 - 2t)} = 3$, for t.

21. $y'y^2 + 2xyy' = 4y$, for y'.

22. $2x - (xy' + yy') + 2yy' = 0$, for y'.

Solve the systems of equations in Exercises 23–27.

23. $\begin{cases} 3x - 2y = 6 \\ y = 2x - 5 \end{cases}$

24. $\begin{cases} x = 7y - 9 \\ 4x - 15y = 26 \end{cases}$

25. $\begin{cases} 2x + 3y = 7 \\ y = -\frac{3}{5}x + 6 \end{cases}$

26. $\begin{cases} 3x - y = 17 \\ -2x - 3y = -4 \end{cases}$

27. $\begin{cases} ax + y = 2a \\ x + ay = 1 + a^2 \end{cases}$

Determine the points of intersection for Exercises 28–29.

28.

$y = x + 1$

$2x + 3y = 12$

29.

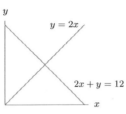

$y = 2x$

$2x + y = 12$

The figures in Problems 30–31 are parallelograms. Find the coordinates of the labeled point(s).

30.

31.

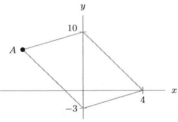

The figures in Problems 32–35 contain a semicircle with the center marked. Find the coordinates of A, a point on the diameter, and B, an extreme point (highest, lowest, or farthest to the right).

32.

33.

34.

35.

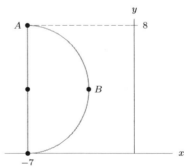

Chapter Two

FUNCTIONS

Contents

2.1 INPUT AND OUTPUT

Finding Output Values: Evaluating a Function

Evaluating a function means calculating the value of a function's output from a particular value of the input.

In the housepainting example on page 4, the notation $n = f(A)$ indicates that the number of gallons of paint n is a function of area A. The expression $f(A)$ represents the output of the function—specifically, the amount of paint required to cover an area of A ft^2. For example, $f(20,000)$ represents the number of gallons of paint required to cover an area of 20,000 ft^2.

Example 1 Using the fact that 1 gallon of paint covers 250 ft^2, evaluate the expression $f(20,000)$.

Solution To evaluate $f(20,000)$, calculate the number of gallons required to cover 20,000 ft^2:

$$f(20,000) = \frac{20,000 \text{ ft}^2}{250 \text{ ft}^2/\text{gallon}} = 80 \text{ gallons of paint.}$$

Evaluating a Function Using a Formula

If we have a formula for a function, we evaluate it by substituting the input value into the formula.

Example 2 The formula for the area of a circle of radius r is $A = q(r) = \pi r^2$. Use the formula to evaluate $q(10)$ and $q(20)$. What do your results tell you about circles?

Solution In the expression $q(10)$, the value of r is 10, so

$$q(10) = \pi \cdot 10^2 = 100\pi \approx 314.$$

Similarly, substituting $r = 20$, we have

$$q(20) = \pi \cdot 20^2 = 400\pi \approx 1257.$$

The statements $q(10) \approx 314$ and $q(20) \approx 1257$ tell us that a circle of radius 10 cm has an area of approximately 314 cm^2 and a circle of radius 20 cm has an area of approximately 1257 cm^2.

Example 3 Let $g(x) = \dfrac{x^2 + 1}{5 + x}$. Evaluate the following expressions.

    (a) $g(3)$ (b) $g(-1)$ (c) $g(a)$

Solution (a) To evaluate $g(3)$, replace every x in the formula with 3:

$$g(3) = \frac{3^2 + 1}{5 + 3} = \frac{10}{8} = 1.25.$$

(b) To evaluate $g(-1)$, replace every x in the formula with (-1):

$$g(-1) = \frac{(-1)^2 + 1}{5 + (-1)} = \frac{2}{4} = 0.5.$$

(c) To evaluate $g(a)$, replace every x in the formula with a:

$$g(a) = \frac{a^2 + 1}{5 + a}.$$

Evaluating a function may involve algebraic simplification, as the following example shows.

Example 4 Let $h(x) = x^2 - 3x + 5$. Evaluate and simplify the following expressions.

(a) $h(2)$ (b) $h(a - 2)$ (c) $h(a) - 2$ (d) $h(a) - h(2)$

Solution Notice that x is the input and $h(x)$ is the output. It is helpful to rewrite the formula as

$$\text{Output} = h(\text{Input}) = (\text{Input})^2 - 3 \cdot (\text{Input}) + 5.$$

(a) For $h(2)$, we have Input $= 2$, so

$$h(2) = (2)^2 - 3 \cdot (2) + 5 = 3.$$

(b) In this case, Input $= a - 2$. We substitute and multiply out

$$\begin{aligned}
h(a - 2) &= (a - 2)^2 - 3(a - 2) + 5 \\
&= a^2 - 4a + 4 - 3a + 6 + 5 \\
&= a^2 - 7a + 15.
\end{aligned}$$

(c) First input a, then subtract 2:

$$\begin{aligned}
h(a) - 2 &= a^2 - 3a + 5 - 2 \\
&= a^2 - 3a + 3.
\end{aligned}$$

(d) Since we found $h(2) = 3$ in part (a), we subtract from $h(a)$:

$$\begin{aligned}
h(a) - h(2) &= a^2 - 3a + 5 - 3 \\
&= a^2 - 3a + 2.
\end{aligned}$$

Finding Input Values: Solving Equations

Given an input, we evaluate the function to find the output. Sometimes the situation is reversed; we know the output and we want to find a corresponding input. If the function is given by a formula, the input values are solutions to an equation.

Example 5 Use the cricket function $T = \frac{1}{4}R + 40$, introduced on page 3, to find the rate, R, at which the snowy tree cricket chirps when the temperature, T, is 76°F.

Solution We want to find R when $T = 76$. Substitute $T = 76$ into the formula and solve the equation

$$76 = \frac{1}{4}R + 40$$

$$36 = \frac{1}{4}R \qquad \text{subtract 40 from both sides}$$

$$144 = R. \qquad \text{multiply both sides by 4}$$

The cricket chirps at a rate of 144 chirps per minute when the temperature is 76°F.

Example 6 Suppose $f(x) = \dfrac{1}{\sqrt{x - 4}}$.

(a) Find an x-value that results in $f(x) = 2$.
(b) Is there an x-value that results in $f(x) = -2$?

Solution (a) To find an x-value that results in $f(x) = 2$, solve the equation

$$2 = \frac{1}{\sqrt{x - 4}}.$$

Square both sides:

$$4 = \frac{1}{x - 4}.$$

Now multiply by $(x - 4)$:

$$4(x - 4) = 1$$
$$4x - 16 = 1$$
$$x = \frac{17}{4} = 4.25.$$

The x-value is 4.25. (Note that the simplification $(x - 4)/(x - 4) = 1$ in the second step was valid because $x - 4 \neq 0$.)

(b) Since $\sqrt{x - 4}$ is nonnegative if it is defined, its reciprocal, $f(x) = \dfrac{1}{\sqrt{x - 4}}$ is also nonnegative if it is defined. Thus, $f(x)$ is not negative for any x input, so there is no x-value that results in $f(x) = -2$.

In the next example, we solve an equation for a quantity that is being used to model a physical quantity; we must choose the solutions that make sense in the context of the model.

Example 7   Let $A = q(r)$ be the area of a circle of radius r, where r is in cm. What is the radius of a circle whose area is 100 cm^2?

Solution   The output $q(r)$ is an area. Solving the equation $q(r) = 100$ for r gives the radius of a circle whose area is 100 cm^2. Since the formula for the area of a circle is $q(r) = \pi r^2$, we solve

$$q(r) = \pi r^2 = 100$$
$$r^2 = \frac{100}{\pi}$$
$$r = \pm\sqrt{\frac{100}{\pi}} = \pm 5.642.$$

We have two solutions for r, one positive and one negative. Since a circle cannot have a negative radius, we take $r = 5.642$ cm. A circle of area 100 cm^2 has a radius of 5.642 cm.

Finding Output and Input Values From Tables and Graphs

The following two examples use function notation with a table and a graph respectively.

Example 8   Table 2.1 shows the revenue, $R = f(t)$, received, by the National Football League,[1] NFL, from network TV as a function of the year, t, since 1975.

(a)   Evaluate and interpret $f(25)$.   (b)   Solve and interpret $f(t) = 1159$.

Table 2.1

Year, t (since 1975)	0	5	10	15	20	25	30
Revenue, R (million $)	201	364	651	1075	1159	2200	2200

Solution   (a) Table 2.1 shows $f(25) = 2200$. Since $t = 25$ in the year 2000, we know that NFL's revenue from TV was $2200 million in the year 2000.

(b) Solving $f(t) = 1159$ means finding the year in which TV revenues were $1159 million; it is $t = 20$. In 1995, NFL's TV revenues were $1159 million.

---

[1]*Newsweek*, January 26, 1998.

Example 9   A man drives from his home to a store and back. The entire trip takes 30 minutes. Figure 2.1 gives his velocity $v(t)$ (in mph) as a function of the time t (in minutes) since he left home. A negative velocity indicates that he is traveling away from the store back to his home.

Figure 2.1: Velocity of a man on a trip to the store and back

Evaluate and interpret:

(a) $v(5)$ (b) $v(24)$ (c) $v(8) - v(6)$ (d) $v(-3)$

Solve for t and interpret:

(e) $v(t) = 15$ (f) $v(t) = -20$ (g) $v(t) = v(7)$

Solution   (a) To evaluate $v(5)$, look on the graph where $t = 5$ minutes. Five minutes after he left home, his velocity is 0 mph. Thus, $v(5) = 0$. Perhaps he had to stop at a light.

(b) The graph shows that $v(24) = -40$ mph. After 24 minutes, he is traveling at 40 mph away from the store, back to his home.

(c) From the graph, $v(8) = 35$ mph and $v(6) = 0$ mph. Thus, $v(8) - v(6) = 35 - 0 = 35$. This shows that the man's speed increased by 35 mph in the interval between $t = 6$ minutes and $t = 8$ minutes.

(d) The quantity $v(-3)$ is not defined since the graph only gives velocities for nonnegative times.

(e) To solve for t when $v(t) = 15$, look on the graph where the velocity is 15 mph. This occurs at $t \approx 0.75$ minute, 3.75 minutes, 6.5 minutes, and 15.5 minutes. At each of these four times the man's velocity was 15 mph.

(f) To solve $v(t) = -20$ for t, we see that the velocity is -20 mph (that is, 20 mph toward home) at $t \approx 19.5$ and $t \approx 29$ minutes.

(g) First we evaluate $v(7) \approx 27$. To solve $v(t) = 27$, we look for the values of t making the velocity 27 mph. One such t is of course $t = 7$; the other t is $t \approx 15$ minutes. These are the two times when the velocity is the same as it is at 7 minutes.

Exercises and Problems for Section 2.1

Skill Refresher

For Exercises S1–S6, expand and simplify.

S1. $5(x - 3)$

S2. $a(2a + 5)$

S3. $(m - 5)(4(m - 5) + 2)$ **S4.** $(x + 2)(3x - 8)$

S5. $3\left(1 + \dfrac{1}{x}\right)$

S6. $3 + 2\left(\dfrac{1}{x}\right)^2 - x$

Solve the equations in Exercises S7–S10.

S7. $x^2 - 9 = 0$

S8. $\sqrt{2x - 1} + 3 = 9$

S9. $\dfrac{21}{z - 5} - \dfrac{13}{z^2 - 5z} = 3$ **S10.** $2x^{\frac{3}{2}} - 1 = 7$

Exercises

1. If $f(t) = t^2 - 4$, **(a)** Find $f(0)$ **(b)** Solve $f(t) = 0$.

2. If $g(x) = x^2 - 5x + 6$, **(a)** Find $g(0)$ **(b)** Solve $g(x) = 0$.

3. If $g(t) = \dfrac{1}{t+2} - 1$, **(a)** Find $g(0)$ **(b)** Solve $g(t) = 0$.

4. If $h(x) = ax^2 + bx + c$, find $h(0)$.

5. If $g(x) = -\frac{1}{2}x^{1/3}$, find $g(-27)$.

6. Let $f(x) = \dfrac{2x+1}{x+1}$. For what value of x is $f(x) = 0.3$?

If $p(r) = r^2 + 5$, evaluate the expressions in Exercises 7–8.

7. $p(7)$ **8.** $p(x) + p(8)$

In Figure 2.2, mark the point(s) representing the statements in Exercises 9–12 and label their coordinates.

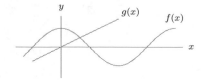

Figure 2.2

9. $f(0) = 2$

10. $f(-3) = f(3) = f(9) = 0$

11. $f(2) = g(2)$

12. $g(x) > f(x)$ for $x > 2$

Problems

13. Let $F = g(t)$ be the number of foxes in a park as a function of t, the number of months since January 1. Evaluate $g(9)$ using Table 1.3 on page 5. What does this tell us about the fox population?

14. Let $F = g(t)$ be the number of foxes in month t in the national park described in Example 5 on page 5. Solve the equation $g(t) = 75$. What does your solution tell you about the fox population?

15. Let $f(x) = 3 + 2x^2$. Find $f\left(\dfrac{1}{3}\right)$ and $\dfrac{f(1)}{f(3)}$. Are they equal?

16. Let $g(x) = x^2 + x$. Find formulas for the following functions. Simplify your answers.

(a) $g(-3x)$ **(b)** $g(1-x)$ **(c)** $g(x+\pi)$

(d) $g(\sqrt{x})$ **(e)** $g(1/(x+1))$ **(f)** $g(x^2)$

17. Let $f(x) = \dfrac{x}{x-1}$.

(a) Find and simplify

(i) $f\left(\dfrac{1}{t}\right)$ (ii) $f\left(\dfrac{1}{t+1}\right)$

(b) Solve $f(x) = 3$.

18. **(a)** Using Figure 2.3, fill in Table 2.2.

Table 2.2

x	-2	-1	0	1	2	3
$h(x)$						

(b) Evaluate $h(3) - h(1)$ **(c)** Evaluate $h(2) - h(0)$

(d) Evaluate $2h(0)$ **(e)** Evaluate $h(1) + 3$

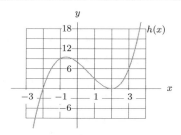

Figure 2.3

19. A ball is thrown up from the ground with initial velocity 64 ft/sec. Its height at time t is

$$h(t) = -16t^2 + 64t.$$

(a) Evaluate $h(1)$ and $h(3)$. What does this tell us about the height of the ball?

(b) Sketch this function. Using a graph, determine when the ball hits the ground and the maximum height of the ball.

20. Let $v(t) = t^2 - 2t$ be the velocity, in ft/sec, of an object at time t, in seconds.

(a) What is the initial velocity, $v(0)$?

(b) When does the object have a velocity of zero?

(c) What is the meaning of the quantity $v(3)$? What are its units?

21. Let $s(t) = 11t^2 + t + 100$ be the position, in miles, of a car driving on a straight road at time t, in hours. The car's velocity at any time t is given by $v(t) = 22t + 1$.

(a) Use function notation to express the car's position after 2 hours. Where is the car then?

(b) Use function notation to express the question, "When is the car going 65 mph?"

(c) Where is the car when it is going 67 mph?

22. Use the letters a, b, c, d, e, h in Figure 2.4 to answer the following questions.

(a) What are the coordinates of the points P and Q?

(b) Evaluate $f(b)$.

(c) Solve $f(x) = e$ for x.

(d) Suppose $c = f(z)$ and $z = f(x)$. What is x?

(e) Suppose $f(b) = -f(d)$. What additional information does this give you?

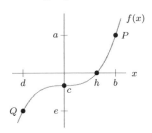

Figure 2.4

23. New York state income tax is based on taxable income, which is part of a person's total income. The tax owed to the state is calculated using the taxable income (not total income). In 2009, for a single person with a taxable income between \$20,000 and \$200,000, the tax owed was \$973 plus 6.85% of the taxable income over \$20,000.[2]

(a) Compute the tax owed by a lawyer whose taxable income is \$68,000.

(b) Consider a lawyer whose taxable income is 80% of her total income, \$$x$, where x is between \$85,000 and \$120,000. Write a formula for $T(x)$, the taxable income.

(c) Write a formula for $L(x)$, the amount of tax owed by the lawyer in part (b).

(d) Use $L(x)$ to evaluate the tax liability for $x = 85,000$ and compare your results to part (a).

24. **(a)** Complete Table 2.3 using

$$f(x) = 2x(x-3) - x(x-5) \quad \text{and} \quad g(x) = x^2 - x.$$

What do you notice? Graph these two functions. Are the two functions the same? Explain.

(b) Complete Table 2.4 using

$$h(x) = x^5 - 5x^3 + 6x + 1 \quad \text{and} \quad j(x) = 2x + 1.$$

What do you notice? Graph these two functions. Are the two functions the same? Explain.

[2]www.nystax.gov, accessed January 4, 2010.

Table 2.3

x	-2	-1	0	1	2
$f(x)$					
$g(x)$					

Table 2.4

x	-2	-1	0	1	2
$h(x)$					
$j(x)$					

Problems 25–26 concern $v = r(s)$, the eyewall wind profile of a hurricane at landfall, where v is the eyewall wind speed (in mph) as a function of s, the height (in meters) above the ground. (The eyewall is the band of clouds that surrounds the eye of the storm.) Let s_0 be the height at which the wind speed is greatest, and let $v_0 = r(s_0)$. Interpret the following in terms of the hurricanes.

25. $r(0.5s_0)$

26. $r(s) = 0.75v_0$

27. Let $h(x) = x^2 + bx + c$. Evaluate and simplify:

(a) $h(1)$

(b) $h(b+1)$

28. If $g(x) = x\sqrt{x} + 100x$, evaluate without a calculator

(a) $g(100)$ **(b)** $g(4/25)$ **(c)** $g(1.21 \cdot 10^4)$

In Problems 29–31, if $f(x) = \dfrac{ax}{a+x}$, find and simplify

29. $f(a)$ **30.** $f(1-a)$ **31.** $f\left(\dfrac{1}{1-a}\right)$

32. Values of f and g are given in Table 2.5.

(a) Evaluate $f(1)$ and $g(3)$.

(b) Describe in full sentences the patterns you see in the values for each function.

(c) Assuming that the patterns you observed in part (b) hold true for all values of x, calculate $f(5)$, $f(-2)$, $g(5)$, and $g(-2)$.

(d) Find possible formulas for $f(x)$ and $g(x)$.

Table 2.5

x	-1	0	1	2	3	4
$f(x)$	-4	-1	2	5	8	11
$g(x)$	4	1	0	1	4	9

73

33. Table 2.6 shows $N(s)$, the number of sections of Economics 101, as a function of s, the number of students in the course. If s is between two numbers listed in the table, then $N(s)$ is the higher number of sections.

Table 2.6

s	50	75	100	125	150	175	200
$N(s)$	4	4	5	5	6	6	7

(a) Evaluate and interpret:

    (i) $N(150)$ (ii) $N(80)$ (iii) $N(55.5)$

(b) Solve for s and interpret:

    (i) $N(s) = 4$ (ii) $N(s) = N(125)$

34. Figure 2.5 shows $y = f(x)$. Label the coordinates of any points on the graph where

(a) $f(c) = 0$.

(b) $f(0) = d$.

Figure 2.5

35. An epidemic of influenza spreads through a city. Figure 2.6 is the graph of $I = f(w)$, where I is the number of individuals (in thousands) infected w weeks after the epidemic begins.

(a) Evaluate $f(2)$ and explain its meaning in terms of the epidemic.

(b) Approximately how many people were infected at the height of the epidemic? When did that occur? Write your answer in the form $f(a) = b$.

(c) Solve $f(w) = 4.5$ and explain what the solutions mean in terms of the epidemic.

(d) The graph used $f(w) = 6w(1.3)^{-w}$. Use the graph to estimate the solution of the inequality $6w(1.3)^{-w} \geq 6$. Explain what the solution means in terms of the epidemic.

Figure 2.6

Problems 36–37 concern studies which indicate that as carbon dioxide (CO_2) levels rise, hurricanes will become more intense.[3] Hurricane intensity is measured in terms of the minimum central pressure P (in mb): the lower the pressure, the more powerful the storm. Since warm ocean waters fuel hurricanes, P is a decreasing function of H, sea surface temperature in °C. Let $P = n(H)$ be the hurricane-intensity function for present-day CO_2 levels, and let $P = N(H)$ be the hurricane-intensity function for future projected CO_2 levels. If H_0 is the average temperature in the Caribbean Sea, what do the following quantities tell you about hurricane intensity?

36. $N(H_0) - n(H_0)$ **37.** $n(H_0 + 1) - n(H_0)$

2.2 DOMAIN AND RANGE

In Example 4 on page 5, we defined R to be the average monthly rainfall at Chicago's O'Hare airport in month t. Although R is a function of t, the value of R is not defined for every possible value of t. For instance, it makes no sense to consider the value of R for $t = -3$, or $t = 8.21$, or $t = 13$ (since a year has 12 months). Thus, although R is a function of t, this function is defined only for certain values of t. Notice also that R, the output value of this function, takes only the values $\{1.8, 2.1, 2.4, 2.5, 2.7, 3.1, 3.2, 3.4, 3.5, 3.7\}$.

A function is often defined only for certain values of the independent variable. Also, the dependent variable often takes on only certain values. This leads to the following definitions:

If $Q = f(t)$, then
- the **domain** of f is the set of input values, t, which yield an output value.
- the **range** of f is the corresponding set of output values, Q.

---

[3] *Journal of Climate*, September 14, 2004, pages 3477–3495.

Thus, the domain of a function is the set of input values, and the range is the set of output values.

If the domain of a function is not specified, we usually assume that it is as large as possible—that is, all numbers that make sense as inputs for the function. For example, if there are no restrictions, the domain of the function $f(x) = x^2$ is the set of all real numbers, because we can substitute any real number into the formula $f(x) = x^2$. Sometimes, however, we may restrict the domain to suit a particular application. If the function $f(x) = x^2$ is used to represent the area of a square of side x, we restrict the domain to positive numbers.

If a function is being used to model a real-world situation, the domain and range of the function are often determined by the constraints of the situation being modeled, as in the next example.

Example 1   The house-painting function $n = f(A)$ in Example 2 on page 4 has domain $A > 0$ because all houses have some positive paintable area. There is a practical upper limit to A because houses cannot be infinitely large, but in principle, A can be as large or as small as we like, as long as it is positive. Therefore we take the domain of f to be $A > 0$.

The range of this function is $n \geq 0$, because we cannot use a negative amount of paint.

Choosing Realistic Domains and Ranges

When a function is used to model a real situation, it may be necessary to modify the domain and range.

Example 2   Algebraically speaking, the formula

$$T = \frac{1}{4}R + 40$$

can be used for all values of R. If we know nothing more about this function than its formula, its domain is all real numbers. The formula for $T = \frac{1}{4}R + 40$ can return any value of T when we choose an appropriate R-value. (See Figure 2.7.) Thus, the range of the function is also all real numbers. However, if we use this formula to represent the temperature, T, as a function of a cricket's chirp rate, R, as we did in Example 1 on page 2, some values of R cannot be used. For example, it does not make sense to talk about a negative chirp rate. Also, there is some maximum chirp rate R_{max} that no cricket can physically exceed. Thus, to use this formula to express T as a function of R, we must restrict R to the interval $0 \leq R \leq R_{max}$ shown in Figure 2.8.

Figure 2.7: Graph showing that any T value can be obtained from some R value

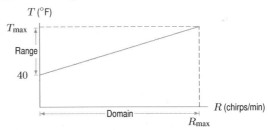

Figure 2.8: Graph showing that if $0 \leq R \leq R_{max}$, then $40 \leq T \leq T_{max}$

The range of the cricket function is also restricted. Since the chirp rate is nonnegative, the smallest value of T occurs when $R = 0$. This happens at $T = 40$. On the other hand, if the temperature gets too hot, the cricket will not be able to keep chirping faster. If the temperature T_{max} corresponds to the chirp rate R_{max}, then the values of T are restricted to the interval $40 \leq T \leq T_{max}$.

Using a Graph to Find the Domain and Range of a Function

A good way to estimate the domain and range of a function is to examine its graph. The domain is the set of input values on the horizontal axis that give rise to a point on the graph; the range is the corresponding set of output values on the vertical axis.

Example 3

A sunflower plant is measured every day t, for $t \geq 0$. The height, $h(t)$ centimeters, of the plant[4] can be modeled by using the *logistic function*

$$h(t) = \frac{260}{1 + 24(0.9)^t}.$$

(a) Using a graphing calculator or computer, graph the height over 80 days.
(b) What is the domain of this function? What is the range? What does this tell you about the height of the sunflower?

Solution

(a) The logistic function is graphed in Figure 2.9.

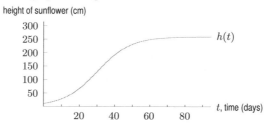

Figure 2.9: Height of sunflower as a function of time

(b) The domain of this function is $t \geq 0$. If we consider the fact that the sunflower dies at some point, then there is an upper bound on the domain, $0 \leq t \leq T$, where T is the day on which the sunflower dies.

To find the range, notice that the smallest value of h occurs at $t = 0$. Evaluating gives $h(0) = 10.4$ cm. This means that the plant was 10.4 cm high when it was first measured on day $t = 0$. Tracing along the graph, $h(t)$ increases. As t-values get large, $h(t)$-values approach, but never reach, 260. This suggests that the range is $10.4 \leq h(t) < 260$. This information tells us that sunflowers typically grow to a height of about 260 cm.

Using a Formula to Find the Domain and Range of a Function

When a function is defined by a formula, its domain and range can often be determined by examining the formula algebraically.

Example 4

State the domain and range of g, where

$$g(x) = \frac{1}{x}.$$

Solution

The domain is all real numbers except those which do not yield an output value. The expression $1/x$ is defined for any real number x except 0 (division by 0 is undefined). Therefore,

Domain: all real x, $x \neq 0$.

---

[4] Adapted from H.S. Reed and R.H. Holland, "Growth of an Annual Plant Helianthus," *Proc. Nat. Acad. Sci.*, 5, 1919.

The range is all real numbers that the formula can return as output values. It is not possible for $g(x)$ to equal zero, since 1 divided by a real number is never zero. All real numbers except 0 are possible output values, since all nonzero real numbers have reciprocals. Thus

$$\text{Range: all real values,} \quad g(x) \neq 0.$$

The graph in Figure 2.10 indicates agreement with these values for the domain and range.

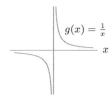

Figure 2.10: Domain and range of $g(x) = 1/x$

Example 5   Find the domain of the function $f(x) = \dfrac{1}{\sqrt{x-4}}$ by examining its formula.

Solution   The domain is all real numbers except those for which the function is undefined. The square root of a negative number is undefined (if we restrict ourselves to real numbers), and so is division by zero. Therefore we need

$$x - 4 > 0.$$

Thus, the domain is all real numbers greater than 4.

$$\text{Domain:} \quad x > 4.$$

In Example 6 on page 69, we saw that for $f(x) = 1/\sqrt{x-4}$, the output, $f(x)$, cannot be negative. Note that $f(x)$ cannot be zero either. (Why?) The range of $f(x) = 1/\sqrt{x-4}$ is $f(x) > 0$. See Exercise 9.

Exercises and Problems for Section 2.2

Skill Refresher

In Exercises S1–S4, for what value(s), if any, are the functions undefined?

S1. $f(x) = \dfrac{x-2}{x-3}$ **S2.** $g(x) = \dfrac{1}{x(x-3)}$

S3. $h(x) = \sqrt{x-15}$ **S4.** $k(x) = \sqrt{15-x}$

Solve the inequalities in Exercises S5–S10.

S5. $x - 8 > 0$ **S6.** $-x + 5 > 0$

S7. $-3(n-4) > 12$ **S8.** $12 \leq 24 - 4a$

S9. $x^2 - 25 > 0$ **S10.** $36 - x^2 \geq 0$

Exercises

In Exercises 1–4, use a graph to find the range of the function on the given domain.

1. $f(x) = \dfrac{1}{x}, \quad -2 \leq x \leq 2$

2. $f(x) = \dfrac{1}{x^2}, \quad -1 \leq x \leq 1$

3. $f(x) = x^2 - 4, \quad -2 \leq x \leq 3$

4. $f(x) = \sqrt{9 - x^2}, \quad -3 \leq x \leq 1$

Find the domain of the functions in Exercises 5–14 algebraically.

5. $f(x) = \dfrac{1}{x + 3}$

6. $p(t) = \dfrac{1}{t^2 - 4}$

7. $f(t) = \dfrac{t - 3}{3t + 9}$

8. $n(q) = \dfrac{1}{q^4 + 2}$

9. $f(x) = \dfrac{1}{\sqrt{x - 4}}$

10. $y(t) = \dfrac{1}{t^4}$

11. $f(x) = \sqrt{x^2 - 4}$

12. $q(r) = \sqrt[3]{r^2 - 16}$

13. $m(x) = x^2 - 9$

14. $t(a) = \sqrt[4]{a - 2}$

Find the domain and range of the functions in Exercises 15–16 algebraically.

15. $m(q) = \dfrac{1}{5}q - 4$

16. $f(x) = \sqrt{15 - 4x}$

Given the domain D of the functions in Exercises 17–20, find possible values for the unknowns a and b (where applicable).

17. $f(x) = \dfrac{1}{x - a}$, D: all real numbers $\neq 3$

18. $p(t) = \dfrac{1}{(2t - a)(t + b)}$, D: all real numbers except 4 and 5.

19. $m(r) = \sqrt{r - a}$, D: all real numbers ≥ -3

20. $n(q) = \sqrt{r^2 + a}$, D: all real numbers

Problems

In Problems 21–22, estimate the domain and range of the function. Assume the entire graph is shown.

21.

22.

23. Give a formula for a function whose domain is all negative values of x except $x = -5$.

24. Give a formula for a function that is undefined for $x = -2$ and for $x < -4$, but is defined everywhere else.

25. A restaurant is open from 2 pm to 2 am each day, and a maximum of 200 clients can fit inside. If $f(t)$ is the number of clients in the restaurant t hours after 2 pm each day, what are a reasonable domain and range for $f(t)$?

26. What is the domain of the function f giving average monthly rainfall at Chicago's O'Hare airport? (See Table 1.2 on page 5.)

27. A movie theater seats 200 people. For any particular show, the amount of money the theater makes is a function of the number of people, n, in attendance. If a ticket costs \$4.00, find the domain and range of this function. Sketch its graph.

28. A car gets the best mileage at intermediate speeds. Graph the gas mileage as a function of speed. Determine a reasonable domain and range for the function and justify your reasoning.

29. (a) Use Table 2.7 to determine the number of calories that a person weighing 200 lb uses in a half–hour of walking.[5]

(b) Table 2.7 illustrates a relationship between the number of calories used per minute walking and a person's weight in pounds. Describe in words what is true about this relationship. Identify the dependent and independent variables. Specify whether it is an increasing or decreasing function.

(c) (i) Graph the linear function for walking, as described in part (b), and estimate its equation.

(ii) Interpret the meaning of the vertical intercept of the graph of the function.

(iii) Specify a meaningful domain and range for your function.

(iv) Use your function to determine how many calories per minute a person who weighs 135 lb uses per minute of walking.

Table 2.7 *Calories per minute as a function of weight*

Activity	100 lb	120 lb	150 lb	170 lb	200 lb	220 lb
Walking	2.7	3.2	4.0	4.6	5.4	5.9
Bicycling	5.4	6.5	8.1	9.2	10.8	11.9
Swimming	5.8	6.9	8.7	9.8	11.6	12.7

In Problems 30–31, find the domain and range of the function.

30. $h(x) = \dfrac{a}{\sqrt{x}}$, where a is a constant

31. $p(x) = |x - b| + 6$, where b is a constant

---

[5] Source: 1993 World Almanac. Speeds assumed are 3 mph for walking, 10 mph for bicycling, and 2 mph for swimming.

32. The last digit, d, of a phone number is a function of n, its position in the phone book. Table 2.8 gives d for the first 10 listings in the 2009 New York State telephone directory.[6] The table shows that the last digit of the first listing is 1, the last digit of the second listing is 5, and so on. In principle we could use a phone book to figure out other values of d. For instance, if $n = 300$, we could count down to the 300th listing in order to determine d. So we write $d = f(n)$.

(a) What is the value of $f(6)$?

(b) Explain how you could use the phone book to find the domain of f.

(c) What is the range of f?

Table 2.8

n	1	2	3	4	5	6	7	8	9	10
d	1	5	1	5	9	9	0	1	1	7

33. In month $t = 0$, a small group of rabbits escapes from a ship onto an island where there are no rabbits. The island rabbit population, $p(t)$, in month t is given by

$$p(t) = \frac{1000}{1 + 19(0.9)^t}, \quad t \geq 0.$$

(a) Evaluate $p(0)$, $p(10)$, $p(50)$, and explain their meaning in terms of rabbits.

(b) Graph $p(t)$ for $0 \leq t \leq 100$. Describe the graph in words. Does it suggest the growth in population you would expect among rabbits on an island?

(c) Estimate the range of $p(t)$. What does this tell you about the rabbit population?

(d) Explain how you can find the range of $p(t)$ from its formula.

34. Bronze is an alloy or mixture of the metals copper and tin. The properties of bronze depend on the percentage of copper in the mix. A chemist decides to study the properties of a given alloy of bronze as the proportion of copper is varied. She starts with 9 kg of bronze that contain 3 kg of copper and 6 kg of tin and either adds or removes copper. Let $f(x)$ be the percentage of copper in the mix if x kg of copper are added ($x > 0$) or removed ($x < 0$).

(a) State the domain and range of f. What does your answer mean in the context of bronze?

(b) Find a formula in terms of x for $f(x)$.

(c) If the formula you found in part (b) was not intended to represent the percentage of copper in an alloy of bronze, but instead simply defined an abstract mathematical function, what would be the domain and range of this function?

35. Let t be time in seconds and let $r(t)$ be the rate, in gallons/second, that water enters a reservoir:

$$r(t) = 800 - 40t.$$

(a) Evaluate the expressions $r(0), r(15), r(25)$, and explain their physical significance.

(b) Graph $y = r(t)$ for $0 \leq t \leq 30$, labeling the intercepts. What is the physical significance of the slope and the intercepts?

(c) For $0 \leq t \leq 30$, when does the reservoir have the most water? When does it have the least water?

(d) What are the domain and range of $r(t)$?

36. The surface area of a cylindrical aluminum can is a measure of how much aluminum the can requires. If the can has radius r and height h, its surface area A and its volume V are given by the equations:

$$A = 2\pi r^2 + 2\pi rh \quad \text{and} \quad V = \pi r^2 h.$$

(a) The volume, V, of a 12 oz cola can is 355 cm^3. A cola can is approximately cylindrical. Express its surface area A as a function of its radius r, where r is measured in centimeters. [Hint: First solve for h in terms of r.]

(b) Graph $A = s(r)$, the surface area of a cola can whose volume is 355 cm^3, for $0 \leq r \leq 10$.

(c) What is the domain of $s(r)$? Based on your graph, what, approximately, is the range of $s(r)$?

(d) The manufacturers wish to use the smallest amount of aluminum (in cm^2) necessary to make a 12-oz cola can. Use your answer in (c) to find the minimum amount of aluminum needed. State the values of r and h that minimize the amount of aluminum used.

(e) The radius of a real 12-oz cola can is about 3.25 cm. Show that real cola cans use more aluminum than necessary to hold 12 oz of cola. Why do you think real cola cans are made in this way?

---

[6]www6.oft.state.ny.us/telecom/phones/techSubRange.do?type=INDIVIDUAL&prefix=A$D-1340452-P=1, accessed February 10, 2010.

2.3 PIECEWISE-DEFINED FUNCTIONS

A function may employ different formulas on different parts of its domain. Such a function is said to be *piecewise defined*. For example, the function graphed in Figure 2.11 has the following formulas:

$$y = x^2 \quad \text{for } x \le 2 \qquad \text{or more compactly} \quad y = \begin{cases} x^2 & \text{for } x \le 2 \\ 6 - x & \text{for } x > 2. \end{cases}$$
$$y = 6 - x \quad \text{for } x > 2$$

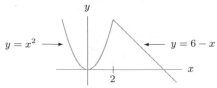

Figure 2.11: Piecewise defined function

Example 1 Graph the function $y = g(x)$ given by the following formulas:

$$g(x) = x + 1 \quad \text{for} \quad x \le 2 \qquad \text{and} \qquad g(x) = 1 \quad \text{for} \quad x > 2.$$

Using bracket notation, this function is written:

$$g(x) = \begin{cases} x + 1 & \text{for } x \le 2 \\ 1 & \text{for } x > 2. \end{cases}$$

Solution For $x \le 2$, graph the line $y = x + 1$. The solid dot at the point $(2, 3)$ shows that it is included in the graph. For $x > 2$, graph the horizontal line $y = 1$. See Figure 2.12. The open circle at the point $(2, 1)$ shows that it is not included in the graph. (Note that $g(2) = 3$, and $g(2)$ cannot have more than one value.)

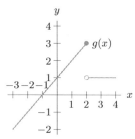

Figure 2.12: Graph of the piecewise defined function g

Example 2 A long-distance calling plan charges 99 cents for any call up to 20 minutes in length and 7 cents for each additional minute or part of a minute.

(a) Use bracket notation to write a formula for the cost, C, of a call as a function of its length t in minutes.
(b) Graph the function.
(c) State the domain and range of the function.

Solution   (a) For $0 < t \leq 20$, the value of C is 99 cents. If $t > 20$, we subtract 20 to find the additional minutes and multiply by the rate, 7 cents per minute.[7] The cost function in cents is thus

$$C = f(t) = \begin{cases} 99 & \text{for } 0 < t \leq 20 \\ 99 + 7(t - 20) & \text{for } t > 20, \end{cases}$$

or, after simplifying,

$$C = f(t) = \begin{cases} 99 & \text{for } 0 < t \leq 20 \\ 7t - 41 & \text{for } t > 20. \end{cases}$$

(b) See Figure 2.13.

(c) Because negative and zero call lengths do not make sense, the domain is $t > 0$. From the graph, we see that the range is $C \geq 99$.

Figure 2.13: Cost of a long-distance phone call

Example 3   The Ironman Triathlon is a race that consists of three parts: a 2.4-mile swim followed by a 112-mile bike race and then a 26.2-mile marathon. A participant swims steadily at 2 mph, cycles steadily at 20 mph, and then runs steadily at 9 mph.[8] Assuming that no time is lost during the transition from one stage to the next, find a formula for the distance covered, d, in miles, as a function of the elapsed time t in hours, from the beginning of the race. Graph the function.

Solution   For each leg of the race, we use the formula Distance = Rate · Time. First, we calculate how long it took for the participant to cover each of the three parts of the race. The first leg took $2.4/2 = 1.2$ hours, the second leg took $112/20 = 5.6$ hours, and the final leg took $26.2/9 \approx 2.91$ hours. Thus, the participant finished the race in $1.2 + 5.6 + 2.91 = 9.71$ hours.

During the first leg, $t \leq 1.2$ and the speed is 2 mph, so

$$d = 2t \quad \text{for} \quad 0 \leq t \leq 1.2.$$

During the second leg, $1.2 < t \leq 1.2 + 5.6 = 6.8$ and the speed is 20 mph. The length of time spent in the second leg is $(t - 1.2)$ hours. Thus, by time t,

$$\text{Distance covered in the second leg} = 20(t - 1.2) \quad \text{for } 1.2 < t \leq 6.8.$$

When the participant is in the second leg, the total distance covered is the sum of the distance covered in the first leg (2.4 miles) plus the part of the second leg that has been covered by time t:

$$d = 2.4 + 20(t - 1.2)$$
$$= 20t - 21.6 \quad \text{for } 1.2 < t \leq 6.8.$$

In the third leg, $6.8 < t \leq 9.71$ and the speed is 9 mph. Since 6.8 hours were spent on the first two parts of the race, the length of time spent on the third leg is $(t - 6.8)$ hours. Thus, by time t,

$$\text{Distance covered in the third leg} = 9(t - 6.8) \quad \text{for } 6.8 < t \leq 9.71.$$

[7] In actuality, most calling plans round the call length to whole minutes or specified fractions of a minute.
[8] Personal communication Susan Reid, Athletics Department, University of Arizona.

When the participant is in the third leg, the total distance covered is the sum of the distances covered in the first leg (2.4 miles) and the second leg (112 miles), plus the part of the third leg that has been covered by time t:

$$d = 2.4 + 112 + 9(t - 6.8)$$
$$= 9t + 53.2 \qquad \text{for } 6.8 < t \leq 9.71.$$

The formula for d is different on different intervals of t:

$$d = \begin{cases} 2t & \text{for} \quad 0 \leq t \leq 1.2 \\ 20t - 21.6 & \text{for} \quad 1.2 < t \leq 6.8 \\ 9t + 53.2 & \text{for} \quad 6.8 < t \leq 9.71. \end{cases}$$

Figure 2.14 gives a graph of the distance covered, d, as a function of time, t. Notice the three pieces.

Figure 2.14: Ironman Triathlon: d as a function of t

The Absolute Value Function

The absolute value of a x, written $|x|$, is defined piecewise:

For positive x, $\quad |x| = x.$

For negative x, $\quad |x| = -x.$

(Remember that $-x$ is a positive number if x is a negative number.) For example, if $x = -3$, then

$$|-3| = -(-3) = 3.$$

For $x = 0$, we have $|0| = 0$. This leads to the following two-part definition:

The **Absolute Value Function** is defined by

$$f(x) = |x| = \begin{cases} x & \text{for} \quad x \geq 0 \\ -x & \text{for} \quad x < 0 \end{cases}.$$

Table 2.9 gives values of $f(x) = |x|$ and Figure 2.15 shows a graph of $f(x)$.

Table 2.9   *Absolute value function*

x	$|x|$
-3	3
-2	2
-1	1
0	0
1	1
2	2
3	3

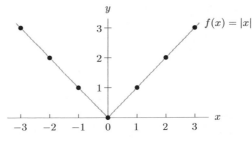

Figure 2.15: Graph of absolute value function

Exercises and Problems for Section 2.3

Skill Refresher

In Exercises S1–S6, write all the possible values for x that match the graph.

S1.

S2.

S3.

S4.

S5.

S6.

In Exercises S7–S10, determine the domain and range of the function.

S7.

S8.

S9.

S10.

Exercises

Graph the piecewise defined functions in Exercises 1–4. Use an open circle to represent a point that is not included and a solid dot to indicate a point that is on the graph.

1. $f(x) = \begin{cases} -1, & -1 \le x < 0 \\ 0, & 0 \le x < 1 \\ 1, & 1 \le x < 2 \end{cases}$

2. $f(x) = \begin{cases} x+1, & -2 \le x < 0 \\ x-1, & 0 \le x < 2 \\ x-3, & 2 \le x < 4 \end{cases}$

3. $f(x) = \begin{cases} x+4, & x \le -2 \\ 2, & -2 < x < 2 \\ 4-x, & x \ge 2 \end{cases}$

4. $f(x) = \begin{cases} x^2, & x \le 0 \\ \sqrt{x}, & 0 < x < 4 \\ x/2, & x \ge 4 \end{cases}$

For Exercises 5–6, find the domain and range.

5. $G(x) = \begin{cases} x+1 & \text{for } x < -1 \\ x^2+3 & \text{for } x \ge -1 \end{cases}$

6. $F(x) = \begin{cases} x^3 & \text{for } x \le 1 \\ 1/x & \text{for } x > 1 \end{cases}$

In Exercises 7–10, write formulas for the functions.

7.

8.

9.

10.

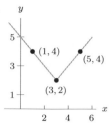

Problems

11. Consider the graph in Figure 2.16. An open circle represents a point that is not included.

    (a) Is y a function of x? Explain.

    (b) Is x a function of y? Explain.

    (c) The domain of $y = f(x)$ is $0 \le x < 4$. What is the range of $y = f(x)$?

Figure 2.16

12. Many people believe that $\sqrt{x^2} = x$. We will investigate this claim graphically and numerically.

    (a) Graph the two functions x and $\sqrt{x^2}$ in the window $-5 \le x \le 5$, $-5 \le y \le 5$. Based on what you see, do you believe that $\sqrt{x^2} = x$? What function does the graph of $\sqrt{x^2}$ remind you of?

    (b) Complete Table 2.10. Based on this table, do you believe that $\sqrt{x^2} = x$? What function does the table for $\sqrt{x^2}$ remind you of? Is this the same function you found in part (a)?

Table 2.10

x	-5	-4	-3	-2	-1	0	1	2	3	4	5
$\sqrt{x^2}$											

    (c) Explain how you know that $\sqrt{x^2}$ is the same as the function $|x|$.

    (d) Graph the function $\sqrt{x^2} - |x|$ in the window $-5 \le x \le 5$, $-5 \le y \le 5$. Explain what you see.

13. (a) Graph $u(x) = |x|/x$ in the window $-5 \le x \le 5$, $-5 \le y \le 5$. Explain what you see.

    (b) Complete Table 2.11. Does this table agree with what you found in part (a)?

Table 2.11

x	-5	-4	-3	-2	-1	0	1	2	3	4	5
$|x|/x$											

    (c) Identify the domain and range of $u(x)$.

    (d) Comment on the claim that $u(x)$ can be written as
$$u(x) = \begin{cases} -1 & \text{if } x < 0, \\ 0 & \text{if } x = 0, \\ 1 & \text{if } x > 0. \end{cases}$$

14. The charge for a taxi ride in New York City is $2.50 upon entry and $0.40 for each $1/5$ of a mile traveled (rounded up to the nearest $1/5$ mile), when the taxicab is traveling at 6 mph or more. In addition, a New York State Tax Surcharge of $0.50 is added to the fare. [9]

    (a) Make a table showing the cost of a trip as a function of its length. Your table should start at zero and go up to two miles in $1/5$-mile intervals.

    (b) What is the cost for a 1.2-mile trip?

    (c) How far can you go for $5.80?

    (d) Graph the cost function in part (a).

15. A museum charges $40 for a group of 10 or fewer people. A group of more than 10 people must, in addition to the $40, pay $2 per person for the number of people above 10. For example, a group of 12 pays $44 and a group of 15 pays $50. The maximum group size is 50.

    (a) Draw a graph that represents this situation.

    (b) What are the domain and range of the cost function?

---

[9] www.nyc.gov/html/tlc/html/passenger/taxicab_rate.shtml, accessed February 11, 2010.

16. A floor-refinishing company charges $1.83 per square foot to strip and refinish a tile floor for up to 1000 square feet. There is an additional charge of $350 for toxic waste disposal for any job that includes more than 150 square feet of tile.

   (a) Express the cost, y, of refinishing a floor as a function of the number of square feet, x, to be refinished.

   (b) Graph the function. Give the domain and range.

17. At a supermarket checkout, a scanner records the prices of the foods you buy. In order to protect consumers, the state of Michigan passed a "scanning law" that says something similar to the following:

> If there is a discrepancy between the price marked on the item and the price recorded by the scanner, the consumer is entitled to receive 10 times the difference between those prices; this amount given must be at least $1 and at most $5. Also, the consumer will be given the difference between the prices, in addition to the amount calculated above.

For example: If the difference is 5¢, you should receive $1 (since 10 times the difference is only 50¢ and you are to receive at least $1), plus the difference of 5¢. Thus, the total you should receive is $1.00 + $0.05 = $1.05.

If the difference is 25¢, you should receive 10 times the difference in addition to the difference, giving $(10)(0.25) + 0.25 = 2.75.

If the difference is 95¢, you should receive $5 (because $10(.95) = 9.50 is more than $5, the maximum penalty), plus 95¢, giving $5 + 0.95 = 5.95.

   (a) What is the lowest possible refund?

   (b) Suppose x is the difference between the price scanned and the price marked on the item, and y is the amount refunded to the customer. Write a formula for y in terms of x. [Hint: Look at the sample calculations.]

   (c) What would the difference between the price scanned and the price marked have to be in order to obtain a $9.00 refund?

   (d) Graph y as a function of x.

18. Seattle City Light charges residents for electricity on a daily basis. There is basic daily charge of 11.57 cents. For each day the first 10 kWh cost 4.59 cents per kWh and any additional kWhs are 9.55 cents per kWh. (A kWh is a unit of energy.)

   (a) Make a table showing the cost in dollars of usage from 0 to 40 kWh in increments of 5 kWh.

   (b) Write a piecewise defined function to describe the usage rate.

---

[10]The Olympic Regional Development Authority.

   (c) What is the cost for 33 kWh?

   (d) How many kWh can you burn on a day for $3?

19. Gore Mountain is a ski resort in the Adirondack mountains in upstate New York. Table 2.12 shows the cost of a weekday ski-lift ticket for various ages and dates.

   (a) Graph cost as a function of age for each time period given. (One graph will serve for times when rates are identical).

   (b) For which age group does the date affect cost?

   (c) Graph cost as a function of date for the age group mentioned in part (b).

   (d) Why does the cost fluctuate as a function of date?

Table 2.12 *Ski-lift ticket prices at Gore Mountain, 1998–1999*[10]

Age	Opening-Dec 12	Dec 13-Dec 24	Dec 25-Jan 3	Jan 4-Jan 15	Jan 16-Jan 18
Up to 6	Free	Free	Free	Free	Free
7–12	$19	$19	$19	$19	$19
13–69	$29	$34	$39	$34	$39
70+	Free	Free	Free	Free	Free

Age	Jan 19-Feb 12	Feb 13-Feb 21	Feb 22-Mar 28	Mar 29-Closing	
Up to 6	Free	Free	Free	Free	
7–12	$19	$19	$19	$19	
13–69	$34	$39	$34	$29	
70+	Free	Free	Free	Free	

In Problems 20–21:

   (a) Use the definition of absolute value to write a piecewise formula for f.

   (b) Graph f.

20. $f(x) = |x^2 - 4|$ **21.** $f(x) = |2x - 6|$

22. If $f(x) = \begin{cases} 1/x & \text{for} \quad x < -1 \\ x^2 & \text{for} \quad -1 \leq x \leq 1 \\ \sqrt{x} & \text{for} \quad x > 1 \end{cases}$ evaluate:

   (a) $f(-2)$

   (b) $f(2)$

   (c) What is the range of f?

23. Let $f(x) = \begin{cases} 3x & \text{for} \quad -1 \leq x \leq 1 \\ -x + 4 & \text{for} \quad 1 < x \leq 5 \end{cases}$

   (a) Find $f(0)$ and $f(3)$.

   (b) Find the domain and range of $f(x)$.

24. Let $g(x) = \begin{cases} -1 & \text{for} \quad x < 0 \\ x^3 & \text{for} \quad x \geq 0 \end{cases}$

(a) Find $g(-2)$, $g(2)$, and $g(0)$.
(b) Find the domain and range of $g(x)$.

25. Use bracket notation to write a formula for the piecewise function that is defined by $y = x^2$ for negative values of x and by $y = x - 1$ for x values that are greater than or equal to zero.

2.4 COMPOSITE AND INVERSE FUNCTIONS

Composition of Functions

Two functions may be connected by the fact that the output of one is the input of the other. For example, to find the cost, C, in dollars, to paint an area A square feet, we need to know the number, n, of gallons of paint required. Since one gallon covers 250 square feet, we have the function $n = f(A) = A/250$. If paint is \$30.50 a gallon, we have the function $C = g(n) = 30.5n$. We substitute $n = f(A)$ into $g(n)$ to find the cost C as a function of A.

Example 1   Find a formula for cost, C, as a function of area, A, to be painted.

Solution   Since we have

$$C = 30.5n \quad \text{and} \quad n = \frac{A}{250},$$

substituting for n in the formula for C gives

$$C = 30.5\frac{A}{250} = 0.122A.$$

We say that C is a "function of a function", or *composite function*. If the function giving C in terms of A is called h, so $C = h(A)$, then we write

$$C = h(A) = g(f(A)).$$

The function h is said to be the *composition* of the functions f and g. We say f is the *inside* function and g is the *outside* function. In this example, the composite function $C = h(A) = g(f(A))$ tells us the cost of painting an area of A square feet.

> For two functions $f(t)$ and $g(t)$, the function $f(g(t))$ is said to be a **composition** of f with g. The function $f(g(t))$ is defined by using the output of the function g as the input to f.

The composite function $f(g(t))$ is defined only for values in the domain of g whose $g(t)$ values are in the domain of f.

Example 2   The air temperature, T, in °F, is given in terms of the chirp rate, R, in chirps per minute, of a snowy tree cricket by the function

$$T = f(R) = \frac{1}{4}R + 40.$$

Suppose one night we record the chirp rate and find that it varies with time, x, according to the function

$$R = g(x) = 20 + x^2 \qquad \text{where } x \text{ is in hours since midnight and } 0 \leq x \leq 10.$$

Find how temperature varies with time by obtaining a formula for h, where $T = h(x)$.

Solution   Since $f(R)$ is a function of R and $R = g(x)$, we see that g is the inside function and f is the outside function. Thus we substitute $R = g(x)$ into f:

$$T = f(R) = f(g(x)) = \frac{1}{4}g(x) + 40 = \frac{1}{4}(20 + x^2) + 40 = \frac{1}{4}x^2 + 45.$$

Thus, for $0 \leq x \leq 10$, we have

$$T = h(x) = \frac{1}{4}x^2 + 45.$$

Example 3 shows another example of composition.

Example 3   Let $f(x) = 2x + 1$ and $g(x) = x^2 - 3$.
(a) Calculate $f(g(3))$ and $g(f(3))$.
(b) Find formulas for $f(g(x))$ and $g(f(x))$.

Solution   (a) We want

$$f(g(3)).$$

We start by evaluating $g(3)$. The formula for g gives $g(3) = 3^2 - 3 = 6$, so

$$f(g(3)) = f(6).$$

The formula for f gives $f(6) = 2 \cdot 6 + 1 = 13$, so

$$f(g(3)) = 13.$$

To calculate $g(f(3))$, we have

$$g(f(3)) = g(7) \quad \text{Because } f(3) = 2 \cdot 3 + 1 = 7$$
$$= 46 \quad \text{Because } g(7) = 7^2 - 3$$

Notice that, $f(g(3)) \neq g(f(3))$. The functions $f(g(x))$ and $g(f(x))$ are different.
(b) In the formula for $f(g(x))$,

$$f(\underbrace{g(x)}_{\text{Input for } f}) = f(x^2 - 3) \quad \text{Because } g(x) = x^2 - 3$$
$$= 2(x^2 - 3) + 1 \quad \text{Because } f(\text{Input}) = 2 \cdot \text{Input} + 1$$
$$= 2x^2 - 5.$$

Check this formula by evaluating $f(g(3))$, which we know to be 13:

$$f(g(3)) = 2 \cdot 3^2 - 5 = 13.$$

In the formula for $g(f(x))$,

$$g(\underbrace{f(x)}_{\text{Input for } g}) = g(2x + 1) \quad \text{Because } f(x) = 2x + 1$$
$$= (2x + 1)^2 - 3 \quad \text{Because } g(\text{Input}) = \text{Input}^2 - 3$$
$$= 4x^2 + 4x - 2.$$

Check this formula by evaluating $g(f(3))$, which we know to be 46:

$$g(f(3)) = 4 \cdot 3^2 + 4 \cdot 3 - 2 = 46.$$

Inverse Functions

The roles of a function's input and output can sometimes be reversed. For example, the population, P, of birds on an island is given, in thousands, by $P = f(t)$, where t is the number of years since 2007. In this function, t is the input and P is the output. If the population is increasing, knowing the population enables us to calculate the year. Thus we can define a new function, $t = g(P)$, which tells us the value of t given the value of P instead of the other way round. For this function, P is the input and t is the output. The functions f and g are called *inverses* of each other. A function which has an inverse is said to be *invertible*.

The fact that f and g are inverse functions means that they go in "opposite directions." The function f takes t as input and outputs P, while g takes P as input and outputs t.

Inverse Function Notation

In the preceding discussion, there was nothing about the names of the two functions that stressed their special relationship. If we want to emphasize that g is the inverse of f, we call it f^{-1} (read "f-inverse"). To express the fact that the population of birds, P, is a function of time, t, we write

$$P = f(t).$$

To express the fact that the time t is also determined by P, so that t is a function of P, we write

$$t = f^{-1}(P).$$

The symbol f^{-1} is used to represent the function that gives the output t for a given input P.

Warning: The -1 that appears in the symbol f^{-1} for the inverse function is not an exponent. Unfortunately, the notation $f^{-1}(x)$ might lead us to interpret it as $(f(x))^{-1} = \frac{1}{f(x)}$. The two expressions are not the same in general: $f^{-1}(x)$ is the output when x is fed into the inverse of f, while $(f(x))^{-1} = \frac{1}{f(x)}$ is the reciprocal of the number we get when x is fed into f.

Example 4 Using $P = f(t)$, where P represents the population, in thousands, of birds on an island and t is the number of years since 2007:

(a) What does $f(4)$ represent?   (b) What does $f^{-1}(4)$ represent?

Solution (a) The expression $f(4)$ is the bird population (in thousands) in the year 2011.
(b) Since f^{-1} is the inverse function, f^{-1} is a function which takes population as input and returns time as output. Therefore, $f^{-1}(4)$ is the number of years after 2007 at which there were 4,000 birds on the island.

Example 5 Suppose that g is an invertible function, with $g(10) = -26$ and $g^{-1}(0) = 7$. What other values of g and g^{-1} do you know?

Solution Because $g(10) = -26$, we know that $g^{-1}(-26) = 10$; because $g^{-1}(0) = 7$, we know that $g(7) = 0$.

Finding a Formula for the Inverse Function

In the next example, we find the formula for an inverse function.

Example 6   The cricket function, which gives temperature, T, in terms of chirp rate, R, is

$$T = f(R) = \frac{1}{4} \cdot R + 40.$$

Find a formula for the inverse function, $R = f^{-1}(T)$.

Solution   The inverse function gives the chirp rate in terms of the temperature, so we solve the following equation for R:

$$T = \frac{1}{4} \cdot R + 40,$$

giving

$$T - 40 = \frac{1}{4} \cdot R$$
$$R = 4(T - 40).$$

Thus, $R = f^{-1}(T) = 4(T - 40)$.

Domain and Range of an Inverse Function

The input values of the inverse function f^{-1} are the output values of the function f. Thus, the domain of f^{-1} is the range of f. For the cricket function, $T = f(R) = \frac{1}{4}R + 40$, if a realistic domain is $0 \le R \le 160$, then the range of f is $40 \le T \le 80$. The domain of f^{-1} is then $40 \le T \le 80$ and the range is $0 \le R \le 160$. See Figure 2.17.

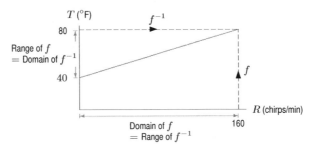

Figure 2.17: Domain and range of an inverse function

A Function and Its Inverse Undo Each Other

Example 7   Calculate the composite functions $f^{-1}(f(R))$ and $f(f^{-1}(T))$ for the cricket example. Interpret the results.

Solution   Since $f(R) = \frac{1}{4}R + 40.$ and $f^{-1}(T) = 4(T - 40)$, we have

$$f^{-1}(f(R)) = f^{-1}\left(\frac{1}{4} \cdot R + 40\right) = 4\left(\left(\frac{1}{4} \cdot R + 40\right) - 40\right) = R.$$
$$f(f^{-1}(T)) = f(4(T - 40)) = \frac{1}{4}(4(T - 40)) + 40 = T.$$

To interpret these results, we use the fact that $f(R)$ gives the temperature corresponding to chirp rate R, and $f^{-1}(T)$ gives the chirp rate corresponding to temperature T. Thus $f^{-1}(f(R))$ gives the chirp rate at temperature $f(R)$, which is R. Similarly, $f(f^{-1}(T))$ gives the temperature at chirp rate $f^{-1}(T)$, which is T.

In Example 7, we see that $f^{-1}(f(R)) = R$ and $f(f^{-1}(T)) = T$. This illustrates the following result, which we see is true in general in Chapter 10.

The functions f and f^{-1} are called inverses because they "undo" each other when composed.

Exercises and Problems for Section 2.4

Skill Refresher

Solve the equations in Exercises S1–S6 for y.

S1. $x = 3y - 4$

S2. $4x - 3y = 7$

S3. $x = \dfrac{2y + 1}{y - 2}$

S4. $x = \sqrt{y} - 2$

S5. $x = y^3 - 4$

S6. $x = 5 - (2y)^3$

Simplify the expressions in Exercises S7–S10.

S7. $5\left(\frac{1}{5}x - 1\right) + 5$

S8. $(2x + 1)^2 - 4$

S9. $3(y - 2)^2 - 7$

S10. $(1 - t)^2 - (1 - t)$

Exercises

In Exercises 1–3, give the meaning and units of the composite function.

1. $A(f(t))$, where $r = f(t)$ is the radius, in centimeters, of a circle at time t minutes, and $A(r)$ is the area, in square centimeters, of a circle of radius r centimeters.

2. $R(f(p))$, where $Q = f(p)$ is the number of barrels of oil sold by a company when the price is p dollars/barrel and $R(Q)$ is the revenue earned in millions of dollars from a sale of Q barrels.

3. $C(A(d))$, where $A(d)$ is the area of a circular pizza with diameter d, and $C(x)$ is the price of pizza with area x.

In Exercises 4–10, use $f(x) = 3x - 1$ and $g(x) = 1 - x^2$.

4. $f(g(0))$

5. $g(f(0))$

6. $g(f(2))$

7. $f(g(2))$

8. $f(g(x))$

9. $f(f(x))$

10. $g(g(x))$

In Exercises 11–15, give the meaning and units of the inverse function. (Assume f is invertible.)

11. $P = f(t)$ is population in millions in year t.

12. $T = f(H)$ is time in minutes to bake a cake at $H°F$.

13. $N = f(t)$ is number of inches of snow in the first t days of January.

14. $x = C(w)$ is calories for w ounces of almonds.

15. $c = P(d)$ is the price, in dollars, for a pizza of diameter d inches.

In Exercises 16–19, find the inverse function.

16. $y = f(t) = 2t + 3$

17. $Q = f(x) = x^3 + 3$

18. $A = f(r) = \pi r^2, r \geq 0$

19. $y = g(s) = 1 + \dfrac{1}{s}$

20. Use the graph in Figure 2.18 to fill in the missing values:

  (a) $f(0) = ?$ **(b)** $f(?) = 0$

  (c) $f^{-1}(0) = ?$ **(d)** $f^{-1}(?) = 0$

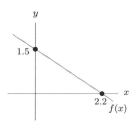

Figure 2.18

21. Use the graph in Figure 2.19 to fill in the missing values:

  (a) $f(0) = ?$ **(b)** $f(?) = 0$

  (c) $f^{-1}(0) = ?$ **(d)** $f^{-1}(?) = 0$

Figure 2.19

Problems

In Problems 22–24, let $n = f(A) = A/250$, where n is the number of gallons of paint needed to paint an area of A square feet.

22. Find a formula for the inverse function $A = f^{-1}(n)$.

23. Interpret and evaluate $f(100)$ and $f^{-1}(100)$.

24. Calculate the composite functions $f^{-1}(f(A))$ and $f(f^{-1}(n))$. Explain the results.

25. Table 2.13 gives values of an invertible function, f.

  (a) Using the table, fill in the missing values:

    (i) $f(0) = ?$ (ii) $f(?) = 0$

    (iii) $f^{-1}(0) = ?$ (iv) $f^{-1}(?) = 0$

  (b) How do the answers to (i)–(iv) in part (a) relate to one another? In particular, how could you have obtained the answers to (iii) and (iv) from the answers to (i) and (ii)?

Table 2.13

x	-2	-1	0	1	2
$f(x)$	5	4	2	0	-3

26. The cost (in dollars) of producing x air conditioners is $C = g(x) = 600 + 45x$. Find a formula for the inverse function $g^{-1}(C)$.

27. The cost of producing q thousand loaves of bread is $C(q)$ dollars. Interpret the following statements in terms of bread; give units.

  (a) $C(5) = 653$

  (b) $C^{-1}(80) = 0.62$

  (c) The solution to $C(q) = 790$ is 6.3

  (d) The solution to $C^{-1}(x) = 1.2$ is 150

28. The cost, C, in thousands of dollars, of producing q kg of a chemical is given by $C = f(q) = 100 + 0.2q$. Find and interpret

  (a) $f(10)$ **(b)** $f^{-1}(200)$ **(c)** $f^{-1}(C)$

29. The perimeter of a square of side s is given by $P = f(s) = 4s$. Find and interpret

  (a) $f(3)$ **(b)** $f^{-1}(20)$ **(c)** $f^{-1}(P)$

30. The gross domestic product (GDP) of the US is given by $G(t)$ where t is the number of years since 1990 and the units of G are billions of dollars.[11]

  (a) What is meant by $G(15) = 12{,}638.4$?

  (b) What is meant by $G^{-1}(14{,}441.4) = 18$?

In Problems 31–33, let $H = f(t) = \frac{5}{9}(t - 32)$, where H is temperature in degrees Celsius and t is in degrees Fahrenheit.

31. Find and interpret the inverse function, $f^{-1}(H)$.

32. Using the results of Problem 31, evaluate and interpret:

  (a) $f(0)$ **(b)** $f^{-1}(0)$

  (c) $f(100)$ **(d)** $f^{-1}(100)$

---

[11]www.bea.gov/national/xls/gdplev.xls, accessed December 21, 2009.

33. The temperature, $t = g(n) = 68 + 10 \cdot 2^{-n}$, in degrees Fahrenheit of a room is a function of the number, n, of hours that the air conditioner has been running. Find and interpret $f(g(n))$. Give units.

34. The period, T, of a pendulum of length l is given by $T = f(l) = 2\pi\sqrt{l/g}$, where g is a constant. Find a formula for $f^{-1}(T)$ and explain its meaning.

35. The area, in square centimeters, of a circle whose radius is r cm is given by $A = \pi r^2$.

   (a) Write this formula using function notation, where f is the name of the function.
   (b) Evaluate $f(0)$.
   (c) Evaluate and interpret $f(r + 1)$.
   (d) Evaluate and interpret $f(r) + 1$.
   (e) What are the units of $f^{-1}(4)$?

36. The area, $A = f(d)$ in^2, of a circular pizza is a function of the diameter d, in inches. A package of pepperoni costs \$2.99 and covers 250 square inches of pizza.

   (a) Write the formula for $f(d)$.
   (b) Find a formula for $C = g(A)$, the cost in dollars of adding pepperoni to a pizza of area A in^2.
   (c) Find and interpret $C = g(f(d))$.
   (d) Evaluate and interpret $f(11)$ and $g(11)$.

37. The radius, r, in centimeters, of a melting snowball is given by $r = 50 - 2.5t$, where t is time in hours. The snowball is spherical, with volume $V = \frac{4}{3}\pi r^3$ cm^3. Find a formula for $V = f(t)$, the volume of the snowball as a function of time.

38. Suppose that $f(x)$ is invertible and that both f and f^{-1} are defined for all values of x. Let $f(2) = 3$ and $f^{-1}(5) = 4$. Evaluate the following expressions, or, if the given information is insufficient, write unknown.

   (a) $f^{-1}(3)$ (b) $f^{-1}(4)$ (c) $f(4)$

39. A circular oil slick is expanding with radius, r in yards, at time t in hours given by $r = 2t - 0.1t^2$, for $0 \le t \le 10$. Find a formula for the area in square yards, $A = f(t)$, as a function of time.

40. Carbon dioxide is one of the greenhouse gases that are believed to affect global warming. Between 2004 and 2008, the concentration of carbon dioxide in the earth's atmosphere increased steadily from 375 parts per million (ppm) to 383 ppm.[12] Let $C(t)$ be the concentration in ppm of carbon dioxide t years after 2004 during these four years.

   (a) State the domain and range of $C(t)$.
   (b) What is the practical meaning of $C(4)$? What is its value?
   (c) What does $C^{-1}(381)$ represent?

41. Let $f(a)$ be the cost in dollars of a pounds of organic apples at Fresh Abundance[13] in November 2009. What do the following statements tell you? What are the units of each of the numbers?

   (a) $f(2) = 2.80$ (b) $f(0.5) = 0.70$
   (c) $f^{-1}(0.35) = 0.25$ (d) $f^{-1}(7) = 5$

42. For $h(x) = \frac{x}{4} + 2$, evaluate $h\left(-\frac{1}{2}\right)$ and $h^{-1}(8)$.

43. For $g(x) = 2x^3 - 1$, evaluate $g(\frac{3}{2})$ and $g^{-1}(-17)$.

In Problems 44–45, find the inverse function.

44. $y = f(x) = 3x - 7$ 45. $y = g(x) = x^3 + 1$

Find the domain and range of the functions in Problems 46–49 algebraically.

46. $t(a) = \sqrt[3]{a + 1}$ 47. $n(r) = r^3 + 2$

48. $m(x) = \dfrac{1}{\sqrt{x - 2}}$ 49. $p(x) = \dfrac{1}{\sqrt{3 - x}}$

50. Table 2.14 gives values for $d = f(v)$, where d, in meters, is the stopping distance for a car traveling at velocity v kilometers per hour.

   (a) Evaluate and interpret $f(60)$.
   (b) Estimate $f(70)$.
   (c) Evaluate and interpret $f^{-1}(70)$.

Table 2.14

v (km/hr)	20	30	40	50	60	80	90	100	120
d (m)	6	10	16	23	30	50	60	70	100

---

[12]The World Almanac and Book of Facts 2010, page 297.
[13]www.freshabundance.com/index.php?main_page=product_info&products_id=254, accessed November 5, 2009.

2.5 CONCAVITY

Concavity and Rates of Change

The graph of a linear function is a straight line because the average rate of change is constant. However, not all graphs are straight lines; they may bend up or down. Consider the salary function $S(t)$ shown in Table 2.15 and Figure 2.20, where t is time in years since being hired. Since the rate of change increases with time, the slope of the graph increases as t increases, so the graph bends upward. We say such graphs are *concave up*.

Table 2.15 *Salary: Increasing rate of change*

t (years)	S ($1000s)	Rate of change $\Delta S/\Delta t$
0	40	
		3.2
10	72	
		5.6
20	128	
		10.2
30	230	
		18.1
40	411	

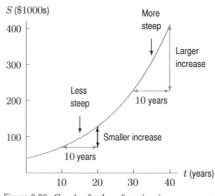

Figure 2.20: Graph of salary function is concave up because rate of change increases

The next example shows that a decreasing function can also be concave up.

Example 1 Table 2.16 shows Q, the quantity of carbon-14 (in μg) in a 200 μg sample remaining after t thousand years. We see from Figure 2.21 that Q is a decreasing function of t, so its rate of change is always negative. What can we say about the concavity of the graph, and what does this mean about the rate of change of the function?

Table 2.16 *Carbon-14: Increasing rate of change*

t (thousand years)	Q (μg)	Rate of change $\Delta Q/\Delta t$
0	200	
		-18.2
5	109	
		-9.8
10	60	
		-5.4
15	33	

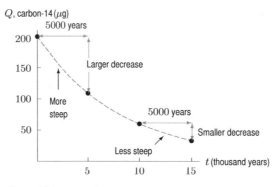

Figure 2.21: Graph of the quantity of carbon-14 is concave up

93

Solution   The graph bends upward, so it is concave up. Table 2.17 shows that the rate of change of the function is increasing, because the rate is becoming less negative. Figure 2.21 shows how the increasing rate of change can be visualized on the graph: the slope is negative and increasing.

Graphs can bend downward; we call such graphs *concave down*.

Example 2   Table 2.17 gives the distance traveled by a cyclist, Karim, as a function of time. What is the concavity of the graph? Was Karim's speed (that is, the rate of change of distance with respect to time) increasing, decreasing, or constant?

Solution   Table 2.17 shows Karim's speed was decreasing throughout the trip. Figure 2.22 shows how the decreasing speed leads to a decreasing slope and a graph which bends downward; thus the graph is concave down.

Table 2.17   *Karim's distance as a function of time, with the average speed for each hour*

t, time (hours)	d, distance (miles)	Average speed, $\Delta d / \Delta t$ (mph)
0	0	
		20 mph
1	20	
		15 mph
2	35	
		10 mph
3	45	
		7 mph
4	52	
		5 mph
5	57	

Figure 2.22: Karim's distance as a function of time

Summary: Increasing and Decreasing Functions; Concavity

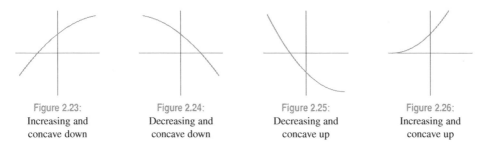

Figure 2.23:
Increasing and
concave down

Figure 2.24:
Decreasing and
concave down

Figure 2.25:
Decreasing and
concave up

Figure 2.26:
Increasing and
concave up

Figures 2.23–2.26 reflect the following relationships between concavity and rate of change:

- If f is a function whose rate of change increases (gets less negative or more positive as we move from left to right[14]), then the graph of f is **concave up**. That is, the graph bends upward.
- If f is a function whose rate of change decreases (gets less positive or more negative as we move from left to right), then the graph of f is **concave down**. That is, the graph bends downward.

If a function has a constant rate of change, its graph is a line and it is neither concave up nor concave down.

Exercises and Problems for Section 2.5

Exercises

Do the graphs of the functions in Exercises 1–8 appear to be concave up, concave down, or neither?

1.

x	0	1	3	6
$f(x)$	1.0	1.3	1.7	2.2

2.

t	0	1	2	3	4
$f(t)$	20	10	6	3	1

3.

4.

5. $y = x^2$

6. $y = -x^2$

7. $y = x^3, x > 0$

8. $y = x^3, x < 0$

9. Calculate successive rates of change for the function, $R(t)$, in Table 2.18 to decide whether you expect the graph of $R(t)$ to be concave up or concave down.

Table 2.18

t	1.5	2.4	3.6	4.8
$R(t)$	-5.7	-3.1	-1.4	0

10. Calculate successive rates of change for the function, $H(x)$, in Table 2.19 to decide whether you expect the graph of $H(x)$ to be concave up or concave down.

Table 2.19

x	12	15	18	21
$H(x)$	21.40	21.53	21.75	22.02

11. Sketch a graph that is everywhere negative, increasing, and concave down.

12. Sketch a graph that is everywhere positive, increasing, and concave up.

Problems

Are the functions in Problems 13–17 increasing or decreasing? What does the scenario tell you about the concavity of the graph modeling it?

13. When money is deposited in the bank, the amount of money increases slowly at first. As the size of the account increases, the amount of money increases more rapidly, since the account is earning interest on the new interest, as well as on the original amount.

14. After a cup of hot chocolate is poured, the temperature cools off very rapidly at first, and then cools off more slowly, until the temperature of the hot chocolate eventually reaches room temperature.

15. When a rumor begins, the number of people who have heard the rumor increases slowly at first. As the rumor spreads, the rate of increase gets greater (as more people continue to tell their friends the rumor), and then slows down again (when almost everyone has heard the rumor).

16. When a drug is injected into a person's bloodstream, the amount of the drug present in the body increases rapidly at first. If the person receives daily injections, the

---

[14] In fact, we need to take the average rate of change over an arbitrarily small interval.

body metabolizes the drug so that the amount of the drug present in the body continues to increase, but at a decreasing rate. Eventually, the quantity levels off at a saturation level.

17. When a new product is introduced, the number of people who use the product increases slowly at first, and then the rate of increase is faster (as more and more people learn about the product). Eventually, the rate of increase slows down again (when most people who are interested in the product are already using it).

18. Graph $f(x)$ with all of these properties:
- $f(0) = 4$
- f is decreasing and concave up for $-\infty < x < 0$
- f is increasing and concave up for $0 < x < 6$
- f is increasing and concave down for $6 < x < 8$
- f is decreasing and concave down for $x > 8$

19. Match each story with the table and graph which best represent it.

(a) When you study a foreign language, the number of new verbs you learn increases rapidly at first, but slows almost to a halt as you approach your saturation level.

(b) You board an airplane in Philadelphia heading west. Your distance from the Atlantic Ocean, in kilometers, increases at a constant rate.

(c) The interest on your savings plan is compounded annually. At first your balance grows slowly, but its rate of growth continues to increase.

(E)

x	0	5	10	15	20	25
y	20	275	360	390	395	399

(F)

x	0	5	10	15	20	25
y	20	36	66	120	220	400

(G)

x	0	5	10	15	20	25
y	20	95	170	245	320	395

20. Match each of the following descriptions with an appropriate graph and table of values.

(a) The weight of your jumbo box of Fruity Flakes decreases by an equal amount every week.

(b) The machinery depreciated rapidly at first, but its value declined more slowly as time went on.

(c) In free fall, your distance from the ground decreases faster and faster.

(d) For a while it looked as if the decline in profits was slowing down, but then they began declining ever more rapidly.

(E)

x	0	1	2	3	4	5
y	400	384	336	256	144	0

(F)

x	0	1	2	3	4	5
y	400	320	240	160	80	0

(G)

x	0	1	2	3	4	5
y	400	184	98	63	49	43

(H)

x	0	1	2	3	4	5
y	412	265	226	224	185	38

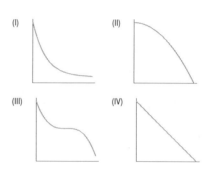

21. An incumbent politician running for reelection declared that the number of violent crimes is no longer rising and is presently under control. Does the graph shown in Figure 2.27 support this claim? Why or why not?

Figure 2.27

96

22. The rate at which water is entering a reservoir is given for time $t > 0$ by the graph in Figure 2.28. A negative rate means that water is leaving the reservoir. In parts (a)–(d), give the largest interval on which:

(a) The volume of water is increasing.

(b) The volume of water is constant.

(c) The volume of water is increasing fastest.

(d) The volume of water is decreasing.

Figure 2.28

23. The relationship between the swimming speed U (in cm/sec) of a salmon to the length l of the salmon (in cm) is given by the function[15]

$$U = 19.5\sqrt{l}.$$

(a) If one salmon is 4 times the length of another salmon, how are their swimming speeds related?

(b) Graph the function $U = 19.5\sqrt{l}$. Describe the graph using words such as increasing, decreasing, concave up, concave down.

(c) Using a property that you described in part (b), answer the question "Do larger salmon swim faster than smaller ones?"

(d) Using a property that you described in part (b), answer the question "Imagine four salmon—two small and two large. The smaller salmon differ in length by 1 cm, as do the two larger. Is the difference in speed between the two smaller fish, greater than, equal to, or smaller than the difference in speed between the two larger fish?"

24. The graph of f is concave down for $0 \leq x \leq 6$. Which is bigger: $\dfrac{f(3) - f(1)}{3 - 1}$ or $\dfrac{f(5) - f(3)}{5 - 3}$? Why?

CHAPTER SUMMARY

- **Input and Output**
  Evaluating functions: finding $f(a)$ for given a.
  Solving equations: finding x if $f(x) = b$ for given b.

- **Domain and Range**
  Domain: set of input values.
  Range: set of output values
  Piecewise defined functions: different formulas on different intervals.

- **Composite Functions**
  Finding $f(g(x))$ given $f(x)$ and $g(x)$.

- **Inverse Functions**
  If $y = f(x)$, then $f^{-1}(y) = x$.
  Evaluating $f^{-1}(b)$. Interpretation of $f^{-1}(b)$.
  Formula for $f^{-1}(y)$ given formula for $f(x)$.

- **Concavity**
  Concave up: increasing rate of change.
  Concave down: decreasing rate of change.

REVIEW EXERCISES AND PROBLEMS FOR CHAPTER TWO

Exercises

In Exercises 1–2, evaluate the function for $x = -7$.

1. $f(x) = x/2 - 1$

2. $f(x) = x^2 - 3$

For Exercises 3–6, calculate exactly the values of y when $y = f(4)$ and of x when $f(x) = 6$.

3. $f(x) = \dfrac{6}{2 - x^3}$

4. $f(x) = \sqrt{20 + 2x^2}$

5. $f(x) = 4x^{3/2}$

6. $f(x) = x^{-3/4} - 2$

7. If $f(x) = 2x + 1$, **(a)** Find $f(0)$ **(b)** Solve $f(x) = 0$.

8. If $f(x) = \dfrac{x}{1 - x^2}$, find $f(-2)$.

9. If $P(t) = 170 - 4t$, find $P(4) - P(2)$.

[15]From K. Schmidt-Nielsen, *Scaling, Why is Animal Size so Important?* (Cambridge: CUP, 1984).

10. Let $h(x) = 1/x$. Find

(a) $h(x+3)$ (b) $h(x) + h(3)$

11. (a) Using Table 2.20, evaluate $f(1)$, $f(-1)$, and $-f(1)$.
(b) Solve $f(x) = 0$ for x.

Table 2.20

x	-1	0	1	2
$f(x)$	0	-1	2	1

12. (a) In Figure 2.29, estimate $f(0)$.
(b) For what x-value(s) is $f(x) = 0$?
(c) For what x-value(s) is $f(x) > 0$?

Figure 2.29

Find the domain and range of functions in Exercises 13–18 algebraically.

13. $q(x) = \sqrt{x^2 - 9}$

14. $m(r) = \dfrac{1}{\sqrt{r^2 - 1}}$

15. $m(x) = 9 - x$

16. $n(x) = 9 - x^4$

17. $m(t) = \dfrac{t}{3} + 2$

18. $s(q) = \dfrac{2q + 3}{5 - 4q}$

19. (a) How can you tell from the graph of a function that an x-value is not in the domain? Sketch an example.
(b) How can you tell from the formula for a function that an x-value is not in the domain? Give an example.

20. Let $g(x) = x^2 + x$. Evaluate and simplify the following.

(a) $-3g(x)$ (b) $g(1) - x$
(c) $g(x) + \pi$ (d) $\sqrt{g(x)}$
(e) $g(1)/(x+1)$ (f) $(g(x))^2$

21. Let $f(x) = 1 - x$. Evaluate and simplify the following.

(a) $2f(x)$ (b) $f(x) + 1$ (c) $f(1 - x)$
(d) $(f(x))^2$ (e) $f(1)/x$ (f) $\sqrt{f(x)}$

In Exercises 22–23, let $f(x) = 3x - 7$ and $g(x) = x^3 + 1$ to find a formula for the function.

22. $f(g(x))$ **23.** $g(f(x))$

In Exercises 24–25, give the meaning and units of the composite function.

24. $a(g(w))$, where $F = g(w)$ is the force, in newtons, on a rocket when the wind speed is w meters/sec and $a(F)$ is the acceleration, in meters/sec^2, when the force is F newtons.

25. $P(f(t))$, where $l = f(t)$ is the length, in centimeters, of a pendulum at time t minutes, and $P(l)$ is the period, in seconds, of a pendulum of length l.

In Exercises 26–33, use $f(x) = x^2 + 1$ and $g(x) = 2x + 3$.

26. $f(g(0))$ **27.** $f(g(1))$ **28.** $g(f(0))$ **29.** $g(f(1))$

30. $f(g(x))$ **31.** $g(f(x))$ **32.** $f(f(x))$ **33.** $g(g(x))$

In Exercises 34–35, give the meaning and units of the inverse function. (Assume f is invertible.)

34. $V = f(t)$ is the speed in km/hr of an accelerating car t seconds after starting.

35. $I = f(r)$ is the interest earned, in dollars, on a $10,000 deposit at an interest rate of $r\%$ per year, compounded annually.

In Exercises 36–37, find the domain and range of the function.

36. $g(x) = a + 1/x$, where a is a constant

37. $q(x) = (x - b)^{1/2} + 6$, where b is a constant

In Exercises 38–39, find the inverse function.

38. $y = g(t) = \sqrt{t} + 1$ **39.** $P = f(q) = 14q - 2$

In Exercises 40–42, let $P = f(t)$ be the population, in millions, of a country at time t in years and let $E = g(P)$ be the daily electricity consumption, in megawatts, when the population is P. Give the meaning and units of the function. Assume both f and g are invertible.

40. $g(f(t))$ **41.** $f^{-1}(P)$ **42.** $g^{-1}(E)$

43. Calculate successive rates of change for the function, $p(t)$, in Table 2.21 to decide whether you expect the graph of $p(t)$ to be concave up or concave down.

Table 2.21

t	0.2	0.4	0.6	0.8
$p(t)$	-3.19	-2.32	-1.50	-0.74

44. If $p(x) = \dfrac{12}{\sqrt{x}}$, evaluate $p(8)$ and $p^{-1}(\sqrt{2})$

45. For $f(x) = 12 - \sqrt{x}$, evaluate $f(16)$ and $f^{-1}(3)$.

In Exercises 46–47, graph the function.

46. $f(x) = \begin{cases} x^2 & \text{for} \quad x \le 1 \\ 2 - x & \text{for} \quad x > 1 \end{cases}$

47. $g(x) = \begin{cases} x + 5 & \text{for} \quad x < 0 \\ x^2 + 1 & \text{for} \quad 0 \le x \le 2 \\ 3 & \text{for} \quad x > 2 \end{cases}$

Problems

48. If $V = \frac{1}{3}\pi r^2 h$ gives the volume of a cone, what is the value of V when $r = 3$ inches and $h = 2$ inches? Give units.

49. Let $q(x) = 3 - x^2$. Evaluate and simplify:

   (a) $q(5)$ **(b)** $q(a)$

   (c) $q(a - 5)$ **(d)** $q(a) - 5$

   (e) $q(a) - q(5)$

50. Let $p(x) = x^2 + x + 1$. Find $p(-1)$ and $-p(1)$. Are they equal?

51. Chicago's average monthly rainfall, $R = f(t)$ inches, is given as a function of month, t, in Table 2.22. (January is $t = 1$.) Solve and interpret:

   (a) $f(t) = 3.7$ **(b)** $f(t) = f(2)$

Table 2.22

t	1	2	3	4	5	6	7	8
R	1.8	1.8	2.7	3.1	3.5	3.7	3.5	3.4

52. Use the graph of $f(x)$ in Figure 2.30 to estimate:

   (a) $f(0)$ **(b)** $f(1)$ **(c)** $f(b)$ **(d)** $f(c)$ **(e)** $f(d)$

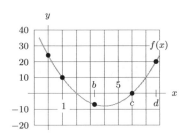

Figure 2.30

53. Let $f(x) = \sqrt{x^2 + 16} - 5$.

   (a) Find $f(0)$

   (b) For what values of x is $f(x)$ zero?

   (c) Find $f(3)$

   (d) What is the vertical intercept of the graph of $f(x)$?

   (e) Where does the graph cross the x-axis?

54. Use the graph in Figure 2.31 to fill in the missing values:

   (a) $f(0) = ?$ **(b)** $f(?) = 0$

   (c) $f^{-1}(0) = ?$ **(d)** $f^{-1}(?) = 0$

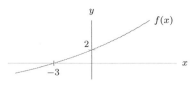

Figure 2.31

55. Use the values of the invertible function in Table 2.23 to find as many values of g^{-1} as possible.

Table 2.23

t	1	2	3	4	5
$y = g(t)$	7	12	13	19	22

56. The formula $V = f(r) = \frac{4}{3}\pi r^3$ gives the volume of a sphere of radius r. Find a formula for the inverse function, $f^{-1}(V)$, giving radius as a function of volume.

57. The formula for the volume of a cube with side s is $V = s^3$. The formula for the surface area of a cube is $A = 6s^2$.

   (a) Find and interpret the formula for the function $s = f(A)$.

   (b) If $V = g(s)$, find and interpret the formula for $g(f(A))$.

58. The area, $A = f(s)$ ft^2, of a square wooden deck is a function of the side s feet. A can of stain costs \$29.50 and covers 200 square feet of wood.

   (a) Write the formula for $f(s)$.

   (b) Find a formula for $C = g(A)$, the cost in dollars of staining an area of A ft^2.

   (c) Find and interpret $C = g(f(s))$.

   (d) Evaluate and interpret, giving units:

      (i) $f(8)$ (ii) $g(80)$ (iii) $g(f(10))$

59. Table 2.24 shows the cost, $C(m)$, in dollars, of a taxi ride as a function of the number of miles, m, traveled.

   (a) Estimate and interpret $C(3.5)$ in practical terms.

   (b) Assume C is invertible. What does $C^{-1}(3.5)$ mean in practical terms? Estimate $C^{-1}(3.5)$.

Table 2.24

m	0	1	2	3	4	5
$C(m)$	0	2.50	4.00	5.50	7.00	8.50

60. The perimeter, in meters, of a square whose side is s meters is given by $P = 4s$.

   (a) Write this formula using function notation, where f is the name of the function.

   (b) Evaluate $f(s + 4)$ and interpret its meaning.

   (c) Evaluate $f(s) + 4$ and interpret its meaning.

   (d) What are the units of $f^{-1}(6)$?

61. **(a)** Find the side, $s = f(d)$, of a square as a function of its diagonal d.

   (b) Find the area, $A = g(s)$, of a square as a function of its side s.

   (c) Find the area $A = h(d)$ as a function of d.

   (d) What is the relation between f, g, and h?

62. Suppose that $j(x) = h^{-1}(x)$ and that both j and h are defined for all values of x. Let $h(4) = 2$ and $j(5) = -3$. Evaluate if possible:

   (a) $j(h(4))$ **(b)** $j(4)$ **(c)** $h(j(4))$

   (d) $j(2)$ **(e)** $h^{-1}(-3)$ **(f)** $j^{-1}(-3)$

   (g) $h(5)$ **(h)** $(h(-3))^{-1}$ **(i)** $(h(2))^{-1}$

63. Let $k(x) = 6 - x^2$.

   (a) Find a point on the graph of $k(x)$ whose x-coordinate is -2.

   (b) Find two points on the graph whose y-coordinates are -2.

   (c) Graph $k(x)$ and locate the points in parts (a) and (b).

   (d) Let $p = 2$. Calculate $k(p) - k(p - 1)$.

64. **(a)** Find a point on the graph of $h(x) = \sqrt{x + 4}$ whose x-coordinate is 5.

   (b) Find a point on the graph whose y-coordinate is 5.

   (c) Graph $h(x)$ and mark the points in parts (a) and (b).

   (d) Let $p = 2$. Calculate $h(p + 1) - h(p)$.

65. Let $t(x)$ be the time required, in seconds, to melt 1 gram of a compound at $x°$C.

   (a) Express the following statement as an equation using $t(x)$: It takes 272 seconds to melt 1 gram of the compound at $400°$C.

   (b) Explain the following equations in words:

      (i) $t(800) = 136$ (ii) $t^{-1}(68) = 1600$

   (c) Above a certain temperature, doubling the temperature, x, halves the melting time. Express this fact with an equation involving $t(x)$.

66. **(a)** The Fibonacci sequence is a sequence of numbers that begins $1, 1, 2, 3, 5, \ldots$. Each term in the sequence is the sum of the two preceding terms. For example,

$$2 = 1 + 1, \quad 3 = 2 + 1, \quad 5 = 2 + 3, \ldots.$$

   Based on this observation, complete the following table of values for $f(n)$, the nth term in the Fibonacci sequence.

n	1	2	3	4	5	6	7	8	9	10	11	12
$f(n)$	1	1	2	3	5							

   (b) The table of values in part (a) can be completed even though we don't have a formula for $f(n)$. Does the fact that we don't have a formula mean that $f(n)$ is not a function?

   (c) Are you able to evaluate the following expressions using parts (a) and (b)? If so, do so; if not, explain why not.

$$f(0), \quad f(-1), \quad f(-2), \quad f(0.5).$$

67. A psychologist conducts an experiment to determine the effect of sleep loss on job performance. Let $p = f(t)$ be the number of minutes it takes the average person to complete a particular task if he or she has lost t minutes of sleep, where $t = 0$ represents exactly 8 hours of sleep. For instance, $f(60)$ is the amount of time it takes the average person to complete the task after sleeping for only 7 hours. Let $p_0 = f(0)$ and let t_1, t_2, and t_3 be positive constants. Explain what the following statements tell you about sleep loss and job performance.

(a) $f(30) = p_0 + 5$
(b) $f(t_1) = 2p_0$
(c) $f(2t_1) = 1.5f(t_1)$
(d) $f(t_2 + 60) = f(t_2 + 30) + 10$

68. Give a formula for a function whose domain is all non-negative values of x except $x = 3$.

69. Give a formula for a function that is undefined for $x = 8$ and for $x < 4$, but is defined everywhere else.

70. Many printing presses are designed with large plates that print a fixed number of pages as a unit. Each unit is called a signature. A particular press prints signatures of 16 pages each. Suppose $C(p)$ is the cost of printing a book of p pages, assuming each signature printed costs $0.14.

(a) What is the cost of printing a book of 128 pages? 129 pages? p pages?
(b) What are the domain and range of C?
(c) Graph $C(p)$ for $0 \le p \le 128$.

71. Table 2.25 shows the population, P, in millions, of Ireland[16] at various times between 1780 and 1910, with t in years since 1780.

(a) When was the population increasing? Decreasing?
(b) For each successive time interval, construct a table showing the average rate of change of the population.
(c) From the table you constructed in part (b), when is the graph of the population concave up? Concave down?
(d) When was the average rate of change of the population the greatest? The least? How is this related to part (c)? What does this mean in human terms?
(e) Graph the data in Table 2.25 and join the points by a curve to show the trend in the data. From this graph identify where the curve is increasing, decreasing, concave up and concave down. Compare your answers to those you got in parts (a) and (c). Identify the region you found in part (d).
(f) Something catastrophic happened in Ireland between 1780 and 1910. When? What happened in Ireland at that time to cause this catastrophe?

Table 2.25 *The population of Ireland from 1780 to 1910, where $t = 0$ corresponds to 1780*

t	0	20	40	60	70	90	110	130
P	4.0	5.2	6.7	8.3	6.9	5.4	4.7	4.4

CHECK YOUR UNDERSTANDING

Are the statements in Problems 1–42 true or false? Give an explanation for your answer.

1. If $f(t) = 3t^2 - 4$ then $f(2) = 0$.

2. If $f(x) = x^2 - 9x + 10$ then $f(b) = b^2 - 9b + 10$.

3. If $f(x) = x^2$ then $f(x + h) = x^2 + h^2$.

4. If $q = \dfrac{1}{\sqrt{z^2 + 5}}$ then the values of z that make $q = \frac{1}{3}$ are $z = \pm 2$.

5. If $W = \dfrac{t + 4}{t - 4}$ then when $t = 8$, $W = 1$.

6. If $f(t) = t^2 + 64$ then $f(0) = 64$.

7. If $f(x) = 0$ then $x = 0$.

8. If $f(x) - x^2 + 2x + 7$ then $f(-x) = f(x)$.

9. If $g(x) = \dfrac{3}{\sqrt{x^2 + 4}}$ then $g(x)$ can never be zero.

10. If $h(p) = -6p + 9$ then $h(3) + h(4) = h(7)$.

11. The domain of a function is the set of input values.

12. If a function is being used to model a real-world situation, the domain and range are often determined by the constraints of the situation being modeled.

13. The domain of $f(x) = \dfrac{4}{x - 3}$ consists of all real numbers x, $x \ne 0$.

14. If $f(x) = \sqrt{2 - x}$, the domain of f consists of all real numbers $x \ge 2$.

15. The range of $f(x) = \dfrac{1}{x}$ is all real numbers.

[16]Adapted from D. N. Burghes and A. D. Wood, *Mathematical Models in the Social, Management and Life Science*, p. 104 (Ellis Horwood, 1980).

16. The range of $y = 4 - \dfrac{1}{x}$ is $0 < y < 4$.

17. If $f(x) = \frac{2}{5}x + 6$ and its domain is $15 \leq x \leq 20$ then the range of f is $12 \leq x \leq 14$.

18. The domain of $f(x) = \dfrac{x}{\sqrt{x^2 + 1}}$ is all real numbers.

19. The graph of the absolute value function $y = |x|$ has a V shape.

20. The domain of $f(x) = |x|$ is all real numbers.

21. If $f(x) = |x|$ and $g(x) = |-x|$ then for all x, $f(x) = g(x)$.

22. If $f(x) = |x|$ and $g(x) = -|x|$ then for all x, $f(x) = g(x)$.

23. If $y = \dfrac{x}{|x|}$ then $y = 1$ for $x \neq 0$.

24. If $f(x) = \begin{cases} 3 & \text{if } x < 0 \\ x^2 & \text{if } 0 \leq x \leq 4 \\ 7 & \text{if } x > 4 \end{cases}$, then $f(3) = 0$.

25. Let $f(x) = \begin{cases} x & \text{if } x < 0 \\ x^2 & \text{if } 0 \leq x \leq 4. \\ -x & \text{if } x > 4 \end{cases}$ If $f(x) = 4$ then $x = 2$.

26. If $f(3) = 5$ and f is invertible, then $f^{-1}(3) = 1/5$.

27. If $h(7) = 4$ and h is invertible, then $h^{-1}(4) = 7$.

28. If $f(x) = \frac{3}{4}x - 6$ then $f^{-1}(8) = 0$.

29. If $R = f(S) = \frac{2}{3}S + 8$ then $S = f^{-1}(R) = \frac{3}{2}(R - 8)$.

30. In general $f^{-1}(x) = (f(x))^{-1}$.

31. If $f(x) = \dfrac{x}{x + 1}$ then $f(t^{-1}) = \dfrac{1/t}{1/t + 1}$.

32. The units of the output of a function are the same as the units of output of its inverse.

33. The functions $f(x) = 2x + 1$ and $g(x) = \frac{1}{2}x - 1$ are inverses.

34. If $q = f(x)$ is the quantity of rice in tons required to feed x million people for a year and $p = g(q)$ is the cost, in dollars, of q tons of rice, then $g(f(x))$ is the dollar cost of feeding x million people for a year.

35. If $f(t) = t + 2$ and $g(t) = 3t$, then $g(f(t)) = 3(t + 2) = 3t + 6$.

36. A fireball has radius $r = f(t)$ meters t seconds after an explosion. The volume of the ball is $V = g(r)$ meter^3 when it has radius r meters. Then the units of measurement of $g(f(t))$ are meter^3/sec.

37. If the graph of a function is concave up, then the average rate of change of a function over an interval of length 1 increases as the interval moves from left to right.

38. The function f in the table could be concave up.

x	-2	0	2	4
$f(x)$	5	6	8	12

39. The function g in the table could be concave down.

t	-1	1	3	5
$g(t)$	9	8	6	3

40. A straight line is concave up.

41. A function can be both decreasing and concave down.

42. If a function is concave up, it must be increasing.

Chapter Three

QUADRATIC FUNCTIONS

Contents

3.1 INTRODUCTION TO THE FAMILY OF QUADRATIC FUNCTIONS

A baseball is "popped" straight up by a batter. The height of the ball above the ground is given by the function $y = f(t) = -16t^2 + 47t + 3$, where t is time in seconds after the ball leaves the bat and y is in feet. See Figure 3.1. Note that the path of the ball is straight up and down, although the graph of height against time is a curve. The ball goes up fast at first and then more slowly because of gravity; thus the graph of its height as a function of time is concave down.

y (feet)

$y = f(t) = -16t^2 + 47t + 3$

Initial
height

3

t (seconds)

3

Figure 3.1: The height of a ball t seconds after being "popped up". (Note: This graph does not represent the ball's path.)

The baseball height function is an example of a *quadratic function*, whose general form is $y = ax^2 + bx + c$. The graph of a quadratic function is a *parabola*. Notice that the function in Figure 3.1 is concave down and has a maximum corresponding to the time at which the ball stops rising and begins to fall back to the earth. The maximum point on the parabola is called the *vertex*. The intersection of the parabola with the horizontal axis gives the times when the height of the ball is zero; these times are the *zeros* of the height function. The horizontal intercepts of a graph occur at the zeros of the function. In this section we examine the zeros and concavity of a quadratic functions, and in the next section we see how to find the vertex.

Finding the Zeros of a Quadratic Function

A natural question to ask is when the ball hits the ground. The graph suggests that $y = 0$ when t is approximately 3. In symbols, the question is: For what value(s) of t does $f(t) = 0$? These are the zeros of the function.

It is easy to find the zeros of a quadratic function if it can be expressed in *factored form*,

$$q(x) = a(x - r)(x - s),$$

where a, r, and s are constants, $a \neq 0$. Then r and s are zeros of the function q.

The baseball function factors as $y = -1(16t + 1)(t - 3)$, so the zeros of f are $t = 3$ and $t = -\frac{1}{16}$. In this problem we are interested in positive values of t, so the ball hits the ground 3 seconds after it was hit. (For more on factoring, see the Skills Review on page 120.)

Example 1 Find the zeros of $f(x) = x^2 - x - 6$.

Solution To find the zeros, set $f(x) = 0$ and solve for x by factoring:

$$x^2 - x - 6 = 0$$
$$(x - 3)(x + 2) = 0.$$

Thus the zeros are $x = 3$ and $x = -2$.

We can also find the zeros of a quadratic function by using the quadratic formula. (See the Skills Review on page 120 to review the quadratic formula.)

Example 2   Find the zeros of $f(x) = x^2 - x - 6$ by using the quadratic formula.

Solution   We solve the equation $x^2 - x - 6 = 0$. For this equation, $a = 1$, $b = -1$, and $c = -6$. Thus

$$x = \frac{-b \pm \sqrt{b^2 - 4ac}}{2a} = \frac{-(-1) \pm \sqrt{(-1)^2 - 4(1)(-6)}}{2(1)}$$

$$= \frac{1 \pm \sqrt{25}}{2} = 3 \text{ or } -2.$$

The zeros are $x = 3$ and $x = -2$, the same as we found by factoring.

Since the zeros of a function occur at the horizontal intercepts of its graph, quadratic functions without horizontal intercepts (such as in the next example) have no zeros.

Example 3   Figure 3.2 shows a graph of $h(x) = -\frac{1}{2}x^2 - 2$. What happens if we try to use algebra to find the zeros of h?

Figure 3.2: Zeros of $h(x) = -(x^2/2) - 2$?

Solution   To find the zeros, we solve the equation

$$-\frac{1}{2}x^2 - 2 = 0$$

$$-\frac{1}{2}x^2 = 2$$

$$x^2 = -4$$

$$x = \pm\sqrt{-4}.$$

Since $\sqrt{-4}$ is not a real number, there are no real solutions, so h has no real zeros. This corresponds to the fact that the graph of h in Figure 3.2 does not cross the x-axis.

Concavity and Quadratic Functions

A quadratic function has a graph that is either concave up or concave down.

Example 4   Let $f(x) = x^2$. Find the average rate of change of f over the consecutive intervals of length 2 starting at $x = -4$ and ending at $x = 4$. What do these rates tell you about the concavity of the graph of f?

Solution   Between $x = -4$ and $x = -2$, we have

$$\text{Average rate of change of } f = \frac{f(-2) - f(-4)}{-2 - (-4)} = \frac{(-2)^2 - (-4)^2}{-2 + 4} = -6.$$

Between $x = -2$ and $x = 0$, we have

$$\text{Average rate of change of } f = \frac{f(0) - f(-2)}{0 - (-2)} = \frac{0^2 - (-2)^2}{0 + 2} = -2.$$

Between $x = 0$ and $x = 2$, we have

$$\text{Average rate of change of } f = \frac{f(2) - f(0)}{2 - 0} = \frac{2^2 - 0^2}{2 - 0} = 2.$$

Between $x = 2$ and $x = 4$, we have

$$\text{Average rate of change of } f = \frac{f(4) - f(2)}{4 - 2} = \frac{4^2 - 2^2}{4 - 2} = 6.$$

Since the rates of change are increasing, the graph is concave up. See Figure 3.3.

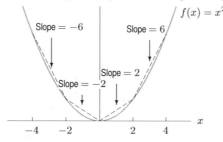

Figure 3.3: Rate of change and concavity of $f(x) = x^2$

Example 5   A high-diver jumps off a 10-meter platform. For t in seconds after the diver leaves the platform until she hits the water, her height h in meters above the water is given by

$$h = f(t) = -4.9t^2 + 8t + 10.$$

The graph of this function is shown in Figure 3.4.

(a) Estimate and interpret the domain and range of the function, and the intercepts of the graph.
(b) Identify the concavity.

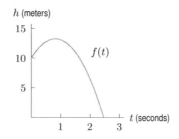

Figure 3.4: Height of diver above water as a function of time

106

Solution

(a) The diver enters the water when her height above the water is 0. This occurs when

$$h = f(t) = -4.9t^2 + 8t + 10 = 0.$$

Using the quadratic formula to solve this equation, we find the only positive solution is $t = 2.462$ seconds. The domain is the interval of time the diver is in the air, which is approximately $0 \leq t \leq 2.462$. To find the range of f, we look for the largest and smallest outputs for h. From the graph, the diver's maximum height appears to occur at about $t = 1$, so we estimate the largest output value for f to be about

$$f(1) = -4.9 \cdot 1^2 + 8 \cdot 1 + 10 = 13.1 \text{ meters.}$$

Thus, the range of f is approximately $0 \leq f(t) \leq 13.1$. Methods to find the exact maximum height are found in Section 3.2.

The vertical intercept of the graph is

$$f(0) = -4.9 \cdot 0^2 + 8 \cdot 0 + 10 = 10 \text{ meters.}$$

The diver's initial height is 10 meters (the height of the diving platform). The horizontal intercept is the point where $f(t) = 0$, which we found in part (a). The diver enters the water approximately 2.462 seconds after leaving the platform.

(b) In Figure 3.4, we see that the graph is bending downward over its entire domain, so it is concave down. This is reflected in Table 3.1, where the rate of change, $\Delta h / \Delta t$, is decreasing.

Table 3.1   *Slope of $f(t) = -4.9t^2 + 8t + 10$*

t (sec)	h (meters)	Rate of change $\Delta h / \Delta t$
0	10	
		5.55
0.5	12.775	
		0.65
1.0	13.100	
		−4.25
1.5	10.975	
		−9.15
2.0	6.400	

Finding a Formula From the Zeros and Vertical Intercept

If we know the zeros and the vertical intercept of a quadratic function, we can use the factored form to find a formula for the function.

Example 6   Find the equation of the parabola in Figure 3.5 using the factored form.

Figure 3.5: Finding a formula for a quadratic from the zeros

Solution   Since the parabola has x-intercepts at $x = 1$ and $x = 3$, its formula can be written as

$$f(x) = a(x - 1)(x - 3).$$

Substituting $x = 0, y = 6$ gives

$$6 = a(3)$$
$$a = 2.$$

Thus, the formula is

$$f(x) = 2(x - 1)(x - 3).$$

Multiplying out gives $f(x) = 2x^2 - 8x + 6$.

Formulas for Quadratic Functions

The function f in Example 6 can be written in at least two different ways.

The form $f(x) = 2x^2 - 8x + 6$ shows the the parabola opens upward, since the coefficient of x^2 is positive and the constant 6 gives the vertical intercept. The form $f(x) = 2(x - 1)(x - 3)$ shows that the parabola crosses the x-axis at $x = 1$ and $x = 3$. In general, we have the following:

The graph of a **quadratic function** is a **parabola**.

The **standard form** for a quadratic function is

$$y = ax^2 + bx + c, \quad \text{where } a, \ b, \ c \text{ are constants, } a \neq 0.$$

The parabola opens upward if $a > 0$ or downward if $a < 0$, and it intersects the y-axis at c.

The **factored form**, when it exists, is

$$y = a(x - r)(x - s), \quad \text{where } a, \ r, \ s \text{ are constants, } a \neq 0.$$

The parabola intersects the x-axis at $x = r$ and $x = s$.

In the next section we look at another form for quadratic functions which shows the vertex of the graph.

Exercises and Problems for Section 3.1

Skill Refresher

Multiply and write the expressions in Problems S1–S2 without parentheses. Gather like terms.

S1. $\left(t^2 + 1\right) 50t - \left(25t^2 + 125\right) 2t$

S2. $\left(A^2 - B^2\right)^2$

For Exercises S3–S8, factor completely if possible.

S3. $u^2 - 2u$

S4. $x^2 + 3x + 2$

S5. $3x^2 - x - 4$

S6. $(s + 2t)^2 - 4p^2$

S7. $16x^2 - 1$

S8. $y^3 - y^2 - 12y$

Solve the equations in Exercises S9–S10.

S9. $x^2 + 7x + 6 = 0$

S10. $2w^2 + w - 10 = 0$

Exercises

Are the functions in Exercises 1–7 quadratic? If so, write the function in the form $f(x) = ax^2 + bx + c$.

1. $f(x) = 2(7 - x)^2 + 1$

2. $L(P) = (P + 1)(1 - P)$

3. $g(m) = m(m^2 - 2m) + 3\left(14 - \dfrac{m^3}{3}\right) + \sqrt{3}m$

4. $h(t) = -16(t - 3)(t + 1)$

5. $R(q) = \dfrac{1}{q^2}(q^2 + 1)^2$

6. $K(x) = 13^2 + 13^x$

7. $T(n) = \sqrt{5} + \sqrt{3n^4} - \sqrt{\dfrac{n^4}{4}}$

8. Find the zeros of $Q(r) = 2r^2 - 6r - 36$ by factoring.

9. Find the zeros of $Q(x) = 5x - x^2 + 3$ using the quadratic formula.

10. Solve for x using the quadratic formula and demonstrate your solution graphically:

    (a) $6x - \frac{1}{3} = 3x^2$ (b) $2x^2 + 7.2 = 5.1x$

In Exercises 11–18, find the zeros (if any) of the function algebraically.

11. $y = (2 - x)(3 - 2x)$ 12. $y = 2x^2 + 5x + 2$

13. $y = 4x^2 - 4x - 8$ 14. $y = 7x^2 + 16x + 4$

15. $y = 5x^2 + 2x - 1$ 16. $y = -17x^2 + 23x + 19$

17. $y = x^4 + 5x^2 + 6$ 18. $y = x - \sqrt{x} - 12$

Problems

In Problems 19–20, find a formula for the quadratic function whose graph has the given properties.

19. A y-intercept of $y = 7$ and x-intercepts at $x = 1, 4$.

20. A y-intercept of $y = 7$ and only one zero at $x = -2$.

21. Use the quadratic formula to find the time at which the baseball in Figure 3.1 on page 104 hits the ground.

22. Is there a quadratic function with zeros $x = 1$, $x = 2$ and $x = 3$?

23. Find two quadratic functions with zeros $x = 1$, $x = 2$.

24. Determine the concavity of the graph of $f(x) = 4 - x^2$ between $x = -1$ and $x = 5$ by calculating average rates of change over intervals of length 2.

25. Graph a quadratic function which has all the following properties: concave up, y-intercept is -6, zeros at $x = -2$ and $x = 3$.

26. Without a calculator, graph $y = 3x^2 - 16x - 12$ by factoring and plotting zeros.

27. Without a calculator, graph the following function by factoring and plotting zeros:

$$y = -4cx + x^2 + 4c^2 \quad \text{for} \quad c > 0.$$

In Problems 28–29, find a formula for the parabola.

30. Using the factored form, find the formula for the parabola whose zeros are $x = -1$ and $x = 5$, and which passes through the point $(-2, 6)$.

31. Write $y = 3(0.5x - 4)(4 - 20x)$ in the form $y = k(x - r)(x - s)$ and give the values of k, r, s.

32. A ball is thrown into the air. Its height (in feet) t seconds later is given by $h(t) = 80t - 16t^2$.

    (a) Evaluate and interpret $h(2)$.
    (b) Solve the equation $h(t) = 80$. Interpret your solutions and illustrate them on a graph of $h(t)$.

33. Let $V(t) = t^2 - 4t + 4$ represent the velocity of an object in meters per second.

    (a) What is the object's initial velocity?
    (b) When is the object not moving?
    (c) Identify the concavity of the velocity graph.

34. A snowboarder slides up from the bottom of a half-pipe and comes down again, sliding with little resistance on the snow. Her height above the edge t seconds after starting up the side is $-4.9t^2 + 14t - 5$ meters.

    (a) What is her height at $t = 0$?
    (b) After how many seconds does she reach the air? Return to the edge of the pipe?
    (c) How long is she in the air?

28.

29.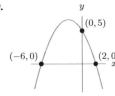

35. The percentage of schools with interactive videodisc players[1] each year from 1992 to 1996 is shown in Table 3.2. If x is in years since 1992, show that this data set can be approximated by the quadratic function $p(x) = -0.8x^2 + 8.8x + 7.2$. What does this model predict for the year 2004? How good is this model for predicting the future?

Table 3.2

Year	1992	1993	1994	1995	1996
Percentage	8	14	21	29.1	29.3

36. Let $f(x) = x^2$ and $g(x) = x^2 + 2x - 8$.

   (a) Graph f and g in the window $-10 \le x \le 10$, $-10 \le y \le 10$. How are the two graphs similar? How are they different?

   (b) Graph f and g in the window $-10 \le x \le 10$, $-10 \le y \le 100$. Why do the two graphs appear more similar on this window than on the window from part (a)?

   (c) Graph f and g in the window $-20 \le x \le 20$, $-10 \le y \le 400$, the window $-50 \le x \le 50$, $-10 \le y \le 2500$, and the window $-500 \le x \le 500$, $-2500 \le y \le 250{,}000$. Describe the change in appearance of f and g on these three successive windows.

37. A relief package is dropped from a moving airplane. The package has an initial forward horizontal velocity and follows a quadratic graph path (instead of dropping straight down). Figure 3.6 shows the height of the package, h, in km, as a function of the horizontal distance, d, in meters, as it drops.

   (a) From what height was the package released?

   (b) How far away from the spot above which it was released does the package hit the ground?

   (c) Write a formula for $h(d)$. [Hint: The package starts falling at the highest point on the graph].

Figure 3.6

3.2   THE VERTEX OF A PARABOLA

In Section 3.1, we looked at the example of a baseball popped upward by a batter. The height of the ball above the ground is given by the quadratic function $y = f(t) = -16t^2 + 47t + 3$, where t is time in seconds after the ball leaves the bat, and y is in feet. See Figure 3.7.

The point on the graph with the largest y value appears to be approximately $(1.5, 37.5)$. (We find the exact value in Example 4 on page 114.) This means that the baseball reaches its maximum

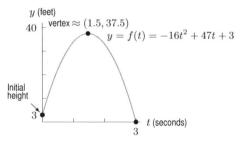

Figure 3.7: Height of baseball at time t

---

[1]Data from R. Famighetti, ed., *The World Almanac and Book of Facts: 1999* (New Jersey: Funk and Wagnalls, 1998).

height of about 37.5 feet about 1.5 seconds after being hit. The maximum point on the parabola is called the *vertex*. For quadratic functions the vertex shows where the function reaches either its maximum value or, in the case of a concave-up parabola, its minimum value.

The vertex of a parabola can be easily determined exactly if the quadratic function is written in the form $y = a(x - h)^2 + k$.

Example 1
(a) Sketch $f(x) = (x + 3)^2 - 4$, and indicate the vertex.
(b) Estimate the coordinates of the vertex from the graph.
(c) Explain how the formula for f can be used to obtain the minimum of f.

Solution
(a) Figure 3.8 shows a sketch of $f(x)$; the vertex gives the minimum value of the function.
(b) The vertex of f appears to be about at the point $(-3, -4)$.
(c) Note that $(x + 3)^2$ is always positive or zero, so $(x + 3)^2$ takes on its smallest value when $x + 3 = 0$, that is, at $x = -3$. At this point $(x + 3)^2 - 4$ takes on its smallest value,

$$f(-3) = (-3 + 3)^2 - 4 = 0 - 4 = -4.$$

Thus, we see that the vertex is exactly at the point $(-3, -4)$.

Figure 3.8: A graph of $f(x) = (x + 3)^2 - 4$

Notice that if we select x-values that are equally spaced to the left and the right of the vertex, the y-values of the function are equal. For example, $f(-2) = f(-4) = -3$. The graph is symmetric about a vertical line that passes through the vertex. This line is called the *axis of symmetry*. The function in Example 1 has axis of symmetry $x = -3$.

The Vertex Form of a Quadratic Function

Writing the function f in Example 1 in the form

$$f(x) = (x + 3)^2 - 4$$

enables us to find the vertex of the graph and the location and value for the minimum of the function. In general, we have the following:

The **vertex form** of a quadratic function is

$$y = a(x - h)^2 + k, \quad \text{where } a, \ h, \ k \text{ are constants}, a \neq 0.$$

The graph of this quadratic function has vertex (h, k) and axis of symmetry $x = h$.

A quadratic function can always be expressed in both standard form and vertex form. For example, for the function $f(x) = (x + 3)^2 - 4$ in Example 1, we convert to standard form by expanding $(x + 3)^2$ and gather like terms, so that f can be written as

$$f(x) = x^2 + 6x + 5.$$

This form shows that the parabola opens upward and that the vertical intercept is 5.

In this case we can also factor f and write it as

$$f(x) = (x + 1)(x + 5).$$

This form shows that the parabola crosses the x-axis at $x = -1$ and $x = -5$. In fact, all three forms share the same constant a, which tells us whether the parabola opens upward or downward. In the function f, we see that $a = 1$.

To convert from vertex form to standard form, we multiply out the squared term. To convert from standard form to vertex form, we *complete the square*.[2]

Example 2   Put each quadratic function into vertex form by completing the square and then graph it.

(a) $s(x) = x^2 - 6x + 8$
(b) $t(x) = -4x^2 - 12x - 8$

Solution   (a) To complete the square, find the square of half of the coefficient of the x-term, $(-6/2)^2 = 9$. Add and subtract this number after the x-term:

$$s(x) = \underbrace{x^2 - 6x + 9}_{\text{Perfect square}} -9 + 8,$$

so

$$s(x) = (x - 3)^2 - 1.$$

The vertex of s is $(3, -1)$ and the axis of symmetry is the vertical line $x = 3$. The parabola opens upward. See Figure 3.9.

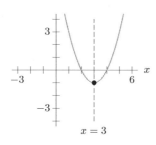

Figure 3.9: $s(x) = x^2 - 6x + 8$

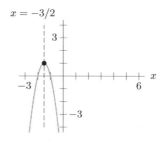

Figure 3.10: $t(x) = -4x^2 - 12x - 8$

[2] A more detailed explanation of this method is in the Skills Review on page 125.

(b) To complete the square, first factor out -4, the coefficient of x^2, giving

$$t(x) = -4(x^2 + 3x + 2).$$

Now add and subtract the square of half the coefficient of the x-term, $(3/2)^2 = 9/4$, inside the parentheses. This gives

$$t(x) = -4\left(\underbrace{x^2 + 3x + \frac{9}{4}}_{\text{Perfect square}} - \frac{9}{4} + 2 \right)$$

$$t(x) = -4\left(\left(x + \frac{3}{2}\right)^2 - \frac{1}{4} \right)$$

$$t(x) = -4\left(x + \frac{3}{2}\right)^2 + 1.$$

The vertex of t is $(-3/2, 1)$, the axis of symmetry is $x = -3/2$, and the parabola opens downward. See Figure 3.10.

Finding a Formula Given the Vertex and Another Point

If we know the vertex of a quadratic function and one other point, we can use the vertex form to find its formula.

Example 3   Find the formula for the quadratic function graphed in Figure 3.11.

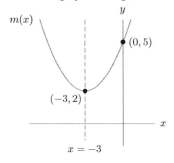

Figure 3.11: Finding a formula for a quadratic from the vertex

Solution   Since the vertex is given, we use the form $m(x) = a(x - h)^2 + k$ to find a, h, and k. The vertex is $(-3, 2)$, so $h = -3$ and $k = 2$. Thus,

$$m(x) = a(x - (-3))^2 + 2,$$

so

$$m(x) = a(x + 3)^2 + 2.$$

To find a, use the y-intercept $(0, 5)$. Substitute $x = 0$ and $y = m(0) = 5$ into the formula for $m(x)$ and solve for a:

$$5 = a(0 + 3)^2 + 2$$
$$3 = 9a$$
$$a = \frac{1}{3}.$$

Thus, the formula is
$$m(x) = \frac{1}{3}(x+3)^2 + 2.$$
If we want the formula in standard form, we multiply out:
$$m(x) = \frac{1}{3}x^2 + 2x + 5.$$

Modeling with Quadratic Functions

In applications, it is often useful to find the maximum or minimum value of a quadratic function. In the next example, we return to the baseball example that started this section.

Example 4   For t in seconds, the height of a baseball in feet is given by the formula
$$y = f(t) = -16t^2 + 47t + 3.$$
Using algebra, find the maximum height reached by the baseball and the time that height is reached.

Solution   The maximum height is at the vertex, so we complete the square to write the function in vertex form:

$$\begin{aligned}
y = f(t) &= -16\left(t^2 - \frac{47}{16}t - \frac{3}{16}\right) \\
&= -16\left(t^2 - \frac{47}{16}t + \left(-\frac{47}{32}\right)^2 - \left(-\frac{47}{32}\right)^2 - \frac{3}{16}\right) \\
&= -16\left(\left(t - \frac{47}{32}\right)^2 - \frac{2209}{1024} - \frac{192}{1024}\right) \\
&= -16\left(\left(t - \frac{47}{32}\right)^2 - \frac{2401}{1024}\right) \\
&= -16\left(t - \frac{47}{32}\right)^2 + \frac{2401}{64}.
\end{aligned}$$

Thus, the vertex is at the point $\left(\frac{47}{32}, \frac{2401}{64}\right)$. This means that the ball reaches it maximum height of 37.516 feet at $t = 1.469$ seconds. Note that these values are in line with the the graphical estimate $(1.5, 37.5)$ from the beginning of the section.

Example 5   A city decides to make a park by fencing off a section of riverfront property. Funds are allotted for 80 meters of fence. The area enclosed will be a rectangle, but only three sides will be enclosed by fence—the other side will be bounded by the river. What is the maximum area that can be enclosed?

Solution   Two sides are perpendicular to the bank of the river and have equal length, which we call h. The other side is parallel to the bank of the river; its length is b. See Figure 3.12. The area, A, of the park is the product of the lengths of adjacent sides, so $A = bh$.
    Since the fence is 80 meters long, we have
$$2h + b = 80$$
$$b = 80 - 2h.$$

Thus,

$$A = bh = (80 - 2h)h$$
$$A = -2h^2 + 80h.$$

The function $A = -2h^2 + 80h$ is quadratic. Since the coefficient of h^2 is negative, the parabola opens downward and we have a maximum at the vertex. The factored form of the quadratic is $A = -2h(h - 40)$, so the zeros are $h = 0$ and $h = 40$. The vertex of the parabola occurs on its axis of symmetry, midway between the zeros at $h = 20$. Substituting $h = 20$ gives the maximum area:

$$A = -2 \cdot 20(20 - 40) = -40(-20) = 800 \text{ meters}^2.$$

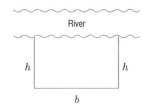

Figure 3.12: A park next to a river

Exercises and Problems for Section 3.2

Skill Refresher

For Exercises S1–S4, complete the square for each expression.

S1. $y^2 - 12y$ **S2.** $s^2 + 6s - 8$

S3. $c^2 + 3c - 7$ **S4.** $4s^2 + s + 2$

In Exercises S5–S7, solve by completing the square.

S5. $r^2 - 6r + 8 = 0$ **S6.** $n^2 = 3n + 18$

S7. $5q^2 - 8 = 2q$

In Exercises S8–S10, solve using factoring, completing the square, or the quadratic formula.

S8. $-3t^2 + 4t + 9 = 0$ **S9.** $n^2 + 4n - 3 = 2$

S10. $2q^2 + 4q - 5 = 8$

Exercises

For the quadratic functions in Exercises 1–2, state the coordinates of the vertex, the axis of symmetry, and whether the parabola opens upward or downward.

1. $f(x) = 3(x - 1)^2 + 2$

2. $g(x) = -(x + 3)^2 - 4$

3. Find the vertex and axis of symmetry of the graph of $v(t) = t^2 + 11t - 4$.

4. Find the vertex and axis of symmetry of the graph of $w(x) = -3x^2 - 30x + 31$.

5. Sketch the quadratic functions given in standard form. Identify the values of the parameters a, b, and c. Label the zeros, axis of symmetry, vertex, and y-intercept.

    (a) $g(x) = x^2 + 3$ **(b)** $f(x) = -2x^2 + 4x + 16$

6. Show that the function $y = -x^2 + 7x - 13$ has no real zeros.

7. Find the value of k so that the graph of $y = (x - 3)^2 + k$ passes through the point $(6, 13)$.

8. The parabola $y = ax^2 + k$ has vertex $(0, -2)$ and passes through the point $(3, 4)$. Find its equation.

In Exercises 9–12, find a formula for the parabola.

9.

10.

11.

12.

For Exercises 13–16, convert the quadratic functions to vertex form by completing the square. Identify the vertex and the axis of symmetry.

13. $f(x) = x^2 + 8x + 3$

14. $g(x) = -2x^2 + 12x + 4$

15. $p(t) = 2t^2 - 0.12t + 0.1$

16. $w(z) = -3z^2 + 9z - 2$

In Exercises 17–19, write the quadratic function in its standard, vertex, and factored forms.

17. $y = -6 + \dfrac{x^2 - x}{2}$

18. $f(t) = \dfrac{5t^2 - 20}{2}$

19. $g(s) = (s - 5)(2s + 3)$

Problems

20. Using the vertex form, find a formula for the parabola with vertex $(2, 5)$ that passes through the point $(1, 2)$.

In Problems 21–24, find a formula for the quadratic function whose graph has the given properties.

21. A vertex at $(4, 2)$ and a y-intercept of $y = 6$.

22. A vertex at $(4, 2)$ and a y-intercept of $y = -4$.

23. A vertex at $(4, 2)$ and zeros at $x = -3, 11$.

24. A vertex at $(-7, -3)$ and contains the point $(-3, -7)$.

25. Let f be a quadratic function whose graph is a concave up parabola with a vertex at $(1, -1)$, and a zero at the origin.

(a) Graph $y = f(x)$.
(b) Determine a formula for $f(x)$.
(c) Determine the range of f.
(d) Find any other zeros.

26. Find the vertex of $y = 0.03x^2 + 1.8x + 2$ exactly. Graph the function, labeling all intercepts.

27. Find the vertex of $y = 26 + 0.4x - 0.01x^2$ exactly. Graph the function, labeling all intercepts.

28. If we know a quadratic function f has a zero at $x = -1$ and vertex at $(1, 4)$, do we have enough information to find a formula for this function? If your answer is yes, find it; if not, give your reasons.

29. If you have a string of length 50 cm, what are the dimensions of the rectangle of maximum area that you can enclose with your string? Explain your reasoning. What about a string of length k cm?

30. A football player kicks a ball at an angle of $37°$ above the ground with an initial speed of 20 meters/second. The height, h, as a function of the horizontal distance traveled, d, is given by:

$$h = 0.75d - 0.0192d^2.$$

(a) Graph the path the ball follows.
(b) When the ball hits the ground, how far is it from the spot where the football player kicked it?
(c) What is the maximum height the ball reaches during its flight?
(d) What is the horizontal distance the ball has traveled when it reaches its maximum height?[3]

----

[3] Adapted from R. Halliday, D. Resnick, and K. Krane, *Physics* (New York: Wiley, 1992), p. 58.

31. A ballet dancer jumps in the air. The height, $h(t)$, in feet, of the dancer at time t, in seconds since the start of the jump, is given by[4]

$$h(t) = -16t^2 + 16Tt,$$

where T is the total time in seconds that the ballet dancer is in the air.

(a) Why does this model apply only for $0 \leq t \leq T$?

(b) When, in terms of T, does the maximum height of the jump occur?

(c) Show that the time, T, that the dancer is in the air is related to H, the maximum height of the jump, by the equation

$$H = 4T^2.$$

CHAPTER SUMMARY

- **General Formulas for Quadratic Functions**
  Standard form:

  $$y = ax^2 + bx + c, a \neq 0$$

  Factored form:

  $$y = a(x - r)(x - s)$$

  Vertex form:

  $$y = a(x - h)^2 + k$$

- **Graphs of Quadratic Functions**
  Graphs are parabolas
  Vertex (h, k)
  Axis of symmetry, $x = h$

Effect of parameter a

Opens upward (concave up) if $a > 0$, minimum at (h, k)

Opens downward (concave down) if $a < 0$, maximum at (h, k)

Factored form displays zeros at $x = r$ and $x = s$

- **Solving Quadratic Equations**
  Factoring
  Quadratic formula

  $$x = \frac{-b \pm \sqrt{b^2 - 4ac}}{2a}$$

  Completing the square

REVIEW EXERCISES AND PROBLEMS FOR CHAPTER THREE

Exercises

Are the functions in Exercises 1–4 quadratic? If so, write the function in the form $f(x) = ax^2 + bx + c$.

1. $f(x) = (2x - 3)(5 - x)$

2. $g(t) = 3(t - 2)^2 + 7$

3. $w(n) = n(n - 3)(n - 2) - n^2(n - 8)$

4. $r(v) = \dfrac{v^2 + \sqrt{2}}{3} + \dfrac{v - 3}{5} + \pi v^2$

In Exercises 5–10, find the zeros (if any) of the function algebraically.

5. $y = 9x^2 + 6x + 1$ **6.** $y = 6x^2 - 17x + 12$

7. $y = 89x^2 + 55x + 34$ **8.** $y = 3x^2 - 2x + 6$

9. $N(t) = t^2 - 7t + 10$ **10.** $Q(r) = 2r^2 - 6r - 36$

11. Show that $y = x^2 - x + 41$ has no real zeros.

12. Find the vertex and axis of symmetry for the parabola whose equation is $y = 3x^2 - 6x + 5$.

In Exercises 13–18, find a possible formula for the parabola with the given conditions.

13. The vertex is $(1, -2)$ and the y-intercept is $y = -5$.

14. The vertex is $(4, -2)$ and the y-intercept is $y = -3$.

15. The vertex is $(7, 3)$ and the parabola contains the point $(3, 7)$.

16. The parabola goes through the origin and its vertex is $(1, -1)$.

17. The x-intercepts are at $x = -1$ and $x = 2$ and $(-2, 16)$ is on the function's graph.

18. The parabola has only one x-intercept at $x = 1/2$ and has a y-intercept at 3.

---

[4]K. Laws, *The Physics of Dance* (Schirmer, 1984).

In Exercises 19–22, find a formula for the parabola.

19.

20.

21.
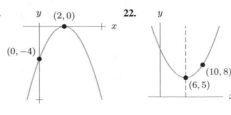

22.

Problems

For each parabola in Problems 23–26, state the coordinates of the vertex, the axis of symmetry, the y-intercept, and whether the curve is concave up or concave down.

23. $y = 2(x - 3/4)^2 - 2/3$ **24.** $y = -1/2(x + 6)^2 - 4$

25. $y = (x - 0.6)^2$ **26.** $y = -0.3x^2 - 7$

In Problems 27–30, write each function in factored form or vertex form and then state its vertex and zeros.

27. $y = 0.3x^2 - 0.6x - 7.2$

28. $y = 2x^2 - 4x - 2$

29. $y = -3x^2 + 24x - 36$

30. $y = 2x^2 + (7/3)x + 1$

31. For x between $x = -2$ and $x = 4$, determine the concavity of the graph of $f(x) = (x-1)^2 + 2$ by calculating average rates of change over intervals of length 2.

32. A tomato is thrown vertically into the air at time $t = 0$. Its height, $d(t)$ (in feet), above the ground at time t (in seconds) is given by

$$d(t) = -16t^2 + 48t.$$

(a) Graph $d(t)$.

(b) Find t when $d(t) = 0$. What is happening to the tomato the first time $d(t) = 0$? The second time?

(c) When does the tomato reach its maximum height?

(d) What is the maximum height that the tomato reaches?

33. When slam-dunking, a basketball player seems to hang in the air at the height of his jump. The height $h(t)$, in feet above the ground, of a basketball player at time t, in seconds since the start of a jump, is given by

$$h(t) = -16t^2 + 16Tt,$$

where T is the total time in seconds that it takes to complete the jump. For a jump that takes 1 second to complete, how much of this time does the basketball player spend at the top 25% of the trajectory? [Hint: Find the maximum height reached. Then find the times at which the height is 75% of this maximum.]

CHECK YOUR UNDERSTANDING

Are the statements in Problems 1–15 true or false? Give an explanation for your answer.

1. The quadratic function $f(x) = x(x + 2)$ is in factored form.

2. If $f(x) = (x + 1)(x + 2)$, then the zeros of f are 1 and 2.

3. A quadratic function whose graph is concave up has a maximum.

4. All quadratic equations have the form $f(x) = ax^2$.

5. If the height above the ground of an object at time t is given by $s(t) = at^2 + bt + c$, then $s(0)$ tells us when the object hits the ground.

6. To find the zeros of $f(x) = ax^2 + bx + c$, solve the equation $ax^2 + bx + c = 0$ for x.

7. Every quadratic equation has two real solutions.

8. There is only one quadratic function with zeros at $x = -2$ and $x = 2$.

9. A quadratic function has exactly two zeros.

10. The graph of every quadratic equation is a parabola.

11. The maximum or minimum point of a parabola is called its vertex.

12. If a parabola is concave up its vertex is a maximum point.

13. If the equation of a parabola is written as $y = a(x - h)^2 + k$, then the vertex is located at the point $(-h, k)$.

14. If the equation of a parabola is written as $y = a(x - h)^2 + k$, then the axis of symmetry is found at $x = h$.

15. If the equation of a parabola is $y = ax^2 + bx + c$ and $a < 0$, then the parabola opens downward.

SKILLS REFRESHER FOR CHAPTER 3: QUADRATIC EQUATIONS

SKILLS FOR FACTORING

Expanding an Expression

The *distributive property* for real numbers a, b, and c tells us that

$$a(b + c) = ab + ac,$$

and

$$(b + c)a = ba + ca.$$

We use the distributive property and the rules of exponents to multiply algebraic expressions involving parentheses. This process is sometimes referred to as *expanding* the expression.

Example 1 Multiply the following expressions and simplify.

(a) $3x^2 \left(x + \frac{1}{6}x^{-3} \right)$ (b) $\left((2t)^2 - 5 \right) \sqrt{t}$

Solution

(a) $3x^2 \left(x + \frac{1}{6}x^{-3} \right) = \left(3x^2\right)(x) + \left(3x^2\right)\left(\frac{1}{6}x^{-3}\right) = 3x^3 + \frac{1}{2}x^{-1}$

(b) $\left((2t)^2 - 5 \right)\sqrt{t} = (2t)^2(\sqrt{t}) - 5\sqrt{t} = \left(4t^2\right)\left(t^{1/2}\right) - 5t^{1/2} = 4t^{5/2} - 5t^{1/2}$

If there are two terms in each factor, then there are four terms in the product:

$$(a + b)(c + d) = a(c + d) + b(c + d) = ac + ad + bc + bd.$$

The following special cases of the above product occur frequently. Learning to recognize their forms aids in factoring.

$$(a + b)(a - b) = a^2 - b^2$$
$$(a + b)^2 = a^2 + 2ab + b^2$$
$$(a - b)^2 = a^2 - 2ab + b^2$$

Example 2 Expand the following and simplify by gathering like terms.

(a) $(5x^2 + 2)(x - 4)$ (b) $(2\sqrt{r} + 2)(4\sqrt{r} - 3)$ (c) $\left(3 - \frac{1}{2}x \right)^2$

Solution

(a) $\left(5x^2 + 2\right)(x - 4) = \left(5x^2\right)(x) + \left(5x^2\right)(-4) + (2)(x) + (2)(-4) = 5x^3 - 20x^2 + 2x - 8$

(b) $(2\sqrt{r} + 2)(4\sqrt{r} - 3) = (2)(4)(\sqrt{r})^2 + (2)(-3)(\sqrt{r}) + (2)(4)(\sqrt{r}) + (2)(-3) = 8r + 2\sqrt{r} - 6$

(c) $\left(3 - \frac{1}{2}x \right)^2 = 3^2 - 2(3)\left(\frac{1}{2}x\right) + \left(-\frac{1}{2}x\right)^2 = 9 - 3x + \frac{1}{4}x^2$

Factoring

To write an expanded expression in factored form, we "un-multiply" the expression. Some techniques for factoring are given in this section. We can check factoring by multiplying the factors.

Removing a Common Factor

It is sometimes useful to factor out the same factor from each of the terms in an expression. This is basically the distributive law in reverse:

$$ab + ac = a(b + c).$$

One special case is removing a factor of -1, which gives

$$-a - b = -(a + b)$$

Another special case is

$$(a - b) = -(b - a)$$

Example 3   Factor the following:

(a) $\dfrac{2}{3}x^2y + \dfrac{4}{3}xy$ (b) $(2p + 1)p^3 - 3p(2p + 1)$ (c) $-\dfrac{s^2t}{8w} - \dfrac{st^2}{16w}$

Solution   (a) $\dfrac{2}{3}x^2y + \dfrac{4}{3}xy = \dfrac{2}{3}xy(x + 2)$

(b) $(2p + 1)p^3 - 3p(2p + 1) = (p^3 - 3p)(2p + 1) = p(p^2 - 3)(2p + 1)$
   (Note that the expression $(2p + 1)$ was one of the factors common to both terms.)

(c) $-\dfrac{s^2t}{8w} - \dfrac{st^2}{16w} = -\dfrac{st}{8w}\left(s + \dfrac{t}{2}\right)$

Grouping Terms

Even though all the terms may not have a common factor, we can sometimes factor by first grouping the terms and then removing a common factor.

Example 4   Factor $x^2 - hx - x + h$.

Solution $x^2 - hx - x + h = \left(x^2 - hx\right) - (x - h) = x(x - h) - (x - h) = (x - h)(x - 1)$

Factoring Quadratics

One way to factor quadratics is to mentally multiply out the possibilities.

Example 5   Factor $t^2 - 4t - 12$.

Solution   If the quadratic factors, it will be of the form

$$t^2 - 4t - 12 = (t + ?)(t + ?).$$

We are looking for two numbers whose product is -12 and whose sum is -4. By trying combinations, we find

$$t^2 - 4t - 12 = (t - 6)(t + 2).$$

Example 6   Factor $4 - 2M - 6M^2$.

Solution   By a similar method to the previous example, we find $4 - 2M - 6M^2 = (2 - 3M)(2 + 2M)$.

Perfect Squares and the Difference of Squares

Recognition of the special products $(x + y)^2$, $(x - y)^2$ and $(x + y)(x - y)$ in expanded form is useful in factoring. Reversing the results given on page 120, we have

$$a^2 + 2ab + b^2 = (a + b)^2,$$
$$a^2 - 2ab + b^2 = (a - b)^2,$$
$$a^2 - b^2 = (a - b)(a + b).$$

When we see squared terms in an expression to be factored, it is often useful to look for one of these forms. The difference of squares identity (the third one listed above) is especially useful.

Example 7   Factor: (a) $16y^2 - 24y + 9$ (b) $25S^2R^4 - T^6$ (c) $x^2(x - 2) + 16(2 - x)$

Solution   (a) $16y^2 - 24y + 9 = (4y - 3)^2$
(b) $25S^2R^4 - T^6 = \left(5SR^2\right)^2 - \left(T^3\right)^2 = \left(5SR^2 - T^3\right)\left(5SR^2 + T^3\right)$
(c) $x^2(x - 2) + 16(2 - x) = x^2(x - 2) - 16(x - 2) = (x - 2)\left(x^2 - 16\right) = (x - 2)(x - 4)(x + 4)$

Solving Quadratic Equations

Example 8   Give exact and approximate solutions to $x^2 = 3$.

Solution   The exact solutions are $x = \pm\sqrt{3}$; approximate ones are $x \approx \pm 1.73$, or $x \approx \pm 1.732$, or $x \approx \pm 1.73205$. (since $\sqrt{3} = 1.732050808\ldots$). Notice that the equation $x^2 = 3$ has only two exact solutions, but many possible approximate solutions, depending on how much accuracy is required.

Solving by Factoring

Some equations can be put into factored form such that the product of the factors is zero. Then we solve by using the fact that if $a \cdot b = 0$, then either a or b (or both) is zero.

Example 9   Solve $(x + 1)(x + 3) = 15$.

Solution   Although it is true that if $a \cdot b = 0$, then $a = 0$ or $b = 0$, it is *not* true that $a \cdot b = 15$ means that $a = 15$ or $b = 15$, or that a and b are 3 and 5. To solve this equation, we expand the left-hand side and rearrange so that the right-hand side is equal to zero:

$$x^2 + 4x + 3 = 15,$$
$$x^2 + 4x - 12 = 0.$$

Then, factoring gives

$$(x - 2)(x + 6) = 0.$$

Thus $x = 2$ and $x = -6$ are solutions.

Example 10   Solve $2(x + 3)^2 = 5(x + 3)$.

Solution   You might be tempted to divide both sides by $(x + 3)$. However, if you do this you will overlook one of the solutions. Instead, write

$$2(x + 3)^2 - 5(x + 3) = 0$$
$$(x + 3)\,(2(x + 3) - 5) = 0$$
$$(x + 3)(2x + 6 - 5) = 0$$
$$(x + 3)(2x + 1) = 0.$$

Thus, $x = -1/2$ and $x = -3$ are solutions.

Note that if we had divided by $(x + 3)$ at the start, we would have lost the solution $x = -3$, which was obtained by setting $x + 3 = 0$.

Solving with the Quadratic Formula

Instead of factoring, we can solve the equation $ax^2 + bx + c = 0$ by using the quadratic formula:

$$x = \frac{-b \pm \sqrt{b^2 - 4ac}}{2a}.$$

The quadratic formula is derived by completing the square for $y = ax^2 + bx + c$. See page 125.

Example 11   Solve $11 + 2x = x^2$.

Solution   The equation is

$$-x^2 + 2x + 11 = 0.$$

The expression on the left does not factor using integers, so we use

$$x = \frac{-2 + \sqrt{4 - 4(-1)(11)}}{2(-1)} = \frac{-2 + \sqrt{48}}{-2} = \frac{-2 + \sqrt{16 \cdot 3}}{-2} = \frac{-2 + 4\sqrt{3}}{-2} = 1 - 2\sqrt{3},$$

$$x = \frac{-2 - \sqrt{4 - 4(-1)(11)}}{2(-1)} = \frac{-2 - \sqrt{48}}{-2} = \frac{-2 - \sqrt{16 \cdot 3}}{-2} = \frac{-2 - 4\sqrt{3}}{-2} = 1 + 2\sqrt{3}.$$

The exact solutions are $x = 1 - 2\sqrt{3}$ and $x = 1 + 2\sqrt{3}$.

The decimal approximations to these numbers $x = 1 - 2\sqrt{3} = -2.464$ and $x = 1 + 2\sqrt{3} = 4.464$ are approximate solutions to this equation. The approximate solutions could also be found directly from a graph or calculator.

Exercises to Skills for Factoring

For Exercises 1–15, expand and simplify.

1. $2(3x - 7)$

2. $-4(y + 6)$

3. $12(x + y)$

4. $-7(5x - 8y)$

5. $x(2x + 5)$

6. $3z(2x - 9z)$

7. $-10r(5r + 6rs)$

8. $x(3x - 8) + 2(3x - 8)$

9. $5z(x - 2) - 3(x - 2)$

10. $(x+1)(x+3)$

11. $(x-2)(x+6)$

12. $(5x-1)(2x-3)$

13. $(y+1)(z+3)$

14. $(12y-5)(8w+7)$

15. $(5z-3)(x-2)$

Multiply and write the expressions in Problems 16–22 without parentheses. Gather like terms.

16. $-(x-3)-2(5-x)$

17. $(x-5)6-5(1-(2-x))$

18. $\left(3x-2x^2\right)4+(5+4x)(3x-4)$

19. $P(p-3q)^2$

20. $4(x-3)^2+7$

21. $-\left(\sqrt{2x}+1\right)^2$

22. $u\left(u^{-1}+2^u\right)2^u$

For Exercises 23–67, factor completely if possible.

23. $2x+6$

24. $3y+15$

25. $5z-30$

26. $4t-6$

27. $10w-25$

28. $3u^4-4u^3$

29. $3u^7+12u^2$

30. $12x^3y^2-18x$

31. $14r^4s^2-21rst$

32. x^2+3x-2

33. x^2-3x+2

34. x^2-3x-2

35. x^2+2x+3

36. x^2-2x-3

37. x^2-2x+3

38. x^2+2x-3

39. $2x^2+5x+2$

40. $2x^2-10x+12$

41. $x^2+3x-28$

42. x^3-2x^2-3x

43. x^3+2x^2-3x

44. $ac+ad+bc+bd$

45. $x^2+2xy+3xz+6yz$

46. $x^2-1.4x-3.92$

47. $a^2x^2-b^2$

48. $\pi r^2+2\pi rh$

49. $B^2-10B+24$

50. c^2+x^2-2cx

51. x^2+y^2

52. a^4-a^2-12

53. $(t+3)^2-16$

54. $x^2+4x+4-y^2$

55. a^3-2a^2+3a-6

56. $b^3-3b^2-9b+27$

57. $c^2d^2-25c^2-9d^2+225$

58. $hx^2+12-4hx-3x$

59. $r(r-s)-2(s-r)$

60. $y^2-3xy+2x^2$

61. $x^2e^{-3x}+2xe^{-3x}$

62. $t^2e^{5t}+3te^{5t}+2e^{5t}$

63. $P(1+r)^2+P(1+r)^2r$

64. $x^2-6x+9-4z^2$

65. $dk+2dm-3ek-6em$

66. $\pi r^2-2\pi r+3r-6$

67. $8gs-12hs+10gm-15hm$

Solve the equations in Exercises 68–93.

68. $y^2-5y-6=0$

69. $4s^2+3s-15=0$

70. $\dfrac{2}{x}+\dfrac{3}{2x}=8$

71. $\dfrac{3}{x-1}+1=5$

72. $\sqrt{y-1}=13$

73. $-16t^2+96t+12=60$

74. $g^3-4g=3g^2-12$

75. $8+2x-3x^2=0$

76. $2p^3+p^2-18p-9=0$

77. $N^2-2N-3=2N(N-3)$

78. $\dfrac{1}{64}t^3=t$

79. $x^2-1=2x$

80. $4x^2-13x-12=0$

81. $60=-16t^2+96t+12$

82. $n^5+80=5n^4+16n$

83. $5a^3+50a^2=4a+40$

84. $y^2 + 4y - 2 = 0$

85. $\dfrac{2}{z - 3} + \dfrac{7}{z^2 - 3z} = 0$

86. $\dfrac{x^2 + 1 - 2x^2}{(x^2 + 1)^2} = 0$

87. $4 - \dfrac{1}{L^2} = 0$

88. $2 + \dfrac{1}{q + 1} - \dfrac{1}{q - 1} = 0$

89. $\sqrt{r^2 + 24} = 7$

90. $\dfrac{1}{\sqrt[3]{x}} = -2$

91. $3\sqrt{x} = \dfrac{1}{2}x$

92. $10 = \sqrt{\dfrac{v}{7\pi}}$

93. $\dfrac{(3x + 4)(x - 2)}{(x - 5)(x - 1)} = 0$

In Exercises 94–97, solve for the indicated variable.

94. $T = 2\pi\sqrt{\dfrac{l}{g}}$, for l.

95. $Ab^5 = C$, for b.

96. $|2x + 1| = 7$, for x.

97. $\dfrac{x^2 - 5mx + 4m^2}{x - m} = 0$, for x

Solve the systems of equations in Exercises 98–102.

98. $\begin{cases} y = 2x - x^2 \\ y = -3 \end{cases}$

99. $\begin{cases} y = 1/x \\ y = 4x \end{cases}$

100. $\begin{cases} x^2 + y^2 = 36 \\ y = x - 3 \end{cases}$

101. $\begin{cases} y = 4 - x^2 \\ y - 2x = 1 \end{cases}$

102. $\begin{cases} y = x^3 - 1 \\ y = e^x \end{cases}$

103. Let ℓ be the line of slope 3 passing through the origin. Find the points of intersection of the line ℓ and the parabola whose equation is $y = x^2$. Sketch the line and the parabola, and label the points of intersection.

Determine the points of intersection for Problems 104–105.

104.

105.

COMPLETING THE SQUARE

An example of changing the form of an expression is the conversion of $ax^2 + bx + c$ into the form $a(x - h)^2 + k$. We make this conversion by *completing the square*, a method for producing a perfect square within a quadratic expression. A perfect square is an expression of the form:

$$(x + n)^2 = x^2 + 2nx + n^2.$$

In order to complete the square in an expression, we must find that number n, which is half the coefficient of x. Before giving a general procedure, let's work through an example.

Example 1   Complete the square to rewrite $x^2 - 10x + 4$ in the form $a(x - h)^2 + k$.

Solution   Step 1: We divide the coefficient of x by 2, giving $\frac{1}{2}(-10) = -5$.
Step 2: We square the result of step 1, giving $(-5)^2 = 25$.
Step 3: Now add and subtract the 25 after the x-term:

$$x^2 - 10x + 4 = x^2 - 10x + 25 - 25 + 4$$
$$= \underbrace{(x^2 - 10x + 25)}_{\text{Perfect square}} - 25 + 4.$$

Step 4: Notice that we have created a perfect square, $x^2 - 10x + 25$. The next step is to factor the perfect square and combine the constant terms, $-25 + 4$, giving the final result:

$$x^2 - 10x + 4 = (x - 5)^2 - 21.$$

Thus, $a = +1$, $h = +5$, and $k = -21$.

Visualizing The Process of Completing The Square

We can visualize how to find the constant that needs to be added to $x^2 + bx$ in order to obtain a perfect square by thinking of $x^2 + bx$ as the area of a rectangle. For example, the rectangle in Figure 3.13 has area $x(x + b) = x^2 + bx$. Now imagine cutting the rectangle into pieces as in Figure 3.14 and trying to rearrange them to make a square, as in Figure 3.15. The corner piece, whose area is $(b/2)^2$, is missing. By adding this piece to our expression, we "complete" the square: $x^2 + bx + (b/2)^2 = (x + b/2)^2$.

Figure 3.13: Rectangle with sides x and $x + b$

Figure 3.14: Cut off 2 strips of width $b/2$

Figure 3.15: Rearrange to see a square with missing corner of area $(b/2)^2$

The procedure we followed can be summarized as follows:

To complete the square in the expression $x^2 + bx + c$, divide the coefficient of x by 2, giving $b/2$. Then add and subtract $(b/2)^2 = b^2/4$ and factor the perfect square:

$$x^2 + bx + c = \left(x + \frac{b}{2}\right)^2 - \frac{b^2}{4} + c.$$

To complete the square in the expression $ax^2 + bx + c$, factor out a first.

The next example has a coefficient a with $a \neq 1$. After factoring out the coefficient, we follow the same steps as in Example 1.

Example 2   Complete the square in the formula $h(x) = 5x^2 + 30x - 10$.

Solution   We first factor out 5:
$$h(x) = 5(x^2 + 6x - 2).$$

Now we complete the square in the expression $x^2 + 6x - 2$.
Step 1: Divide the coefficient of x by 2, giving 3.
Step 2: Square the result: $3^2 = 9$.
Step 3: Add the result after the x term, then subtract it:
$$h(x) = 5(\underbrace{x^2 + 6x + 9}_{\text{Perfect square}} -9 - 2).$$

Step 4: Factor the perfect square and simplify the rest:
$$h(x) = 5\left((x + 3)^2 - 11\right).$$

Now that we have completed the square, we can multiply by the 5:
$$h(x) = 5(x + 3)^2 - 55.$$

Deriving the Quadratic Formula

We derive a general formula to find the zeros of $q(x) = ax^2 + bx + c$, with $a \neq 0$, by completing the square. To find the zeros, set $q(x) = 0$:
$$ax^2 + bx + c = 0.$$

Before we complete the square, we factor out the coefficient of x^2:
$$a\left(x^2 + \frac{b}{a}x + \frac{c}{a}\right) = 0.$$

Since $a \neq 0$, we can divide both sides by a:
$$x^2 + \frac{b}{a}x + \frac{c}{a} = 0.$$

To complete the square, we add and then subtract $((b/a)/2)^2 = b^2/(4a^2)$:
$$\underbrace{x^2 + \frac{b}{a}x + \frac{b^2}{4a^2}}_{\text{Perfect square}} - \frac{b^2}{4a^2} + \frac{c}{a} = 0.$$

We factor the perfect square and simplify the constant term, giving:
$$\left(x + \frac{b}{2a}\right)^2 - \left(\frac{b^2 - 4ac}{4a^2}\right) = 0 \qquad \text{since } \frac{-b^2}{4a^2} + \frac{c}{a} = \frac{-b^2}{4a^2} + \frac{4ac}{4a^2} = -\left(\frac{b^2 - 4ac}{4a^2}\right)$$

$$\left(x + \frac{b}{2a}\right)^2 = \frac{b^2 - 4ac}{4a^2} \qquad \text{adding } \tfrac{b^2-4ac}{4a^2} \text{ to both sides}$$

$$x + \frac{b}{2a} = \pm\sqrt{\frac{b^2 - 4ac}{4a^2}} = \frac{\pm\sqrt{b^2 - 4ac}}{2a} \qquad \text{taking the square root}$$

$$x = \frac{-b}{2a} \pm \frac{\sqrt{b^2 - 4ac}}{2a} \qquad \text{subtracting } b/2a$$

$$x = \frac{-b \pm \sqrt{b^2 - 4ac}}{2a}.$$

Exercises to Skills for Completing the Square

For Exercises 1–8, complete the square for each expression.

1. $x^2 + 8x$

2. $w^2 + 7w$

3. $2r^2 + 20r$

4. $3t^2 + 24t - 13$

5. $a^2 - 2a - 4$

6. $n^2 + 4n - 5$

7. $3r^2 + 9r - 4$

8. $12g^2 + 8g + 5$

In Exercises 9–12, rewrite in the form $a(x - h)^2 + k$.

9. $x^2 - 2x - 3$

10. $10 - 6x + x^2$

11. $-x^2 + 6x - 2$

12. $3x^2 - 12x + 13$

In Exercises 13–22, complete the square to find the vertex of the parabola.

13. $y = x^2 + 6x + 3$

14. $y = x^2 - x + 4$

15. $y = -x^2 - 8x + 2$

16. $y = x^2 - 3x - 3$

17. $y = -x^2 + x - 6$

18. $y = 3x^2 + 12x$

19. $y = -4x^2 + 8x - 6$

20. $y = 5x^2 - 5x + 7$

21. $y = 2x^2 - 7x + 3$

22. $y = -3x^2 - x - 2$

In Exercises 23–29, solve by completing the square.

23. $g^2 = 2g + 24$

24. $p^2 - 2p = 6$

25. $d^2 - d = 2$

26. $2r^2 + 4r - 5 = 0$

27. $2s^2 = 1 - 10s$

28. $7r^2 - 3r - 6 = 0$

29. $5p^2 + 9p = 1$

In Exercises 30–35, solve by using the quadratic formula.

30. $n^2 - 4n - 12 = 0$

31. $2y^2 + 5y = -2$

32. $6k^2 + 11k = -3$

33. $w^2 + w = 4$

34. $z^2 + 4z = 6$

35. $2q^2 + 6q - 3 = 0$

In Exercises 36–46, solve using factoring, completing the square, or the quadratic formula.

36. $r^2 - 2r = 8$

37. $s^2 + 3s = 1$

38. $z^3 + 2z^2 = 3z + 6$

39. $25u^2 + 4 = 30u$

40. $v^2 - 4v - 9 = 0$

41. $3y^2 = 6y + 18$

42. $2p^2 + 23 = 14p$

43. $2w^3 + 24 = 6w^2 + 8w$

44. $4x^2 + 16x - 5 = 0$

45. $49m^2 + 70m + 22 = 0$

46. $8x^2 - 1 = 2x$

Chapter Four

EXPONENTIAL FUNCTIONS

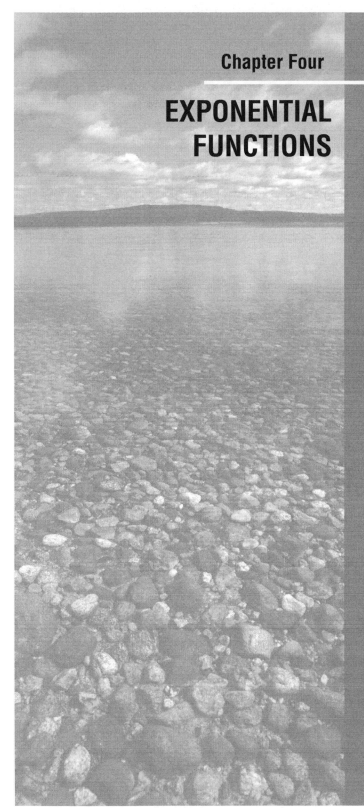

Contents

4.1 INTRODUCTION TO THE FAMILY OF EXPONENTIAL FUNCTIONS

Growing at a Constant Percent Rate

Linear functions represent quantities that change at a constant rate. In this section we introduce functions that change at a constant *percent* rate, the *exponential functions*.

Salary Raises

Example 1 After graduation from college, you will probably be looking for a job. Suppose you are offered a job at a starting salary of $40,000 per year. To strengthen the offer, the company promises annual raises of 6% per year for at least the first five years after you are hired. Let's compute your salary for the first few years.

If t represents the number of years since the beginning of your contract, then for $t = 0$, your salary is $40,000$. At the end of the first year, when $t = 1$, your salary increases by 6% so

$$\text{Salary when } t = 1 = \text{Original salary} + 6\% \text{ of Original salary}$$
$$= 40{,}000 + 0.06 \cdot 40{,}000$$
$$= 42{,}400 \text{ dollars.}$$

After the second year, your salary again increases by 6%, so

$$\text{Salary when } t = 2 = \text{Former salary} + 6\% \text{ of Former salary}$$
$$= 42{,}400 + 0.06 \cdot 42{,}400$$
$$= 44{,}944 \text{ dollars.}$$

Notice that your raise is higher in the second year than in the first since the second 6% increase applies both to the original $40,000 salary and to the $2400 raise given in the first year.

Salary calculations for four years have been rounded and recorded in Table 4.1. At the end of the third and fourth years your salary again increases by 6%, and your raise is larger each year. Not only are you given the 6% increase on your original salary, but your raises earn raises as well.

Table 4.1 *Raise amounts and resulting salaries for a person earning 6% annual salary increases*

Year	Raise amount ($)	Salary ($)
0		40,000.00
1	2400.00	42,400.00
2	2544.00	44,944.00
3	2696.64	47,640.64
4	2858.44	50,499.08

Figure 4.1: Salary over a 20-year period

Figure 4.1 shows salary over a 20-year period assuming that the annual increase remains 6%. Since the rate of change of your salary (in dollars per year) is not constant, the graph of this function is not a line. The salary increases at an increasing rate, giving the graph its upward curve. A function that increases at a constant percent rate is said to increase exponentially.

Population Growth

Exponential functions provide a reasonable model for many growing populations.

Example 2 During the 2000s, the population of Mexico increased at a constant annual percent rate of 1.2%.[1] Since the population grew by the same percent each year, it can be modeled by an exponential function.

Let's calculate the population of Mexico for the years after 2000. In 2000, the population was 100 million. The population grew by 1.2%, so

$$\text{Population in 2001} = \text{Population in 2000} + 1.2\% \text{ of Population in 2000}$$
$$= 100 + 0.012(100)$$
$$= 100 + 1.2 = 101.2 \text{ million.}$$

Similarly,

$$\text{Population in 2002} = \text{Population in 2001} + 1.2\% \text{ of Population in 2001}$$
$$= 101.2 + 0.012(101.2)$$
$$= 101.2 + 1.2144 = 102.4144 \text{ million.}$$

The calculations for years 2000 through 2007 have been rounded and recorded in Table 4.2. The population of Mexico increased by slightly more each year than it did the year before, because each year the increase is 1.2% of a larger number.

Table 4.2   *Calculated values for the population of Mexico*

Year	ΔP, increase in population	P, population (millions)
2000	—	100
2001	1.2	101.2
2002	1.21	102.41
2003	1.23	103.64
2004	1.25	104.89
2005	1.26	106.15
2006	1.27	107.42
2007	1.29	108.71

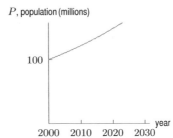

Figure 4.2: The projected population of Mexico, assuming 1.2% annual growth

Figure 4.2 gives a graph of the population of Mexico over a 30-year period, assuming a 1.2% annual growth rate. Notice that this graph curves upward like the graph in Figure 4.1.

Radioactive Decay

Exponential functions can also model decreasing quantities. A quantity which decreases at a constant percent rate is said to be decreasing exponentially.

Example 3 Carbon-14 is used to estimate the age of organic compounds. Over time, radioactive carbon-14 decays into a stable form. The decay rate is 11.4% every 1000 years. For example, if we begin with a 200-microgram (μg) sample of carbon-14 then

---

[1] http://www.census.gov/ipc/www/idb/country.php, accessed May 23, 2010.

131

$$\frac{\text{Amount remaining}}{\text{after 1000 years}} = \text{Initial amount} - 11.4\% \text{ of Initial amount}$$
$$= 200 - 0.114 \cdot 200$$
$$= 177.2 \ \mu g.$$

Similarly,

$$\frac{\text{Amount remaining}}{\text{after 2000 years}} = \frac{\text{Amount remaining}}{\text{after 1000 years}} - 11.4\% \text{ of } \frac{\text{Amount remaining}}{\text{after 1000 years}}$$
$$= 177.2 - 0.114 \cdot 177.2 \approx 156.999 \ \mu g,$$

and

$$\frac{\text{Amount remaining}}{\text{after 3000 years}} = \frac{\text{Amount remaining}}{\text{after 2000 years}} - 11.4\% \text{ of } \frac{\text{Amount remaining}}{\text{after 2000 years}}$$
$$= 156.999 - 0.114 \cdot 156.999 \approx 139.101 \ \mu g.$$

These calculations are recorded in Table 4.3. During each 1000-year period, the amount of carbon-14 that decays is smaller than in the previous period. This is because we take 11.4% of a smaller quantity each time.

Table 4.3   *The amount of carbon-14 remaining over time*

Years elapsed	Amount decayed (μg)	Amount remaining (μg)
0	—	200.0
1000	22.8	177.2
2000	20.201	156.999
3000	17.898	139.101

Figure 4.3: Amount of carbon-14 over 10,000 years

Figure 4.3 shows the amount of carbon-14 left from a 200 μg sample over 10,000 years. Because the amount decreases by a smaller amount over each successive time interval, the graph is not linear but bends upward, hence is concave up.

Growth Factors and Percent Growth Rates

The Growth Factor of an Increasing Exponential Function

The salary in Example 1 increases by 6% every year. We say that the annual percent growth rate is 6%. But there is another way to think about the growth of this salary. We know that each year,

$$\text{New salary} = \text{Old salary} + 6\% \text{ of Old salary}.$$

We can rewrite this as follows:

$$\text{New salary} = 100\% \text{ of Old salary} + 6\% \text{ of Old salary}.$$

So

$$\text{New salary} = 106\% \text{ of Old salary}.$$

Since $106\% = 1.06$, we have

$$\text{New salary} = 1.06 \cdot \text{Old salary}.$$

We call 1.06 the *growth factor*.

The Growth Factor of a Decreasing Exponential Function

In Example 3, the carbon-14 changes by -11.4% every 1000 years. The negative growth rate tells us that the quantity of carbon-14 decreases over time. We have

$$\text{New amount} = \text{Old amount} - 11.4\% \text{ of Old amount},$$

which can be rewritten as

$$\text{New amount} = 100\% \text{ of Old amount} - 11.4\% \text{ of Old amount}.$$

So,

$$\text{New amount} = 88.6\% \text{ of Old amount}.$$

Since $88.6\% = 0.886$, we have

$$\text{New amount} = 0.886 \cdot \text{Old amount}.$$

We call 0.886 the growth factor even though the amount of carbon-14 is decreasing. Although it may sound strange to refer to 0.886 as the growth factor, rather than the decay factor, we use "growth factor" to describe both increasing and decreasing quantities.

A General Formula for the Family of Exponential Functions

Because it grows at a constant percentage rate each year, the salary, S, in Example 1 is an example of an exponential function. We want a formula for S in terms of t, the number of years since being hired. Since the annual growth factor is 1.06, we know that for each year,

$$\text{New salary} = \text{Old salary} \cdot 1.06.$$

Thus, after one year, or when $t = 1$,

$$S = \underbrace{40{,}000}_{\text{Old salary}}(1.06).$$

Similarly, when $t = 2$,

$$S = \underbrace{40{,}000(1.06)}_{\text{Old salary}}(1.06) = 40{,}000(1.06)^2.$$

Here there are *two* factors of 1.06 because the salary has increased by 6% twice. When $t = 3$,

$$S = \underbrace{40{,}000(1.06)^2}_{\text{Old salary}}(1.06) = 40{,}000(1.06)^3$$

and continues in this pattern so that after t years have elapsed,

$$S = 40{,}000 \underbrace{(1.06)(1.06)\ldots(1.06)}_{t \text{ factors of } 1.06} = 40{,}000(1.06)^t.$$

After t years the salary has increased by a factor of 1.06 a total of t times. Thus,

$$S = 40{,}000(1.06)^t.$$

These results, which are summarized in Table 4.4, are the same as in Table 4.1. Notice that in this formula we assume that t is an integer, $t \geq 0$, since the raises are given only once a year.

Table 4.4 *Salary after t years*

t (years)	S, salary ($)
0	40,000
1	$40{,}000(1.06) = 42{,}400.00$
2	$40{,}000(1.06)^2 = 44{,}944.00$
3	$40{,}000(1.06)^3 = 47{,}640.64$
t	$40{,}000(1.06)^t$

This salary formula can be written as

$$S = \text{Initial salary} \cdot (\text{Growth factor})^t.$$

In general, we have:

An **exponential function** $Q = f(t)$ has the formula

$$f(t) = ab^t, \quad a \neq 0, b > 0,$$

where a is the initial value of Q (at $t = 0$) and b, the base, is the growth factor. The growth factor is given by

$$b = 1 + r$$

where r is the decimal representation of the percent rate of change.
- If there is exponential growth, then $r > 0$ and $b > 1$.
- If there is exponential decay, then $r < 0$ and $0 < b < 1$.

The constants a and b are called *parameters.*. The base b is restricted to positive values because if $b < 0$ then b^t is undefined for some exponents t, for example, $t = 1/2$.

Every function in the form $f(t) = ab^t$ with the input, t, in the exponent is an exponential function, provided $a \neq 0$. Note that if $b = 1$, then $f(t) = a \cdot 1^t = a$ and $f(t)$ is a constant, so when $b = 1$, the function is generally not considered exponential. Graphs showing exponential growth and decay are in Figures 4.4 and 4.5. Notice that in both cases the graph is concave up.

Figure 4.4: Exponential growth: $b > 1$ Figure 4.5: Exponential decay: $0 < b < 1$

Example 4   Use the formula $S = 40,000(1.06)^t$ to calculate your salary after 4 years, 12 years, and 40 years.

Solution   After 4 years, $t = 4$, and we have
$$S = 40,000(1.06)^4 \approx \$50,499.08.$$
Notice that this agrees with Table 4.1 on page 130. After 12 years, $t = 12$, and we have
$$S = 40,000(1.06)^{12} \approx \$80,487.86.$$
After 12 years, the salary has more than doubled from the initial salary of $\$40,000$. When $t = 40$ we have
$$S = 40,000(1.06)^{40} \approx \$411,428.72.$$
Thus if you work for 40 years and consistently earn 6% annual raises, your salary will be over $\$400,000$ a year.

Example 5   Carbon-14 decays at a rate of 11.4% every 1000 years. Write a formula for the quantity, Q, of a 200-μg sample remaining as a function of time, t, in thousands of years.

Solution   The growth factor of carbon-14 over 1000 years is $1 - 0.114 = 0.886$. Originally, there are 200 μg, so the quantity remaining after t thousand years is given by
$$Q = 200(0.886)^t.$$

Example 6   Using Example 2 on page 131, find a formula for P, the population of Mexico (in millions), in year t where $t = 0$ represents the year 2000.

Solution   In 2000, the population of Mexico was 100 million, and it was growing at a constant 1.2% annual rate. The growth factor is $b = 1 + 0.012 = 1.012$, and $a = 100$, so
$$P = 100(1.012)^t.$$
Because the growth factor may change eventually, this formula may not give accurate results for large values of t.

Example 7   What does the formula $P = 100(1.012)^t$ predict when $t = 0$? When $t = -5$? What do these values tell you about the population of Mexico?

Solution   If $t = 0$, then , since $(1.012)^0 = 1$, we have
$$P = 100(1.012)^0 = 100.$$
This makes sense because $t = 0$ stands for 2000, and in 2000 the population was 100 million. When $t = -5$ we have
$$P = 100(1.012)^{-5} \approx 94.210.$$
To make sense of this number, we must interpret the year $t = -5$ as five years before 2000; that is, as the year 1995. If the population of Mexico had been growing at a 1.2% annual rate from 1995 onward, then it was 94.21 million in 1995.

Example 8   On August 2, 1988, a US District Court judge imposed a fine on the city of Yonkers, New York, for defying a federal court order involving housing desegregation.[2] The fine started at $\$100$ for the first day and was to double daily until the city chose to obey the court order.

(a) What was the daily percent growth rate of the fine?
(b) Find a formula for the fine as a function of t, the number of days since August 2, 1988.
(c) If Yonkers waited 30 days before obeying the court order, what would the fine have been?

---
[2] *The Boston Globe*, August 27, 1988.

135

Solution
(a) Since the fine increased each day by a factor of 2, the fine grew exponentially with growth factor $b = 2$. To find the percent growth rate, we set $b = 1 + r = 2$, from which we find $r = 1$, or 100%. Thus the daily percent growth rate is 100%. This makes sense because when a quantity increases by 100%, it doubles in size.

(b) If t is the number of days since August 2, the formula for the fine, P in dollars, is

$$P = 100 \cdot 2^t.$$

(c) After 30 days, the fine is $P = 100 \cdot 2^{30} \approx 1.074 \cdot 10^{11}$ dollars, or \$107,374,182,400.

Exercises and Problems for Section 4.1

Skill Refresher

In Exercises S1–S2, express the percentages in decimal form. In Exercises S3–S4, express the decimals as a percent.

S1. 6% **S2.** 0.6% **S3.** 0.0012 **S4.** 1.23

Exercises

Are the functions in Exercises 1–9 exponential? If so, write the function in the form $f(t) = ab^t$.

1. $g(w) = 2\left(2^{-w}\right)$

2. $m(t) = (2 \cdot 3^t)^3$

3. $f(x) = \dfrac{3^{2x}}{4}$

4. $G(t) = 3(t)^t$

5. $q(r) = \dfrac{-4}{3^r}$

6. $j(x) = 2^x 3^x$

7. $Q(t) = 8^{t/3}$

8. $K(x) = \dfrac{2^x}{3 \cdot 3^x}$

9. $p(r) = 2^r + 3^r$

What is the growth factor in Exercises 10–13? Assume time is measured in the units given.

10. Water usage is increasing by 3% per year.

11. A city grows by 28% per decade.

12. A diamond mine is depleted by 1% per day.

13. A forest shrinks 80% per century.

In Exercises 14–17, give the starting value a, the growth factor b, and the growth rate r if $Q = ab^t = a(1 + r)^t$.

14. $Q = 1750(1.593)^t$

15. $Q = 34.3(0.788)^t$

16. $Q = 79.2(1.002)^t$

17. $Q = 0.0022(2.31)^{-3t}$

Problems

18. The populations, P, of six towns with time t in years are given by

(i) $P = 1000(1.08)^t$

(ii) $P = 600(1.12)^t$

(iii) $P = 2500(0.9)^t$

(iv) $P = 1200(1.185)^t$

(v) $P = 800(0.78)^t$

(vi) $P = 2000(0.99)^t$

(a) Which towns are growing in size? Which are shrinking?

(b) Which town is growing the fastest? What is the annual percent growth rate for that town?

(c) Which town is shrinking the fastest? What is the annual percent "decay" rate for that town?

(d) Which town has the largest initial population (at $t = 0$)? Which town has the smallest?

19. The value, V, of a \$100,000 investment that earns 3% annual interest is given by $V = f(t)$ where t is in years. How much is the investment worth in 3 years?

20. An investment decreases by 5% per year for 4 years. By what total percent does it decrease?

21. Without a calculator, match each of the formulas to one of the graphs in Figure 4.6.

(a) $y = 0.8^t$

(b) $y = 5(3)^t$

(c) $y = -6(1.03)^t$

(d) $y = 15(3)^{-t}$

(e) $y = -4(0.98)^t$ **(f)** $y = 82(0.8)^{-t}$

(i) y (ii) y

(iii) y (iv) y

Figure 4.6

In Problems 22–27, the initial value (at year $t = 0$) and the percent change per year of a quantity Q are given.

(a) Write a formula for Q as a function of t.

(b) What is the value of Q when $t = 10$?

22. Initial amount 2000; increasing by 5% per year

23. Initial amount 35; decreasing by 8% per year

24. Initial amount 112.8; decreasing by 23.4% per year

25. Initial amount 5.35; increasing by 0.8% per year

26. Initial amount 5; increasing by 100% per year

27. Initial amount 0.2; decreasing by 0.5% per year

28. Figure 4.7 is the graph of $f(x) = 4 \cdot b^x$. Find the slope of the line segment PQ in terms of b.

Figure 4.7

29. In 2010, the population of a country was 70 million and growing at a rate of 1.9% per year. Assuming the percentage growth rate remains constant, express the population, P, as a function of t, the number of years after 2010.

30. The mass, Q, of a sample of tritium (a radioactive isotope of hydrogen), decays at a rate of 5.626% per year. Write a function giving the mass of a 726-gram sample after a time, t, in years. Graph this decay function.

31. In 2010 the number of people infected by a virus was P_0. Due to a new vaccine, the number of infected people has decreased by 20% each year since 2010. In other words, only 80% as many people are infected each year as were infected the year before. Find a formula for $P = f(n)$, the number of infected people n years after 2010. Graph $f(n)$. Explain, in terms of the virus, why the graph has the shape it does.

32. Every year, a lake becomes more polluted, and 2% fewer organisms can live in it. If in 2011 there are one million organisms, write an equation relating O, the number of organisms, to time, t, in years since 2011.

33. (a) The annual inflation rate is 3.5% per year. If a movie ticket costs $7.50, find a formula for p, the price of the ticket t years from today, assuming that movie tickets keep up with inflation.

(b) According to your formula, how much will movie tickets cost in 20 years?

34. The value V of an investment in year t is given by $V = 2500(1.0325)^t$. Describe the investment in words.

35. A typical cup of coffee contains about 100 mg of caffeine and every hour approximately 16% of the amount of caffeine in the body is metabolized and eliminated.

(a) Write C, the amount of caffeine in the body in mg, as a function of t, the number of hours since the coffee was consumed.

(b) How much caffeine is in the body after 5 hours?

36. Grinnell Glacier in Glacier National Park in the US covered about 142 acres in 2007 and was shrinking at a rate of about 4.4% per year.[3]

(a) Write a formula for the size, S, of the Grinnell Glacier, in acres, as a function of years t since 2007.

(b) Use the model to predict the size of the glacier in the year 2015.

(c) According to the model, how many acres of ice were lost from the glacier between 2007 and 2010?

37. In January 2005, the population of California was 36.8 million and growing at an annual rate of 1.3%. Assume that growth continues at the same rate.

(a) By how much will the population increase between 2005 and 2030? Between 2030 and 2055?

(b) Explain how you can tell before doing the calculations which of the two answers in part (a) is larger.

38. A cold yam is placed in a hot oven. Newton's Law of Heating tells us that the difference between the oven's temperature and the yam's temperature decays exponentially with time. The yam's temperature is initially 0°F,

---

[3]"Warming climate shrinking Glacier Park's glaciers", www.usatoday.com, October 15, 2007.

the oven's temperature is $300°$F, and the temperature difference decreases by 3% per minute. Find a formula for $Y(t)$, the yam's temperature at time t.

39. The population of India was about 1.15 billion people in 2010 and was growing at a rate of about 1.35% per year.

  (a) Write a formula for the population, P, of India, in billions, as a function of years t since 2010.
  (b) If the growth rate stays constant, predict the population of India in the year 2015 and the year 2020.
  (c) Find the rate of change of India's population, in million people per year, during the year 2010.
  (d) Find the rate of change of India's population, in people per minute, during the year 2010.

40. Polluted water is passed through a series of filters. Each filter removes 85% of the remaining impurities. Initially, the untreated water contains impurities at a level of 420 parts per million (ppm). Find a formula for L, the remaining level of impurities, after the water has been passed through a series of n filters.

41. In 2007, world solar photovoltaic (PV) market installations totaled 2826 megawatts and were growing at a rate of 62% per year. In the same year, Japan's PV market installations totaled 230 megawatts and were declining at a rate of 23% per year.[4]

  (a) Use the information given to predict PV market installations in the world and in Japan in the year 2012.
  (b) What percent of world PV market installations were in Japan in 2007? In 2012?

Write the exponential function $y = 5(0.5)^{t/3}$ in the forms given in Problems 42–43. Give the values of all constants.

42. $y = ab^t$ **43.** $y = a \cdot 4^{kt}$

44. Write the following exponential function in standard form, $f(t) = ab^t$, giving the values of a and b:

$$f(t) = \frac{60}{5 \cdot 2^{t/11.2}}.$$

45. In the year 2009, a total of 13.4 million passengers took a cruise vacation.[5] The global cruise industry has been growing at a rate of approximately 5% per year for the last five years.

  (a) Write a formula to approximate the number, N, of cruise passengers (in millions) t years after 2009.
  (b) How many cruise passengers are predicted in the year 2015? Approximately how many passengers went on a cruise in the year 2005?

46. The amount (in milligrams) of a drug in the body t hours after taking a pill is given by $A(t) = 25(0.85)^t$.

  (a) What is the initial dose given?
  (b) What percent of the drug leaves the body each hour?
  (c) What is the amount of drug left after 10 hours?
  (d) After how many hours is there less than 1 milligram left in the body?

47. Every year, teams from 64 colleges qualify to compete in the NCAA basketball playoffs. For each round, every team is paired with an opponent. A team is eliminated from the tournament once it loses a round. So, at the end of a round, only one half the number of teams move on to the next round. Let $N(r)$ be the number of teams remaining in competition after r rounds of the tournament have been played.

  (a) Find a formula for $N(r)$ and graph $y = N(r)$.
  (b) In 2009 the North Carolina Tar Heels defeated the Michigan State Spartans 89-72. How many rounds did #1 seed North Carolina have to go through to win the championship game?

48. The UN Food and Agriculture Organization estimates that 2.17% of the world's natural forests existing in 1990 were gone by the end of the decade. In 1990, the world's forest cover stood at 4077 million hectares.[6]

  (a) How many million hectares of natural forests were lost during the 1990s?
  (b) How many million hectares of natural forests existed in the year 2000?
  (c) Write an exponential formula approximating the number of million hectares of natural forest in the world t years after 1990.
  (d) What was the annual percent decay rate during the 1990s?
  (e) During the years 2000 through 2005, the world's natural forests decreased by approximately 0.18% per year. Approximately how many million hectares of natural forests existed in the year 2005?

49. Forty percent of a radioactive substance decays in five years. By what percent does the substance decay each year?

50. The population of a small town increases by a growth factor of 1.134 over a two-year period.

  (a) By what percent does the town increase in size during the two-year period?
  (b) If the town grows by the same percent each year, what is its annual percent growth rate?

---

[4] www.solarbuzz.com/marketbuzz2008. Accessed February, 2010.
[5] http://www.f-cca.com, accessed May 25, 2010.
[6] www.fao.org/forestry/fra/fra/2005/en/, accessed January 2, 2010.

51. The *Home* section of many Sunday newspapers includes a mortgage table similar to Table 4.5.[7] The table gives the monthly payment per $1000 borrowed for loans at various interest rates and time periods. Determine the monthly payment on a

(a) $60,000 mortgage at 4% for fifteen years.
(b) $60,000 mortgage at 4% for thirty years.
(c) $60,000 mortgage at 6% for fifteen years.
(d) Over the life of the loan, how much money would be saved on a 15-year mortgage of $60,000 if the rate were 4% instead of 6%?
(e) Over the life of the loan, how much money would be saved on an 4% mortgage of $60,000 if the term of the loan was fifteen years rather than thirty years?

Table 4.5

Interest rate (%)	15-year loan	20-year loan	25-year loan	30-year loan
4.00	7.40	6.06	5.28	4.77
4.50	7.65	6.33	5.56	5.07
5.00	7.91	6.60	5.85	5.37
5.50	8.17	6.88	6.14	5.68
6.00	8.44	7.16	6.44	6.00
6.50	8.71	7.46	6.75	6.32
7.00	8.99	7.75	7.07	6.65
7.50	9.27	8.06	7.39	6.99
8.00	9.56	8.36	7.72	7.34

52. You owe $2000 on a credit card. The card charges 1.5% monthly interest on your balance, and requires a minimum monthly payment of 2.5% of your balance. All transactions (payments and interest charges) are recorded at the end of the month. You make only the minimum required payment every month and incur no additional debt.

(a) Complete Table 4.6 for a twelve-month period.
(b) What is your unpaid balance after one year has passed? At that time, how much of your debt have you paid off? How much money in interest charges have you paid your creditors?

Table 4.6

Month	Balance	Interest	Minimum payment
0	$2000.00	$30.00	$50.00
1	$1980.00	$29.70	$49.50
2	$1960.20		
⋮			

53. A one-page letter is folded into thirds to go into an envelope. If it were possible to repeat this kind of tri-fold 20 times, how many miles thick would the letter be? (A stack of 150 pieces of stationery is one inch thick; 1 mile = 5280 feet.)

Problems 54–55 concern ISO A-series paper, commonly used in many countries. $A0$ is the largest sheet, $A1$ next largest, and so on, with $A4$ being somewhat similar to the 8.5 by 11 inch paper standard in the US. The width in millimeters (mm) of a sheet of A_n paper in this series is given by the formula[8]

$$f(n) = 1000 \cdot 2^{-\frac{1}{4} - \frac{n}{2}}.$$

54. Show that this is an exponential function by writing it in standard form, $f(n) = ab^n$, . What do the values of a and b tell you about A-series paper?

55. Evaluate and simplify the ratio $f(n+2)/f(n)$. What does your answer tell you about A-series paper?

Use Figure 4.8 in Problems 56–59.

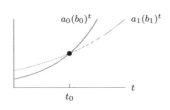

Figure 4.8

56. Which is greater, a_0 or a_1?

57. Which is greater, b_0 or b_1?

58. What happens to t_0 if a_0 is increased while the other quantities remain fixed?

59. What happens to t_0 if b_1 is decreased while the other quantities remain fixed?

[7]http://www.drcalculator.com, accessed January 1, 2010.
[8]Actual paper sizes are rounded to the nearest mm, so this formula is only approximate. See /www.cl.cam.ac.uk/~mgk25/iso-paper.html, accessed February 24, 2008.

60. The figure shows graphs of two functions:

$$f(t) = a_0 \cdot 2^{-t/\tau_0}$$
$$g(t) = a_1 \cdot 2^{-t/\tau_1}.$$

Which is larger, a_0 or a_1? τ_0 or τ_1?

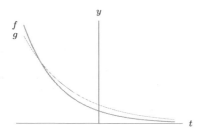

61. Let P be the number of students in a school district, N be the size of the tax base (in households), and r be the average annual tax rate (in $/household).

(a) Find a formula for R, the total tax revenue, in terms of N and r.

(b) Find a formula for A, the average revenue per student.

(c) Suppose the tax base goes up by 2% and the tax rate is raised by 3%. Find formulas for the new tax base and tax rate in terms of N and r.

(d) Using your answer to part (c), find a formula for the new total tax revenue in terms of R. By what percent did R increase?

(e) Over the time period in part (c), the student population rises by 8%. Find a formula for the new average revenue in terms of A. Did the average revenue rise or fall? By how much?

4.2 COMPARING EXPONENTIAL AND LINEAR FUNCTIONS

The exponential function $Q = ab^t$ represents a quantity changing at a constant percent rate. In this section we compare exponential and linear models and we fit exponential models to data from tables and graphs.

Identifying Linear and Exponential Functions From a Table

Table 4.7 gives values of a linear and an exponential function. Notice that the value of x changes by equal steps of $\Delta x = 5$. The function f could be linear because the difference between consecutive values of $f(x)$ is constant: $f(x)$ increases by 15 each time x increases by 5.

Table 4.7 *Two functions, one linear and one exponential*

x	20	25	30	35	40	45
$f(x)$	30	45	60	75	90	105
$g(x)$	1000	1200	1440	1728	2073.6	2488.32

On the other hand, the difference between consecutive values of $g(x)$ is *not* constant:

$$1200 - 1000 = 200$$
$$1440 - 1200 = 240$$
$$1728 - 1440 = 288.$$

Thus, g is not linear. However, the *ratio* of consecutive values of $g(x)$ is constant:

$$\frac{1200}{1000} = 1.2, \quad \frac{1440}{1200} = 1.2, \quad \frac{1728}{1440} = 1.2,$$

and so on. Note that $1200 = 1.2(1000)$, $1440 = 1.2(1200)$, $1728 = 1.2(1440)$. Thus, each time x increases by 5, the value of $g(x)$ increases by a factor of 1.2. This pattern of constant ratios is indicative of exponential functions. In general:

> For a table of data that gives y as a function of x and in which Δx is constant:
> - If the *difference* of consecutive y-values is constant, the table could represent a linear function.
> - If the *ratio* of consecutive y-values is constant, the table could represent an exponential function.

Finding a Formula for an Exponential Function

To find a formula for the exponential function in Table 4.7, we must determine the values of a and b in the formula $g(x) = ab^x$. The table tells us that $ab^{20} = 1000$ and that $ab^{25} = 1200$. Taking the ratio gives

$$\frac{ab^{25}}{ab^{20}} = \frac{1200}{1000} = 1.2.$$

Notice that the value of a cancels in this ratio, so

$$\frac{ab^{25}}{ab^{20}} = b^5 = 1.2.$$

We solve for b by raising each side to the $(1/5)^{\text{th}}$ power:

$$(b^5)^{1/5} = b = 1.2^{1/5} \approx 1.03714.$$

Now that we have the value of b, we can solve for a. Since $g(20) = ab^{20} = 1000$, we have

$$a(1.03714)^{20} = 1000$$
$$a = \frac{1000}{1.03714^{20}} \approx 482.253.$$

Thus, a formula for g is $g(x) = 482.253(1.037)^x$. (Note: We could have used $g(25)$ or any other value from the table to find a.)

Modeling Linear and Exponential Growth Using Two Data Points

If we are given two data points, we can fit either a line or an exponential function to the points. The following example compares the predictions made by a linear model and an exponential model fitted to the same data.

Example 1
At time $t = 0$ years, a species of turtle is released into a wetland. When $t = 4$ years, a biologist estimates there are 300 turtles in the wetland. Three years later, the biologist estimates there are 450 turtles. Let P represent the size of the turtle population in year t.

(a) Find a formula for $P = f(t)$ assuming linear growth. Interpret the slope and P-intercept of your formula in terms of the turtle population.

(b) Now find a formula for $P = g(t)$ assuming exponential growth. Interpret the parameters of your formula in terms of the turtle population.

(c) In year $t = 12$, the biologist estimates that there are 900 turtles in the wetland. What does this indicate about the two population models?

Solution (a) Assuming linear growth, we have $P = f(t) = b + mt$, and

$$m = \frac{\Delta P}{\Delta t} = \frac{450 - 300}{7 - 4} = \frac{150}{3} = 50.$$

Calculating b gives

$$300 = b + 50 \cdot 4$$
$$b = 100,$$

so $P = f(t) = 100 + 50t$. This formula tells us that 100 turtles were originally released into the wetland and that the number of turtles increases at the constant rate of 50 turtles per year.

(b) Assuming exponential growth, we have $P = g(t) = ab^t$. The values of a and b are calculated from the ratio

$$\frac{ab^7}{ab^4} = \frac{450}{300},$$

so

$$b^3 = 1.5.$$

Thus,

$$b = (1.5)^{1/3} \approx 1.145.$$

Using the fact that $g(4) = ab^4 = 300$ to find a gives

$$a(1.145)^4 = 300$$
$$a = \frac{300}{1.145^4} \approx 175, \quad \text{Rounding to the nearest whole turtle}$$

so $P = g(t) = 175(1.145)^t$. This formula tells us that 175 turtles were originally released into the wetland and the number increases at about 14.5% per year.

(c) In year $t = 12$, there are approximately 900 turtles. The linear function from part (a) predicts

$$P = 100 + 50 \cdot 12 = 700 \text{ turtles.}$$

The exponential formula from part (b), however, predicts

$$P = 175(1.145)^{12} \approx 889 \text{ turtles.}$$

The fact that 889 is closer to the observed value of 900 turtles suggests that, during the first 12 years, exponential growth is a better model of the turtle population than linear growth. The two models are graphed in Figure 4.9.

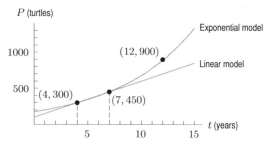

Figure 4.9: Comparison of the linear and exponential models of the turtle population

Similarities and Differences Between Linear and Exponential Functions

In some ways the general formulas for linear and exponential functions are similar. If y is a linear function of x and x is a positive integer, we can write $y = b + mx$ as

$$y = b + \underbrace{m + m + m + \ldots + m}_{x \text{ times}}.$$

Similarly, if y is an exponential function of x, so that $y = a \cdot b^x$ and x is a positive integer, we can write

$$y = a \cdot \underbrace{b \cdot b \cdot b \cdot \ldots \cdot b}_{x \text{ times}}.$$

So linear functions involve repeated sums whereas exponential functions involve repeated products. In both cases, x determines the number of repetitions.

There are other similarities between the formulas for linear and exponential functions. In the formula $y = b + mx$, b tells us the y-intercept and m tells us how the function is changing. In the formula $y = a \cdot b^x$, a tells us the y-intercept and b tells us how the function is changing.

Example 2   The following tables contain values from an exponential or linear function. For each table, decide if the function is linear or exponential, and find a possible formula for the function.

(a)

x	$f(x)$
0	65
1	75
2	85
3	95
4	105

(b)

x	$g(x)$
0	400
1	600
2	900
3	1350
4	2025

Solution   (a) The function values increase by 10 as x increases by 1, so this is a linear function with slope $m = 10$. Since $f(0) = 65$, the vertical intercept is 65. A possible formula is

$$f(x) = 65 + 10x.$$

(b) The function is not linear, since $g(x)$ increases by different amounts as x increases by 1. To determine whether g might be exponential, we look at ratios of consecutive values:

$$\frac{600}{400} = 1.5, \quad \frac{900}{600} = 1.5, \quad \frac{1350}{900} = 1.5, \quad \frac{2025}{1350} = 1.5.$$

Each time x increases by 1, the value of $g(x)$ increases by a factor of 1.5. This is an exponential function with growth factor 1.5. Since $g(0) = 400$, the vertical intercept is 400. A possible formula is

$$g(x) = 400(1.5)^x.$$

Exponential Growth Will Always Outpace Linear Growth in the Long Run

Figure 4.9 shows the graphs of the linear and exponential models for the turtle population from Example 1. The graphs highlight the fact that, although these two graphs remain fairly close for the first ten or so years, the exponential model predicts explosive growth later on.

It can be shown that an exponentially increasing quantity will, in the long run, always outpace a linearly increasing quantity. This fact led the 19th-century clergyman and economist Thomas Malthus to make some rather gloomy predictions, which are illustrated in the next example.

Example 3 The population of a country is initially 2 million people and is increasing at 4% per year. The country's annual food supply is initially adequate for 4 million people and is increasing at a constant rate adequate for an additional 0.5 million people per year.

(a) Based on these assumptions, in approximately what year will this country first experience shortages of food?

(b) If the country doubled its initial food supply, would shortages still occur? If so, when? (Assume the other conditions do not change).

(c) If the country doubled the rate at which its food supply increases, in addition to doubling its initial food supply, would shortages still occur? If so, when? (Again, assume the other conditions do not change.)

Solution Let P represent the country's population (in millions) and N the number of people the country can feed (in millions). The population increases at a constant percent rate, so it can be modeled by an exponential function. The initial population is $a = 2$ million people and the annual growth factor is $b = 1 + 0.04 = 1.04$, so a formula for the population is

$$P = 2(1.04)^t.$$

In contrast, the food supply increases by a constant amount each year and is therefore modeled by a linear function. The initial food supply is adequate for $b = 4$ million people and the growth rate is $m = 0.5$ million per year, so the number of people that can be fed is

$$N = 4 + 0.5t.$$

(a) Figure 4.10(a) gives the graphs of P and N over a 105-year span. For many years, the food supply is far in excess of the country's needs. However, after about 78 years the population has begun to grow so rapidly that it catches up to the food supply and then outstrips it. After that time, the country will suffer from shortages.

(b) If the country can initially feed eight million people rather than four, the formula for N is

$$N = 8 + 0.5t.$$

However, as we see from Figure 4.10(b), this measure only buys the country three or four extra years with an adequate food supply. After 81 years, the population is growing so rapidly that the head start given to the food supply makes little difference.

(c) If the country doubles the rate at which its food supply increases, from 0.5 million per year to 1.0 million per year, the formula for N is

$$N = 8 + 1.0t.$$

Unfortunately the country still runs out of food eventually. Judging from Figure 4.10(c), this happens in about 102 years.

Figure 4.10: These graphs illustrate the fact that an exponentially growing population eventually outstrips a linearly growing food supply

144

Malthus believed that populations increase exponentially while food production increases linearly. The last example explains his gloomy predictions: Malthus believed that any population eventually outstrips its food supply, leading to famine and war.

Exercises and Problems for Section 4.2

Skill Refresher

In Exercises S1–S4, write each of the following with single positive exponents.

S1. $b^4 \cdot b^6$

S2. $8g^3 \cdot (-4g)^2$

S3. $\dfrac{18a^{10}b^6}{6a^3b^{-4}}$

S4. $\dfrac{(2a^3b^2)^3}{(4ab^{-4})^2}$

In Exercises S5–S6, evaluate the functions for $t = 0$ and $t = 3$.

S5. $f(t) = 5.6(1.043)^t$

S6. $g(t) = 12{,}837(0.84)^t$

In Exercises S7–S10, solve for x.

S7. $4x^3 = 20$

S8. $\dfrac{5x^3}{x^5} = 125$

S9. $\dfrac{4x^8}{3x^3} = 7$

S10. $\sqrt{4x^3} = 5$

Exercises

1. Write a formula for the price p of a gallon of gas in t days if the price is \$2.50 on day $t = 0$ and the price is:

(a) Increasing by \$0.03 per day.
(b) Decreasing by \$0.07 per day.
(c) Increasing by 2% per day.
(d) Decreasing by 4% per day.

2. A population has size 5000 at time $t = 0$, with t in years.

(a) If the population decreases by 100 people per year, find a formula for the population, P, at time t.
(b) If the population decreases by 8% per year, find a formula for the population, P, at time t.

3. The following formulas give the populations (in 1000s) of four different cities, A, B, C, and D, where t is in years. Which are changing exponentially? Describe in words how each of these populations is changing over time. Graph those that are exponential.

$$P_A = 200 + 1.3t, \quad P_B = 270(1.021)^t,$$

$$P_C = 150(1.045)^t, \quad P_D = 600(0.978)^t.$$

4. In an environment with unlimited resources and no predators, a population tends to grow by the same percentage each year. Should a linear or exponential function be used to model such a population? Why?

5. Find $g(t) = ab^t$ if $g(10) = 50$ and $g(30) = 25$.

6. Find a formula for $f(x)$, an exponential function such that $f(-8) = 200$ and $f(30) = 580$.

7. Suppose that $f(x)$ is exponential and that $f(-3) = 54$ and $f(2) = \frac{2}{9}$. Find a formula for $f(x)$.

8. Find a formula for $f(x)$, an exponential function such that $f(2) = 1/27$ and $f(-1) = 27$.

9. Find the equation of an exponential curve through the points $(-1, 2), (1, 0.3)$.

For Exercises 10–15, find a formula for the exponential function.

10.

11.

12.

13.

14. **15.**

16. (a) Make a table of values for $P = f(t) = 1000(1.2)^t$, for $t = 0, 1, 2, 3, 4, 5$.

(b) Calculate each of the ratios of successive terms:

$$\frac{f(1)}{f(0)}, \quad \frac{f(2)}{f(1)}, \quad \frac{f(3)}{f(2)}, \quad \frac{f(4)}{f(3)}, \quad \frac{f(5)}{f(4)}.$$

(c) Discuss the results. Why is this outcome to be expected?

x	0	5	10	15	20
$f(x)$	95.4	85.9	77.3	69.6	62.6
$g(x)$	44.8	40.9	36.8	32.5	28.0
$h(x)$	37.3	36.6	35.9	35.2	34.5

In Exercises 17–18, find exponential functions for the graphs shown in the figures, or explain why this is not possible.

The tables in Exercises 22–25 contain values from an exponential or a linear function. In each problem:

(a) Decide if the function is linear or exponential.

(b) Find a possible formula for each function and graph it.

17.

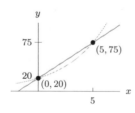

18.

22.

x	$f(x)$
0	12.5
1	13.75
2	15.125
3	16.638
4	18.301

23.

x	$g(x)$
0	0
1	2
2	4
3	6
4	8

19. Find a possible formula for the exponential function g given that the points $(2.3, 0.4)$ and $(3.5, 0.1)$ are on its graph.

20. Find a possible formula for the exponential function f given $f(-5) = 22$ and $f(17) = 46$.

21. Which (if any) of the functions in the table could be linear? Which could be exponential? (Note that table values may reflect rounding.)

24.

x	$h(x)$
0	14
1	12.6
2	11.34
3	10.206
4	9.185

25.

x	$i(x)$
0	18
1	14
2	10
3	6
4	2

Problems

26. Graphs of a linear and an exponential function are shown in Figure 4.11. Find formulas for each of the functions.

Figure 4.11

27. Let $p(x) = 2 + x$ and $q(x) = 2^x$. Estimate the values of x such that $p(x) < q(x)$.

28. If $f(x) = 12 + 20x$ and $g(x) = \frac{1}{2} \cdot 3^x$, for what values of x is $g(x) < f(x)$?

29. Find formulas for the exponential functions in Figure 4.12.

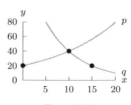

Figure 4.12

Decide whether the functions in Problems 30–32 could be approximately linear, approximately exponential, or are neither. For those that could be nearly linear or nearly exponential, find a formula.

30.

t	3	10	14
$Q(t)$	7.51	8.7	9.39

31.

t	5	9	15
$R(t)$	2.32	2.61	3.12

32.

t	5	12	16
$S(t)$	4.35	6.72	10.02

33. Figure 4.13 shows the balance, P, in a bank account.

   (a) Find a possible formula for $P = f(t)$ assuming the balance grows exponentially.

   (b) What was the initial balance?

   (c) What annual interest rate does the account pay?

Figure 4.13

34. Suppose the city of Yonkers is offered two alternative fines by the judge. (See Example 8 on page 135.)

     Penalty A: $1 million on August 2 and the fine increases by $10 million each day thereafter.

     Penalty B: 1¢ on August 2 and the fine doubles each day thereafter.

   (a) If the city of Yonkers plans to defy the court order until the end of the month (August 31), compare the fines incurred under Penalty A and Penalty B.

   (b) If t represents the number of days after August 2, express the fine incurred as a function of t under

     (i) Penalty A   (ii) Penalty B

   (c) Assume your formulas in part (b) holds for $t \geq 0$, is there a time such that the fines incurred under both penalties are equal? If so, estimate that time.

35. A 1987 treaty to protect the ozone layer produced dramatic declines in global production, P, of chlorofluorocarbons (CFCs). See Figure 4.14.[9] Find a formula for P as an exponential function of the number of years, t, since 1989. What was the annual percent decay rate?

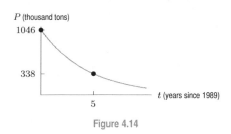

Figure 4.14

36. Figure 4.15 gives the voltage, $V(t)$, across a circuit element at time t seconds. For $t < 0$, the voltage is a constant 80 volts; for $t \geq 0$, the voltage decays exponentially.

   (a) Find a piecewise formula for $V(t)$.

   (b) At what value of t will the voltage reach 0.1?

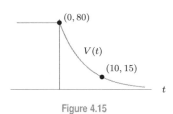

Figure 4.15

37. Short track 500m speed skating became a Winter Olympic event in 1994, and Chae Ji-Hoon of Korea won the event that year with a time of 43.45 seconds. In 2006, Apolo Ohno of the US won the event with a time of 41.94 seconds. Find a formula for the predicted winning time in the 500m speed skating event as a function of the number of years since 1994, and predict the winning time in 2018, if we assume the decrease in time is

   (a) Linear   **(b)** Exponential

---

[9]These numbers reflect the volume of the major CFCs multiplied by their respective ozone-depleting potentials (ODPs), as reported by the U. N. Environmental Programme Ozone Secretariat. See hq.uncp.org/ozone, accessed November, 2001.

38. There were 178.8 million licensed drivers in the US in 1989 and 187.2 million in 1999.[10] Find a formula for the number, N, of licensed drivers in the US as a function of t, the number of years since 1989, assuming growth is

   (a) Linear   **(b)** Exponential

39. In year $t = 0$ a lake is estimated to have about 3500 trout in it. Ten years later, at $t = 10$, the population of trout is believed to be about 1700.

   (a) Write a formula for the size of the population P as a function of year t if we assume the decrease is linear. What is the rate of change, in fish per year, of the function over the ten-year period?

   (b) Write a formula for the size of the population P as a function of year t if we assume the decrease is exponential. What is the percent rate of change, in percent per year, of the function over the ten-year period?

   (c) Graph the two functions on the same coordinate system. Indicate the points at $t = 0$ and $t = 10$.

40. Cocoa production[11] is shown in Table 4.8 for the world and the Ivory Coast, in millions of tons, as a function of the number of years since 2000. In each case, determine if production is better modeled with a linear or an exponential function and find a formula for the function.

Table 4.8

Years since 2000	0	1	2	3	4
World cocoa production	3.1	3.875	4.844	6.055	7.568
Ivory Coast cocoa production	1.3	1.34	1.38	1.42	1.46

41. The average gain in life expectancy at birth in the US has remained almost constant for 150 years, at an increase of 3 months in life expectancy per year.[12] Assume that this rate of increase continues. Life expectancy in the US in 2009 was 78.1 years.

   (a) Is life expectancy increasing linearly or exponentially?

   (b) Find a formula for life expectancy, L, in years, in the US at birth as a function of the number of years t since 2000.

   (c) What is the predicted life expectancy for babies born in 2050?

42. In terms of the initial population P_0, what is the value of the population at the end of 10 years, given each of the following assumptions? Graph each population against time.

   (a) A population decreases linearly and the decrease is 10% in the first year.

   (b) A population decreases exponentially at the rate of 10% a year.

43. The number of asthma sufferers in the world was about 84 million in 1990 and 300 million in 2009.[13] Let N represent the number of asthma sufferers (in millions) worldwide t years after 1990.

   (a) Write N as a linear function of t. What is the slope? What does it tell you about asthma sufferers?

   (b) Write N as an exponential function of t. What is the growth factor? What does it tell you about asthma sufferers?

   (c) How many asthma sufferers are predicted worldwide in the year 2020 with the linear model? With the exponential model?

44. In 2000, the population of a town was 20,000, and it grew by 4.14% that year. By 2010, the town's population had reached 30,000.

   (a) Can this population be best described by a linear or an exponential model, or neither? Explain.

   (b) If possible, find a formula for $P(t)$, this population t years after 2000.

45. In 2000, the population of a town was 18,500 and it grew by 250 people by the end of the year. By 2010, its population had reached 22,500.

   (a) Can this population be best described by a linear or an exponential model, or neither? Explain.

   (b) If possible, find a formula for $P(t)$, the population t years after 2000.

4.3 GRAPHS OF EXPONENTIAL FUNCTIONS

As with linear functions, an understanding of the significance of the parameters a and b in the formula $Q = ab^t$ helps us analyze and compare exponential functions.

---

[10] *The World Almanac* 2002 (New York: World Almanac Education Group, Inc., 2002), p. 228.

[11] Adapted from www.treecrops.org/crops/cocoaoutlook, accessed November, 2009.

[12] "The Science of Living Longer", Time Magazine, February 22, 2010.

[13] www.healthylifestyle-solutions.blogspot.com, accessed January 2, 2010.

Graphs of the Exponential Family: The Effect of the Parameter a

In the formula $Q = ab^t$, the value of a tells us where the graph crosses the Q-axis, since a is the value of Q when $t = 0$. In Figure 4.16 each graph has the same value of b but different values of a and thus different vertical intercepts.

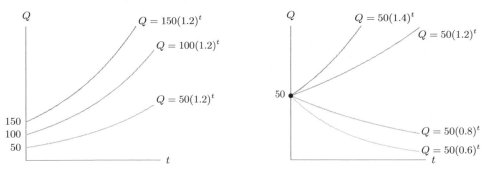

Figure 4.16: Graphs of $Q = a(1.2)^t$ for $a = 50, 100,$ and 150 Figure 4.17: Graphs of $Q = 50b^t$ for $b = 0.6, 0.8, 1.2$ and 1.4

Graphs of the Exponential Family: The Effect of the Parameter b

The growth factor, b, is called the *base* of an exponential function. Provided a is positive, if $b > 1$, the graph climbs when read from left to right, and if $0 < b < 1$, the graph falls when read from left to right.

Figure 4.17 shows how the value of b affects the steepness of the graph of $Q = ab^t$. Each graph has a different value of b but the same value of a (and thus the same Q-intercept). For $b > 1$, the greater the value of b, the more rapidly the graph rises. For $0 < b < 1$, the smaller the value of b, the more rapidly the graph falls. In every case, however, the graph is concave up.

Horizontal Asymptotes

The t-axis is a *horizontal asymptote* for the graph of $Q = ab^t$, because Q approaches 0 as t gets large, either positively or negatively. For exponential decay, such as $Q = f(t) = a(0.6)^t$ in Figure 4.17, the value of Q approaches 0 as t gets large and positive. We write

$$Q \to 0 \quad \text{as} \quad t \to \infty.$$

This means that Q is as close to 0 as we like for all sufficiently large values of t. We say that the *limit* of $f(t)$ as t goes to infinity is 0, and we write

$$\lim_{t \to \infty} f(t) = 0.$$

For exponential growth, the value of Q approaches zero as t grows more negative. (See Figure 4.29 on page 159.) In this case, we write

$$Q \to 0 \quad \text{as} \quad t \to -\infty.$$

This means that Q is as close to 0 as we like for all sufficiently large negative values of t. Using limit notation, we write

$$\lim_{t \to -\infty} f(t) = 0.$$

We make the following definition:

> The horizontal line $y = k$ is a **horizontal asymptote** of a function, f, if the function values get arbitrarily close to k as x gets large (either positively or negatively or both). We describe this behavior using the notation
>
> $$f(x) \to k \quad \text{as} \quad x \to \infty$$
>
> or
>
> $$f(x) \to k \quad \text{as} \quad x \to -\infty.$$
>
> Alternatively, using limit notation, we write
>
> $$\lim_{x \to \infty} f(x) = k \quad \text{or} \quad \lim_{x \to -\infty} f(x) = k.$$

Example 1 A capacitor is the part of an electrical circuit that stores electric charge. The quantity of charge stored decreases exponentially with time. Stereo amplifiers provide a familiar example: When an amplifier is turned off, the display lights fade slowly because it takes time for the capacitors to discharge. (Thus, it can be unsafe to open a stereo or a computer immediately after it is turned off.)

If t is the number of seconds after the circuit is switched off, suppose that the quantity of stored charge (in micro-coulombs) is given by

$$Q = 200(0.9)^t, \quad t \geq 0.$$

(a) Describe in words how the stored charge changes over time.

(b) What quantity of charge remains after 10 seconds? 20 seconds? 30 seconds? 1 minute? 2 minutes? 3 minutes?

(c) Graph the charge over the first minute. What does the horizontal asymptote of the graph tell you about the charge?

Solution (a) The charge is initially 200 micro-coulombs. Since $b = 1 + r = 0.9$, we have $r = -0.10$, which means that the charge level decreases by 10% each second.

(b) Table 4.9 gives the value of Q at $t = 0, 10, 20, 30, 60, 120,$ and 180. Notice that as t increases, Q gets closer and closer to, but does not quite reach, zero. The charge stored by the capacitor is getting smaller, but never completely vanishes.

(c) Figure 4.18 shows Q over a 60-second interval. The horizontal asymptote at $Q = 0$ corresponds to the fact that the charge gets very small as t increases. After 60 seconds, for all practical purposes, the charge is zero.

Table 4.9 *Charge (in micro-coulombs) stored by a capacitor over time*

t (seconds)	Q, charge level
0	200
10	69.736
20	24.315
30	8.478
60	0.359
120	0.000646
180	0.00000116

Figure 4.18: The charge stored by a capacitor over one minute

Solving Exponential Equations Graphically

We are often interested in solving equations involving exponential functions. In the following examples, we do this graphically. In Section 5.1, we will see how to solve equations using logarithms.

Example 2   In Example 8 on page 135, the fine, P, imposed on the city of Yonkers is given by $P = 100 \cdot 2^t$ where t is the number of days after August 2. In 1988, the annual budget of the city was $337 million. If the city chose to disobey the court order, at what point would the fine have wiped out the entire annual budget?

Solution   We need to find the day on which the fine reaches $337 million. That is, we must solve the equation

$$100 \cdot 2^t = 337,000,000.$$

Using a computer or graphing calculator we can graph $P = 100 \cdot 2^t$ to find the point at which the fine reaches 337 million. From Figure 4.19, we see that this occurs between $t = 21$ and $t = 22$. At day $t = 21$, August 23, the fine is:

$$P = 100 \cdot 2^{21} = 209,715,200$$

or just over $200 million. On day $t = 22$, the fine is

$$P = 100 \cdot 2^{22} = 419,430,400$$

or almost $420 million—quite a bit more than the city's entire annual budget!

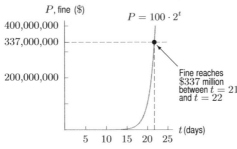

Figure 4.19: The fine imposed on Yonkers exceeds $337 million after 22 days

Figure 4.20: Solving the equation $200(0.886)^t = 25$

Example 3   A 200-μg sample of carbon-14 decays according to the formula

$$Q = 200(0.886)^t$$

where t is in thousands of years. Estimate when there is 25 μg of carbon-14 left.

Solution   We must solve the equation

$$200(0.886)^t = 25.$$

At the moment, we cannot find a formula for the solution to this equation. However, we can estimate the solution graphically. Figure 4.20 shows a graph of $Q = 200(0.886)^t$ and the line $Q = 25$. The amount of carbon-14 decays to 25 micrograms at $t \approx 17.180$. Since t is measured in thousands of years, this means in about 17,180 years.

Finding an Exponential Function for Data

The data in Table 4.10 gives population data for the Houston Metro Area since 1900. (2010 is estimated.) In Section 1.6, we saw how to fit a linear function to data, but the data points shown in Figure 4.21 suggests that it may make more sense to fit the data using an exponential function.

Table 4.10 *Population (in thousands) of Houston Metro Area, t years after 1900*

t	N	t	N
0	184	60	1583
10	236	70	2183
20	332	80	3122
30	528	90	3733
40	737	100	4672
50	1070	110	5937

Figure 4.21: Houston population data with an exponential model

Using an exponential regression feature on a calculator or computer, the following exponential function was found:

$$P = 190(1.034)^t.$$

This equation fits the data nicely, with $a = 190$ being close to the initial data value of 184. The graph in Figure 4.21 shows that $b = 1.034$ is a suitable growth factor and the population was increasing at a rate of about 3.4% per year between 1900 and 2010.

Exercises and Problems for Section 4.3

Exercises

1. (a) Make a table of values for $f(x) = 2^x$ for $x = -3, -2, -1, 0, 1, 2, 3$.
   (b) Graph $f(x)$. Describe the graph in words.

2. (a) Make a table of values for $f(x) = \left(\frac{1}{2}\right)^x$ for $x = -3, -2, -1, 0, 1, 2, 3$.
   (b) Graph $f(x)$. Describe the graph in words.

3. The graphs of $f(x) = (1.1)^x$, $g(x) = (1.2)^x$, and $h(x) = (1.25)^x$ are in Figure 4.22. Explain how you can match these formulas and graphs without a calculator.

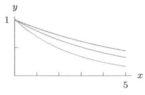

Figure 4.22

4. The graphs of $f(x) = (0.7)^x$, $g(x) = (0.8)^x$, and $h(x) = (0.85)^x$ are in Figure 4.23. Explain how you can match these formulas and graphs without a calculator.

Figure 4.23

In Problems 5–10, will the graphs of the two functions cross in the first quadrant? Explain your reasoning without using a calculator.

5. $f(x) = 10(1.03)^x$; $g(x) = 2(1.05)^x$

6. $f(x) = 250(1.2)^x$; $g(x) = 300(1.3)^x$

7. $f(x) = 10(1.05)^x$; $g(x) = 9(0.95)^x$

8. $f(x) = 5(0.8)^x$; $g(x) = 2(1.05)^x$

152

9. $f(x) = 500(0.8)^x$; $g(x) = 450(0.7)^x$

10. $f(x) = 1000(0.9)^x$; $g(x) = 875(0.95)^x$

For Exercises 11–14, use Figure 4.24. Assume the equations for A, B, C, and D can all be written in the form $y = ab^t$.

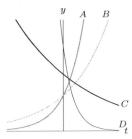

Figure 4.24

11. Which function has the largest value for a?

12. Which two functions have the same value for a?

13. Which function has the smallest value for b?

14. Which function has the largest value for b?

15. The volume of biodegradable material in a compost pile is shown in Figure 4.25, with time t measured in weeks. Use the graph to estimate:

  (a) The volume after 5 weeks.

(b) The number of weeks until the volume is 20 ft^3.

Figure 4.25

16. Solve $y = 46(1.1)^x$ graphically for x if $y = 91$.

17. Solve $p = 22(0.87)^q$ graphically for q if $p = 10$.

18. Solve $4m = 17(2.3)^w$ graphically for w if $m = 12$.

19. Solve $P/7 = (0.6)^t$ graphically for t if $P = 2$.

20. If $b > 1$, what is the horizontal asymptote of $y = ab^t$ as $t \to -\infty$?

21. If $0 < b < 1$, what is the horizontal asymptote of $y = ab^t$ as $t \to \infty$?

22. If the exponential function ab^x has the property that $\lim_{x \to \infty} ab^x = 0$, what can you say about the value of b?

Problems

In Problems 23–27, graph $f(x)$, a function defined for all real numbers and satisfying the condition.

23. $f(x) \to 3$ as $x \to -\infty$

24. $\lim_{x \to \infty} f(x) = 5$

25. $\lim_{x \to -\infty} f(x) = 2$ and $\lim_{x \to \infty} f(x) = -1$

26. $f(x) \to 0$ as $x \to -\infty$ and $f(x) \to -\infty$ as $x \to \infty$

27. $f(x)$ has a horizontal asymptote of $y = 5$.

In Problems 28–29, assume that all important features are shown in the graph of $y = f(x)$. Estimate

  (a) $\lim_{x \to -\infty} f(x)$ **(b)** $\lim_{x \to \infty} f(x)$

28.

29.

30. Let $f(x) = 5 + 3(0.9)^x$. As $x \to \infty$, what happens to $f(x)$? Does this function have a horizontal asymptote, and if so, what is it? Justify your answer both analytically and graphically.

31. Consider the exponential functions graphed in Figure 4.26 and the six constants a, b, c, d, p, q.

  (a) Which of these constants are definitely positive?

  (b) Which of these constants are definitely between 0 and 1?

  (c) Which of these constants could be between 0 and 1?

  (d) Which two of these constants are definitely equal?

  (e) Which one of the following pairs of constants could be equal?

    a and p b and d b and q d and q

Figure 4.26

32. Set a window of $-4 \leq x \leq 4, -1 \leq y \leq 6$ and graph the following functions using several different values of a for each. Include some values of a with $a < 1$.

   (a) $y = a2^x$, $0 < a < 5$.
   (b) $y = 2a^x$, $0 < a < 5$.

33. For which value(s) of a and b is $y = ab^x$ an increasing function? A decreasing function? Concave up?

34. What are the domain and range of the exponential function $Q = ab^t$ where a and b are both positive constants?

Problems 35–36 use Figure 4.27, where y_0 is the y-coordinate of the point of intersection of the graphs. Describe what happens to y_0 if the following changes are made, assuming the other quantities remain the same.

Figure 4.27

35. r is increased   **36.** a is increased

37. The city of Baltimore has been declining in population for the last fifty years.[14] In the year 2000, the population of Baltimore was 651 thousand and declining at a rate of 0.75% per year. If this trend continues:

   (a) Give a formula for the population of Baltimore, P, in thousands, as a function of years, t, since 2000.
   (b) What is the predicted population in 2010?
   (c) To two decimal places, estimate t when the population is 550 thousand.

38. Let $P = f(t) = 1000(1.04)^t$ be the population of a community in year t.

   (a) Evaluate $f(0)$ and $f(10)$. What do these expressions represent in terms of the population?
   (b) Using a calculator or a computer, find appropriate viewing windows on which to graph the population for the first 10 years and for the first 50 years. Give the viewing windows you used and sketch the resulting graphs.
   (c) If the percentage growth rate remains constant, approximately when will the population reach 2500 people?

39. Suppose you use your calculator to graph $y = 1.04^{5x}$. You correctly enter $y = 1.04\hat{\ }(5x)$ and see the graph in Figure 4.28. A friend graphed the function by entering $y = 1.04\hat{\ }5x$ and said, "The graph is a straight line, so I must have the wrong window." Explain why changing the window will not correct your friend's error.

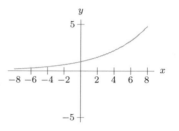

Figure 4.28

40. Suppose y, the number of cases of a disease, is reduced by 10% each year.

   (a) If there are initially 10,000 cases, express y as a function of t, the number of years elapsed.
   (b) How many cases will there be 5 years from now?
   (c) How long does it take to reduce the number of cases to 1000?

41. The earth's atmospheric pressure, P, in terms of height above sea level is often modeled by an exponential decay function. The pressure at sea level is 1013 millibars and that the pressure decreases by 14% for every kilometer above sea level.

   (a) What is the atmospheric pressure at 50 km?
   (b) Estimate the altitude h at which the pressure equals 900 millibars.

---

[14]*The World Almanac and Book of Facts 2006* (New York), p. 480.

42. The population of a colony of rabbits grows exponentially. The colony begins with 10 rabbits; five years later there are 340 rabbits.

    (a) Give a formula for the population of the colony of rabbits as a function of the time.

    (b) Use a graph to estimate how long it takes for the population of the colony to reach 1000 rabbits.

43. Let f be a piecewise-defined function given by

$$f(x) = \begin{cases} 2^x, & x < 0 \\ 0, & x = 0 \\ 1 - \frac{1}{2}x, & x > 0. \end{cases}$$

    (a) Graph f for $-3 \le x \le 4$.

    (b) The domain of $f(x)$ is all real numbers. What is its range?

    (c) What are the intercepts of f?

    (d) What happens to $f(x)$ as $x \to \infty$ and $x \to -\infty$?

    (e) Over what intervals is f increasing? Decreasing?

44. Table 4.11 shows the concentration of theophylline, a common asthma drug, in the blood stream as a function of time after injection of a 300-mg initial dose.[15] It is claimed that this data set is consistent with an exponential decay model $C = ab^t$ where C is the concentration and t is the time.

    (a) Estimate the values of a and b, using ratios to estimate b. How good is this model?

    (b) Use a calculator or computer to find the exponential regression function for concentration as a function of time. Compare answers from parts (a) and (b).

Table 4.11

Time (hours)	0	1	3	5	7	9
Concentration (mg/l)	12.0	10.0	7.0	5.0	3.5	2.5

45. Table 4.12 shows global wind energy generating capacity, W (in megawatts), as a function of the number of years, t, since 1995.[16]

    (a) Plot the data and explain why it is reasonable to approximate these data with an exponential function.

    (b) Use a calculator or computer to fit an exponential function to these data.

    (c) What annual percent growth rate does the exponential model show?

Table 4.12

t	0	1	2	3	4
W	4780	6070	7640	10,150	13,930
t	5	6	7	8	9
W	18,450	24,930	32,037	39,664	47,760

46. Three scientists, working independently of each other, arrive at the following formulas to model the spread of a species of mussel in a system of fresh water lakes:

$$f_1(x) = 3(1.2)^x, \quad f_2(x) = 3(1.21)^x, \quad f_3(x) = 3.01(1.2)^x,$$

where $f_n(x)$, $n = 1, 2, 3$, is the number of individual mussels (in 1000s) predicted by model number n to be living in the lake system after x months have elapsed.

    (a) Graph these three functions for $0 \le x \le 60$, $0 \le y \le 40{,}000$.

    (b) The graphs of these three models do not seem all that different from each other. But do the three functions make significantly different predictions about the future mussel population? To answer this, graph the difference function, $f_2(x) - f_1(x)$, of the population sizes predicted by models 1 and 2, as well as the difference functions, $f_3(x) - f_1(x)$ and $f_3(x) - f_2(x)$. (Use the same window as in part (a).)

    (c) Based on your graphs in part (b), discuss the assertion that all three models are in good agreement as far as long-range predictions of mussel population are concerned. What conclusions can you draw about exponential functions in general?

4.4 APPLICATIONS TO COMPOUND INTEREST

What is the difference between a bank account that pays 12% interest once per year and one that pays 1% interest every month? Imagine we deposit $1000 into the first account. Then, after 1 year, we have (assuming no other deposits or withdrawals)

$$\$1000(1.12) = \$1120.$$

---

[15] Based on D. N. Burghes, I. Huntley, and J. McDonald, *Applying Mathematics* (Ellis Horwood, 1982).

[16] The Worldwatch Institute, *Vital Signs* 2005 (New York: W.W. Norton & Company, 2005), p. 35.

But if we deposit $1000 into the second account, then after 1 year, or 12 months, we have

$$\$1000 \underbrace{(1.01)(1.01)\dots(1.01)}_{\text{12 months of 1\% monthly interest}} = 1000(1.01)^{12} = \$1126.83.$$

Thus, we earn $6.83 more in the second account than in the first. To see why this happens, notice that the 1% interest we earn in January itself earns interest at a rate of 1% per month. Similarly, the 1% interest we earn in February earns interest, and so does the interest earned in March, April, May, and so on. The extra $6.83 comes from interest earned on interest. This effect is known as *compounding*. We say that the first account earns 12% interest *compounded annually* and the second account earns 12% interest *compounded monthly*.

Nominal Versus Effective Rate

The expression 12% compounded monthly means that interest is added twelve times per year and that $12\%/12 = 1\%$ of the current balance is added each time. We refer to the 12% as the *nominal rate* (nominal means "in name only"). When the interest is compounded more frequently than once a year, the account effectively earns more than the nominal rate. Thus, we distinguish between nominal rate and *effective annual rate*, or *effective rate*. The effective annual rate tells you how much interest the investment actually earns. In the US, the effective annual rate is sometimes called the APY (annual percentage yield).

Example 1 What are the nominal and effective annual rates of an account paying 12% interest, compounded annually? Compounded monthly?

Solution Since an account paying 12% annual interest, compounded annually, grows by exactly 12% in one year, we see that its nominal rate is the same as its effective rate: both are 12%.

The account paying 12% interest, compounded monthly, also has a nominal rate of 12%. On the other hand, since it pays 1% interest every month, after 12 months, its balance increases by a factor of

$$\underbrace{(1.01)(1.01)\dots(1.01)}_{\text{12 months of 1\% monthly growth}} = 1.01^{12} \approx 1.1268250.$$

Thus, effectively, the account earns 12.683% interest in a year, so its effective rate is 12.683%.

Example 2 What is the effective annual rate of an account that pays interest at the nominal rate of 6% per year, compounded daily? Compounded hourly?

Solution Since there are 365 days in a year, daily compounding pays interest at the rate of

$$\frac{6\%}{365} = 0.0164384\% \text{ per day.}$$

Thus, the daily growth factor is

$$1 + \frac{0.06}{365} = 1.000164384.$$

If at the beginning of the year the account balance is P, after 365 days the balance is

$$P \cdot \underbrace{\left(1 + \frac{0.06}{365}\right)^{365}}_{\substack{\text{365 days of} \\ \text{0.0164384\% daily interest}}} = P \cdot (1.0618313).$$

Thus, this account earns interest at the effective annual rate of 6.18313%.

Notice that daily compounding results in a higher rate than yearly compounding (6.183% versus 6%), because with daily compounding the interest has the opportunity to earn interest.

If interest is compounded hourly, since there are $24 \cdot 365$ hours in a year, the balance at year's end is

$$P \cdot \left(1 + \frac{0.06}{24 \cdot 365}\right)^{24 \cdot 365} = P \cdot (1.0618363).$$

The effective rate is now 6.18363% instead of 6.18313%—that is, just slightly better than the rate of the account that compounds interest daily. The effective rate increases with the frequency of compounding.

In the previous examples, we computed the growth factor for one year. We now compute the growth factor over t years.

Example 3   At the beginning of the year you deposit P dollars in an account paying interest at the nominal rate of 4% per year compounded quarterly. By what factor does P grow in 3 years?

Solution   Compounding quarterly pays interest at the rate of

$$\frac{4\%}{4} = 1\% \text{ per quarter.}$$

Thus, the quarterly growth factor is $1 + 0.01 = 1.01$. At the beginning of the year the account balance is P. After one year the balance is

$$P \cdot \underbrace{\left(1 + \frac{0.04}{4}\right)^4}_{\substack{\text{4 quarters(1 year) of} \\ \text{1\% quarterly interest}}} = P \cdot (1.0406).$$

So after three years the balance is

$$P \cdot \left(1 + \frac{0.04}{4}\right)^4 \cdot \left(1 + \frac{0.04}{4}\right)^4 \cdot \left(1 + \frac{0.04}{4}\right)^4 = P \cdot \underbrace{\left(1 + \frac{0.04}{4}\right)^{4 \cdot 3}}_{\substack{\text{3 years of} \\ \text{1\% quarterly interest}}} = P \cdot (1.126825).$$

After three years the initial account balance P grows by a factor of 1.126825.

To summarize:

> If interest at an annual rate of r is compounded n times a year, then r/n times the current balance is added n times a year. Therefore, with an initial deposit of $\$P$, the balance t years later is
> $$B = P \cdot \left(1 + \frac{r}{n}\right)^{nt}.$$
> Note that r is the nominal rate; for example, $r = 0.05$ if the annual rate is 5%.

Exercises and Problems for Section 4.4

Exercises

1. An account pays interest at a nominal rate of 8% per year. Find the effective annual yield if interest is compounded

   (a) Monthly   (b) Weekly
   (c) Daily

2. What is the effective annual yield if a deposit of $1000 grows to $3500 in 15 years?

3. An investment grows by 5% per year for 20 years. By what percent does it increase over the 20-year period?

4. An investment decreases by 50% over an 8-year period. At what effective annual percent rate does it decrease?

5. Suppose $1000 is deposited into an account paying interest at a nominal rate of 8% per year. Find the balance three years later if the interest is compounded

   (a) Monthly   (b) Weekly
   (c) Daily

6. A bank pays interest at the nominal rate of 1.3% per year. What is the effective annual rate if compounding is:

   (a) Annual   (b) Monthly

In Exercises 7–10, what is the balance after 1 year if an account containing $500 earns the stated yearly nominal interest, compounded

(a) Annually   (b) Weekly (52 weeks per year)

(c) Every minute (525,600 per year)

7. 1%   **8.** 3%   **9.** 5%   **10.** 8%

In Exercises 11–14, what are the nominal and effective annual rates for an account paying the stated annual interest, compounded

(a) Annually?   (b) Quarterly?

(c) Daily?

11. 1%   **12.** 100%   **13.** 3%   **14.** 6%

Problems

15. An investment grows by 3% per year for 10 years. By what percent does it increase over the 10-year period?

16. An investment grows by 30% over a 5-year period. What is its effective annual percent growth rate?

17. An investment decreases by 60% over a 12-year period. At what effective annual percent rate does it decrease?

18. If you need $25,000 six years from now, what is the minimum amount of money you need to deposit into a bank account that pays 5% annual interest, compounded:

    (a) Annually   (b) Monthly   (c) Daily

    (d) Your answers get smaller as the number of times of compounding increases. Why is this so?

19. A sum of $850 is invested for 10 years and the interest is compounded quarterly. There is $1000 in the account at the end of 10 years. What is the nominal annual rate?

20. If the balance, M, at time t in years, of a bank account that compounds its interest payments monthly is given by

    $$M = M_0(1.07763)^t,$$

    (a) What is the effective annual rate for this account?
    (b) What is the nominal annual rate?

21. Suppose $300 was deposited into one of five bank accounts and t is time in years. For each verbal description (i)–(v), state which formulas (a)–(e) could represent it.

    (a) $B = 300(1.2)^t$ (b) $B = 300(1.12)^t$
    (c) $B = 300(1.06)^{2t}$ (d) $B = 300(1.06)^{t/2}$
    (e) $B = 300(1.03)^{4t}$

    (i) This investment earned 12% annually, compounded annually.
    (ii) This investment earned, on average, more than 1% each month.
    (iii) This investment earned 12% annually, compounded semi-annually.
    (iv) This investment earned, on average, less than 3% each quarter.
    (v) This investment earned, on average, more than 6% every 6 months.

22. Without making any calculations, briefly describe in words what the following formulas tell you about the value of the investments they describe. Be specific. Note that units are in dollars and years.

    (a) $V = 1500(1.077)^t$
    (b) $V = 9500(0.945)^t$
    (c) $V = 1000 \cdot 3^{t/5}$
    (d) $V = 500\left(1 + \frac{0.04}{12}\right)^{12t}$

4.5 THE NUMBER e

An irrational number, introduced by Euler[17] in 1727, is so important that it is given a special name, e. Its value is approximately $e \approx 2.71828\ldots$. It is often used for the base, b, of the exponential function. Base e is called the *natural base*. This may seem mysterious, as what could possibly be natural about using an irrational base such as e? The answer is that the formulas of calculus are much simpler if e is used as the base for exponentials. Some of the remarkable properties of the number e are introduced in Problems 52–53 on page 167. Since $2 < e < 3$, the graph of $Q = e^t$ lies between the graphs of $Q = 3^t$ and $Q = 2^t$. See Figure 4.29.

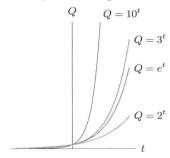

Figure 4.29: Graphs of exponential functions with various bases

Exponential Functions with Base e

Since any positive base b can be written as a power of e:

$$b = e^k,$$

any exponential function $Q = ab^t$ can be rewritten in terms of e:

$$Q = ab^t = a\left(e^k\right)^t = ae^{kt}.$$

If $b > 1$, then k is positive; if $0 < b < 1$, then k is negative. The constant k is called the *continuous growth rate*. In general:

For the exponential function $Q = ab^t$, the **continuous growth rate**, k, is given by solving $e^k = b$. Then

$$Q = ae^{kt}.$$

If a is positive,
- If $k > 0$, then Q is increasing.
- If $k < 0$, then Q is decreasing.

The value of the continuous growth rate, k, may be given as a decimal or a percent. If t is in years, for example, then the units of k are given per year; if t is in minutes, then k is given per minute.

Example 1   Give the continuous growth rate of each of the following functions and graph each function:
$$P = 5e^{0.2t}, \qquad Q = 5e^{0.3t}, \qquad \text{and} \quad R = 5e^{-0.2t}.$$

[17]Leonhard Euler (1707-1783), a Swiss mathematician, introduced e, $f(x)$ notation, π, and i (for $\sqrt{-1}$).

Solution   The function $P = 5e^{0.2t}$ has a continuous growth rate of 20%, and $Q = 5e^{0.3t}$ has a continuous 30% growth rate. The function $R = 5e^{-0.2t}$ has a continuous growth rate of -20%. The negative sign in the exponent tells us that R is decreasing instead of increasing.

Because $a = 5$ in all three formulas, all three functions cross the vertical axis at 5. Note that the graphs of these functions in Figure 4.30 have the same shape as the exponential functions in Section 4.3. They are concave up and have horizontal asymptotes of $y = 0$. (Note that $P \to 0$ and $Q \to 0$ as $t \to -\infty$, whereas $R \to 0$ as $t \to \infty$.)

Figure 4.30: Exponential functions with different continuous growth rates

Example 2   A population increases from 7.3 million at a continuous rate of 2.2% per year. Write a formula for the population, and estimate graphically when the population reaches 10 million.

Solution   We express the formula in base e since the continuous growth rate is given. If P is the population (in millions) in year t, then

$$P = 7.3e^{0.022t}.$$

See Figure 4.31. We see that $P = 10$ when $t \approx 14.3$. Thus, it takes about 14.3 years for the population to reach 10 million.

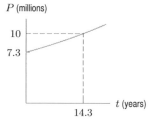

Figure 4.31: Estimating when the
population reaches 10 million

Example 3   Caffeine leaves the body at a continuous rate of 17% per hour. How much caffeine is left in the body 8 hours after drinking a cup of coffee containing 100 mg of caffeine?

Solution   If A is the amount of caffeine in the body t hours after drinking the coffee, then

$$A = 100e^{-0.17t}.$$

Note that the continuous growth rate is -17% since A is decreasing. After 8 hours, we have $A = 100e^{-0.17(8)} = 25.67$ mg.

The Difference Between Annual and Continuous Growth Rates

If $P = P_0(1.07)^t$, with t in years, we say that P is growing at an *annual* rate of 7%. If $P = P_0e^{0.07t}$, with t in years, we say that P is growing at a *continuous* rate of 7% per year. Since

$e^{0.07} = 1.0725\ldots$, we can rewrite $P_0 e^{0.07t} = P_0(1.0725)^t$. In other words, a 7% continuous rate and a 7.25% annual rate generate the same increases in P. We say the two rates are equivalent.

We can check that $e^{0.0677} = 1.07\ldots$, so a 7% annual growth rate is equivalent to a 6.77% continuous growth rate. The continuous growth rate is always smaller than the equivalent annual rate.

The bank account example at the start of the previous section reminds us why a quantity growing at continuous rate of 7% per year increases faster than a quantity growing at an annual rate of 7%: In the continuous case, the interest earns more interest.

Connection: The Number e and Compound Interest

The number e has a surprising relationship with compound interest when the compounding period is made smaller and smaller.

If $1.00 is invested in a bank account that pays 100% interest once a year, then, assuming no other deposits or withdrawals, after one year we have

$$\$1.00(1 + 100\%) = \$2.00.$$

Now we decrease the compounding period. Suppose $1.00 is invested in a bank account that pays 100% nominal interest compounded n times a year; then

$$\text{Balance after one year} = \$1.00 \left(1 + \frac{100\%}{n}\right)^n$$

As the frequency of compounding increases, the balance increases, because the interest earns more. How large can the balance grow? Table 4.13 shows the balance after one year as the interest is calculated more and more frequently. It appears that the balance approaches $e = 2.71828182\ldots$.

Assuming that the initial balance of $1 is growing at a continuous rate of 100%, the balance after one year would be $1 \cdot e^1 = e$ dollars, so the surprising relationship arises from the fact that by increasing the compounding frequency we get the effect of continuous growth that we discussed earlier.

Table 4.13 *Balance after 1 year, 100% nominal interest, various compounding frequencies*

Frequency	Approximate balance
1 (annually)	$2.00
2 (semi-annually)	$2.25
4 (quarterly)	$2.441406
12 (monthly)	$2.613035
365 (daily)	$2.714567
8760 (hourly)	$2.718127
525,600 (each minute)	$2.718279
31,536,000 (each second)	$2.718282

In Example 2 of Section 4.4 we calculated the effective interest rates for two accounts with a 6% per year nominal interest rate, but different compounding periods. We see that the account with more frequent compounding earns a higher effective rate, though the increase is small. Compounding

161

more and more frequently—every minute or every second or many times per second—increases the effective rate still further. However, there is again a limit to how much an account can earn by increasing the frequency of compounding.

Table 4.14   *Effect of increasing the frequency of compounding, 6% nominal interest*

Compounding frequency	Annual growth factor	Effective annual rate
Annually	1.0600000	6%
Monthly	1.0616778	6.16778%
Daily	1.0618313	6.18313%
Hourly	1.0618363	6.18363%
⋮	⋮	⋮
Continuously	$e^{0.06} \approx 1.0618365$	6.18365%

Table 4.14 shows several compounding periods with their annual growth factors and effective annual rates. As the compounding periods become shorter, we discover that the growth factor approaches $e^{0.06}$. Using a calculator, we check that the final value for the annual growth factors in Table 4.14 is given by

$$e^{0.06} \approx 1.0618365,$$

If an account with a 6% nominal interest rate per year delivers an annual growth factor of $e^{0.06}$, we say that the interest has been *compounded continuously*. In general:

> If interest on an initial deposit of \$$P$ is *compounded continuously* at a nominal rate of r per year, the balance t years later can be calculated using the formula
>
> $$B = Pe^{rt}.$$
>
> For example, if the nominal rate is 6%, then $r = 0.06$.

It is important to realize that the functions $B = Pe^{0.06t}$ and $B = P(1.0618365)^t$ both give the balance in a bank account growing at a continuous rate of 6% per year. These formulas both represent the *same* exponential function—they just describe it in different ways.[18]

Example 4   In November 2005, the Wells Fargo Bank offered interest at a 2.323% continuous yearly rate.[19] Find the effective annual rate.

Solution   Since $e^{0.02323} = 1.0235$, the effective annual rate is 2.35%. As expected, the effective annual rate is larger than the continuous yearly rate.

Example 5   Which is better: An account that pays 8% annual interest compounded quarterly or an account that pays 7.95% annual interest compounded continuously?

---

[18]Actually, this is not precisely true, because we rounded off when we found $b = 1.0618365$. However, we can find b to as many digits as we want, and to this extent the two formulas are the same.

[19]http://money.cnn.com/2005/11/30/debt/informa_rate, accessed November 30, 2005.

Solution   The account that pays 8% interest compounded quarterly pays 2% interest 4 times a year. Thus, in one year the balance is

$$P(1.02)^4 \approx P(1.08243),$$

which means the effective annual rate is 8.243%.

The account that pays 7.95% interest compounded continuously has a year-end balance of

$$Pe^{0.0795} \approx P(1.08275),$$

so the effective annual rate is 8.275%. Thus, 7.95% compounded continuously pays more than 8% compounded quarterly.

Exercises and Problems for Section 4.5

Skill Refresher

In Exercises S1–S4, using a calculator approximate to 3 decimal places.

S1. $e^{0.07}$ **S2.** $10e^{-0.14}$ **S3.** $\dfrac{2}{\sqrt[3]{e}}$ **S4.** e^{3e}

In Exercises S5–S8, evaluate the functions for $t = 0$ and $t = 4$.

S5. $f(t) = 2.3e^{0.3t}$

S6. $g(t) = 4.2e^{-0.12t}$

S7. $h(t) = 153 + 8.6e^{0.43t}$

S8. $k(t) = 289 - 4.7e^{-0.0018t}$

In Exercises S9–S15, write the function in the form $f(t) = ae^{kt}$.

S9. $f(t) = \left(3e^{0.04t}\right)^3$ **S10.** $g(z) = 5e^{7z} \cdot e^{4z} \cdot 3e^{z}$

S11. $Q(t) = e^{7-3t}$ **S12.** $Q(t) = \sqrt{e^{3+6t}}$

S13. $m(x) = \dfrac{7e^{0.2x}}{\sqrt{3e^{x}}}$ **S14.** $P(t) = \left(2\sqrt[3]{e^{5t}}\right)^4$

S15. $H(r) = \dfrac{\left(e^{0.4r}\right)^2}{6e^{0.15r}}$

Exercises

1. Without a calculator, match the functions $y = e^x$, $y = 2e^x$, and $y = 3e^x$ to the graphs in Figure 4.32.

Figure 4.32

2. Without a calculator, match the functions $y = 2^x$, $y = 3^x$, and $y = e^x$ with the graphs in Figure 4.33.

Figure 4.33

3. Without a calculator, match the functions (a)–(d) with the graphs (I)–(IV) in Figure 4.34.

   (a) $e^{0.25t}$ **(b)** $(1.25)^t$ **(c)** $(1.2)^t$ **(d)** $e^{0.3t}$

Figure 4.34

4. Without graphing on a calculator, match the functions (a)–(d) with the graphs (I)–(IV) in Figure 4.35.

(a) 1.5^x (b) $e^{0.45x}$ (c) $e^{0.47x}$ (d) $e^{0.5x}$

Figure 4.35

5. Without a calculator, match the functions $y = e^x$, $y = e^{-x}$, and $y = -e^x$ to the graphs in Figure 4.36.

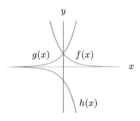

Figure 4.36

6. Without a calculator, match each formula to one of the graphs (I)–(IV) in Figure 4.37.

(a) $e^{-0.01t}$ (b) $e^{0.05t}$ (c) $e^{-0.10t}$ (d) $e^{0.20t}$

Figure 4.37

7. Without a calculator, match the functions (a)–(d) with the graphs (I)–(IV) in Figure 4.38.

(a) $y = e^x$ (b) $y = e^{-x}$

(c) $y = e^{-2x}$ (d) $y = e^{-3x}$

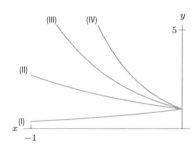

Figure 4.38

Problems

8. Without a calculator, arrange the following quantities in ascending order:

(a) $3^{2.2}, e^{2.2}, (\sqrt{2})^{2.2}$
(b) $3^{-2.2}, e^{-2.2}$

In Problems 9–12, find the limits.

9. $\lim_{x \to \infty} e^{-3x}$ 10. $\lim_{t \to -\infty} 5e^{0.07t}$

11. $\lim_{t \to \infty} (2 - 3e^{-0.2t})$ 12. $\lim_{t \to -\infty} 2e^{-0.1t+6}$

13. If $\lim_{t \to \infty} ae^{kt} = \infty$, what can you say about the values of a and k?

In Problems 14–19, a quantity Q is changing over time t.

(a) What is the quantity at time $t = 0$?

(b) Is the quantity increasing or decreasing over time?

(c) What is the percent per unit time growth or decay rate?

(d) Is the growth rate continuous?

14. $Q = 25e^{0.032t}$ 15. $Q = 2.7(0.12)^t$

16. $Q = 158(1.137)^t$ 17. $Q = 0.01e^{-0.2t}$

18. $Q = 50e^{1.05t}$ 19. $Q = 2^t$

In Problems 20–22, an initial quantity Q_0 and a growth rate are given. Give a formula for quantity Q as a function of time t, and find the value of the quantity at $t = 10$, if we assume that the growth rate is:

(a) Not continuous   (b) Continuous

20. $Q_0 = 100;$ growth rate of 5% per unit time

21. $Q_0 = 8;$ growth rate of 12% per unit time

22. $Q_0 = 500;$ decay rate of -7% per unit time

23. A population of 3.2 million grows at a constant percentage rate.

  (a) What is the population one century later if there is:

    (i) An annual growth rate of 2%

    (ii) A continuous growth rate of 2% per year

  (b) Explain how you can tell which of the answers would be larger before doing the calculations.

24. The following formulas each describe the size of an animal population, P, in t years since the start of the study. Describe the growth of each population in words.

  (a) $P = 200(1.028)^t$ (b) $P = 50e^{-0.17t}$
  (c) $P = 1000(0.89)^t$ (d) $P = 600e^{0.20t}$
  (e) $P = 2000 - 300t$ (f) $P = 600 + 50t$

25. A town has population 3000 people at year $t = 0$. Write a formula for the population, P, in year t if the town

  (a) Grows by 200 people per year.
  (b) Grows by 6% per year.
  (c) Grows at a continuous rate of 6% per year.
  (d) Shrinks by 50 people per year.
  (e) Shrinks by 4% per year.
  (f) Shrinks at a continuous rate of 4% per year.

26. A population is 25,000 in year $t = 0$ and grows at a continuous rate of 7.5% per year.

  (a) Find a formula for $P(t)$, the population in year t.
  (b) By what percent does the population increase each year? Why is this more than 7.5%?

27. A population grows from its initial level of 22,000 at a continuous growth rate of 7.1% per year.

  (a) Find a formula for $P(t)$, the population in year t.
  (b) By what percent does the population increase each year?

28. An investment of $7000 earns interest at a continuous annual rate of 5.2%. What is the investment's value in 7 years?

29. Without making any calculations, describe in words what the following formulas tell you about the value of three different investments. Be specific. Note that units are in dollars and years.

  (a) $V = 1000e^{0.115t}$ (b) $V = 1000 \cdot 2^{t/6}$
  (c) $V = 1000(1.122)^t$

30. Calculate the amount of money in a bank account if $2000 is deposited for 15 years at an interest rate of

  (a) 5% annually
  (b) 5% continuously per year

31. At time t in years, the value, V, of an investment of $1000 is given by $V = 1000e^{0.02t}$. When is the investment worth $3000?

32. How long does it take an investment to double if it grows according to the formula $V = 537e^{0.015t}$? Assume t is in years.

33. From time $t = 0$, with t in years, a $1200 deposit in a bank account grows according to the formula

$$B = 1200e^{0.03t}.$$

  (a) What is the balance in the account at the end of 100 years?
  (b) When does the balance first go over $50,000?

34. The same amount of money is deposited into two different bank accounts paying the same nominal rate, one compounded annually and the other compounded continuously. Which curve in Figure 4.39 corresponds to which compounding method? What is the initial deposit?

Figure 4.39

35. Find the effective annual yield and the continuous growth rate if $Q = 5500\,e^{0.19\,t}$.

36. If $5000 is deposited in an account paying a nominal interest rate of 4% per year, how much is in the account 10 years later if interest is compounded

  (a) Annually?
  (b) Continuously?

37. Find the effective annual rate if $1000 is deposited at 5% annual interest, compounded continuously.

38. An investment of $500 earns interest at a 6.75% continuous annual rate. Give a formula $V = ab^t$ for the investment's value in year t, and state the values of a, b, and the annual growth rate r.

39. A bank account pays 6% annual interest. As the number of compounding periods increases, the effective interest rate earned also rises.

    (a) Find the annual interest rate earned by the account if the interest is compounded:

        (i) Quarterly   (ii) Monthly

        (iii) Weekly   (iv) Daily

    (b) Evaluate $e^{0.06}$, where $e = 2.71828\ldots$ Explain what your result tells you about the bank account.

40. Three different investments are given.

    (a) Find the balance of each of the investments after a two-year period.

    (b) Rank them from best to worst in terms of rate of return. Explain your reasoning.

- Investment A: $875 deposited at 13.5% per year compounded daily for 2 years.
- Investment B: $1000 deposited at 6.7% per year compounded continuously for 2 years.
- Investment C: $1050 deposited at 4.5% per year compounded monthly for 2 years.

41. Rank the following three bank deposit options from best to worst.

- Bank A: 7% compounded daily
- Bank B: 7.1% compounded monthly
- Bank C: 7.05% compounded continuously

42. Which is better, an account paying 5.3% interest compounded continuously or an account paying 5.5% interest compounded annually? Justify your answer.

43. The GDP of Chile was 145.8 billion dollars in 2007 and was growing at a continuous rate of 5.1% per year.[20]

    (a) Find a formula for G, the GDP of Chile in billion dollars, as a function of t, the number of years since 2007.

    (b) By what percent does the GDP increase each year?

    (c) Use your answer to part (b) to write a formula for G as a function of t using the form $G = ab^t$

    (d) Graph your answers to part (a) and part (c) on the same axes. Explain what you see.

44. Which is larger after 5 years: an investment of $1000 earning 5% per year compounded monthly or an investment of $1100 earning 4% per year compounded continuously? Which is larger after 10 years? Justify your answers.

45. One bank pays 5% interest compounded annually and another bank pays 5% interest compounded continuously. Given a deposit of $10,000, what is the difference in the balance between the two banks in 8 years?

46. An investment of $1000 earns 8% interest compounded continuously. An investment of $1500 earns 6% interest compounded annually. Figure 4.40 shows the balance of the two investments over time.

    (a) Which graph goes with which investment?

    (b) Use a graph of the two functions to estimate the time until the balances are equal.

Figure 4.40

47. What can you say about the value of the constants a, k, b, l in Figure 4.41?

Figure 4.41

48. World poultry production was 94.7 million tons in the year 2009 and increasing at a continuous rate of 1.1% per year.[21] Assume that this growth rate continues.

    (a) Write an exponential formula for world poultry production, P, in million tons, as a function of the number of years, t, since 2009.

    (b) Use the formula to estimate world poultry production in the year 2015.

    (c) Use a graph to estimate the year in which world poultry production goes over 110 million tons.

---

[20]www.nationmaster.com, accessed February 2010.

[21]www.sourcejuice.com/1266927/2009/10/19/world-poultry-production-growth-but-decline-trade, accessed Jan., 2010.

49. A radioactive substance decays at a continuous rate of 14% per year, and 50 mg of the substance is present in the year 2009.

   (a) Write a formula for the amount present, A (in mg), t years after 2009.

   (b) How much will be present in the year 2019?

   (c) Estimate when the quantity drops below 5 mg.

50. The annual inflation rate, r, for a five-year period is given in Table 4.15.

   (a) By what total percent did prices rise between the start of 2000 and the end of 2004?

   (b) What is the average annual inflation rate for this time period?

   (c) At the beginning of 2000, a shower curtain costs $20. Make a prediction for the good's cost at the beginning of 2010, using the average inflation rate found in part (b).

Table 4.15

t	2000	2001	2002	2003	2004
r	3.4%	2.8%	1.6%	2.3%	2.7%

51. In the 1980s a northeastern bank experienced an unusual robbery. Each month an armored car delivered cash deposits from local branches to the main office, a trip requiring only one hour. One day, however, the delivery was six hours late. This delay turned out to be a scheme devised by an employee to defraud the bank. The armored car drivers had lent the money, a total of approximately $200,000,000, to arms merchants, who then used it as collateral against the purchase of illegal weapons. The interest charged for this loan was 20% per year compounded continuously. How much was the fee for the six-hour period?

52. This problem explores the value of $(1+1/n)^n$ for integer values of n as n gets large.

   (a) Use a calculator or computer to evaluate $(1+1/n)^n$, correct to seven decimal places, for $n = 1000$, $10{,}000$, $100{,}000$, and $1{,}000{,}000$. Does $(1+1/n)^n$ appear to be an increasing or decreasing function of n?

   (b) The limit of the sequence of values in part (a) is $e = 2.718281828\ldots$. What power of 10 is needed to give a value of e correct to 6 decimal places?

   (c) What happens if you evaluate $(1 + 1/n)^n$ using much larger values of n? For example, try $n = 10^{16}$ on a calculator.

53. With more terms giving a better approximation, it can be shown that

$$e = 1 + \frac{1}{1} + \frac{1}{1 \cdot 2} + \frac{1}{1 \cdot 2 \cdot 3} + \frac{1}{1 \cdot 2 \cdot 3 \cdot 4} + \cdots.$$

   (a) Use a calculator to sum the five terms shown.

   (b) Find the sum of the first seven terms.

   (c) Compare your sums with the calculator's displayed value for e (which you can find by entering $e\,\hat{}\,1$) and state the number of correct digits in the five- and seven-term sum.

   (d) How many terms of the sum are needed in order to give a nine-decimal-digit approximation equal to the calculator's displayed value for e?

CHAPTER SUMMARY

- **Exponential Functions**
  Value of $f(t)$ changes at constant percent rate with respect to t.
- **General Formula for Exponential Functions**
  Exponential function: $f(t) = ab^t$, $b > 0$.
  f increasing for $b > 1$, decreasing for $0 < b < 1$.
     Growth factor: $b = 1 + r$.
     Growth rate: r, percent change as a decimal.
- **Comparing Linear and Exponential Functions**
  An increasing exponential function eventually overtakes any linear function.
- **Graphs of Exponential Functions**
  Concavity; asymptotes; effect of parameters a and b.
  Solving exponential equations graphically; finding an exponential function for data.
- **The Number e**
  Continuous growth: $f(t) = ae^{kt}$.
  f is increasing for $k > 0$, decreasing for $k < 0$.
  Continuous growth rate: k.
- **Compound Interest**
  For compounding n times per year, balance,
  $$B = P\left(1 + \frac{r}{n}\right)^{nt}.$$
  For continuous compounding, $B = Pe^{kt}$.
  Nominal rate, r or k, versus effective rate earned over one year.
- **Horizontal Asymptotes and Limits to Infinity**

REVIEW EXERCISES AND PROBLEMS FOR CHAPTER FOUR

Exercises

In Exercises 1–6, you start with 500 items. How many do you have after the following change?

1. 10% increase

2. 100% increase

3. 1% decrease

4. 42% decrease

5. 42% increase followed by 42% decrease

6. 42% decrease followed by 42% increase

7. Find a formula for $P = f(t)$, the size of a population that begins in year $t = 0$ with 2200 members and decreases at a 3.2% annual rate.

8. Without a calculator or computer, match each exponential formula to one of the graphs I–VI.

   (a) $10(1.2)^t$ (b) $10(1.5)^t$ (c) $20(1.2)^t$
   (d) $30(0.85)^t$ (e) $30(0.95)^t$ (f) $30(1.05)^t$

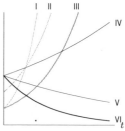

9. A quantity increases from 10 to 12. By what percent has it increased? Now suppose that it had increased from 100 to 102. What is the percent increase in this case?

10. Determine whether the function whose values are in Table 4.16 could be exponential.

Table 4.16

x	1	2	4	5	8	9
$f(x)$	4096	1024	64	16	0.25	0.0625

In Problems 11–14, could the function be linear or exponential or is it neither? Write possible formulas for the linear or exponential functions.

11.

r	1	3	7	15	31
$p(r)$	13	19	31	55	103

12.

x	6	9	12	18	24
$q(x)$	100	110	121	146.41	177.16

13.

x	10	12	15	16	18
$f(x)$	1	2	4	8	16

14.

t	1	2	3	4	5
$g(t)$	512	256	128	64	32

Problems

15. In 2010, the cost of a train ticket from Boston to New York was $95.[22] Assume that the price rises by 7% per year. Make a table showing the price of tickets each year until 2014.

16. Radioactive gallium-67 decays by 1.48% every hour; there are 100 milligrams initially.

    (a) Find a formula for the amount of gallium-67 remaining after t hours.
    (b) How many milligrams are left after 24 hours? After 1 week?

17. A bank pays interest at the nominal rate of 4.2% per year. What is the effective annual rate if compounding is:

(a)   Annual   (b)   Monthly   (c)   Continuous

18. Explain the difference between linear and exponential growth. That is, without writing down any formulas, describe how linear and exponential functions progress differently from one value to the next.

In Problems 19–24, find formulas for the exponential functions satisfying the given conditions.

19. $h(0) = 3$ and $h(1) = 15$

20. $f(3) = -3/8$ and $f(-2) = -12$

---

[22]http://www.amtrak.com, accessed May 23, 2010.

21. $g(1/2) = 4$ and $g(1/4) = 2\sqrt{2}$

22. $g(0) = 5$ and $g(-2) = 10$

23. $g(1.7) = 6$ and $g(2.5) = 4$

24. $f(1) - 4$ and $f(3) - d$

25. Suppose $f(-3) = 5/8$ and $f(2) = 20$. Find a formula for f assuming it is:

    (a) Linear   **(b)** Exponential

For Problems 26–31, find formulas for the exponential functions.

26.

27.

28.

29.

30.

31.

32. Find possible formulas for the functions in Figure 4.42.

Figure 4.42

33. Let $P(t)$ be the population of a country, in millions, t years after 1990, with $P(7) = 3.21$ and $P(13) = 3.75$.

    (a) Find a formula for $P(t)$ assuming it is linear. Describe in words the country's annual population growth given this assumption.

    (b) Find a formula for $P(t)$ assuming it is exponential. Describe in words the country's annual population growth given this assumption.

34. A population has size 100 at time $t = 0$, with t in years.

    (a) If the population grows by 10 people per year, find a formula for the population, P, at time t.

    (b) If the population grows by 10% per year, find a formula for the population, P, at time t.

    (c) Graph both functions on the same axes.

Find the limits in Problems 35–40.

35. $\lim\limits_{x \to \infty} 257(0.93)^x$ **36.** $\lim\limits_{t \to \infty} 5.3e^{-0.12t}$

37. $\lim\limits_{x \to -\infty} (15 - 5e^{3x})$ **38.** $\lim\limits_{t \to -\infty} (21(1.2)^t + 5.1)$

39. $\lim\limits_{x \to \infty} (7.2 - 2e^{3x})$ **40.** $\lim\limits_{x \to -\infty} (5e^{-7x} + 1.5)$

41. In 1940, there were about 10 brown tree snakes per square mile on the island of Guam, and in 2002, there were about 20,000 per square mile.[23] Find an exponential formula for the number, N, of brown tree snakes per square mile on Guam t years after 1940. What was, on average, the annual percent increase in the population during this period?

42. A 2010 Lexus LS costs $64,680.[24] Assume that the car depreciates a total of 42% during its first 5 years.

    (a) Suppose the depreciation is exponential. Find a formula for the value of the car at time t.

[23]*Science News*, Vol. 162, August 10, 2002, p. 85.
[24]http://www.lexus.com, accessed November, 2009.

(b) Suppose instead that the depreciation is linear. Find a formula for the value of the car at time t.

(c) If this were your car and you were trading it in after 4 years, which depreciation model would you prefer (exponential or linear)?

43. Table 4.17 gives the approximate number of cell phone subscribers, S, in the United States.[25]

(a) Explain how you know an exponential function fits the data. Find a formula for S in terms of t, the number of years since 2001.

(b) Interpret the growth rate in terms of cell phone subscribers.

(c) In 2008, there were 262.7 million subscribers. Does this fit the pattern?

Table 4.17

Year	2001	2002	2003	2004	2005	2006
Subscribers (m.)	128.4	140.8	158.7	182.1	207.9	233

44. Find the annual growth rates of a quantity which:

(a) Doubles in size every 7 years

(b) Triples in size every 11 years

(c) Grows by 3% per month

(d) Grows by 18% every 5 months

In Problems 45–48, graph $f(x)$, a function defined for all real numbers and satisfying the condition.

45. $f(x) \to 5$ as $x \to \infty$

46. $f(x) \to 3$ as $x \to \infty$ and $f(x) \to -2$ as $x \to -\infty$

47. $\lim_{x \to -\infty} f(x) = -4$

48. $\lim_{x \to -\infty} f(x) = 0$ and $\lim_{x \to \infty} f(x) = -\infty$

49. The functions $f(x) = (\frac{1}{2})^x$ and $g(x) = 1/x$ are similar in that they both tend toward zero as x becomes large. Using a calculator, determine which function, f or g, approaches zero faster.

In Problems 50–51, graph the function to find horizontal asymptotes.

50. $f(x) = 8 - 2^x$

51. $f(x) = 3^{-x^2} + 2$

52. Without making any calculations, briefly describe the following investments, where t is in years. Be specific.

(a) $V = 2500e^{-0.0434t}$

(b) $V = 4000(1.005)^{12t}$

(c) $V = 8000 \cdot 2^{-t/14}$

(d) $V = 5000 + 250(t - 10)$

53. Without making any calculations, briefly describe in words what the following formulas tell you about the size of the animal populations they describe. Be specific. Note that t is in years.

(a) $P = 5200(1.118)^t$

(b) $P = 4600(1.01)^{12t}$

(c) $P = 3800 \left(\frac{1}{2}\right)^{t/12}$

(d) $P = 8000e^{0.0778t}$

(e) $P = 1675 - 25(t - 30)$

54. Without a calculator, match each of the following formulas to one of the graphs in Figure 4.6.

(a) $y = 8.3e^{-t}$ **(b)** $y = 2.5e^t$ **(c)** $y = -4e^{-t}$

55. If t is in years, the formulas for dollar balances of two different bank accounts are:

$$f(t) = 1100(1.05)^t \quad \text{and} \quad g(t) = 1500e^{0.05t}.$$

(a) Describe in words the bank account modeled by f.

(b) Describe the account modeled by g. State the effective annual yield.

56. Accion is a non-profit microlending organization which makes small loans to entrepreneurs who do not qualify for bank loans.[26] A New York woman who sells clothes from a cart has the choice of a $1000 loan from Accion to be repaid by $1150 a year later and a $1000 loan from a loan shark with an annual interest rate of 22%, compounded annually.

(a) What is the annual interest rate charged by Accion?

(b) To pay off the loan shark for a year's loan of $1000, how much would the woman have to pay?

(c) Which loan is a better deal for the woman? Why?

57. Write $p(x) = \dfrac{7e^{6x} \cdot \sqrt{e} \cdot (2e^x)^{-1}}{10e^{4x}}$ in the form $p(x) = ae^x$. All constants should be expressed exactly.

In Problems 58–59, write each function in standard form. Note that one of them is linear and one exponential.

58. $r(v) = vj^w - 4tj^w + kvj^w$

59. $s(w) = vj^w - 4tj^w + kvj^w$

[25]www.infoplease.com/ipa/A0933563.html, accessed December 22, 2009.
[26]http://www.accionusa.org/, accessed November, 2005.

Problems 60–61 concern ISO A- and B-series paper, commonly used in many countries. The width in millimeters (mm) of a sheet of A_n paper in this series is given by the formula[27]

$$f(n) = 1000 \cdot 2^{-\frac{1}{4}-\frac{n}{2}}.$$

The width $g(n)$ of a sheet of B_n paper is the geometric mean of the widths of A_n paper and the next larger size, A_{n-1} paper. Since the geometric mean of two quantities p and q is the square root of their product, this means

$$g(n) = \sqrt{f(n) \cdot f(n-1)}.$$

60. Evaluate $g(1)$. What does your answer tell you about B-series paper?

61. Show that g is an exponential function by writing it in standard form.

62. The figure gives graphs of two functions, f and g. Explain why not both of these functions can be exponential.

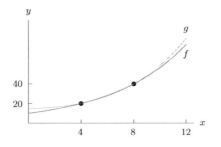

63. Write a paragraph that compares the function $f(x) = a^x$, where $a > 1$, and $g(x) = b^x$, where $0 < b < 1$. Include graphs in your answer.

Problems 64–67 use Figure 4.43, which shows $f(x) = ab^x$ and $g(x) = cd^x$ on three different scales. Their point of intersection is marked.

Figure 4.43

64. Which is larger, a or c?

65. Which is larger, b or d?

66. Rank in order from least to greatest: x_1, x_2, x_3.

67. Match f and g to the graphs labeled (i)–(iv) in (b) and (c).

68. On November 27, 1993, the *New York Times* reported that wildlife biologists have found a direct link between the increase in the human population in Florida and the decline of the local black bear population. From 1953 to 2009, the human population increased, on average, at a rate of 6% per year, while the black bear population decreased at a rate of 6% per year. In 1953 the black bear population was 11,000.

   (a) The 2009 human population of Florida was 16 million. What was the human population in 1953?

   (b) Find the black bear population for 2009.

   (c) Had this trend continued,[28] when would the black bear population have numbered less than 100?

69. **(a)** Using a computer or calculator, graph $f(x) = 2^x$.

   (b) Find the slope of the line tangent to f at $x = 0$ to an accuracy of two decimals. [Hint: Zoom in on the graph until it is indistinguishable from a line and estimate the slope using two points on the graph.]

   (c) Find the slope of the line tangent to $g(x) = 3^x$ at $x = 0$ to an accuracy of two decimals.

   (d) Find b (to two decimals) such that the line tangent to the function $h(x) = b^x$ at $x = 0$ has slope 1.

70. Sales of energy-efficient compact fluorescent lamps in China have been growing approximately exponentially. Table 4.18 shows the sales in millions.[29]

   (a) Use a calculator or computer to find the exponential regression function for sales, S (in millions), as a function of the number of years, t, since 1994.

---

[27]Actual paper sizes are rounded to the nearest mm, so this formula is only approximate. See http://www.cl.cam.ac.uk/˜mgk25/iso-paper.html, accessed February 24, 2008.

[28]Since 1993, the black bear population has in fact remained stable: www.myfwc.com/bear, accessed January 5, 2006.

[29]S. Nadel and Hong, "Market Data on Efficient Lighting," Right Light 6 Conference, Session 8, May, 2005.

(b) Plot the function with the data. Does it appear to fit the data well?

(c) What annual percent growth rate does the exponential model show?

(d) If this growth rate continues, what sales are predicted in the year 2010?

Table 4.18

Year	1994	1996	1998	2000	2002	2003
Sales (millions)	20	30	60	125	295	440

Find possible formulas for the functions in Problems 71–73.

71. V gives the value of an account that begins in year $t = 0$ with \$12,000 and earns 4.2% annual interest, compounded continuously.

72. The exponential function $p(t)$ given that $p(20) = 300$ and $p(50) = 40$.

73. The linear function $q(x)$ whose graph intersects the graph of $y = 5000e^{-x/40}$ at $x = 50$ and $x = 150$.

74. An investment worth $V = \$2500$ in year $t = 0$ earns 4.2% annual interest, compounded continuously. Find a formula for V in terms of t.

75. A population is represented by $P = 12{,}000e^{-0.122t}$. Give the values of a, k, b, and r, where $P = ae^{kt} = ab^t$. What do these values tell you about the population?

76. This problem uses a calculator or computer to explore graphically the value of $(1 + 1/x)^x$ as x gets large.

(a) Graph $y = (1 + 1/x)^x$ for $1 \leq x \leq 10$.

(b) Are the values of y in part (a) increasing or decreasing?

(c) Do the values of y in part (a) appear to approach a limiting value?

(d) Graph $y = (1 + 1/x)^x$, for $1 \leq x \leq 100$, and then for $1 \leq x \leq 1000$. Do the y values appear to approach a limiting value? If so, approximately what is it?

(e) Graph $y = (1 + 1/x)^x$ and $y = e$ on the same axes, for $1 \leq x \leq 10{,}000$. What does the graph suggest?

(f) By checking $x = 10{,}000$, $x = 20{,}000$, and so on, decide how large (as a multiple of 10,000) x should be to give a value of e correct to 4 decimal places.

77. Hong Kong shifted from British to Chinese rule in 1997. Figure 4.44 shows[30] the number of people who emigrated from Hong Kong during each of the years from 1980 to 1992.

(a) Find an exponential function that approximates the data.

(b) What does the model predict about the number of emigrants in 1997?

(c) Briefly explain why this model is or is not useful to predict emigration in the year 2010.

Figure 4.44

78. Before the AIDS epidemic, Botswana[31] had a rapidly growing population, as shown in Table 4.19. In 2005, the population started falling.

(a) Fit an exponential growth model, $P = ab^t$, to this data set, where P is the population in millions and t measures the years since 1975 in 5-year intervals—so $t = 1$ corresponds to 1980. Estimate a and b. Plot the data set and $P = ab^t$ on the same graph.

(b) Starting from 1975, how long does it take for the population of Botswana to double? When is the population of Botswana projected to exceed 214 million, the 1975 population of the US?

Table 4.19

Year	1975	1980	1985	1990
Population (millions)	0.755	0.901	1.078	1.285

Problems 79–80 use Figure 4.45, where t_0 is the t-coordinate of the point of intersection of the graphs. Describe what happens to t_0 if the following changes are made, assuming the other quantities remain the same.

---

[30] Adapted from the *New York Times*, July 5, 1995.
[31] N. Keyfitz, *World Population Growth and Aging* (Chicago: University of Chicago Press), 1990.

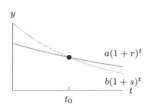

Figure 4.45

79. b is decreased

80. r is increased

81. It is a well-documented fact that the earning power of men is higher than that of women.[32] Table 4.20 gives the median income of year-round full-time workers in the US in dollars.

    (a) Plot the data and connect the points.

    (b) Let t be the year. Construct two functions of the form $W(t) = ae^{b(t-1950)}$, one each for the men's and women's earning power data.

    (c) Graph the two functions from 1950 to 2000 and again from 2000 to 2080.

    (d) Do the graphs in part (c) predict women's salaries will catch up with men's? If so, when?

    (e) Comment on your predictions in part (d).

Table 4.20

Year	1950	1960	1970	1980	1990	2000
Female	953	1261	2237	4920	10,070	16,063
Male	2570	4080	6670	12,530	20,293	28,343

82. According to a letter to the *New York Times* on April 10, 1993, "... the probability of [a driver's] involvement in a single-car accident increases exponentially with increasing levels of blood alcohol." The letter goes on to state that when a driver's blood-alcohol content (BAC) is 0.15, the risk of such an accident is about 25 times greater than for a nondrinker.

    (a) Let p_0 be a nondrinker's probability of being involved in a single-car accident. Let $f(x)$ be the probability of an accident for a driver whose blood alcohol level is x. Find a formula for $f(x)$. (This only makes sense for some values of x.)

    (b) At the time of the letter, the legal definition of intoxication was a BAC of 0.1 or higher. According to your formula for $f(x)$, how many times more likely to be involved in a single-car accident was a driver at the legal limit than a nondrinker?

    (c) Suppose that new legislation is proposed to change the definition of legal intoxication. The new definition states that a person is legally intoxicated when their likelihood of involvement in a single-car accident is three times that of a non-drinker. To what BAC would the new definition of legal intoxication correspond?

Pure water is not perfectly clear—it has a bluish cast—because it absorbs light differently at different wavelengths. The table gives values of the *absorption coefficient* $\mu(\lambda)$, in units of cm^{-1}, as a function of the wavelength λ in nanometers or nm.[33] If light of wavelength λ nanometers (nm) travels through l cm of water, the percent transmitted (without being absorbed) is given by

$$T_\lambda(l) = e^{-\mu(\lambda) \cdot l}.$$

Note that here, T_λ is the name of the function. Answer Problems 83–84.

color	λ	$\mu(\lambda)$	color	λ	$\mu(\lambda)$
violet	400	0.000066	yellow	570	0.000695
indigo	445	0.000075	orange	590	0.001351
blue	475	0.000114	red	650	0.003400
green	510	0.000325	—	—	—

83. What percent of red light will be transmitted after passing through 200 cm of water?

84. What percent of blue light will be transmitted over the same distance?

---

[32]*The World Almanac and Book of Facts 2006*, p. 84.

[33]Note that aside from absorption, optical scattering also plays a role. See http://omlc.ogi.edu/spectra/water/data/pope97.dat, http://eosweb.larc.nasa.gov/EDDOCS/Wavelengths_for_Colors.html, and http://en.wikipedia.org/wiki/Color_of_water, accessed February 29, 2008.

CHECK YOUR UNDERSTANDING

Are the statements in Problems 1–32 true or false? Give an explanation for your answer.

1. Exponential functions are functions that increase or decrease at a constant percent rate.

2. The independent variable in an exponential function is always found in the exponent.

3. If $y = 40(1.05)^t$ then y is an exponential function of t.

4. The following table shows a function that could be exponential.

x	1	2	4	5	6
y	1	2	4	7	11

5. If your salary, S, grows by 4% each year, then $S = S_0(0.04)^t$ where t is in years.

6. If $f(t) = 4(2)^t$ then $f(2) = 64$.

7. If $f(t) = 3(\frac{2}{5})^t$ then f is a decreasing function.

8. If $Q = f(t) = 1000(0.5)^t$ then when $Q = 125, t = 3$.

9. If $Q = f(t) = ab^t$ then a is the initial value of Q.

10. If we are given two data points, we can find a linear function and an exponential function that go through these points.

11. A population that has 1000 members and decreases at 10% per year can be modeled as $P = 1000(0.10)^t$.

12. A positive increasing exponential function always becomes larger than any increasing linear function in the long run.

13. A possible formula for an exponential function that passes through the point $(0, 1)$ and the point $(2, 10)$ is $y = 4.5t + 1$.

14. If a population increases by 50% each year, then in two years it increases by 100%.

15. In the formula $Q = ab^t$, the value of a tells us where the graph crosses the Q-axis.

16. In the formula $Q = ab^t$, if $a > 1$, the graph always rises as we read from left to right.

17. The symbol e represents a constant whose value is approximately 2.71828.

18. If $f(x) \to k$ as $x \to \infty$ we say that the line $y = k$ is a horizontal asymptote.

19. Exponential graphs are always concave up.

20. If there are 110 grams of a substance initially and its decay rate is 3% per minute, then the amount after t minutes is $Q = 110(0.03)^t$ grams.

21. If a population had 200 members at time zero and was growing at 4% per year, then the population size after t years can be expressed as $P = 200(1.04)^t$.

22. If $P = 5e^{0.2t}$, we say the continuous growth rate of the function is 2%.

23. If $P = 4e^{-0.90t}$, we say the continuous growth rate of the function is 10%.

24. If $Q = 3e^{0.2t}$, then when $t = 5, Q = 3$.

25. If $Q = Q_0 e^{kt}$, with Q_0 positive and k negative, then Q is decreasing.

26. If an investment earns 5% compounded monthly, its effective rate will be more than 5%.

27. If a $500 investment earns 6% per year, compounded quarterly, we can find the balance after three years by evaluating the formula $B = 500(1 + \frac{6}{4})^{3 \cdot 4}$.

28. If interest on a $2000 investment is compounded continuously at 3% per year, the balance after five years is found by evaluating the formula $B = 2000e^{(0.03)(5)}$.

29. Investing $10,000 for 20 years at 5% earns more if interest is compounded quarterly than if it is compounded annually.

30. Investing $P for $T years always earns more if interest is compounded continuously than if it is compounded annually.

31. There is no limit to the amount a twenty-year $10,000 investment at 5% interest can earn if the number of times the interest is compounded becomes greater and greater.

32. If you put $1000 into an account that earns 5.5% compounded continuously, then it takes about 18 years for the investment to grow to $2000.

SKILLS REFRESHER FOR CHAPTER 4: EXPONENTS

We list the definition and properties that are used to manipulate exponents.

Definition of Zero, Negative, and Fractional Exponents
If m and n are positive integers:[34]

- $a^0 = 1$
- $a^{-n} = \dfrac{1}{a^n}$
- $a^{1/n} = \sqrt[n]{a}$, the nth root of a
- $a^{m/n} = \sqrt[n]{a^m} = (\sqrt[n]{a})^m$

Properties of Exponents

- $a^m \cdot a^n = a^{m+n}$ For example, $2^4 \cdot 2^3 = (2 \cdot 2 \cdot 2 \cdot 2) \cdot (2 \cdot 2 \cdot 2) = 2^7$.
- $\dfrac{a^m}{a^n} = a^{m-n}, a \neq 0$ For example, $\dfrac{2^4}{2^3} = \dfrac{2 \cdot 2 \cdot 2 \cdot 2}{2 \cdot 2 \cdot 2} = 2^1$.
- $(a^m)^n = a^{mn}$ For example, $(2^3)^2 = 2^3 \cdot 2^3 = 2^6$.
- $(ab)^n = a^n b^n$
- $\left(\dfrac{a}{b}\right)^n = \dfrac{a^n}{b^n}, \quad b \neq 0$

Be aware of the following notational conventions:

$$ab^n = a(b^n), \qquad \text{but } ab^n \neq (ab)^n,$$
$$-b^n = -(b^n), \qquad \text{but } -b^n \neq (-b)^n,$$
$$-ab^n = (-a)(b^n).$$

For example, $-2^4 = -(2^4) = -16$, but $(-2)^4 = (-2)(-2)(-2)(-2) = +16$. Also, be sure to realize that for $n \neq 1$,

$$(a+b)^n \neq a^n + b^n \qquad \text{Power of a sum} \neq \text{Sum of powers.}$$

Example 1   Evaluate without a calculator:

(a) $(27)^{2/3}$ (b) $(4)^{-3/2}$ (c) $8^{1/3} - 1^{1/3}$

Solution   (a) We have $(27)^{2/3} = \sqrt[3]{27^2} = \sqrt[3]{729} = 9$, or, equivalently, $(27)^{2/3} = \left(27^{1/3}\right)^2 = \left(\sqrt[3]{27}\right)^2 = 3^2 = 9$.

(b) We have $(4)^{-3/2} = (2)^{-3} = \dfrac{1}{2^3} = \dfrac{1}{8}$.

(c) We have $8^{1/3} - 1^{1/3} = 2 - 1 = 1$.

---

[34] We assume that the base is restricted to the values for which the power is defined.

Example 2   Use the rules of exponents to simplify the following:

(a) $\dfrac{100x^2y^4}{5x^3y^2}$

(b) $\dfrac{y^4(x^3y^{-2})^2}{2x^{-1}}$

(c) $\sqrt[3]{-8x^6}$

(d) $\left(\dfrac{M^{1/5}}{3N^{-1/2}}\right)^2$

Solution   (a) We have

$$\frac{100x^2y^4}{5x^3y^2} = 20(x^{2-3})(y^{4-2}) = 20x^{-1}y^2 = \frac{20y^2}{x}.$$

(b) We have

$$\frac{y^4\left(x^3y^{-2}\right)^2}{2x^{-1}} = \frac{y^4x^6y^{-4}}{2x^{-1}} = \frac{y^{(4-4)}x^{(6-(-1))}}{2} = \frac{y^0x^7}{2} = \frac{x^7}{2}.$$

(c) We have

$$\sqrt[3]{-8x^6} = \sqrt[3]{-8} \cdot \sqrt[3]{x^6} = -2x^2.$$

(d) We have

$$\left(\frac{M^{1/5}}{3N^{-1/2}}\right)^2 = \frac{\left(M^{1/5}\right)^2}{\left(3N^{-1/2}\right)^2} = \frac{M^{2/5}}{3^2N^{-1}} = \frac{M^{2/5}N}{9}.$$

Example 3   Solve for x:

(a) $\dfrac{10x^7}{4x^2} = 37$

(b) $\dfrac{x^2}{3x^5} = 10$

(c) $\sqrt{9x^5} = 10$

Solution   (a) We have

$$\frac{10x^7}{4x^2} = 37$$
$$2.5x^5 = 37$$
$$x^5 = 14.8$$
$$x = (14.8)^{1/5} = 1.714.$$

(b) We have

$$\frac{x^2}{3x^5} = 10$$
$$\frac{1}{3}x^{-3} = 10$$
$$\frac{1}{x^3} = 30$$
$$x^3 = \frac{1}{30}$$
$$x = \left(\frac{1}{30}\right)^{1/3} = 0.322.$$

(c) We have

$$\sqrt{9x^5} = 10$$
$$3x^{5/2} = 10$$
$$x^{5/2} = \frac{10}{3}$$
$$x = \left(\frac{10}{3}\right)^{2/5} = 1.619.$$

Exercises to Skills for Chapter 4

For Exercises 1–33, evaluate without a calculator.

1. $(-5)^2$ **2.** 11^2 **3.** 10^4

4. $(-1)^{13}$ **5.** $\dfrac{5^3}{5^2}$ **6.** $\dfrac{10^8}{10^5}$

7. $\dfrac{6^4}{6^4}$ **8.** $\sqrt{4}$ **9.** $\sqrt{4^2}$

10. $\sqrt{4^4}$ **11.** $\sqrt{(-4)^2}$ **12.** $\dfrac{1}{7^{-2}}$

13. $\dfrac{2^7}{2^3}$ **14.** $(-1)^{445}$ **15.** -11^2

16. $\left(5^0\right)^3$ **17.** $2.1\left(10^3\right)$ **18.** $16^{1/2}$

19. $16^{1/4}$ **20.** $16^{3/4}$ **21.** $16^{5/4}$

22. $16^{5/2}$ **23.** $100^{5/2}$ **24.** $\sqrt{(-4)^2}$

25. $(-1)^3\sqrt{36}$ **26.** $(0.04)^{1/2}$ **27.** $(-8)^{2/3}$

28. 3^{-1} **29.** $3^{-3/2}$ **30.** 25^{-1}

31. 25^{-2} **32.** $(1/27)^{-1/3}$ **33.** $(0.125)^{1/3}$

Simplify the expressions in Exercises 34–55 and leave without radicals if possible. Assume all variables are positive.

34. $\sqrt{x^4}$ **35.** $\sqrt{y^8}$

36. $\sqrt{w^8 z^4}$ **37.** $\sqrt{x^5 y^4}$

38. $\sqrt{49w^9}$ **39.** $\sqrt{25x^3 z^4}$

40. $\sqrt{r^2}$ **41.** $\sqrt{r^3}$

42. $\sqrt{r^4}$ **43.** $\sqrt{64s^7}$

44. $\sqrt{50x^4 y^6}$ **45.** $\sqrt{48u^{10} v^{12} y^5}$

46. $\sqrt{6s^2 t^3 v^5}\sqrt{6st^5 v^3}$ **47.** $\left(S\sqrt{16xt^2}\right)^2$

48. $\sqrt{e^{2x}}$ **49.** $(3AB)^{-1}\left(A^2 B^{-1}\right)^2$

50. $e^{kt}\cdot e^3\cdot e$ **51.** $\sqrt{M+2}(2+M)^{3/2}$

52. $\left(y^{-2}e^y\right)^2$ **53.** $\dfrac{a^{n+1}3^{n+1}}{a^n 3^n}$

54. $\left(a^{-1}+b^{-1}\right)^{-1}$

55. $\left(\dfrac{35(2b+1)^9}{7(2b+1)^{-1}}\right)^2$ (Do not expand $(2b+1)^9$.)

If possible, evaluate the quantities in Exercises 56–64. Check your answers with a calculator.

56. $(-32)^{3/5}$ **57.** $-32^{3/5}$ **58.** $-625^{3/4}$

59. $(-625)^{3/4}$ **60.** $(-1728)^{4/3}$ **61.** $64^{-3/2}$

62. $-64^{3/2}$ **63.** $(-64)^{3/2}$ **64.** $81^{5/4}$

In Exercises 65–66, solve for x.

65. $7x^4 = 20x^2$ **66.** $2(x+2)^3 = 100$

In Exercises 67–68, use algebra to find the point of intersection.

67.

68.

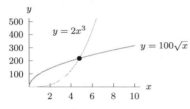

Are the statements in Exercises 69–74 true or false?

69. $x^2y^5 = (xy)^{10}$

70. $5u^2 + 5u^3 = 10u^5$

71. $(3r)^2 9s^2 = 81r^2s^2$

72. $\sqrt[3]{-64b^3c^6} = -4bc^2$

73. $-4w^2 - 3w^3 = -w^2(4 + 3w)$

74. $(u + v)^{-1} = \dfrac{1}{u} + \dfrac{1}{v}$

Solve the equations in Exercises 75–76 in terms of r and s, given that

$$2^r = 5 \quad \text{and} \quad 2^s = 7.$$

75. $2^x = 35$.

76. $2^x = 140$.

Let $2^a = 5$ and $2^b = 7$. Using exponent rules, solve the equations in Exercises 77–82 in terms of a and b.

77. $5^x = 32$

78. $7^x = \dfrac{1}{8}$

79. $25^x = 64$

80. $14^x = 16$

81. $5^x = 7$

82. $0.4^x = 49$

178

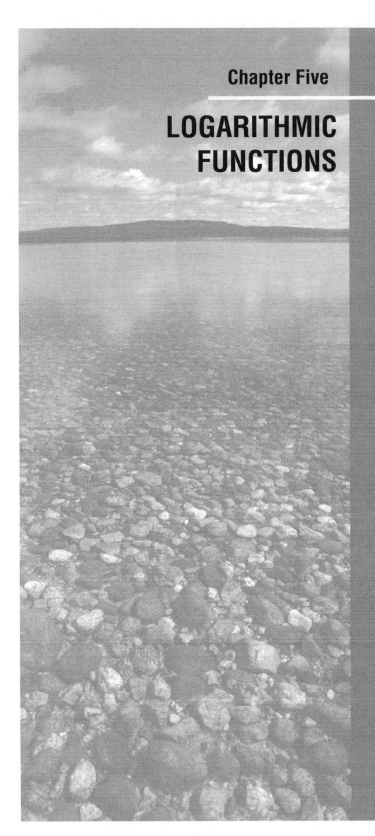

Chapter Five

LOGARITHMIC FUNCTIONS

Contents

5.1 LOGARITHMS AND THEIR PROPERTIES

What Is a Logarithm?

Suppose that a population grows according to the formula $P = 10^t$, where P is the colony size at time t, in hours. When will the population be 2500? We want to solve the following equation for t:

$$10^t = 2500.$$

In Section 4.2, we used a graphical method to approximate t. This time, we introduce a function that returns precisely the exponent of 10 we need.

Since $10^3 = 1000$ and $10^4 = 10,000$, and $1000 < 2500 < 10,000$, the exponent we are looking for is between 3 and 4. But how do we find the exponent exactly?

To answer this question, we define the *common logarithm function*, or simply the *log function*, written $\log_{10} x$, or $\log x$, as follows.

If x is a positive number,

$$\log x \text{ is the exponent of 10 that gives } x.$$

In other words, if

$$y = \log x \quad \text{then} \quad 10^y = x.$$

For example, $\log 100 = 2$, because 2 is the exponent of 10 that gives 100, or $10^2 = 100$.

To solve the equation $10^t = 2500$, we must find the power of 10 that gives 2500. Using the log button on a calculator, we can approximate this exponent. We find

$$\log 2500 \approx 3.398, \quad \text{which means that} \quad 10^{3.398} \approx 2500.$$

As predicted, this exponent is between 3 and 4. The precise exponent is $\log 2500$; the approximate value is 3.398. Thus, it takes roughly 3.4 hours for the population to reach 2500.

Example 1   Rewrite the following statements using exponents instead of logs.

    (a) $\log 100 = 2$ (b) $\log 0.01 = -2$ (c) $\log 30 = 1.477$

Solution   For each statement, we use the fact that if $y = \log x$ then $10^y = x$.

    (a) $2 = \log 100$ means that $10^2 = 100$.

    (b) $-2 = \log 0.01$ means that $10^{-2} = 0.01$.

    (c) $1.477 = \log 30$ means that $10^{1.477} = 30$. (Actually, this is only an approximation. Using a calculator, we see that $10^{1.477} = 29.9916\ldots$ and that $\log 30 = 1.47712125\ldots$.)

Example 2   Rewrite the following statements using logs instead of exponents.

    (a) $10^5 = 100,000$ (b) $10^{-4} = 0.0001$ (c) $10^{0.8} = 6.3096$.

Solution   For each statement, we use the fact that if $10^y = x$, then $y = \log x$.
(a) $10^5 = 100{,}000$ means that $\log 100{,}000 = 5$.
(b) $10^{-4} = 0.0001$ means that $\log 0.0001 = -4$.
(c) $10^{0.8} = 6.3096$ means that $\log 6.3096 = 0.8$. (This, too, is only an approximation because $10^{0.8}$ actually equals $6.30957344\ldots$.)

Logarithms Are Exponents

Note that logarithms are just exponents! Thinking in terms of exponents is often a good way to answer a logarithm problem.

Example 3   Without a calculator, evaluate the following, if possible:

(a) $\log 1$ (b) $\log 10$ (c) $\log 1{,}000{,}000$

(d) $\log 0.001$ (e) $\log \dfrac{1}{\sqrt{10}}$ (f) $\log(-100)$

Solution   (a) We have $\log 1 = 0$, since $10^0 = 1$.
(b) We have $\log 10 = 1$, since $10^1 = 10$.
(c) Since $1{,}000{,}000 = 10^6$, the exponent of 10 that gives $1{,}000{,}000$ is 6. Thus, $\log 1{,}000{,}000 = 6$.
(d) Since $0.001 = 10^{-3}$, the exponent of 10 that gives 0.001 is -3. Thus, $\log 0.001 = -3$.
(e) Since $1/\sqrt{10} = 10^{-1/2}$, the exponent of 10 that gives $1/\sqrt{10}$ is $-\frac{1}{2}$. Thus $\log(1/\sqrt{10}) = -\frac{1}{2}$.
(f) Since 10 to any power is positive, -100 cannot be written as a power of 10. Thus, $\log(-100)$ is undefined.

Logarithmic and Exponential Functions Are Inverses

The operation of taking a logarithm "undoes" the exponential function; the logarithm and the exponential are inverse functions. For example, $\log(10^6) = 6$ and $10^{\log 6} = 6$. In particular,

$$
\begin{array}{l}
\text{For any } N, \\
\qquad \log(10^N) = N \\
\text{and for } N > 0, \\
\qquad 10^{\log N} = N.
\end{array}
$$

Example 4   Evaluate without a calculator: (a) $\log\left(10^{8.5}\right)$ (b) $10^{\log 2.7}$ (c) $10^{\log(x+3)}$

Solution   Using $\log(10^N) = N$ and $10^{\log N} = N$, we have:
(a) $\log\left(10^{8.5}\right) = 8.5$ (b) $10^{\log 2.7} = 2.7$ (c) $10^{\log(x+3)} = x + 3$
You can check the first two results on a calculator.

Properties of Logarithms

In Chapter 4, we saw how to solve exponential equations such as $100 \cdot 2^t = 337{,}000{,}000$, graphically. To use logarithms to solve these equations, we use the properties of logarithms, which are justified on page 184.

Properties of the Common Logarithm
- By definition, $y = \log x$ means $10^y = x$.
- In particular,
$$\log 1 = 0 \quad \text{and} \quad \log 10 = 1.$$
- The functions 10^x and $\log x$ are inverses, so they "undo" each other:
$$\log(10^x) = x \qquad \text{for all } x,$$
$$10^{\log x} = x \qquad \text{for } x > 0.$$
- For a and b both positive and any value of t,
$$\log(ab) = \log a + \log b$$
$$\log\left(\frac{a}{b}\right) = \log a - \log b$$
$$\log(b^t) = t \cdot \log b.$$

We can now use logarithms to solve the equation that we solved graphically in Section 4.2.

Example 5   Solve $100 \cdot 2^t = 337{,}000{,}000$ for t.

Solution   Dividing both sides of the equation by 100 gives
$$2^t = 3{,}370{,}000.$$
Taking logs of both sides gives
$$\log\left(2^t\right) = \log(3{,}370{,}000).$$
Since $\log(2^t) = t \cdot \log 2$, we have
$$t \log 2 = \log(3{,}370{,}000),$$
so, solving for t, we have
$$t = \frac{\log(3{,}370{,}000)}{\log 2} = 21.684.$$
In Example 2 on page 151, we found the graphical approximation of between 21 and 22 days as the time for the Yonkers fine to exceed the city's annual budget.

The Natural Logarithm

When e is used as the base for exponential functions, computations are easier with the use of another logarithm function, called log base e. The log base e is used so frequently that it has its own notation: $\ln x$, read as the *natural log of* x. We make the following definition:

For $x > 0$,

$$\ln x \text{ is the power of } e \text{ that gives } x$$

or, in symbols,

$$\ln x - y \quad \text{means} \quad e^y = x,$$

and y is called the **natural logarithm** of x.

Just as the functions 10^x and $\log x$ are inverses, so are e^x and $\ln x$. The function $\ln x$ has similar properties to the common log function:

Properties of the Natural Logarithm
- By definition, $y = \ln x$ means $x = e^y$.
- In particular,

$$\ln 1 = 0 \quad \text{and} \quad \ln e = 1.$$

- The functions e^x and $\ln x$ are inverses, so they "undo" each other:

$$\ln(e^x) = x \qquad \text{for all } x$$
$$e^{\ln x} = x \qquad \text{for } x > 0.$$

- For a and b both positive and any value of t,

$$\ln(ab) = \ln a + \ln b$$
$$\ln\left(\frac{a}{b}\right) = \ln a - \ln b$$
$$\ln(b^t) = t \cdot \ln b.$$

Example 6 Solve for x:

(a) $5e^{2x} = 50$ (b) $3^x = 100$.

Solution   (a) We first divide both sides by 5 to obtain

$$e^{2x} = 10.$$

Taking the natural log of both sides, we have

$$\ln(e^{2x}) = \ln 10$$
$$2x = \ln 10$$
$$x = \frac{\ln 10}{2} \approx 1.151.$$

(b) Taking natural logs of both sides,

$$\ln(3^x) = \ln 100$$
$$x \ln 3 = \ln 100$$
$$x = \frac{\ln 100}{\ln 3} \approx 4.192.$$

For more practice with logarithms, see the Skills Review on page 219.

Misconceptions and Calculator Errors Involving Logs

It is important to know how to use the properties of logarithms. It is equally important to recognize statements that are *not* true. Beware of the following:

- $\log(a + b)$ is not the same as $\log a + \log b$
- $\log(a - b)$ is not the same as $\log a - \log b$
- $\log(ab)$ is not the same as $(\log a)(\log b)$
- $\log\left(\dfrac{a}{b}\right)$ is not the same as $\dfrac{\log a}{\log b}$
- $\log\left(\dfrac{1}{a}\right)$ is not the same as $\dfrac{1}{\log a}$.

There are no formulas to simplify either $\log(a+b)$ or $\log(a-b)$. Also the expression $\log 5x^2$ is not the same as $2 \cdot \log 5x$, because the exponent, 2, applies only to the x and not to the 5. However, it is correct to write

$$\log 5x^2 = \log 5 + \log x^2 = \log 5 + 2\log x.$$

Using a calculator to evaluate expressions like $\log(\frac{17}{3})$ requires care. On some calculators, entering $\log 17/3$ gives 0.410, which is incorrect. This is because the calculator assumes that you mean $(\log 17)/3$, which is not the same as $\log(17/3)$. Notice also that

$$\frac{\log 17}{\log 3} \approx \frac{1.230}{0.477} \approx 2.579,$$

which is not the same as either $(\log 17)/3$ or $\log(17/3)$. Thus, the following expressions are all different:

$$\log \frac{17}{3} \approx 0.753, \qquad \frac{\log 17}{3} \approx 0.410, \qquad \text{and} \qquad \frac{\log 17}{\log 3} \approx 2.579.$$

Justification of $\log(a \cdot b) = \log a + \log b$ and $\log(a/b) = \log a - \log b$

If a and b are both positive, we can write $a = 10^m$ and $b = 10^n$, so $\log a = m$ and $\log b = n$. Then, the product $a \cdot b$ can be written

$$a \cdot b = 10^m \cdot 10^n = 10^{m+n}.$$

Therefore $m + n$ is the power of 10 needed to give $a \cdot b$, so

$$\log(a \cdot b) = m + n,$$

which gives

$$\log(a \cdot b) = \log a + \log b.$$

Similarly, the quotient a/b can be written as

$$\frac{a}{b} = \frac{10^m}{10^n} = 10^{m-n}.$$

Therefore $m - n$ is the power of 10 needed to give a/b, so

$$\log\left(\frac{a}{b}\right) = m - n,$$

and thus

$$\boxed{\log\left(\frac{a}{b}\right) = \log a - \log b.}$$

Justification of $\log(b^t) = t \cdot \log b$

Suppose that b is positive, so we can write $b = 10^k$ for some value of k. Then

$$b^t = (10^k)^t.$$

We have rewritten the expression b^t so that the base is a power of 10. Using a property of exponents, we can write $(10^k)^t$ as 10^{kt}, so

$$b^t = (10^k)^t = 10^{kt}.$$

Therefore kt is the power of 10 which gives b^t, so

$$\log(b^t) = kt.$$

But since $b = 10^k$, we know $k = \log b$. This means

$$\log(b^t) = (\log b)t = t \cdot \log b.$$

Thus, for $b > 0$ we have

$$\boxed{\log\left(b^t\right) = t \cdot \log b.}$$

Exercises and Problems for Section 5.1

Skill Refresher

Without using logs or a calculator, solve the equations in Exercises S1–S10 if possible.

S1. $10^x = 1,000,000$ **S2.** $10^t = 0.01$

S3. $e^z = \sqrt{e^3}$ **S4.** $10^x = 1$

S5. $e^w = 0$ **S6.** $e^{3x} = \dfrac{1}{e^5}$

S7. $\sqrt{e^{9t}} = e^7$ **S8.** $10^{-x} = -1,000$

S9. $10^{2t} = \sqrt[4]{0.1}$ **S10.** $e^{3x} = \sqrt[3]{e^5}$

Exercises

Rewrite the statements in Exercises 1–6 using exponents instead of logs.

1. $\log 19 = 1.279$ **2.** $\log 4 = 0.602$

3. $\ln 26 = 3.258$ **4.** $\ln(0.646) = -0.437$

5. $\log P = t$ **6.** $\ln q = z$

Rewrite the statements in Exercises 7–10 using logs.

7. $10^8 = 100,000,000$ **8.** $e^{-4} = 0.0183$

9. $10^v = \alpha$ **10.** $e^a = b$

11. Evaluate without a calculator.

  (a) $\log 1000$ (b) $\log \sqrt{1000}$ (c) $\log(10^0)$

  (d) $\log \sqrt{10}$ (e) $\log(10^5)$ (f) $\log(10^2)$

  (g) $\log\left(\dfrac{1}{\sqrt{10}}\right)$ (h) $10^{\log 100}$ (i) $10^{\log 1}$

  (j) $10^{\log(0.01)}$

12. Evaluate without a calculator.

  (a) $\ln 1$ (b) $\ln e^0$ (c) $\ln e^5$

  (d) $\ln \sqrt{e}$ (e) $e^{\ln 2}$ (f) $\ln\left(\dfrac{1}{\sqrt{e}}\right)$

Solve the equations in Exercises 13–18 using logs.

13. $2^x = 11$

14. $(1.45)^x = 25$

15. $e^{0.12x} = 100$

16. $10 = 22(0.87)^q$

17. $48 = 17(2.3)^w$

18. $2/7 = (0.6)^{2t}$

Problems

19. Express the following in terms of x without logs.

  (a) $\log 100^x$ **(b)** $1000^{\log x}$ **(c)** $\log 0.001^x$

20. Express the following in terms of x without natural logs.

  (a) $\ln e^{2x}$

  (b) $e^{\ln(3x+2)}$

  (c) $\ln\left(\dfrac{1}{e^{5x}}\right)$

  (d) $\ln\sqrt{e^x}$

21. Evaluate the following pairs of expressions without using a calculator. What do you notice?

  (a) $\log(10 \cdot 100)$ and $\log 10 + \log 100$

  (b) $\log(100 \cdot 1000)$ and $\log 100 + \log 1000$

  (c) $\log\left(\dfrac{10}{100}\right)$ and $\log 10 - \log 100$

  (d) $\log\left(\dfrac{100}{1000}\right)$ and $\log 100 - \log 1000$

  (e) $\log(10^2)$ and $2\log 10$

  (f) $\log(10^3)$ and $3\log 10$

22. **(a)** Write the general formulas reflected in what you observed in Problem 21.

  (b) Apply these formulas to rewrite $\log\left(\dfrac{AB}{C}\right)^p$ at least two different ways.

23. True or false?

  (a) $\log AB = \log A + \log B$

  (b) $\dfrac{\log A}{\log B} = \log A - B$

  (c) $\log A \log B = \log A + \log B$

  (d) $p \cdot \log A = \log A^p$

  (e) $\log\sqrt{x} = \frac{1}{2}\log x$

  (f) $\sqrt{\log x} = \log(x^{1/2})$

Use properties of logarithms to solve for x in Problems 24–29. Assume a, b, M, and N are constants.

24. $\log(3 \cdot 2^x) = 8$

25. $\ln(25(1.05)^x) = 6$

26. $\ln(ab^x) = M$

27. $\log(MN^x) = a$

28. $\ln(3x^2) = 8$

29. $\log(5x^3) = 2$

30. A graph of $P = 25(1.075)^t$ is given in Figure 5.1.

  (a) What is the initial value of P (when $t = 0$)? What is the percent growth rate?

  (b) Use the graph to estimate the value of t when $P = 100$.

(c) Use logs to find the exact value of t when $P = 100$.

Figure 5.1

31. A graph of $Q = 10e^{-0.15t}$ is given in Figure 5.2.

  (a) What is the initial value of Q (when $t = 0$)? What is the continuous percent decay rate?

  (b) Use the graph to estimate the value of t when $Q = 2$.

  (c) Use logs to find the exact value of t when $Q = 2$.

Figure 5.2

32. Let $u = \log 2$ and $v = \log 3$. Evaluate the following expressions in terms of u and/or v. For example, $\log 9 = \log(3^2) = 2\log 3 = 2v$.

  (a) $\log 6$ **(b)** $\log 0.08$ **(c)** $\log\sqrt{\frac{3}{2}}$ **(d)** $\log 5$

33. Without using a calculator, write the following quantities in terms of $\log 15$ and/or $\log 5$.

  (a) $\log 3$ **(b)** $\log 25$ **(c)** $\log 75$

34. Find a possible formula for the exponential function S in Figure 5.3, if $R(x) = 5.1403(1.1169)^x$.

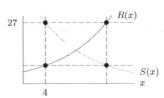

Figure 5.3

In Problems 35–51, solve the equations exactly for x or t.

35. $91 = 46(1.1)^x$

36. $84(0.74)^t = 38$

37. $e^{0.044t} = 6$

38. $200 \cdot 2^{t/5} = 355.$

39. $e^{x+4} = 10$

40. $e^{x+5} = 7 \cdot 2^x$

41. $0.4(\frac{1}{3})^{3x} = 7 \cdot 2^{-x}$

42. $\log_3 3^{5x+1} = 2$

43. $400e^{0.1x} = 500e^{0.08x}$

44. $6000 \left(\frac{1}{2}\right)^{t/15} = 1000$

45. $e^{x+4} = 10$

46. $ab^x = c$

47. $Pe^{kx} = Q$

48. $58e^{4t+1} = 30$

49. $\log(2x + 5) \cdot \log(9x^2) = 0$

50. $\log(1 - x) - \log(1 + x) = 2$

51. $\log(2x + 5) \cdot \log(9x^2) = 0$

52. Solve each of the following equations exactly for x.

(a) $e^{2x} + e^{2x} = 1$ (b) $2e^{3x} + e^{3x} = b$

53. If we square a positive quantity n, we double its log: $\log(n^2) = 2\log n$. Briefly describe what happens to the log when we double a positive quantity n.

54. Consider the exponential function $Q = r \cdot s^t$. Letting $q = \ln Q$, show that q is a linear function of t by writing it in the form $q = b + mt$. State the values of m and b.

55. The *arithmetic mean* of two numbers is half their sum, and the *geometric mean* is the square root of their product. Using log properties, show how we can think of the log of the geometric mean of v and w as the arithmetic mean of two related numbers, p and q.

56. Because they are so large, it is impossible to compare directly the two numbers[1]

$$A = 2^{2^{2^{83}}} \quad \text{and} \quad B = 3^{3^{3^{52}}}.$$

Instead, first simplify $\ln(\ln A)$ and $\ln(\ln B)$, and then use a calculator to determine which is larger, A or B.

57. Both of these numbers are slightly larger than 1:

$$A = 5^{3^{-47}} \quad \text{and} \quad B = 7^{5^{-32}}.$$

Which is larger? Explain your reasoning.

5.2 LOGARITHMS AND EXPONENTIAL MODELS

The log function is often useful when answering questions about exponential models. Logarithms "undo" exponentials—because the log is the inverse of the exponential function—so logs are used to solve many exponential equations.

Example 1   In Example 3 on page 151 we solved the equation $200(0.886^t) = 25$ graphically, where t is in thousands of years. We found that a 200 microgram sample of carbon-14 decays to 25 micrograms in approximately 17,200 years. Now solve $200(0.886)^t = 25$ using logarithms.

Solution   First, isolate the power on one side of the equation

$$200(0.886^t) = 25$$
$$0.886^t = 0.125.$$

---

[1] Adapted from Robert P. Munafo's website on large numbers. These numbers are given as examples of Class-4 numbers. A Class-3 number is too large to be evaluated exactly on a computer; a Class-4 number is one whose *logarithm* is too large to be evaluated exactly. See http://www.mrob.com/pub/index.html, accessed April 7, 2008.

Take the log of both sides, and use the fact that $\log(0.886^t) = t \log 0.886$. Then

$$\log(0.886^t) = \log 0.125$$
$$t \log 0.886 = \log 0.125,$$

so

$$t = \frac{\log 0.125}{\log 0.886} \approx 17.180 \text{ thousand years.}$$

This answer is close to the value we found from the graph, 17,200.

Example 2   The US population, P, in millions, is currently growing according to the formula[2]

$$P = 299e^{0.009t},$$

where t is in years since 2006. When is the population predicted to reach 350 million?

Solution   We want to solve the following equation for t:

$$299e^{0.009t} = 350.$$

Dividing by 299 gives

$$e^{0.009t} = \frac{350}{299},$$

so $0.009t$ is the power of e which gives $350/299$. Thus, by the definition of the natural log,

$$0.009t = \ln\left(\frac{350}{299}\right).$$

Solving for t and evaluating $\ln(350/299)$ on a calculator gives

$$t = \frac{\ln(350/299)}{0.009} = 17.5 \text{ years.}$$

The US population is predicted to reach 350 million during the year 2024.

Example 3   The population of City A begins with 50,000 people and grows at 3.5% per year. The population of City B begins with a larger population of 250,000 people but grows at the slower rate of 1.6% per year. Assuming that these growth rates hold constant, will the population of City A ever catch up to the population of City B? If so, when?

Solution   If t is time measured in years and P_A and P_B are the populations of these two cities, then

$$P_A = 50{,}000(1.035)^t \quad \text{and} \quad P_B = 250{,}000(1.016)^t.$$

We want to solve the equation

$$50{,}000(1.035)^t = 250{,}000(1.016)^t.$$

We first get the exponential terms together by dividing both sides of the equation by $50{,}000(1.016)^t$:

$$\frac{(1.035)^t}{(1.016)^t} = \frac{250{,}000}{50{,}000} = 5.$$

Since $\dfrac{a^t}{b^t} = \left(\dfrac{a}{b}\right)^t$, this gives

$$\left(\frac{1.035}{1.016}\right)^t = 5.$$

_____

[2]Based on data from www.census.gov and www.cia.gov/cia/publications/factbook, accessed July 31, 2006.

Taking logs of both sides and using $\log b^t = t \log b$, we have

$$\log \left(\frac{1.035}{1.016} \right)^t = \log 5$$

$$t \log \left(\frac{1.035}{1.016} \right) = \log 5$$

$$t = \frac{\log 5}{\log(1.035/1.016)} \approx 86.865.$$

Thus, the cities' populations will be equal in just under 87 years. To check this, notice that when $t = 86.865$,

$$P_A = 50{,}000(1.035)^{86.865} = 992{,}575$$

and

$$P_B = 250{,}000(1.016)^{86.865} = 992{,}572.$$

The answers are not exactly equal because we rounded off the value of t. Rounding can introduce significant errors, especially when logs and exponentials are involved. Using $t = 86.86480867$, the computed values of P_A and P_B agree to three decimal places.

Doubling Time

Eventually, any exponentially growing quantity doubles, or increases by 100%. Since its percent growth rate is constant, the time it takes for the quantity to grow by 100% is also a constant. This time period is called the *doubling time*.

Example 4 (a) Find the time needed for the turtle population described by the function $P = 175(1.145)^t$ to double its initial size.

(b) How long does this population take to quadruple its initial size? To increase by a factor of 8?

Solution (a) The initial size is 175 turtles; doubling this gives 350 turtles. We need to solve the following equation for t:

$$175(1.145)^t = 350$$

$$1.145^t = 2$$

$$\log \left(1.145^t \right) = \log 2$$

$$t \cdot \log 1.145 = \log 2$$

$$t = \frac{\log 2}{\log 1.145} \approx 5.119 \text{ years.}$$

We check this by noting that

$$175(1.145)^{5.119} = 350,$$

which is double the initial population. In fact, at any time it takes the turtle population about 5.119 years to double in size.

(b) Since the population function is exponential, it increases by 100% every 5.119 years. Thus it doubles its initial size in the first 5.119 years, quadruples its initial size in two 5.119 year periods, or 10.238 years, and increases by a factor of 8 in three 5.119 year periods, or 15.357 years. We check this by noting that

$$175(1.145)^{10.238} = 700,$$

or 4 times the initial size, and that

$$175(1.145)^{15.357} = 1400,$$

or 8 times the initial size.

Example 5 A population doubles in size every 20 years. What is its continuous growth rate?

Solution We are not given the initial size of the population, but we can solve this problem without that information. Let the symbol P_0 represent the initial size of the population. We have $P = P_0 e^{kt}$. After 20 years, $P = 2P_0$, and so

$$P_0 e^{k \cdot 20} = 2P_0$$
$$e^{20k} = 2$$
$$20k = \ln 2 \qquad \text{Taking ln of both sides}$$
$$k = \frac{\ln 2}{20} \approx 0.03466.$$

Thus, the population grows at the continuous rate of 3.466% per year.

Example 6 Interest rates in Brazil have fluctuated widely since 1995: investments in Brazil in different years were expected to double in value at wildly different rates.[3] The Brazilian currency is the real.

(a) An investment purchased in May 1995 has a value, V, in reals, t years later, given by

$$V = 100{,}000 \cdot 2^t.$$

  (i) How much was the investment worth in May 1996? 1997? 1998?
  (ii) What is the doubling time?

(b) An investment purchased in January 2009 is expected to have value, Z, in reals, t years later, given by

$$Z = 100{,}000 \cdot 2^{t/6}.$$

  (i) How much is it expected to be worth in January 2015? 2021?
  (ii) What is the doubling time?

(c) Suppose an investment's value t years after 2011 is predicted to be $100{,}000 \cdot 2^{t/n}$.

  (i) How much is the investment expected to be worth after n years?
  (ii) What is its doubling time?

Solution (a) (i) May 1996 is one year after the investment began, so $t = 1$, and

$$V = 100{,}000 \cdot 2^1 = 200{,}000.$$

May 1997 is two years after the investment began, so $t = 2$, and

$$V = 100{,}000 \cdot 2^2 = 400{,}000.$$

May 1998 is three years after the investment began, so $t = 3$, and

$$V = 100{,}000 \cdot 2^3 = 800{,}000.$$

  (ii) The value of the investment, which started at 100,000 reals, doubles each year, so the doubling time is 1 year. Since the formula is

$$V = 100{,}000 \cdot 2^t = 100{,}000(1 + 1)^t,$$

the growth rate is $1 = 100\%$ per year.

[3] www.latin-focus.com/latinfocus/countries/brazil/brainter.htm, accessed January 10, 2010.

    (b) (i) January 2015 is six years after the investment begins, so $t = 6$, and $t/6 = 1$, giving

$$Z = 100{,}000 \cdot 2^1 = 200{,}000.$$

             January 2021 is twelve years after the investment begins, so $t = 12$, and $t/6 = 2$, giving

$$Z - 100{,}000 \cdot 2^2 = 400{,}000.$$

      (ii) Note that the value of the investment doubles every 6 years, so the doubling time is 6 years. Since $Z = 100{,}000 \cdot 2^{t/6}$, when $t = 6$, the growth factor is $2^{6/6} = 2$, as expected.

    (c) (i) After n years, the investment is worth $100{,}000 \cdot 2^{n/n} = 100{,}000 \cdot 2^1 = 200{,}000$.

      (ii) We see that the value of the investment doubles after the first n years, so the doubling time is n years. Algebraically, we see that when $t = n$, the growth factor becomes

$$2^{t/n} = 2^{n/n} = 2^1 = 2,$$

    so we see that the investment doubles in n years.

Half-Life

Just as an exponentially growing quantity doubles in a fixed amount of time, an exponentially decaying quantity decreases by a factor of 2 in a fixed amount of time, called the *half-life* of the quantity.

Example 7   Carbon-14 decays radioactively at a constant annual rate of 0.0121%. Show that the half-life of carbon-14 is about 5728 years.

Solution   We are not given an initial amount of carbon-14, but we can solve this problem without that information. Let the symbol Q_0 represent the initial quantity of carbon-14 present. The growth rate is -0.000121 because carbon-14 is decaying. So the growth factor is $b = 1 - 0.000121 = 0.999879$. Thus, after t years the amount left will be

$$Q = Q_0(0.999879)^t.$$

We want to find how long it takes for the quantity to drop to half its initial level. Thus, we need to solve for t in the equation

$$\frac{1}{2}Q_0 = Q_0(0.999879)^t.$$

Dividing each side by Q_0, we have

$$\frac{1}{2} = 0.999879^t.$$

Taking logs

$$\log \frac{1}{2} = \log\left(0.999879^t\right)$$

$$\log 0.5 = t \cdot \log 0.999879$$

$$t = \frac{\log 0.5}{\log 0.999879} \approx 5728.143.$$

Thus, no matter how much carbon-14 there is initially, after about 5728 years, half will remain.

Similarly, we can determine the growth rate given the half-life or doubling time.

Example 8   The quantity, Q, of a substance decays according to the formula $Q = Q_0 e^{-kt}$, where t is in minutes. The half-life of the substance is 11 minutes. What is the value of k?

Solution   We know that after 11 minutes, $Q = \frac{1}{2} Q_0$. Thus, solving for k, we get

$$Q_0 e^{-k \cdot 11} = \frac{1}{2} Q_0$$

$$e^{-11k} = \frac{1}{2}$$

$$-11k = \ln \frac{1}{2}$$

$$k = \frac{\ln(1/2)}{-11} \approx 0.06301,$$

so $k = 0.063$ per minute. This substance decays at the continuous rate of 6.301% per minute.

Converting Between $Q = ab^t$ and $Q = ae^{kt}$

Any exponential function can be written in either of the two forms:

$$Q = ab^t \qquad \text{or} \qquad Q = ae^{kt}.$$

If $b = e^k$, so $k = \ln b$, the two formulas represent the same function.

Example 9   Convert the exponential function $P = 175(1.145)^t$ to the form $P = ae^{kt}$.

Solution   Since the new formula represents the same function, we want $P = 175$ when $t = 0$. Thus, substituting $t = 0$ gives $175 = ae^{k(0)} = a$, so $a = 175$. The parameter a in both functions represents the initial population. For all t,

$$175(1.145)^t = 175(e^k)^t,$$

so we must find k such that

$$e^k = 1.145.$$

Therefore k is the power of e that gives 1.145. By the definition of ln, we have

$$k = \ln 1.145 \approx 0.1354.$$

Therefore,

$$P = 175e^{0.1354t}.$$

Example 10   Convert the formula $Q = 7e^{0.3t}$ to the form $Q = ab^t$.

Solution   Using the properties of exponents,

$$Q = 7e^{0.3t} = 7(e^{0.3})^t.$$

Using a calculator, we find $e^{0.3} \approx 1.3499$, so

$$Q = 7(1.3499)^t.$$

Example 11   Assuming t is in years, find the continuous and annual percent growth rates in Examples 9 and 10.

Solution   In Example 9, the annual percent growth rate is 14.5% and the continuous percent growth rate per year is 13.54%. In Example 10, the continuous percent growth rate is 30% and the annual percent growth rate is 34.99%.

Example 12   Find the continuous percent growth rate of $Q = 200(0.886)^t$, where t is in thousands of years.

Solution   Since this function describes exponential decay, we expect a negative value for k. We want

$$e^k = 0.886.$$

Solving for k gives

$$k = \ln(0.886) = -0.12104.$$

So we have $Q = 200e^{-0.12104t}$ and the continuous growth rate is -12.104% per thousand years.

Exponential Growth Problems That Cannot Be Solved by Logarithms

Some equations with the variable in the exponent cannot be solved using logarithms.

Example 13   With t in years, the population of a country (in millions) is given by $P = 2(1.02)^t$, while the food supply (in millions of people that can be fed) is given by $N = 4 + 0.5t$. Determine the year in which the country first experiences food shortages.

Solution   The country starts to experience shortages when the population equals the number of people that can be fed—that is, when $P = N$. We attempt to solve the equation $P = N$ by using logs:

$$2(1.02)^t = 4 + 0.5t$$
$$1.02^t = 2 + 0.25t \qquad \text{Dividing by 2}$$
$$\log 1.02^t = \log(2 + 0.25t)$$
$$t \log 1.02 = \log(2 + 0.25t).$$

Unfortunately, we cannot isolate t, so, this equation cannot be solved using logs. However, we can approximate the solution of the original equation numerically or graphically, as shown in Figure 5.4. The two functions, P and N, are equal when $t \approx 199.381$. Thus, it will be almost 200 years before shortages occur.

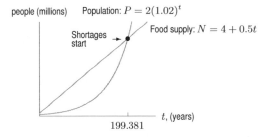

Figure 5.4: Finding the intersection of linear and exponential graphs

Exercises and Problems for Section 5.2

Skill Refresher

For Exercises S1–S4, simplify the expression if possible.

S1. $10^{-\log 5x}$

S2. $e^{-3\ln t}$

S3. $t\ln e^{t/2}$

S4. $10^{2+\log x}$

In Exercises S5–S10, solve for x.

S5. $4^x = 9$

S6. $e^x = 8$

S7. $2e^x = 13$

S8. $e^{7x} = 5e^{3x}$

S9. $\log(2x + 7) = 2$

S10. $\log(2x) = \log(x + 10)$

Exercises

For Exercises 1–2, write the exponential function in the form $y = ab^t$. Find b accurate to four decimal places. If t is measured in years, give the percent annual growth or decay rate and the continuous percent growth or decay rate per year.

1. $y = 25e^{0.053t}$

2. $y = 100e^{-0.07t}$

For Exercises 3–4, write the exponential function in the form $y = ae^{kt}$. Find k accurate to four decimal places. If t is measured in years, give the percent annual growth rate and the continuous percent growth rate per year.

3. $y = 6000(0.85)^t$

4. $y = 5(1.12)^t$

In Exercises 5–8, convert to the form $Q = ab^t$.

5. $Q = 4e^{7t}$

6. $Q = 0.3e^{0.7t}$

7. $Q = \dfrac{14}{5}e^{0.03t}$

8. $Q = e^{-0.02t}$

In Exercises 9–12, convert to the form $Q = ae^{kt}$.

9. $Q = 12(0.9)^t$

10. $Q = 16(0.487)^t$

11. $Q = 14(0.862)^{1.4t}$

12. $Q = 721(0.98)^{0.7t}$

In Exercises 13–20, give the starting value a, the growth rate r, and the continuous growth rate k.

13. $Q = 230(1.182)^t$

14. $Q = 0.181\left(e^{0.775}\right)^t$

15. $Q = 0.81(2)^t$

16. $Q = 5 \cdot 2^{t/8}$

17. $Q = 12.1 \cdot 10^{-0.11t}$

18. $Q = 40e^{(t-5)/12}$

19. $Q = 2e^{(1-3t/4)}$

20. $Q = 2^{-(t-5)/3}$

Problems

Find the doubling time in Exercises 21–24.

21. A population growing according to $P = P_0e^{0.2t}$.

22. A city is growing by 26% per year.

23. A bank account is growing by 2.7% per year.

24. A company's profits are increasing by an annual growth factor of 1.12.

Find the half-lives of the substances in Exercises 25–27.

25. Tritium, which decays at a rate of 5.471% per year.

26. Einsteinium-253, which decays at a rate of 3.406% per day.

27. A radioactive substance that decays at a continuous rate of 11% per minute.

28. You place $800 in an account that earns 4% annual interest, compounded annually. How long will it be until you have $2000?

29. (a) What annual interest rate, compounded continuously, is equivalent to an annual rate of 8%, compounded annually?

(b) What annual interest rate, compounded annually, is equivalent to an annual rate of 6%, compounded continuously?

30. A population grows from 11000 to 13000 in three years. Assuming the growth is exponential, find the:

(a) Annual growth rate   (b) Continuous growth rate

(c) Why are your answers to parts (a) and (b) different?

31. A $5000 investment earns 7.2% annual interest, and an $8000 investment earns 5.4%, both compounded annually. How long will it take for the smaller investment to catch up to the larger one?

32. A $9000 investment earns 5.6% annual interest, and a $4000 investment earns 8.3%, both compounded continuously. When will the smaller catch up to the larger?

33. A population doubles in size every 15 years. Assuming exponential growth, find the

    (a) Annual growth rate   **(b)** Continuous growth rate

34. A population increases from 5.2 million at an annual rate of 3.1%. Find the continuous growth rate.

35. The half-life of nicotine in the body is 2 hours. What is the continuous decay rate?

36. If 17% of a radioactive substance decays in 5 hours, what is the half-life of the substance?

37. Total power generated by wind worldwide doubles every 3 years.[4] In 2008, world wind-energy generating capacity was about 90 thousand megawatts. Find the continuous growth rate and give a formula for wind generating capacity W (in thousand megawatts) as a function of t, number of years since 2008.

38. Sketch the exponential function $y = u(t)$ given that it has a starting value of 0.8 and a doubling time of 12 years. Label the axes and indicate the scale.

39. A town has 5000 people in year $t = 0$. Calculate how long it takes for the population P to double once, twice, and three times, assuming that the town grows at a constant rate of

    (a) 500 people per year.
    (b) 5% per year.

40. **(a)** Estimate the doubling time of the exponential function shown in Figure 5.5.
    (b) Use the doubling time to find the continuous percent growth rate and give a formula for the function.

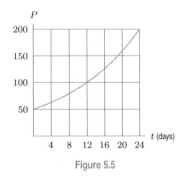

Figure 5.5

---
[4]World Wind Energy Report 2008.

41. **(a)** The quantity of caffeine in the body after drinking a cup of coffee is shown in Figure 5.6. Estimate the half-life of caffeine.
    (b) Use the half-life to find the continuous percent decay rate and give a formula for Q as function of t.

Figure 5.6

42. The temperature, H, in °F, of a cup of coffee t hours after it is set out to cool is given by the equation:

$$H = 70 + 120(1/4)^t.$$

    (a) What is the coffee's temperature initially (that is, at time $t = 0$)? After 1 hour? 2 hours?
    (b) How long does it take the coffee to cool down to 90°F? 75°F?

43. Use algebra to show that the time it takes for a quantity growing exponentially to double is independent of the starting quantity and the time. To do this, let d represent the time it takes for P to double. Show that if P becomes $2P$ at time $t + d$, then d depends only on the growth factor b, but not on the starting quantity a and time t. (Assume $P \neq 0$.)

44. Prices climb at a constant 3% annual rate.

    (a) By what percent will prices have climbed after 5 years?
    (b) How long will it take for prices to climb 25%?

45. The growth of an animal population, P, is described by the function $P = 300 \cdot 2^{t/20}$.

    (a) How large is this population in year $t = 0$? $t = 20$?
    (b) When does this population reach 1000?

46. Find values for a, b, k, s where

$$f(t) = ab^t = ae^{kt} = a \cdot 2^{t/s},$$

given that $f(-20) = 5$ and $f(40) = 30$.

47. (a) Find the time required for an investment to triple in value if it earns 4% annual interest, compounded continuously.
(b) Now find the time required assuming that the interest is compounded annually.

48. The world's population is aging. The approximate world population age 80 or older[5] is given in Table 5.1.

(a) Find a formula for P, the number of people in the world age 80 or older, in millions, as a function of time, t, in years since 2005. Use the form $P = ab^t$. What is the annual percent rate of increase?
(b) Convert to the form $P = ae^{kt}$. What is the continuous percent increase per year?
(c) Find the doubling time.

Table 5.1

t (year)	2005	2006	2007	2008	2009
P (millions)	89.144	92.175	95.309	98.550	101.901

49. Technetium-99m is a radioactive substance used to diagnose brain diseases. Its half-life is approximately 6 hours. Initially you have 200 mg of technetium-99m.

(a) Write an equation that gives the amount of technetium-99m remaining after t hours.
(b) Determine the number of hours needed for your sample to decay to 120 mg.
(c) Determine the concavity of the graph that models the half-life of technetium-99m using average rates of change over intervals of length 2 between $t = 0$ and $t = 6$.

50. The US census projects the population of the state of Washington using the function $N(t) = 5.4e^{0.013t}$, where $N(t)$ is in millions and t is in years since 1995.

(a) What is the population's continuous growth rate?
(b) What is the population of Washington in year $t = 0$?
(c) How many years is it before the population triples?
(d) In what year does this model indicate a population of only one person? Is this reasonable or unreasonable?

51. In 1991, the body of a man was found in melting snow in the Alps of Northern Italy. An examination of the tissue sample revealed that 46% of the carbon-14 present in his body at the time of his death had decayed. The half-life of carbon-14 is approximately 5728 years. How long ago did this man die?

52. A manager at Saks Fifth Avenue wants to estimate the number of customers to expect on the last shopping day before Christmas. She collects data from three previous years, and determines that the crowds follow the same general pattern. When the store opens at 10 am, 500 people enter, and the total number in the store doubles every 40 minutes. When the number of people in the store reaches 10,000, security guards need to be stationed at the entrances to control the crowds. At what time should the guards be commissioned?

53. Figure 5.7 shows the graphs of the exponential functions f and g, and the linear function, h.

(a) Find formulas for f, g, and h.
(b) Find the exact value(s) of x such that $f(x) = g(x)$.
(c) Estimate the value(s) of x such that $f(x) = h(x)$.

Figure 5.7

Problems 54–55 involve the Rule of 70, which gives quick estimates of the doubling time of an exponentially growing quantity. If $r\%$ is the annual growth rate of the quantity, then the Rule of 70 says

$$\text{Doubling time in years} \approx \frac{70}{r}.$$

54. Use the Rule of 70 to estimate how long it takes a $1000 investment to double if it grows at the following annual rates: 1%, 2%, 5%, 7%, 10%. Compare with the actual doubling times.

55. Using natural logs, solve for the doubling time for $Q = ae^{kt}$. Use your result to explain why the Rule of 70 works.

56. A person's blood alcohol content (BAC) is a measure of how much alcohol is in the blood stream. When a person stops drinking, the BAC declines over time as the alcohol is metabolized. The BAC, Q, of a person t minutes after the he stops drinking is given by

$$Q = Q_0 e^{-t/\tau},$$

where Q_0 is the person's initial BAC and τ is known as the *elimination time*. How long does it take for a person's BAC to drop from 0.10 to 0.04 if the elimination time is 2.5 hours?

57. The size of a population, P, of toads t years after it is introduced into a wetland is given by

$$P = \frac{1000}{1 + 49(1/2)^t}.$$

(a) How many toads are there in year $t = 0$? $t = 5$? $t = 10$?

---
[5]UN Department of Economic and Social Affairs, 2009.

(b) How long does it take for the toad population to reach 500? 750?

(c) What is the maximum number of toads that the wetland can support?

58. Write the exponential function $y = ab^t$ in the form

$$y = e^{k(t-t_0)}.$$

Give k and t_0 in terms of a and b.

59. *Gompertz functions* can be used to model population growth.[6] Solve $f(t) = 3$ for t for the particular Gompertz function

$$f(t) = 6e^{-0.5e^{-0.1t}}.$$

60. (a) Rewrite the equation $23\,(1.36)^t = 85$ in the form $e^{k+rt} = e^s$. State the values of the constants $k, r,$ and s.

(b) Solve the original equation in terms of $k, r,$ and s, then give a numerical approximation.

61. (a) Rewrite the equation $1.12^t = 6.3$ in the form $10^{vt} = 10^w$. State the values of the constants v and w.

(b) Solve the original equation in terms of v and w, then give a numerical approximation.

5.3 THE LOGARITHMIC FUNCTION

The Graph, Domain, and Range of the Common Logarithm

In Section 5.1 we defined the log function (to base 10) for all positive numbers. In other words,

Domain of $\log x$ is all positive numbers.

By considering its graph in Figure 5.8, we determine the range of $y = \log x$. The log graph crosses the x-axis at $x = 1$, because $\log 1 = \log(10^0) = 0$. The graph climbs to $y = 1$ at $x = 10$, because $\log 10 = \log(10^1) = 1$. In order for the log graph to climb to $y = 2$, the value of x must reach 100, or 10^2, and in order for it to climb to $y = 3$, the value of x must be 10^3, or 1000. To reach the modest height of $y = 20$ requires x to equal 10^{20}, or 100 billion billion! The log function increases so slowly that it often serves as a benchmark for other slow-growing functions. Nonetheless, the graph of $y = \log x$ eventually climbs to any value we choose.

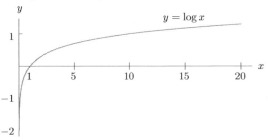

Figure 5.8: The log function grows very rapidly for $0 < x < 1$ and very slowly for $x > 1$. It has a vertical asymptote at $x = 0$ but never touches the y-axis

Although x cannot equal zero in the log function, we can choose $x > 0$ to be as small as we like. As x decreases toward zero, the values of $\log x$ get large and negative. For example,

$$\log 0.1 = \log 10^{-1} = -1,$$
$$\log 0.01 = \log 10^{-2} = -2,$$
$$\vdots \qquad \vdots$$
$$\log 0.0000001 = \log 10^{-7} = -7,$$

---

[6] See http://en.wikipedia.org/wiki/Gompertz_curve, accessed April 13, 2008.

and so on. So small positive values of x give exceedingly large negative values of y. The graph has a vertical asymptote at $x = 0$ and

$$\text{Range of } \log x \text{ is all real numbers.}$$

The log function is increasing and its graph is concave down, since its rate of change is decreasing.

Graphs of the Inverse Functions $y = \log x$ and $y = 10^x$

The fact that $y = \log x$ and $y = 10^x$ are inverses means that their graphs are related. Looking at Tables 5.2 and 5.3, we see that the point $(0.01, -2)$ is on the graph of $y = \log x$ and the point $(-2, 0.01)$ is on the graph of $y = 10^x$. In general, if the point (a, b) is on the graph of $y = \log x$, the point (b, a) is on the graph of $y = 10^x$. Thus, the graph of $y = \log x$ is the graph of $y = 10^x$ with x- and y-axes interchanged. If the x- and y-axes have the same scale, this is equivalent to reflecting the graph of $y = 10^x$ across the diagonal line $y = x$. See Figure 5.9.

Table 5.2 *Log function*

x	$y = \log x$
0.01	-2
0.1	-1
1	0
10	1
100	2
1000	3

Table 5.3 *Exponential function*

x	$y = 10^x$
-2	0.01
-1	0.1
0	1
1	10
2	100
3	1000

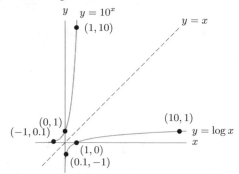

Figure 5.9: The functions $y = \log x$ and $y = 10^x$ are inverses of one another

Graph of Natural Logarithm

In addition to similar algebraic properties, the natural log and the common log have similar graphs.

Example 1 Graph $y = \ln x$ for $0 < x < 10$.

Solution Values of $\ln x$ are in Table 5.4. Like the common log, the natural log is only defined for $x > 0$ and has a vertical asymptote at $x = 0$. The graph is slowly increasing and concave down.

Table 5.4 *Values of* $\ln x$ *(rounded)*

x	$\ln x$
0	Undefined
1	0
2	0.7
e	1
3	1.1
4	1.4
$\vdots$	$\vdots$

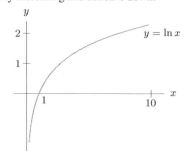

Figure 5.10: Graph of the natural logarithm

The functions $y = \ln x$ and $y = e^x$ are inverses. If the scales on the axes are the same, their graphs are reflections of one another across the line $y = x$. See Figure 5.11. For example, the vertical asymptote of the logarithm is the reflection of the horizontal asymptote of the exponential. On page 201, we see how to write asymptotes in limit notation.

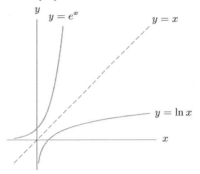

Figure 5.11: The functions $y = \ln x$ and $y = e^x$ are inverses of one another

Chemical Acidity

Logarithms are useful in measuring quantities whose magnitudes vary widely, such as acidity (pH), sound (decibels), and earthquakes (the Richter scale). In chemistry, the acidity of a liquid is expressed using pH. The acidity depends on the hydrogen ion concentration in the liquid (in moles per liter); this concentration is written $[H^+]$. The greater the hydrogen ion concentration, the more acidic the solution. The pH is defined as:

$$\text{pH} = -\log[H^+].$$

Example 2   The hydrogen ion concentration of seawater is $[H^+] = 1.1 \cdot 10^{-8}$. Estimate the pH of seawater. Then check your answer with a calculator.

Solution   We want to estimate pH $= -\log(1.1 \cdot 10^{-8})$. Since $1.1 \cdot 10^{-8} \approx 10^{-8}$ and $\log 10^{-8} = -8$, we know that
$$\text{pH} = -\log(1.1 \cdot 10^{-8}) \approx -(-8) = 8.$$
Using a calculator, we have
$$\text{pH} = -\log(1.1 \cdot 10^{-8}) = 7.959.$$

Example 3   A vinegar solution has a pH of 3. Determine the hydrogen ion concentration.

Solution   Since $3 = -\log[H^+]$, we have $-3 = \log[H^+]$. This means that $10^{-3} = [H^+]$. So the hydrogen ion concentration is 10^{-3} moles per liter.

Logarithms and Orders of Magnitude

We often compare sizes or quantities by computing their ratios. If A is twice as tall as B, then
$$\frac{\text{Height of } A}{\text{Height of } B} = 2.$$

If one object is 10 times heavier than another, we say it is an *order of magnitude* heavier. If one quantity is two factors of 10 greater than another, we say it is two orders of magnitude greater, and so on. For example, the value of a dollar is two orders of magnitude greater than the value of a penny, because we have

$$\frac{\$1}{\$0.01} = 100 = 10^2.$$

The order of magnitude is the logarithm of their ratio.

Example 4 The sound intensity of a refrigerator motor is 10^{-11} watts/cm^2. A typical school cafeteria has sound intensity of 10^{-8} watts/cm^2. How many orders of magnitude more intense is the sound of the cafeteria?

Solution To compare the two intensities, we compute their ratio:

$$\frac{\text{Sound intensity of cafeteria}}{\text{Sound intensity of refrigerator}} = \frac{10^{-8}}{10^{-11}} = 10^{-8-(-11)} = 10^3.$$

Thus, the sound intensity of the cafeteria is 1000 times greater than the sound intensity of the refrigerator. The log of this ratio is 3. We say that the sound intensity of the cafeteria is three orders of magnitude greater than the sound intensity of the refrigerator.

Decibels

The intensity of audible sound varies over an enormous range. The range is so enormous that we consider the logarithm of the sound intensity. This is the idea behind the *decibel* (abbreviated dB). To measure a sound in decibels, the sound's intensity, I, is compared to the intensity of a standard benchmark sound, I_0. The intensity of I_0 is defined to be 10^{-16} watts/cm^2, roughly the lowest intensity audible to humans. The comparison between a sound intensity I and the benchmark sound intensity I_0 is made as follows:

$$\text{Noise level in decibels} = 10 \cdot \log\left(\frac{I}{I_0}\right).$$

For instance, let's find the decibel rating of the refrigerator in Example 4. First, we find how many orders of magnitude more intense the refrigerator sound is than the benchmark sound:

$$\frac{I}{I_0} = \frac{\text{Sound intensity of refrigerator}}{\text{Benchmark sound intensity}} = \frac{10^{-11}}{10^{-16}} = 10^5.$$

Thus, the refrigerator's intensity is 5 orders of magnitude more than I_0, the benchmark intensity. We have

$$\text{Decibel rating of refrigerator} = 10 \cdot \underbrace{\text{Number of orders of magnitude}}_{5} = 50 \text{ dB}.$$

Note that 5, the number of orders of magnitude, is the log of the ratio I/I_0. We use the log function because it "counts" the number of powers of 10. Thus if N is the decibel rating, then

$$N = 10 \log\left(\frac{I}{I_0}\right).$$

Example 5 (a) If a sound doubles in intensity, by how many units does its decibel rating increase?

(b) Loud music can measure 110 dB whereas normal conversation measures 50 dB. How many times more intense is loud music than normal conversation?

Solution (a) Let I be the sound's intensity before it doubles. Once doubled, the new intensity is $2I$. The decibel rating of the original sound is $10 \log(I/I_0)$, and the decibel rating of the new sound is $10 \log(2I/I_0)$. The difference in decibel ratings is given by

$$\text{Difference in decibel ratings} = 10 \log\left(\frac{2I}{I_0}\right) - 10 \log\left(\frac{I}{I_0}\right)$$

$$= 10 \left(\log\left(\frac{2I}{I_0}\right) - \log\left(\frac{I}{I_0}\right)\right) \qquad \text{Factoring out 10}$$

$$= 10 \cdot \log\left(\frac{2I/I_0}{I/I_0}\right) \qquad \text{Using the property } \log a - \log b = \log(a/b)$$

$$= 10 \cdot \log 2 \qquad \text{Canceling } I/I_0$$

$$\approx 3.010 \text{ dB.} \qquad \text{Because } \log 2 \approx 0.3$$

Thus, if the sound intensity is doubled, the decibel rating goes up by approximately 3 dB.

(b) If I_M is the sound intensity of loud music, then

$$10 \log\left(\frac{I_M}{I_0}\right) = 110 \text{ dB.}$$

Similarly, if I_C is the sound intensity of conversation, then

$$10 \log\left(\frac{I_C}{I_0}\right) = 50 \text{ dB.}$$

Computing the difference of the decibel ratings gives

$$10 \log\left(\frac{I_M}{I_0}\right) - 10 \log\left(\frac{I_C}{I_0}\right) = 60.$$

Dividing by 10 gives

$$\log\left(\frac{I_M}{I_0}\right) - \log\left(\frac{I_C}{I_0}\right) = 6$$

$$\log\left(\frac{I_M/I_0}{I_C/I_0}\right) = 6 \qquad \text{Using the property } \log b - \log a = \log(b/a)$$

$$\log\left(\frac{I_M}{I_C}\right) = 6 \qquad \text{Canceling } I_0$$

$$\frac{I_M}{I_C} = 10^6. \qquad \log x = 6 \text{ means that } x = 10^6$$

So $I_M = 10^6 I_C$, which means that loud music is 10^6 times, or one million times, as intense as normal conversation.

Asymptotes and Limit Notation

In Section 4.3 we saw that the graph of an exponential function has a horizontal asymptote. In Figure 5.9 on page 198, we see that $y = 10^x$ has horizontal asymptote $y = 0$, because

$$\text{as } x \to -\infty, \quad 10^x \to 0.$$

Correspondingly, as x gets closer to zero, $y = \log x$ takes on larger and larger negative values. We write

$$\text{as } x \to 0^+, \qquad \log x \to -\infty.$$

The notation $x \to 0^+$ is read "x approaches zero from the right" and means that we are choosing smaller and smaller positive values of x—that is, we are sliding toward $x = 0$ through small positive values. We say the graph of the log function $y = \log x$ has a *vertical asymptote* of $x = 0$.

To describe vertical asymptotes in general, we use the notation

$$x \to a^+$$

to mean that x slides toward a from the right (that is, through values larger than a) and

$$x \to a^-$$

to mean that x slides toward a from the left (that is, through values smaller than a).

If $f(x) \to \infty$ as $x \to a^+$, we say the *limit* of $f(x)$ as x approaches a from the right is infinity,[7] and write

$$\lim_{x \to a^+} f(x) = \infty.$$

If $f(x) \to \infty$ as $x \to a^-$, we write

$$\lim_{x \to a^-} f(x) = \infty.$$

If both $\lim_{x \to a^+} f(x) = \infty$ and $\lim_{x \to a^-} f(x) = \infty$, we say the limit of $f(x)$ as x approaches a is infinity, and write

$$\lim_{x \to a} f(x) = \infty.$$

Similarly, we can write

$$\lim_{x \to a^+} f(x) = -\infty \quad \text{or} \quad \lim_{x \to a^-} f(x) = -\infty \quad \text{or} \quad \lim_{x \to a} f(x) = -\infty.$$

We summarize the information about both horizontal and vertical asymptotes:

Let $y = f(x)$ be a function and let a be a finite number.
- The graph of f has a **horizontal asymptote** of $y = a$ if

$$\lim_{x \to \infty} f(x) = a \quad \text{or} \quad \lim_{x \to -\infty} f(x) = a \qquad \text{or both.}$$

- The graph of f has a **vertical asymptote** of $x = a$ if

$$\lim_{x \to a^+} f(x) = \infty \text{ or } \lim_{x \to a^+} f(x) = -\infty \text{ or } \lim_{x \to a^-} f(x) = \infty \text{ or } \lim_{x \to a^-} f(x) = -\infty.$$

Notice that the process of finding a vertical asymptote is different from the process for finding a horizontal asymptote. Vertical asymptotes occur where the function values grow larger and larger, either positively or negatively, as x approaches a finite value (i.e. where $f(x) \to \infty$ or $f(x) \to -\infty$ as $x \to a$). Horizontal asymptotes are determined by whether the function values approach a finite number as x takes on large positive or large negative values (i.e., as $x \to \infty$ or $x \to -\infty$).

Exercises and Problems for Section 5.3

Skill Refresher

For Exercises S1–S2, evaluate without a calculator.

S1. $\log 0.0001$

S2. $\dfrac{\log 100^6}{\log 100^2}$

---
[7]Some authors say that these limits do not exist.

For Exercises S3–S4, rewrite the exponential equation in equivalent logarithmic form.

S3. $10^5 = 100,000$ **S4.** $e^2 = 7.389$

For Exercises S5–S6, rewrite the logarithmic equation in equivalent exponential form.

S5. $-\ln x = 12$ **S6.** $\log(x + 3) = 2$

For Exercises S7–S8, if possible, write the expression using sums and/or differences of logarithmic expressions that do not contain the logarithms of products, quotients or powers.

S7. $\ln(x(7 - x)^3)$ **S8.** $\ln\left(\dfrac{xy^2}{z}\right)$

For Exercises S9–S10, rewrite the expression as a single logarithm.

S9. $\ln x^3 + \ln x^2$ **S10.** $\frac{1}{3}\log 8 - \frac{1}{2}\log 25$

Exercises

1. What is the equation of the asymptote of the graph of $y = 10^x$? Of the graph of $y = 2^x$? Of the graph of $y = \log x$?

2. What is the equation for the asymptote of the graph of $y = e^x$? Of the graph of $y = e^{-x}$? Of the graph of $y = \ln x$?

3. Without a calculator, match the functions $y = 10^x$, $y = e^x$, $y = \log x$, $y = \ln x$ with the graphs in Figure 5.12.

Figure 5.12

4. Without a calculator, match the functions $y = 2^x$, $y = e^{-x}$, $y = 3^x$, $y = \ln x$, $y = \log x$ with the graphs in Figure 5.13.

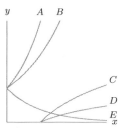

Figure 5.13

Graph the functions in Problems 5–8. Label all asymptotes and intercepts.

5. $y = 2 \cdot 3^x + 1$ 6. $y = -e^{-x}$

7. $y = \log(x - 4)$ 8. $y = \ln(x + 1)$

In Problems 9–10, graph the function. Identify any vertical asymptotes. State the domain of the function.

9. $y = 2\ln(x - 3)$ 10. $y = 1 - \ln(2 - x)$

11. What is the value (if any) of the following?
    (a) 10^{-x} as $x \to \infty$ (b) $\log x$ as $x \to 0^+$

12. What is the value (if any) of the following?
    (a) e^x as $x \to -\infty$ (b) $\ln x$ as $x \to 0^+$

13. Find (a) $\lim_{x \to 0^+} \log x$ (b) $\lim_{x \to 0^-} \ln(-x)$

In Exercises 14–18, find the hydrogen ion concentration, $[H^+]$, for the substances.[8] [Hint: pH $= -\log[H^+]$.]

14. Lye, with a pH of 13.

15. Battery acid, with a pH of 1.

16. Baking soda, with a pH of 8.3.

17. Tomatoes, with a pH of 4.5.

18. Hydrochloric acid, with a pH of 0.

---

[8] Data from www.miamisci.org/ph/hhoh.html, accessed November, 2001.

Problems

19. Immediately following the gold medal performance of the US women's gymnastic team in the 1996 Olympic Games, an NBC commentator, John Tesh, said of one team member: "Her confidence and performance have grown logarithmically." He clearly thought this was an enormous compliment. Is it a compliment? Is it realistic?

20. Match the statements (a)–(d) with the functions (I)–(IV).

(a) $\lim_{x \to 0^+} f(x) = -\infty$ (b) $\lim_{x \to 0^-} f(x) = 0$

(c) $\lim_{x \to \infty} f(x) = \infty$ (d) $\lim_{x \to -\infty} f(x) = 0$

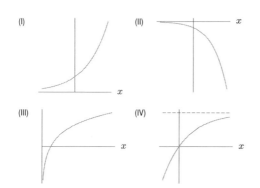

21. Match the graphs (a)–(c) to one of the functions $r(x)$, $s(x)$, $t(x)$ whose values are in the tables.

x	2	4	10
$r(x)$	1	1.301	1.699

x	0.5	5	10
$s(x)$	-0.060	0.379	0.699

x	0.1	2	100
$t(x)$	-3	0.903	6

In Problems 22–26, sound in decibels is measured by comparing the sound intensity, I, to a benchmark sound I_0 with intensity 10^{-16} watts/cm^2. Then,

$$\text{Noise level in decibels} = 10 \log(I/I_0).$$

22. The noise level of a whisper is 30 dB. Compute the sound intensity of a whisper.

23. Death of hearing tissue begins to occur at a noise level of 180 dB. Compute the sound's intensity at this noise level.

24. Denver Broncos fans recently broke the world record for "loudest roar" at a sports event.[9] A crowd of 76,000 fans reached a noise level of 128.7 dB. The previous world record of 125.4 dB was held by soccer fans in Dublin, Ireland. How many times more intense was the roar of the crowd of Denver Broncos fans than the roar of the soccer fans in Ireland?

25. Sound A measures 30 decibels and sound B is 5 times as loud as sound A. What is the decibel rating of sound B to the nearest integer?

26. (a) Let D_1 and D_2 represent the decibel ratings of sounds of intensity I_1 and I_2, respectively. Using log properties, find a simplified formula for the difference between the two ratings, $D_2 - D_1$, in terms of the two intensities, I_1 and I_2.

(b) If a sound's intensity doubles, how many decibels louder does the sound become?

Problems 27–30 use the *Richter scale* for the strength of an earthquake. The strength, W, of the seismic waves of an earthquake are compared to the strength, W_0, of the seismic waves of a standard earthquake. The Richter scale rating, M, is

$$M = \log\left(\frac{W}{W_0}\right).$$

27. In 2008 the Sichuan earthquake in China had a Richter-scale rating of 7.9. How many times more powerful were the seismic waves of the Sichuan earthquake than standard seismic waves?

28. In 1986 the worst nuclear power plant accident in history occurred in Chernobyl, Ukraine. The explosion resulted in seismic waves with a Richter scale rating of 3.5. How many times stronger were the seismic waves of the Chernobyl disaster than standard seismic waves?

---

[9]See http://www.encyclopedia.com/doc/1G1-65629077.html, accessed January 8, 2010.

29. Let M_1 and M_2 be the magnitude of two earthquakes whose seismic waves are of sizes W_1 and W_2, respectively. Using log properties, find a simplified formula for the difference $M_2 - M_1$ in terms of W_1 and W_2.

30. The 1989 earthquake in California had a rating of 7.1 on the Richter scale. How many times larger than the California earthquake were the seismic waves in the March 2005 earthquake off the coast of Sumatra, which measured 8.7 on the Richter scale? Give your answer to the nearest integer.

31. **(a)** Using the definition of pH on page 199, find the concentrations of hydrogen ions in solutions with

    (i) pH $= 2$ (ii) pH $= 4$ (iii) pH $= 7$

  (b) A high concentration of hydrogen ions corresponds to an acidic solution. From your answer to part (a), decide if solutions with high pHs are more or less acidic than solutions with low pHs.

32. **(a)** A 12-oz cup of coffee contains about $2.41 \cdot 10^{18}$ hydrogen ions. What is the concentration (moles/liter) of hydrogen ions in a 12-oz cup of coffee? [Hint: One liter equals 30.3 oz. One mole of hydrogen ions equals $6.02 \cdot 10^{23}$ hydrogen ions.]

  (b) Based on your answer to part (a) and the formula for pH, what is the pH of a 12-oz cup of coffee?

33. **(a)** The pH of lemon juice is about 2.3. What is the concentration of hydrogen ions in lemon juice?

  (b) A person squeezes 2 oz of lemon juice into a cup. Based on your answer to part (a), how many hydrogen ions does this juice contain?

In Problems 34–39, find possible formulas for the functions using logs or exponentials.

40. Give the domain of $y = \dfrac{1}{2 - \sqrt{7 - e^{2t}}}$.

5.4 LOGARITHMIC SCALES

The Solar System and Beyond

Table 5.5 gives the distance from the sun to a number of different astronomical objects. The planet Mercury is 58,000,000 km from the sun, the earth is 149,000,000 km from the sun, and Pluto is 5,900,000,000 km, or almost 6 billion kilometers from the sun. The table also gives the distance to Proxima Centauri, the star closest to the sun, and to the Andromeda Galaxy, the spiral galaxy closest to our own galaxy, the Milky Way.

Table 5.5 *Distance from the sun to various astronomical objects*

Object	Distance (million km)		
Mercury	58	Saturn	1426
Venus	108	Uranus	2869
Earth	149	Neptune	4495
Mars	228	Pluto	5900
Jupiter	778	Proxima Centauri	$4.1 \cdot 10^7$
		Andromeda Galaxy	$2.4 \cdot 10^{13}$

Linear Scales

We can represent the information in Table 5.5 graphically in order to get a better feel for the distances involved. Figure 5.14 shows the distance from the sun to the first five planets on a *linear scale*, which means that the evenly spaced units shown in the figure represent equal distances. In this case, each unit represents 100 million kilometers.

Figure 5.14: The distance from the sun of the first five planets (in millions of kilometers)

The drawback of Figure 5.14 is that the scale is too small to show all of the astronomical distances described by the table. For example, to show the distance to Pluto on this scale would require over six times the space on the page. Even worse, assuming that each 100 million km unit on the scale measures half an inch on the printed page, we would need 3 miles of paper to show the distance to Proxima Centauri!

You might conclude that we could fix this problem by choosing a larger scale. In Figure 5.15 each unit on the scale is 1 billion kilometers. Notice that all five planets shown by Figure 5.14 are crowded into the first unit of Figure 5.15; even so, the distance to Pluto barely fits. The distances to the other objects certainly don't fit. For instance, to show the Andromeda Galaxy, Figure 5.15 would have to be almost 200,000 miles long. Choosing an even larger scale will not improve the situation.

Figure 5.15: The distance to all nine planets (in billions of kilometers)

Logarithmic Scales

We conclude that the data in Table 5.5 cannot easily be represented on a linear scale. If the scale is too small, the more distant objects do not fit; if the scale is too large, the less distant objects are indistinguishable. The problem is not that the numbers are too big or too small; the problem is that the numbers vary too greatly in size.

We consider a different type of scale on which equal distances are not evenly spaced. All the objects from Table 5.5 are represented in Figure 5.16. The nine planets are still cramped, but it is possible to tell them apart. Each tick mark on the scale in Figure 5.16 represents a distance ten times larger than the one before it. This kind of scale is called *logarithmic*.

Figure 5.16: The distance from the sun (in millions of kilometers)

How Do We Plot Data on a Logarithmic Scale?

A logarithmic scale is marked with increasing powers of 10: 10^1, 10^2, 10^3, and so on. Notice that even though the distances in Figure 5.16 are not evenly spaced, the exponents are evenly spaced. Therefore the distances in Figure 5.16 are spaced according to their logarithms.

In order to plot Mercury's distance from the sun, 58 million kilometers, we use the fact that

$$10 < 58 < 100,$$

so Mercury's distance is between 10^1 and 10^2, as shown in Figure 5.16. To plot Mercury's distance more precisely, calculate $\log 58 = 1.763$, so $10^{1.763} = 58$, and use 1.763 to represent Mercury's position. See Figure 5.17.

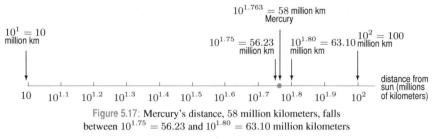

Figure 5.17: Mercury's distance, 58 million kilometers, falls between $10^{1.75} = 56.23$ and $10^{1.80} = 63.10$ million kilometers

Example 1   Where should Saturn be on the logarithmic scale? What about the Andromeda Galaxy?

Solution   Saturn's distance is 1426 million kilometers, so we want the exponent of 10 that gives 1426, which is

$$\log 1426 \approx 3.154119526.$$

Thus $10^{3.154} \approx 1426$, so we use 3.154 to indicate Saturn's distance.

Similarly, the distance to the Andromeda Galaxy is $2.4 \cdot 10^{13}$ million kilometers, and since

$$\log(2.4 \cdot 10^{13}) \approx 13.38,$$

we use 13.38 to represent the galaxy's distance. See Figure 5.18.

Figure 5.18: Saturn's distance is $10^{3.154}$ and the Andromeda Galaxy's distance is $10^{13.38}$

Logs of Small Numbers

The history of the world, like the distance to the stars and planets, involves numbers of vastly different sizes. Table 5.6 gives the ages of certain events[10] and the logarithms of their ages. The logarithms have been used to plot the events in Figure 5.19.

---

[10]*CRC Handbook,* 75th ed., sec. 14-8.

Table 5.6   *Ages of various events in earth's history and logarithms of the ages*

Event	Age (millions of years)	log (age)	Event	Age (millions of years)	log (age)
Man emerges	1	0	Rise of dinosaurs	245	2.39
Ape-man fossils	5	0.70	Vertebrates appear	570	2.76
Rise of cats, dogs, pigs	37	1.57	First plants	2500	3.40
Demise of dinosaurs	67	1.83	Earth forms	4450	3.65

Figure 5.19: Logarithmic scale showing the ages of various events (in millions of years ago)

The events described by Table 5.6 all happened at least 1 million years ago. How do we indicate events which occurred less than 1 million years ago on the log scale?

Example 2   Where should the building of the pyramids be indicated on the log scale?

Solution   The pyramids were built about 5000 years ago, or

$$\frac{5000}{1,000,000} = 0.005 \text{ million years ago.}$$

Notice that 0.005 is between 0.001 and 0.01, that is,

$$10^{-3} < 0.005 < 10^{-2}.$$

Since

$$\log 0.005 \approx -2.30,$$

we use -2.30 for the pyramids. See Figure 5.20.

Figure 5.20: Logarithmic scale showing the ages of various events. Note that events that are less than 1 million years old are indicated by negative exponents

Another Way to Label a Log Scale

In Figures 5.19 and 5.20, the log scale has been labeled so that exponents are evenly spaced. Another way to label a log scale is with the values themselves instead of the exponents. This has been done in Figure 5.21.

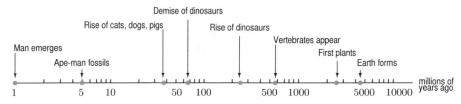

Figure 5.21: Axis labeled using actual values, not logs

Notice the characteristic way that the labels and tick marks "pile up" on each interval. The even spacing between exponents on log scales leads to uneven spacing in values. Although the values 10, 20, 30, 40, and 50 are evenly spaced, their corresponding exponents are not: $\log 10 = 1$, $\log 20 = 1.30$, $\log 30 = 1.48$, $\log 40 = 1.60$, and $\log 50 = 1.70$. Therefore, when we label an axis according to values on a scale that is spaced according to exponents, the labels get bunched up.

Log-Log Scales

Table 5.7 shows the average metabolic rate in kilocalories per day (kcal/day) for animals of different weights.[11] (A kilocalorie is the same as a standard nutritional calorie.) For instance, a 1-lb rat consumes about 35 kcal/day, whereas a 1750-lb horse consumes almost 9500 kcal/day.

Table 5.7   *The metabolic rate (in kcal/day) for animals of different weights*

Animal	Weight (lbs)	Rate (kcal/day)
Rat	1	35
Cat	8	166
Human	150	2000
Horse	1750	9470

It is not practical to plot these data on an ordinary set of axes. The values span too broad a range. However, we can plot the data using log scales for both the horizontal (weight) axis and the vertical (rate) axis. See Figure 5.22. Figure 5.23 shows a close-up view of the data point for cats to make it easier to see how the labels work. Once again, notice the characteristic piling up of labels and gridlines. This happens for the same reason as in Figure 5.21.

Figure 5.22: Metabolic rate (in kcal/hr) plotted against body weight   Figure 5.23: A close-up view of the Cat data point

[11]*The New York Times*, January 11, 1999.

209

Using Logs to Fit an Exponential Function to Data

In Section 1.6 we used linear regression to find the equation for a line of best fit for a set of data. What if the data do not lie close to a straight line, but instead approximate the graph of some other function? In this section we see how logarithms help us fit data with an exponential function of the form $Q = a \cdot b^t$.

Sales of Compact Discs

Table 5.8 shows the fall in the sales of vinyl long-playing records (LPs) and the rise of compact discs (CDs) during for the years 1982 through 1993.[12]

Table 5.8 *CD and LP sales*

t, years since 1982	c, CDs (millions)	l, LPs (millions)
0	0	244
1	0.8	210
2	5.8	205
3	23	167
4	53	125
5	102	107
6	150	72
7	207	35
8	287	12
9	333	4.8
10	408	2.3
11	495	1.2

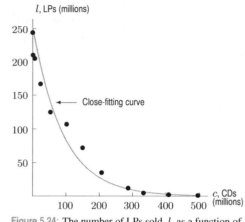

Figure 5.24: The number of LPs sold, l, as a function of number of CDs sold, c

From Table 5.8, we see that as CD sales rose dramatically during the 1980s and early 1990s, LP sales declined equally dramatically. Figure 5.24 shows the number of LPs sold in a given year as a function of the number of CDs sold that year.

Using a Log Scale to Linearize Data

In Section 5.4, we saw that a log scale allows us to compare values that vary over a wide range. Let's see what happens when we use a log scale to plot the data shown in Figure 5.24. Table 5.9 shows values $\log l$, where l is LP sales. These are plotted against c, CD sales, in Figure 5.25. Notice that plotting the data in this way tends to *linearize* the graph—that is, make it look more like a line. A line has been drawn in to emphasize the trend in the data.

Finding a Formula for the Curve

We say that the data in the third column of Table 5.9 have been *transformed*. A calculator or computer gives a regression line for the transformed data:[13]

$$y = 5.52 - 0.011c.$$

---

[12]Data from Recording Industry Association of America, Inc., 1998.

[13]The values obtained by a computer or another calculator may vary slightly from the ones given.

Table 5.9 *Values of $y = \ln l$ and c.*

c, CDs	l, LPs	$y = \ln l$
0	244	5.50
0.8	210	5.35
5.8	205	5.32
23	167	5.12
53	125	4.83
102	107	4.67
150	72	4.28
207	35	3.56
287	12	2.48
333	4.8	1.57
408	2.3	0.83
495	1.2	0.18

Figure 5.25: The y-axis of this graph gives the natural log of LP sales

Notice that this equation gives y in terms of c. To transform the equation back to our original variables, l and c, we substitute $\ln l$ for y, giving

$$\ln l = 5.52 - 0.011c.$$

We solve for l by raising e to both sides:

$$e^{\ln l} = e^{5.52 - 0.011c}$$
$$= (e^{5.52})(e^{-0.011c}). \qquad \text{Using an exponent rule}$$

Since $e^{\ln l} = l$ and $e^{5.52} \approx 250$, we have

$$l = 250e^{-0.011c}.$$

This is the equation of the curve in Figure 5.24.

Fitting an Exponential Function to Data

In general, to fit an exponential formula, $N = ae^{kt}$, to a set of data of the form (t, N), we use three steps. First, we transform the data by taking the natural log of both sides and making the substitution $y = \ln N$. This leads to the equation

$$y = \ln N = \ln\left(ae^{kt}\right)$$
$$= \ln a + \ln e^{kt}$$
$$= \ln a + kt.$$

Setting $b = \ln a$ gives a linear equation with k as the slope and b as the y-intercept:

$$y = b + kt.$$

Secondly, we can now use linear regression on the variables t and y. (Remember that $y = \ln N$.) Finally, as step three, we transform the linear regression equation back into our original variables by substituting $\ln N$ for y and solving for N.

211

Exercises and Problems for Section 5.4

In Exercises S1–S6, write the numbers in scientific notation.

S1. One million four hundred fifty-five thousand

S2. Four hundred twenty three billion

S3. 64.7×10^3 **S4.** 12,310,000

S5. 0.00036   **S6.** 0.00471

In Exercises S7–S10, without a calculator, determine between which two powers of ten the following numbers lie.

S7. 12,500   **S8.** 0.000881

S9. $\frac{1}{3}$ **S10.** $3,850 \cdot 10^8$

Exercises

In Exercises 1–4, you wish to graph the quantities on a standard piece of paper. On which should you use a logarithmic scale? On which a linear scale? Why?

Figure 5.26

1. The wealth of 20 different people, one of whom is a multi-billionaire.

2. The number of diamonds owned by 20 people, one of whom is a multi-billionaire.

3. The number of meals per week eaten in restaurants for a random sample of 20 people worldwide.

4. The number of tuberculosis bacteria in 20 different people, some never exposed to the disease, some slightly exposed, some with mild cases, and some dying of it.

5. **(a)** Use a calculator to fill in the following tables (round to 4 decimal digits).

n	1	2	3	4	5	6	7	8	9
$\log n$									

n	10	20	30	40	50	60	70	80	90
$\log n$									

    (b) Using the results of part (a), plot the integer points 2 through 9 and the multiples of 10 from 20 to 90 on the log scaled axis shown in Figure 5.26.

For the tables in Exercises 6–8,

    (a) Use linear regression to find a linear function $y = b + mx$ that fits the data. Record the correlation coefficient.

    (b) Use linear regression on the values x and $\ln y$ to fit a function of the form $\ln y = b + mx$. Record the correlation coefficient. Convert to an exponential function $y = ae^{kx}$.

    (c) Compare the correlation coefficients. Graph the data and the two functions to assess which function fits best.

6.

x	y
30	70
85	120
122	145
157	175
255	250
312	300

7.

x	y
8	23
17	150
23	496
26	860
32	2720
37	8051

8.

x	y
3.2	35
4.7	100
5.1	100
5.5	150
6.8	200
7.6	300

Problems

9. The signing of the Declaration of Independence is marked on the log scale in Figure 5.20 on page 208. To two decimal places, what is its position?

10. **(a)** Draw a line segment about 5 inches long. On it, choose an appropriate linear scale and mark points that represent the integral powers of two from zero to the sixth power. What is true about the location of the points as the exponents get larger?

    (b) Draw a second line segment. Repeat the process in (a) but this time use a logarithmic scale so that the units are now powers of ten. What do you notice about the location of these points?

11. Figure 5.27 shows the prices of seven different items, with the scale markings representing the logarithm of the price in dollars. Give the approximate price of each item, and explain why a log scale was necessary.

      A B C   D   E   F   G

      0   1   2   3   4   5   6   7   log(price)

      Figure 5.27

12. Microfinance refers to financial services, such as loans, offered to people with very low incomes. Table 5.10 shows the number of microborrowers in 2006.[14]

    (a) Plot the data (in millions of borrowers) on a linear scale.
    (b) Plot the data on a logarithmic scale.
    (c) Which scale is more appropriate? Why?

Table 5.10

Region	Borrowers (millions)
A: Africa	8.4
B: Asia	112.7
C: Eastern Europe and Central Asia	3.4
D: Latin America and the Caribbean	6.8
E: Middle East and North Africa	1.7
F: North America and Western Europe	0.05

13. The usual distances for track (running) events are 100 meters, 200 meters, 400 meters, 800 meters, 1500 meters, 3000 meters, 5000 meters, and 10,000 meters.

    (a) Plot the length of each track event on a linear scale.
    (b) Plot the length of each track event on a logarithmic scale.
    (c) Which scale, (a) or (b), is more useful to the runner?
    (d) On each figure identify the point corresponding to 50 meters.

14. Table 5.11 shows the numbers of deaths in 2006 due to various causes in the US.[15]

    (a) Explain why a log scale is necessary to plot the data from Table 5.11.
    (b) Find the log of each value given.
    (c) Plot the data using a log scale. Label each point with the related cause.

Table 5.11

Cause	Deaths
Scarlet fever	2
Whooping cough	9
Asthma	3613
HIV	12,113
Kidney diseases	46,095
Accidents	121,599
Malignant neoplasms	559,888
Cardiovascular disease	823,746
All causes	2,426,264

15. Table 5.12 shows the dollar value of some items in 2004. Plot and label these values on a log scale.

Table 5.12

Item	Dollar value	Item	Dollar value
Pack of gum	0.50	New house	264,400
Movie ticket	9.00	Lottery winnings	100 million
New computer	1200	Bill Gates' worth	46.6 bn
Year at college	27,500	National debt	7,500 bn
Luxury car	60,400	US GDP	11,700 bn

16. Table 5.13 shows the sizes of various organisms. Plot and label these values on a log scale.

Table 5.13

Animal	Size (cm)	Animal	Size (cm)
Virus	0.0000005	Domestic cat	60
Bacterium	0.0002	Wolf (with tail)	200
Human cell	0.002	Thresher shark	600
Ant	0.8	Giant squid	2200
Hummingbird	12	Sequoia	7500

17. (a) Plot the data in Table 5.14.
    (b) What kind of function might the data from part (a) represent?
    (c) Now plot $\log y$ versus x instead of y versus x. What do you notice?

Table 5.14

x	0.2	1.3	2.1	2.8	3.4	4.5
y	5.7	12.3	21.4	34.8	52.8	113.1

18. (a) Complete the Table 5.15 with values of $y = 3^x$.
    (b) Complete Table 5.16 with values for $y = \log(3^x)$. What kind of function is this?
    (c) Complete tables for $f(x) = 2 \cdot 5^x$ and $g(x) = \log(2 \cdot 5^x)$. What kinds of functions are these?
    (d) What seems to be true about a function which is the logarithm of an exponential function? Is this true in general?

Table 5.15

x	0	1	2	3	4	5
$y = 3^x$						

Table 5.16

x	0	1	2	3	4	5
$y = \log(3^x)$						

---

[14]Based on data in Daley-Harris, *State of the Microsummit Campaign Report 2007*, p. 22.
[15]www.cdc.gov/nchs/data/nvsr/nvsr58/nvsr58_01.pdf, accessed May 30, 2010.

19. Repeat part (b) and (c) of Problem 18 using the natural log function. Is your answer to part (d) the same?

20. Table 5.17 shows newspapers' share of the expenditure of national advertisers. Using the method of Problem 22, fit an exponential function of the form $y = ae^{kx}$ to the data, where y is percent share and x is the number of years since 1950.

Table 5.17 *Newspapers' share of advertising*

	1950	1960	1970	1980	1990	1992
x	0	10	20	30	40	42
y	16.0	10.8	8.0	6.7	5.8	5.0

21. To study how recognition memory decreases with time, the following experiment was conducted. The subject read a list of 20 words slowly aloud, and later, at different time intervals, was shown a list of 40 words containing the 20 words that he or she had read. The percentage, P, of words recognized was recorded as a function of t, the time elapsed in minutes. Table 5.18 shows the averages for 5 different subjects.[16] This is modeled by $P = a \ln t + b$.

(a) Find $\ln t$ for each value of t, and then use regression on a calculator or computer to estimate a and b.

(b) Graph the data points and regression line on a coordinate system of P against $\ln t$.

(c) When does this model predict that the subjects will recognize no words? All words?

(d) Graph the data points and curve $P = a \ln t + b$ on a coordinate system with P against t, with $0 \le t \le 10{,}500$.

Table 5.18 *Percentage of words recognized*

t, min	5	15	30	60	120	240
$P\%$	73.0	61.7	58.3	55.7	50.3	46.7
t, min	480	720	1440	2880	5760	10,080
$P\%$	40.3	38.3	29.0	24.0	18.7	10.3

22. Table 5.19 shows the value, y, of US imports from China with x in years since 2002.

(a) Find a formula for a linear function $y = b + mx$ that approximates the data.

(b) Find $\ln y$ for each y value, and use the x and $\ln y$ values to find a formula for a linear function $\ln y = b + mx$ that approximates the data.

(c) Use the equation in part (b) to find an exponential function of the form $y = ae^{kx}$ that fits the data.

Table 5.19 *Value of US imports from China in millions of dollars*

	2002	2003	2004	2005	2006	2007	2008
x	0	1	2	3	4	5	6
y	125,193	152,436	196,682	243,470	287,774	321,443	337,773

23. Table 5.20 gives the length ℓ (in cm) and weight w (in gm) of 16 different fish known as threadfin bream (*Nemipterus marginatus*) found in the South China Sea.[17]

(a) Let $W = \ln w$ and $L = \ln \ell$. For these sixteen data points, plot W on the vertical axis and L on the horizontal axis. Describe the resulting scatterplot.

(b) Fitting a line to the scatterplot you drew in part (a), find a possible formula for W in terms of L.

(c) Based on your formula for part (b), find a possible formula for w in terms of ℓ.

(d) Comment on your formula, keeping in mind what you know about units as well the typical relationship between weight, volume, and length.

Table 5.20 *Length and weight of fish*

Type	1	2	3	4	5	6	7	8
ℓ	8.1	9.1	10.2	11.9	12.2	13.8	14.8	15.7
w	6.3	9.6	11.6	18.5	26.2	36.1	40.1	47.3
Type	9	10	11	12	13	14	15	16
ℓ	16.6	17.7	18.7	19.0	20.6	21.9	22.9	23.5
w	65.6	69.4	76.4	82.5	106.6	119.8	169.2	173.3

24. A light, flashing regularly, consists of cycles, each cycle having a dark phase and a light phase. The frequency of this light is measured in cycles per second. As the frequency is increased, the eye initially perceives a series of flashes of light, then a coarse flicker, a fine flicker, and ultimately a steady light. The frequency at which the flickering disappears is called the fusion frequency.[18] Table 5.21 shows the results of an experiment[19] in which the fusion frequency F was measured as a function of the light intensity I. It is modeled by $F = a \ln I + b$.

(a) Find $\ln I$ for each value of I, and then use linear regression on a calculator or computer to estimate a and b in the equation $F = a \ln I + b$.

(b) Plot F against $\ln I$, showing the data points and the line.

---

[16]Adapted from D. Lewis, *Quantitative Methods in Psychology* (New York: McGraw-Hill, 1960).

[17]Data taken from *Introduction to Tropical Fish Stock Assessment* by Per Sparre, Danish Institute for Fisheries Research, and Siebren C. Venema, FAO Fisheries Department, available at http://www.fao.org/docrep/W5449E/w5449e00.htm. This source cites the following original reference: Pauly, D., 1983. Some simple methods for the assessment of tropical fish stocks.

[18]R. S. Woodworth, *Experimental Psychology* (New York: Holt and Company, 1948).

[19]D. Lewis, *Quantitative Methods in Psychology* (New York: McGraw-Hill, 1960).

(c) Plot F against I, showing the data points and the curve and give its equation.

(d) The units of I are arbitrary, that is, not given. If the units of I were changed, which of the constants a and b would be affected, and in what way?

Table 5.21 *Fusion frequency, F, as a function of the light intensity, I*

I	0.8	1.9	4.4	10.0	21.4	48.4	92.5	218.7	437.3	980.0
F	8.0	12.1	15.2	18.5	21.7	25.3	28.3	31.9	35.2	38.2

CHAPTER SUMMARY

- **Logarithms**
  Common log: $y = \log x$ means $10^y = x$.
    $\log 10 = 1, \log 1 = 0$.
  Natural log: $y = \ln x$ means $e^y = x$.
    $\ln e = 1, \ln 1 = 0$.

- **Properties of Logs**

  $\log(ab) = \log a + \log b$ $\ln(ab) = \ln a + \ln b$.

  $\log(a/b) = \log a - \log b$ $\ln(a/b) = \ln a - \ln b$.

  $\log(b^t) = t \log b$ $\ln(b^t) = t \ln b$.

  $\log(10^x) = 10^{\log x} = x$ $\ln(e^x) = e^{\ln x} = x$.

- **Converting Between Base b and Base e**
  If $Q = ab^t$ and $Q = ae^{kt}$, then $k = \ln b$.

- **Solving Equations Using Logs**
  Solve equations such as $ab^t = c$ and $ae^{kt} = c$ using logs.
  Not all exponential equations can be solved with logs, e.g. $2^t = 3 + t$.

- **Logarithmic Functions**
  Graph; domain; range; concavity; asymptotes.

- **Applications of Logarithms**
  Doubling time; half life;
  Chemical acidity; orders of magnitude; decibels.

- **Logarithmic Scales**
  Plotting data; log-log scales. Linearizing data and fitting curves to data using logs.

- **Limits and Limits from the Right and from the Left**

REVIEW EXERCISES AND PROBLEMS FOR CHAPTER FIVE

Exercises

In Exercises 1–2, convert to the form $Q = ab^t$.

1. $Q = 7e^{-10t}$ **2.** $Q = 5e^t$

In Exercises 3–6, convert to the form $Q = ae^{kt}$.

3. $Q = 4 \cdot 7^t$ **4.** $Q = 2 \cdot 3^t$

5. $Q = 4 \cdot 8^{1.3t}$ **6.** $Q = 973 \cdot 6^{2.1t}$

Solve the equations in Exercises 7–22 exactly if possible.

7. $1.04^t = 3$ **8.** $e^{0.15t} = 25$

9. $3(1.081)^t = 14$ **10.** $40e^{-0.2t} = 12$

11. $5(1.014)^{3t} = 12$ **12.** $5(1.15)^t = 8(1.07)^t$

13. $5(1.031)^x = 8$ **14.** $4(1.171)^x = 7(1.088)^x$

15. $3\log(2x+6) = 6$ **16.** $1.7(2.1)^{3x} = 2(4.5)^x$

17. $3^{4\log x} = 5$ **18.** $100^{2x+3} = \sqrt[3]{10,000}$

19. $13e^{0.081t} = 25e^{0.032t}$ **20.** $87e^{0.066t} = 3t + 7$

21. $\dfrac{\log x^2 + \log x^3}{\log(100x)} = 3$

22. $\log x + \log(x-1) = \log 2$

In Exercises 23–25, simplify fully.

23. $\log\left(100^{x+1}\right)$ **24.** $\ln\left(e \cdot e^{2+M}\right)$

25. $\ln(A+B) - \ln(A^{-1} + B^{-1})$

In Exercises 26–31, state the domain of the function and identify any vertical asymptote of its graph. You need not graph the function.

26. $y = \ln(x+8)$ **27.** $y = \log(x-20)$

28. $y = \log(12-x)$ **29.** $y = \ln(300-x)$

30. $y = \ln\left(x - e^2\right)$ **31.** $y = \log(x+15)$

In Exercises 32–37, say where you would mark the given animal lifespan on an inch scale, where 0 inches represents $10^0 = 1$ year and 5 inches represents $10^5 = 100,000$ years. Give your answer to the nearest tenth of an inch.[20]

32. A colony of quaking aspen in Utah is estimated to be 80,000 years old.

33. A bristlecone pine in California named Methuselah is es-

timated by ring count to be 4838 years old.

34. A specimen of antarctic sponge is estimated to be 1550 years old.

35. The Puget Sound saltwater clam called a geoduck can live for 160 years.

36. The oldest recorded dog lived 29 years.

37. The common house mouse can live 4 years in captivity.

Problems

38. Suppose that $x = \log A$ and that $y = \log B$. Write the following expressions in terms of x and y.

(a) $\log(AB)$ (b) $\log(A^3 \cdot \sqrt{B})$

(c) $\log(A - B)$ (d) $\dfrac{\log A}{\log B}$

(e) $\log \dfrac{A}{B}$ (f) AB

39. Let $p = \ln m$ and $q = \ln n$. Write the following expressions in terms of p and/or q without using logs.

(a) $\ln(nm^4)$ (b) $\ln\left(\dfrac{1}{n}\right)$

(c) $\dfrac{\ln m}{\ln n}$ (d) $\ln(n^3)$

40. Let $x = 10^U$ and $y = 10^V$. Write the following expressions in terms of U and/or V without using logs.

(a) $\log xy$ (b) $\log\left(\dfrac{x}{y}\right)$

(c) $\log x^3$ (d) $\log\left(\dfrac{1}{y}\right)$

41. Solve the following equations. Give approximate solutions if exact ones can't be found.

(a) $e^{x+3} = 8$ (b) $4(1.12^x) = 5$

(c) $e^{-0.13x} = 4$ (d) $\log(x - 5) = 2$

(e) $2\ln(3x) + 5 = 8$ (f) $\ln x - \ln(x-1) = 1/2$

(g) $e^x = 3x + 5$ (h) $3^x = x^3$

(i) $\ln x = -x^2$

42. Solve for x exactly.

(a) $\dfrac{3^x}{5^{x-1}} = 2^{x-1}$

(b) $-3 + e^{x+1} = 2 + e^{x-2}$

(c) $\ln(2x - 2) - \ln(x - 1) = \ln x$

(d) $9^x - 7 \cdot 3^x = -6$

(e) $\ln\left(\dfrac{e^{4x} + 3}{e}\right) = 1$

(f) $\dfrac{\ln(8x) - 2\ln(2x)}{\ln x} = 1$

In Problems 43–46, , the Richter scale ratings for two earthquakes are M_1 and M_2, with $M_2 > M_1$. If the earthquakes have seismic waves of sizes W_1 and W_2, respectively, then

$$M_2 - M_1 = \log\left(\frac{W_2}{W_1}\right).$$

How many times greater than the smaller one are the seismic waves for the larger one?

43. $M_1 = 4.2$ and $M_2 = 6.4$

44. $M_1 = 5.3$ and $M_2 = 5.8$

45. $M_1 = 4.4$ and $M_2 = 5.6$

46. $M_1 = 5.7$ and $M_2 = 8.1$

47. With t in years, the formulas for dollar balances of two bank accounts are:

$$f(t) = 1100(1.05)^t \quad \text{and} \quad g(t) = 1500e^{0.05t}.$$

(a) Describe in words the bank account modeled by f.

(b) Describe the account modeled by g. State the effective annual rate.

(c) What continuous interest rate has the same effective growth rate as f?

48. (a) Let $B = 5000(1.06)^t$ give the balance of a bank account after t years. If the formula for B is written $B = 5000e^{kt}$, estimate the value of k correct to four decimal places. What is the financial meaning of k?

(b) The balance of a bank account after t years is given by the formula $B = 7500e^{0.072t}$. If the formula for B is written $B = 7500b^t$, find b exactly, and give the value of b correct to four decimal places. What is the financial meaning of b?

49. The number of bacteria present in a culture after t hours is given by the formula $N = 1000e^{0.69t}$.

(a) How many bacteria will there be after $1/2$ hour?

(b) How long before there are 1,000,000 bacteria?

(c) What is the doubling time?

---

[20]From http://en.wikipedia.org/wiki/Maximum_life_span and http://en.wikipedia.org/wiki/List_of_long-living_organisms, accessed June, 2010.

50. In 2010, the population of the country Erehwon was 50 million people and increasing by 2.9% every year. The population of the country Ecalpon, on other hand, was 45 million people and increasing by 3.2% every year.

   (a) For each country, write a formula expressing the population as a function of time t, where t is the number of years since 2010.

   (b) Find the value(s) of t, if any, when the two countries have the same population.

   (c) When is the population of Ecalpon double that of Erehwon?

51. The price $P(t) = 5(2)^{t/7}$ of a good is rising due to inflation, where t is time in years.

   (a) What is the doubling time?

   (b) What is the annual inflation rate?

52. Let $P = 15(1.04)^t$ give the population (in thousands) of a town, with t in years.

   (a) Describe the population growth in words.

   (b) If the formula for P is written $P = 15(b)^{12t}$, find b exactly. What is the meaning of b in the context of the population?

   (c) If the formula for P is written $P = 15(2)^{t/c}$, find the value of c correct to 2 decimals. What is the meaning of c in this context?

In Problems 53–55, use $v(t) = 20e^{0.2t}$ and $w(t) = 12e^{0.22t}$.

53. Solve $v(t) = 30$ exactly.

54. Solve $3v(2t) = 2w(3t)$ exactly.

55. Find the doubling time of w.

56. A calculator confirms that $5 \approx 10^{0.7}$. Show how to use this fact to approximate the value of $\log 25$.

57. **(a)** What are the domain and range of $f(x) = 10^x$? What is the asymptote of $f(x) = 10^x$?

   (b) What does your answer to part (a) tell you about the domain, range, and asymptotes of $g(x) = \log x$?

58. What is the domain of $y = \ln(x^2 - x - 6)$?

59. **(a)** Plot the data given by Table 5.22. What kind of function might fit this data well?

   (b) Using the substitution $z = \ln x$, transform the data in Table 5.22, and compile your results into a new table. Plot the transformed data as $\ln x$ versus y.

   (c) What kind of function gives a good fit to the plot you made in part (b)? Find a formula for y in terms of z that fits the data well.

   (d) Using the formula from part (c), find a formula for y in terms of x that gives a good fit to the data in Table 5.22.

(e) What does your formula from part (d) tell you about x as a function of y (as opposed to y as a function of x)?

Table 5.22

x	0.21	0.55	1.31	3.22	5.15	12.48
y	−11	−2	6.5	16	20.5	29

60. Radioactive carbon-14 decays according to the function $Q(t) = Q_0 e^{-0.000121t}$ where t is time in years, $Q(t)$ is the quantity remaining at time t, and Q_0 is the amount of present at time $t = 0$. Estimate the age of a skull if 23% of the original quantity of carbon-14 remains.

61. Suppose 2 mg of a drug is injected into a person's bloodstream. As the drug is metabolized, the quantity diminishes at the continuous rate of 4% per hour.

   (a) Find a formula for $Q(t)$, the quantity of the drug remaining in the body after t hours.

   (b) By what percent does the drug level decrease during any given hour?

   (c) The person must receive an additional 2 mg of the drug whenever its level has diminished to 0.25 mg. When must the person receive the second injection?

   (d) When must the person receive the third injection?

62. A rubber ball is dropped onto a hard surface from a height of 6 feet, and it bounces up and down. At each bounce it rises to 90% of the height from which it fell.

   (a) Find a formula for $h(n)$, the height reached by the ball on bounce n.

   (b) How high will the ball bounce on the 12th bounce?

   (c) How many bounces before the ball rises no higher than an inch?

63. Oil leaks from a tank. At hour $t = 0$ there are 250 gallons of oil in the tank. Each hour after that, 4% of the oil leaks out.

   (a) What percent of the original 250 gallons has leaked out after 10 hours? Why is it less than $10 \cdot 4\% = 40\%$?

   (b) If $Q(t) = Q_0 e^{kt}$ is the quantity of oil remaining after t hours, find the value of k. What does k tell you about the leaking oil?

64. Before the advent of computers, logarithms were calculated by hand. Various tricks were used to evaluate different logs. One such trick exploits the fact that $2^{10} \approx 1000$. (It actually equals 1024.) Using this fact and the log properties, show that

   (a) $\log 2 \approx 0.3$ **(b)** $\log 7 \approx 0.85$

65. A googol is the number 1 followed by 100 zeros, or 10^{100}. A googolplex is the number 1 followed by a googol zeros, or 10^{googol}. Evaluate:

(a) $\sqrt{\log{(\text{googol})}}$ **(b)** $\log{\sqrt{\text{googol}}}$

(c) $\sqrt{\log{(\text{googolplex})}}$

66. Since $e = 2.718\ldots$ we know that $2 < e < 3$, which means that $2^2 < e^2 < 3^2$. Without using a calculator, explain why

(a) $1 < \ln 3 < 2$ **(b)** $1 < \ln 4 < 2$

67. Simplify the expression $\sqrt{1000^{\frac{1}{12} \cdot \log k}}$. Your answer should be exact and should not involve exponents or logs, though it may involve radicals.

CHECK YOUR UNDERSTANDING

Are the statements in Problems 1–37 true or false? Give an explanation for your answer.

1. The log of 2000 is less than 3.

2. The inverse of $y = \ln x$ is $y = e^x$.

3. If $2^x = 1024$ then $x = 10$.

4. If a quantity grew to 4 times its original amount in 8 hours then its doubling time is one-half hour.

5. If the function $y = ab^t$ is converted to the form $y = ae^{kt}$, k is always equal to $\ln b$.

6. If x is a positive number, $\log x$ is the exponent of 10 that gives x.

7. If $10^y = x$ then $\log x = y$.

8. The quantity 10^{-k} is a negative number when k is positive.

9. For any n, we have $\log(10^n) = n$.

10. If $n > 0$, then $10^{\log n} = n$.

11. If a and b are positive, $\log\left(\dfrac{a}{b}\right) = \dfrac{\log a}{\log b}$.

12. If a and b are positive, $\ln(a + b) = \ln a + \ln b$.

13. For any value a, $\log a = \ln a$.

14. For any value x, $\ln(e^{2x}) = 2x$.

15. The function $y = \log x$ has an asymptote at $y = 0$.

16. The graph of the function $y = \log x$ is concave down.

17. The reflected graph of $y = \log x$ across the line $y = x$ is the graph of $y = 10^x$.

18. If $y = \log \sqrt{x}$ then $y = \frac{1}{2} \log x$.

19. The function $y = \log(b^t)$ is always equal to $y = (\log b)^t$.

20. The values of $\ln e$ and $\log 10$ are both 1.

21. If $7.32 = e^t$ then $t = \dfrac{7.32}{e}$.

22. If $50(0.345)^t = 4$, then $t = \dfrac{\log(4/50)}{\log 0.345}$.

23. If $ab^t = n$, then $t = \dfrac{\log(n/a)}{\log b}$.

24. The doubling time of a quantity $Q = Q_0 e^{kt}$ is the time it takes for any t-value to double.

25. The half-life of a quantity is the time it takes for the quantity to be reduced by half.

26. If the half-life of a substance is 5 hours then there will be $\frac{1}{4}$ of the substance in 25 hours.

27. If $y = 6(3)^t$, then $y = 6e^{(\ln 3)t}$.

28. If a population doubles in size every 20 years, its annual continuous growth rate is 20%.

29. If $Q = Q_0 e^{kt}$, then $t = \dfrac{\ln(Q/Q_0)}{k}$.

30. Log scales provide a way to graph quantities that have vastly different magnitudes.

31. An elephant weighs about 8000 pounds. Its weight, plotted on a log scale, would be a little before 4.

32. A virus has a cell size of about 0.0000005 cm. On a log scale, its size would be plotted at about 7.

33. The closest star outside our solar system is about 26,395,630,000,000 miles away from Earth. This distance, plotted on a log scale, would occur a little after 26.

34. In a graph made using a log-log scale, consecutive powers of 10 are equally spaced on the horizontal axis and on the vertical axis.

35. One million and one billion differ by one order of magnitude.

36. After fitting a data set with both an exponential function, $y = Ae^{kx}$, and a power function, $y = Bx^n$, we must have $B = A$.

37. Given the points on a cubic curve, $(1, 1)$, $(2, 8)$, $(3, 27)$ and $(4, 64)$ it is not possible to fit an exponential function to this data.

SKILLS REFRESHER FOR CHAPTER 5: LOGARITHMS

We list the definitions and properties of the common and natural logarithms.

> **Properties of Logarithms** If $M, N > 0$:
> - Logarithm of a product: $\qquad \log MN = \log M + \log N \qquad \ln MN = \ln M + \ln N$
> - Logarithm of a quotient: $\qquad \log M/N = \log M - \log N \qquad \ln M/N = \ln M - \ln N$
> - Logarithm of a power: $\qquad \log M^P = P \log M \qquad \ln M^P = P \ln M$
> - Logarithm of 1: $\qquad \log 1 = 0 \qquad \ln 1 = 0$
> - Logarithm of the base: $\qquad \log 10 = 1 \qquad \ln e = 1$

Be aware of the following two common errors,

$$\log(M + N) \neq (\log M)(\log N)$$

and

$$\log(M - N) \neq \frac{\log M}{\log N}.$$

> **Relationships Between Logarithms and Exponents**
> - $\log N = x$ if and only if $10^x = N \qquad \ln N = x$ if and only if $e^x = N$
> - $\log 10^x = x \qquad \ln e^x = x$
> - $10^{\log x} = x$, for $x > 0 \qquad e^{\ln x} = x$, for $x > 0$

Example 1   Evaluate without a calculator:

    (a) $\log 10{,}000$ (b) $\ln 1$

Solution   (a) Common logarithms are powers of 10. The power of 10 needed to get 10,000 is 4, so $\log 10{,}000 = 4$.

    (b) Natural logarithms are powers of e. The power of e needed to get 1 is zero, so $\ln 1 = 0$.

Example 2   Write the equation in exponential form:

    (a) $\log x = -3$ (b) $\ln x = \sqrt{2}$

Solution   (a) By definition $\log x = -3$ means $10^{-3} = x$.

    (b) By definition $\ln x = \sqrt{2}$ means $e^{\sqrt{2}} = x$.

Example 3   Write the equation in logarithmic form:

    (a) $10^x = 1000$ (b) $10^{-2} = 0.01$ (c) $e^{-1} = 0.368$

Solution   (a) By definition $10^x = 1000$ means $\log 1000 = x$.

    (b) By definition $10^{-2} = 0.01$ means $\log 0.01 = -2$.

    (c) By definition $e^{-1} = 0.368$ means $\ln 0.368 = -1$.

Example 4   Write the expression using sums and/or differences of logarithmic expressions that do not contain the logarithms of products, quotients or powers.

(a) $\log(10x)$

(b) $\ln\left(\dfrac{e^2}{\sqrt{x}}\right)$

Solution   (a)

$$\log(10x) = \log 10 + \log x \quad \text{Logarithm of a product}$$
$$= 1 + \log x. \quad \text{Logarithm of the base}$$

(b)

$$\ln\left(\frac{e^2}{\sqrt{x}}\right) = \ln e^2 - \ln \sqrt{x} \quad \text{Logarithm of a quotient}$$
$$= \ln e^2 - \ln x^{1/2}$$
$$= 2\ln e - \frac{1}{2}\ln x \quad \text{Logarithm of a power}$$
$$= 2 \cdot 1 - \frac{1}{2}\ln x \quad \text{Logarithm of the base}$$
$$= 2 - \frac{1}{2}\ln x.$$

Example 5   Write the expression as a single logarithm.

(a) $\ln x - 2\ln y$

(b) $3(\log x + \frac{4}{3}\log y)$

Solution   (a)

$$\ln x - 2\ln y = \ln x - \ln y^2 \quad \text{Logarithm of a power}$$
$$= \ln\left(\frac{x}{y^2}\right). \quad \text{Logarithm of a quotient}$$

(b)

$$3\left(\log x + \frac{4}{3}\log y\right) = 3\log x + 4\log y$$
$$= \log x^3 + \log y^4 \quad \text{Logarithm of a power}$$
$$= \log(x^3 y^4). \quad \text{Logarithm of a product}$$

Example 6   Express in terms of x without logarithms.

(a) $e^{3\ln x}$

(b) $\log 10^{2x}$

Solution   (a)

$$e^{3\ln x} = e^{\ln x^3} \quad \text{Logarithm of a power}$$
$$= x^3. \quad \text{Logarithm of the base}$$

(b) $\log 10^{2x} = 2x.$ Logarithm of the base

Example 7   Solve the equation for x.

    (a) $12e^x = 5$ (b) $2^{-3x} = 17$

Solution   (a)

$$12e^x = 5$$
$$e^x = \frac{5}{12} \quad \text{Dividing by 12}$$
$$\ln e^x = \ln\left(\frac{5}{12}\right) \quad \text{Taking ln of both sides}$$
$$x = \ln\left(\frac{5}{12}\right). \quad \text{Logarithm of the base}$$

(b)

$$2^{-3x} = 17$$
$$\log 2^{-3x} = \log 17 \quad \text{Taking logs of both sides}$$
$$-3x \log 2 = \log 17 \quad \text{Logarithm of a power}$$
$$-3x = \frac{\log 17}{\log 2} \quad \text{Dividing by log 2}$$
$$x = -\frac{\log 17}{3 \log 2}. \quad \text{Dividing by -3}$$

Example 8   Solve the equation for x.

    (a) $2(\log(2x + 50)) - 4 = 0$ (b) $\ln(x + 2) = 3$

Solution   (a)

$$2(\log(2x + 50)) - 4 = 0$$
$$2(\log(2x + 50)) = 4$$
$$\log(2x + 50) = 2$$
$$10^{\log(2x+50)} = 10^2 \quad \text{Converting to exponential form}$$
$$2x + 50 = 10^2$$
$$2x + 50 = 100$$
$$2x = 50$$
$$x = 25.$$

(b)

$$\ln(x + 2) = 3$$
$$e^{\ln(x+2)} = e^3 \quad \text{Raise } e \text{ to each side}$$
$$x + 2 = e^3$$
$$x = e^3 - 2.$$

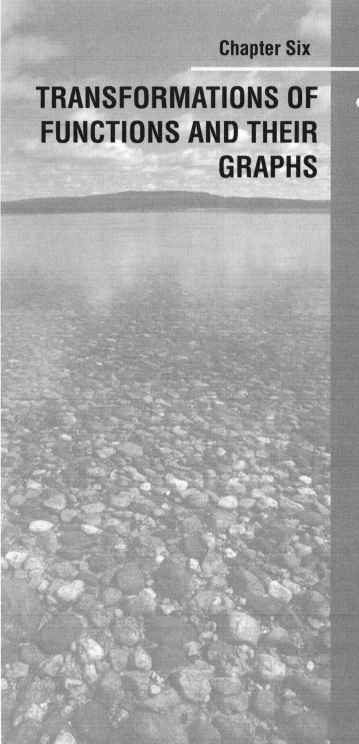

Chapter Six

TRANSFORMATIONS OF FUNCTIONS AND THEIR GRAPHS

Contents

6.1 VERTICAL AND HORIZONTAL SHIFTS

Suppose we shift the graph of a function vertically or horizontally, giving the graph of a new function. In this section we see the relationship between the formulas for the original function and the new function.

Vertical Shift: The Heating Schedule for an Office Building

We start with an example of a vertical shift in the context of the heating schedule for a building.

Example 1 To save money, an office building is kept warm only during business hours. Figure 6.1 shows the temperature, H, in °F, as a function of time, t, in hours after midnight. At midnight ($t = 0$), the building's temperature is 50°F. This temperature is maintained until 4 am. Then the building begins to warm up so that by 8 am the temperature is 70°F. At 4 pm the building begins to cool. By 8 pm, the temperature is again 50°F.

Suppose that the building's superintendent decides to keep the building 5°F warmer than before. Sketch a graph of the new function.

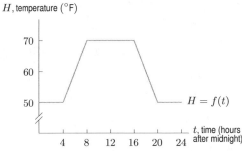

Figure 6.1: The heating schedule at an office building, $H = f(t)$

Figure 6.2: Graph of new heating schedule, $H = p(t)$, obtained by shifting original graph, $H = f(t)$, upward by 5 units

Solution The graph of f, the heating schedule function of Figure 6.1, is shifted upward by 5 units. The new heating schedule, $H = p(t)$, is graphed in Figure 6.2. The building's overnight temperature is now 55°F instead of 50°F and its daytime temperature is 75°F instead of 70°F. The 5°F increase in temperature corresponds to the 5-unit vertical shift in the graph.

Example 2 What is the relationship between the formula for $f(t)$, the original heating schedule and $p(t)$, the new heating schedule?

Solution   The temperature under the new schedule, $p(t)$, is always $5°F$ warmer than the temperature under the old schedule, $f(t)$. Thus,

$$\underset{\text{at time } t}{\text{New temperature}} = \underset{\text{at time } t}{\text{Old temperature}} + 5.$$

Writing this algebraically:

$$\underbrace{p(t)}_{\substack{\text{New temperature} \\ \text{at time } t}} = \underbrace{f(t)}_{\substack{\text{Old temperature} \\ \text{at time } t}} + 5.$$

The relationship between the formulas for p and f is given by the equation $p(t) = f(t) + 5$.

We can get information from the relationship $p(t) = f(t) + 5$, although we do not have an explicit formula for f or p.

Suppose we need to know the temperature at 6 am under the schedule $p(t)$. The graph of $f(t)$ shows that under the old schedule $f(6) = 60$. Substituting $t = 6$ into the equation relating f and p gives $p(6)$:

$$p(6) = f(6) + 5 = 60 + 5 = 65.$$

Thus, at 6 am the temperature under the new schedule is $65°F$.

Example 3   Find $r(t)$, the formula for the heating schedule if at each time the temperature is $2°F$ lower than the original temperature.

Solution   Since

$$\underset{\text{at time } t}{\text{New temperature}} = \underset{\text{at time } t}{\text{Old temperature}} - 2$$

we have

$$\underbrace{r(t)}_{\substack{\text{New temperature} \\ \text{at time } t}} = \underbrace{f(t)}_{\substack{\text{Old temperature} \\ \text{at time } t}} - 2.$$

The graph of $r(t)$ is the graph of f shifted down by 2 units.

Generalizing these observations to any function g:

If $g(x)$ is a function and k is a positive constant, then the graph of
- $y = g(x) + k$ is the graph of $y = g(x)$ shifted vertically upward by k units.
- $y = g(x) - k$ is the graph of $y = g(x)$ shifted vertically downward by k units.

Horizontal Shift: The Heating Schedule

Example 4   The superintendent then changes the original heating schedule to start two hours earlier. The building now begins to warm at 2 am instead of 4 am, reaches $70°F$ at 6 am instead of 8 am, begins cooling off at 2 pm instead of 4 pm, and returns to $50°F$ at 6 pm instead of 8 pm. How are these changes reflected in the graph of the heating schedule?

Solution   Figure 6.3 gives a graph of $H = q(t)$, the new heating schedule, which is obtained by shifting the graph of the original heating schedule, $H = f(t)$, two units to the left.

Figure 6.3: Graph of new heating schedule, $H = q(t)$, found by shifting, f, the original graph 2 units to the left

Notice that the upward shift in Example 1 results in a warmer temperature, whereas the leftward shift in Example 4 results in an earlier schedule.

Example 5   In Example 4 the heating schedule was changed to 2 hours earlier, shifting the graph horizontally 2 units to the left. Find a formula for q, this new schedule, in terms of f, the original schedule.

Solution   The old schedule always reaches a given temperature 2 hours after the new schedule. For example, at 4 am the temperature under the new schedule reaches 60°. The temperature under the old schedule reaches 60° at 6 am, 2 hours later. The temperature reaches 65° at 5 am under the new schedule, but not until 7 am, under the old schedule. In general, we see that

$$\begin{array}{ccc} \text{Temperature under new schedule} & & \text{Temperature under old schedule} \\ \text{at time } t & = & \text{at time } (t + 2), \text{ two hours later.} \end{array}$$

Algebraically, we have
$$q(t) = f(t + 2).$$
This is a formula for q in terms of f.

Let's check the formula from Example 5 by using it to calculate $q(14)$, the temperature under the new schedule at 2 pm. The formula gives
$$q(14) = f(14 + 2) = f(16).$$
Figure 6.1 shows that $f(16) = 70$. Thus, $q(14) = 70$. This agrees with Figure 6.3.

Example 6   Suppose now the heating schedule is made 1 hour later than it was originally. Find the function $s(t)$ that describes this schedule.

Solution   The new schedule reaches a particular temperature 1 hour later than the original. For example, under the old schedule, the temperature reaches 60°F at 6 am, while it reaches 60°F at 7 am under the new schedule. Thus

$$\begin{array}{ccc} \text{Temperature under new schedule} & & \text{Temperature under old schedule} \\ \text{at time } t & = & \text{at time } (t - 1), \text{ one hour earlier.} \end{array}$$

Thus, we have
$$s(t) = f(t - 1).$$
The graph of $s(t)$ is the graph of f shifted to the right by 1 unit.

Generalizing these observations to any function g:

If $g(x)$ is a function and k is a positive constant, then the graph of
- $y = g(x + k)$ is the graph of $y = g(x)$ shifted horizontally to the left by k units.
- $y = g(x - k)$ is the graph of $y = g(x)$ shifted horizontally to the right by k units.

A vertical or horizontal shift of the graph of a function is called a *translation* because it does not change the shape of the graph, but simply translates it to another position in the plane. Shifts or translations are the simplest examples of *transformations* of a function. We will see others in later sections of Chapter 6.

Inside Versus Outside Changes

Since the horizontal shift in the heating schedule, $q(t) = f(t + 2)$, involves a change to the input value, it is called an *inside change* to f. Similarly the vertical shift, $p(t) = f(t) + 5$, is called an *outside change* because it involves changes to the output value.

Example 7   If $n = f(A)$ gives the number of gallons of paint needed to cover a house of area A ft^2, explain the meaning of the expressions $f(A + 10)$ and $f(A) + 10$ in the context of painting.

Solution   These two expressions are similar in that they both involve adding 10. However, for $f(A + 10)$, the 10 is added on the inside, so 10 is added to the area, A. Thus,

$$n = f(\underbrace{A + 10}_{\text{Area}}) = \begin{array}{c}\text{Amount of paint needed} \\ \text{to cover an area of } (A + 10) \text{ ft}^2\end{array} = \begin{array}{c}\text{Amount of paint needed to cover} \\ \text{an area 10 ft}^2 \text{ larger than } A.\end{array}$$

The expression $f(A) + 10$ represents an outside change. We are adding 10 to $f(A)$, which represents an amount of paint, not an area. We have

$$n = \underbrace{f(A)}_{\substack{\text{Amount} \\ \text{of paint}}} + 10 = \begin{array}{c}\text{Amount of paint needed} \\ \text{to cover region of area } A\end{array} + 10 \text{ gals} = \begin{array}{c}10 \text{ gallons more paint than} \\ \text{amount needed to cover area } A.\end{array}$$

In $f(A + 10)$, we added 10 square feet on the inside of the function, which means that the area to be painted is now 10 ft^2 larger. In $f(A) + 10$, we added 10 gallons to the outside, which means that we have 10 more gallons of paint than we need.

Combining Horizontal and Vertical Shifts

We have seen how a function's formula changes when we shift its graph horizontally or vertically. What happens when we shift it both horizontally and vertically?

Example 8   Let r be the transformation of the heating schedule function, $H = f(t)$, given by

$$r(t) = f(t - 2) - 5.$$

(a) Sketch the graph of $H = r(t)$.
(b) Describe in words the heating schedule determined by r.

Solution   (a) To graph r, we break this transformation into two steps. First, we sketch a graph of $H = f(t - 2)$. This is an inside change to the function f and it results in the graph of f being shifted 2 units to the right. Next, we sketch a graph of $H = f(t - 2) - 5$. This graph can be found by shifting our sketch of $H = f(t - 2)$ down 5 units. The resulting graph is shown in Figure 6.4. The graph of r is the graph of f shifted 2 units to the right and 5 units down.
(b) The function r represents a schedule that is both 2 hours later and 5 degrees cooler than the original schedule.

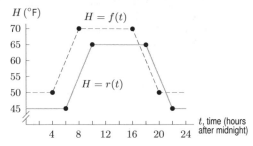

Figure 6.4: Graph of $r(t) = f(t - 2) - 5$ is graph of $H = f(t)$ shifted right by 2 and down by 5

We can use transformations to relate unfamiliar functions to functions we already know.

Example 9   A graph of $f(x) = x^2$ is in Figure 6.5. Define g by shifting the graph of f to the right 2 units and down 1 unit; see Figure 6.6. Find a formula for g in terms of f. Find a formula for g in terms of x.

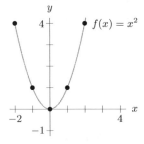

Figure 6.5: The graph of $f(x) = x^2$

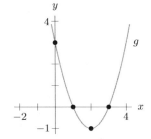

Figure 6.6: The graph of g, a transformation of f

Solution   The graph of g is the graph of f shifted to the right 2 units and down 1 unit, so a formula for g is $g(x) = f(x - 2) - 1$. Since $f(x) = x^2$, we have $f(x - 2) = (x - 2)^2$. Therefore,

$$g(x) = (x - 2)^2 - 1.$$

It is a good idea to check by graphing $g(x) = (x - 2)^2 - 1$ and comparing the graph with Figure 6.6.

Exercises and Problems for Section 6.1

Skill Refresher

In Exercises S1–S4, evaluate each function at $x = 4$.

S1. $f(x) = \sqrt{x}$ **S2.** $g(x) = \sqrt{x} + 6$

S3. $h(x) = \sqrt{x} - 3$ **S4.** $k(x) = \sqrt{x + 5}$

In Exercises S5–S8, solve for x.

S5. $e^x = 1$ **S6.** $e^{x-5} = 1$

S7. $e^{x+8} = 1$ **S8.** $e^x - 3 = 1$

S9. Describe shift(s) that can be applied to the graph of $f(x) = \ln x$ to obtain a graph of the following:

  (a) $y = \ln(x - 4)$ **(b)** $y = \ln(x) - 7$

  (c) $y = \ln(x + \sqrt{2})$ **(d)** $y = \ln(x - 3) + 5$

S10. Describe shift(s) that can be applied to the graph of $f(x) = \dfrac{1}{x}$ to obtain a graph of the following:

  (a) $y = \dfrac{1}{x + 8}$ **(b)** $y = \dfrac{1}{x} + 3$

  (c) $y = \dfrac{1}{x} - \dfrac{1}{5}$ **(d)** $y = \dfrac{1}{x - 2} - \ln 7$

Exercises

1. Using Table 6.1, complete the tables for g, h, k, m, where:

  (a) $g(x) = f(x - 1)$ **(b)** $h(x) = f(x + 1)$

  (c) $k(x) = f(x) + 3$ **(d)** $m(x) = f(x - 1) + 3$

Explain how the graph of each function relates to the graph of $f(x)$.

Table 6.1

x	-2	-1	0	1	2
$f(x)$	-3	0	2	1	-1

x	-1	0	1	2	3
$g(x)$					

x	-3	-2	-1	0	1
$h(x)$					

x	-2	-1	0	1	2
$k(x)$					

x	-1	0	1	2	3
$m(x)$					

2. Match the graphs in (a)–(f) with the formulas in (i)–(vi).

  (i) $y = |x|$ (ii) $y = |x| - 1.2$

  (iii) $y = |x - 1.2|$ (iv) $y = |x| + 2.5$

  (v) $y = |x + 3.4|$ (vi) $y = |x - 3| + 2.7$

(a) (b)

(c) (d)

(e) (f)

3. The graph of $f(x)$ contains the point $(3, -4)$. What point must be on the graph of

  (a) $f(x) + 5$?   **(b)** $f(x + 5)$?

  (c) $f(x - 3) - 2$?

In Exercises 4–7, graph the transformations of $f(x)$ in Figure 6.7.

Figure 6.7

4. $y = f(x + 2)$ **5.** $y = f(x) + 2$

6. $y = f(x - 1) - 5$ **7.** $y = f(x + 6) - 4$

8. Let $f(x) = 4^x$, $g(x) = 4^x + 2$, and $h(x) = 4^x - 3$. What is the relationship between the graph of $f(x)$ and the graphs of $h(x)$ and $g(x)$?

9. Let $f(x) = \left(\frac{1}{3}\right)^x$, $g(x) = \left(\frac{1}{3}\right)^{x+4}$, and $h(x) = \left(\frac{1}{3}\right)^{x-2}$. How do the graphs of $g(x)$ and $h(x)$ compare to the graph of $f(x)$?

10. The domain of the function $g(x)$ is $-2 < x < 7$. What is the domain of $g(x - 2)$?

11. The range of the function $R(s)$ is $100 \leq R(s) \leq 200$. What is the range of $R(s) - 150$?

12. The figure gives a graph of f. Sketch a graph of $y = f(x + 3) + 3$. Label all important features.

Write a formula and graph the transformations of $m(n) = \frac{1}{2}n^2$ in Exercises 13–20.

13. $y = m(n) + 1$ **14.** $y = m(n + 1)$

15. $y = m(n) - 3.7$ **16.** $y = m(n - 3.7)$

17. $y = m(n) + \sqrt{13}$ **18.** $y = m(n + 2\sqrt{2})$

19. $y = m(n + 3) + 7$ **20.** $y = m(n - 17) - 159$

Write a formula and graph the transformations of $k(w) = 3^w$ in Exercises 21–26.

21. $y = k(w) - 3$ **22.** $y = k(w - 3)$

23. $y = k(w) + 1.8$ **24.** $y = k(w + \sqrt{5})$

25. $y = k(w + 2.1) - 1.3$ **26.** $y = k(w - 1.5) - 0.9$

Problems

27. (a) Using Table 6.2, evaluate

    (i) $f(x)$ for $x = 6$.

    (ii) $f(5) - 3$.

    (iii) $f(5 - 3)$.

    (iv) $g(x) + 6$ for $x = 2$.

    (v) $g(x + 6)$ for $x = 2$.

    (vi) $3g(x)$ for $x = 0$.

    (vii) $f(3x)$ for $x = 2$.

    (viii) $f(x) - f(2)$ for $x = 8$.

    (ix) $g(x + 1) - g(x)$ for $x = 1$.

(b) Solve

    (i) $g(x) = 6$.   (ii) $f(x) = 574$.

    (iii) $g(x) = 281$.

(c) The values in the table were obtained using the formulas $f(x) = x^3 + x^2 + x - 10$ and $g(x) = 7x^2 - 8x - 6$. Use the table to find two solutions to the equation $x^3 + x^2 + x - 10 = 7x^2 - 8x - 6$.

Table 6.2

x	0	1	2	3	4	5	6	7	8	9
$f(x)$	-10	-7	4	29	74	145	248	389	574	809
$g(x)$	-6	-7	6	33	74	129	198	281	378	489

28. The graph of $y = m(r)$ is given in Figure 6.8. The graph of each function in parts (a) – (d) resulted from translations of $y = m(r)$. Give a formula for each of these functions in terms of m.

Figure 6.8

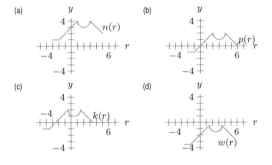

32. (a) Let $f(x) = \left(\dfrac{x}{2}\right)^3 + 2$. Calculate $f(-6)$.

(b) Solve $f(x) = -6$.

(c) Find points that correspond to parts (a) and (b) on the graph of $f(x)$ in Figure 6.11.

(d) Calculate $f(4) - f(2)$. Draw a vertical line segment on the y-axis that illustrates this calculation.

(e) If $a = -2$, compute $f(a + 4)$ and $f(a) + 4$.

(f) In part (e), what x-value corresponds to $f(a + 4)$? To $f(a) + 4$?

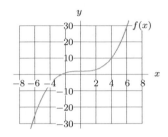

Figure 6.11

29. Figure 6.9 shows the graph $y = f(x)$. Give a formula in terms of f for the graph of the function in Figure 6.10. Your formula should be of the form $y = f(x - h) + k$ for appropriate constants h and k.

Figure 6.9   Figure 6.10

30. Judging from their graphs, find a formula for $g(x)$ in terms of $f(x)$.

31. The graph of $g(x)$ contains the point $(-2, 5)$. Write a formula for a translation of g whose graph contains the point

(a) $(-2, 8)$ **(b)** $(0, 5)$

33. The function $P(t)$ gives the number of people in a certain population in year t. Interpret in terms of population:

(a) $P(t) + 100$ **(b)** $P(t + 100)$

In Problems 34–35, let $s(t)$ denote the average weight (in pounds) of a baby at age t months.

34. The weight, V, of a particular baby named Jonah is related to the average weight function $s(t)$ by the equation

$$V = s(t) + 2.$$

Find Jonah's weight at ages $t = 3$ and $t = 6$ months. What can you say about Jonah's weight in general?

35. The weight, W, of another baby named Ben is related to $s(t)$ by the equation

$$W = s(t + 4).$$

What can you say about Ben's weight at age $t = 3$ months? At $t = 6$ months? Assuming that babies increase in weight over the first year of life, decide if Ben is of average weight for his age, above average, or below average.

36. The function $g(x)$ is obtained by shifting the graph of $y = x^2$. If $g(3) = 16$, give a possible formula for g when

   (a) g is the result of applying only a horizontal shift to $y = x^2$.

   (b) g is the result of applying only a vertical shift to $y = x^2$.

   (c) g is the result of applying a horizontal shift right 2 units and an appropriate vertical shift of $y = x^2$.

37. Describe a series of shifts that translates the graph of $y = (x + 3)^3 - 1$ onto the graph of $y = x^3$.

38. Graph $f(x) = \ln(|x - 3|)$ and $g(x) = \ln(|x|)$. Find the vertical asymptotes of both functions.

39. Graph $y = \log x$, $y = \log(10x)$, and $y = \log(100x)$. How do the graphs compare? Use a property of logs to show that the graphs are vertical shifts of one another.

40. Table 6.3 contains values of $g(t)$. Each function in parts (a)–(e) is a translation of $g(t)$. Find a possible formula for each of these functions in terms of g.

Table 6.3

t	-1	-0.5	0	0.5	1
$g(t)$	0.5	0.8	1.0	0.9	0.6

(a)

t	-1	-0.5	0	0.5	1
$a(t)$	1.0	1.3	1.50	1.4	1.1

(b)

t	-1	-0.5	0	0.5	1
$b(t)$	1.0	0.9	0.6	0.1	-0.4

(c)

t	-1	-0.5	0	0.5	1
$c(t)$	0.7	0.6	0.3	-0.2	-0.7

(d)

t	-1	-0.5	0	$.5$	1
$d(t)$	0	0.5	0.8	1.0	0.9

(e)

t	-1	-0.5	0	0.5	1
$e(t)$	1.2	1.7	2.0	2.2	2.1

41. Graph $y = x^2 - 10x + 25$ and $y = x^2$. Use a shift transformation to explain the relationship between the two graphs.

42. Let $f(x) = x^2$ and let $g(x) = (x - 3)^2 + 2$.

   (a) Give the formula for g in terms of f, and describe the relationship between f and g in words.

   (b) Is g a quadratic function? If so, find its standard form and the parameters a, b, and c.

   (c) Graph g, labeling all important features.

In Problems 43–48, explain in words the effect of the transformation on the graph of $q(z)$. Assume a, b are positive constants.

43. $q(z) + 3$ **44.** $q(z) - a$

45. $q(z + 4)$ **46.** $q(z - a)$

47. $q(z + b) - a$ **48.** $q(z - 2b) + ab$

49. Let $S(d)$ give the height of high tide in Seattle on a specific day, d, of the year. Use shifts of the function $S(d)$ to find formulas for each of the following functions:

   (a) $T(d)$, the height of high tide in Tacoma on day d, given that high tide in Tacoma is always one foot higher than high tide in Seattle.

   (b) $P(d)$, the height of high tide in Portland on day d, given that high tide in Portland is the same height as the previous day's high tide in Seattle.

50. Table 6.4 contains values of $f(x)$. Each function in parts (a)–(c) is a translation of $f(x)$. Find a possible formula for each of these functions in terms of f. For example, given the data in Table 6.5, you could say that $k(x) = f(x) + 1$.

Table 6.4

x	0	1	2	3	4	5	6	7
$f(x)$	0	0.5	2	4.5	8	12.5	18	24.5

Table 6.5

x	0	1	2	3	4	5	6	7
$k(x)$	1	1.5	3	5.5	9	13.5	19	25.5

(a)

x	0	1	2	3	4	5	6	7
$h(x)$	-2	-1.5	0	2.5	6	10.5	16	22.5

(b)

x	0	1	2	3	4	5	6	7
$g(x)$	0.5	2	4.5	8	12.5	18	24.5	32

(c)

x	0	1	2	3	4	5	6	7
$i(x)$	-1.5	0	2.5	6	10.5	16	22.5	30

51. Tables 6.6 and 6.7 give values of functions v and w. Given that $w(x) = v(x - h) + k$, find the constants h and k.

Table 6.6

x	$v(x)$
-2	11
-1	17
0	20
1	17
2	11

Table 6.7

x	$w(x)$
3	4
4	10
5	13
6	10
7	4

52. For $t \geq 0$, let $H(t) = 68 + 93(0.91)^t$ give the temperature of a cup of coffee in degrees Fahrenheit t minutes after it is brought to class.

(a) Find formulas for $H(t + 15)$ and $H(t) + 15$.
(b) Graph $H(t)$, $H(t + 15)$, and $H(t) + 15$.
(c) Describe in practical terms a situation modeled by the function $H(t + 15)$. What about $H(t) + 15$?
(d) Which function, $H(t+15)$ or $H(t)+15$, approaches the same final temperature as the function $H(t)$? What is that temperature?

53. At a jazz club, the cost of an evening is based on a cover charge of $20 plus a beverage charge of $7 per drink.

(a) Find a formula for $t(x)$, the total cost for an evening in which x drinks are consumed.
(b) If the price of the cover charge is raised by $5, express the new total cost function, $n(x)$, as a transformation of $t(x)$.
(c) The management increases the cover charge to $30, leaves the price of a drink at $7, but includes the first two drinks for free. For $x \geq 2$, express $p(x)$, the new total cost, as a transformation of $t(x)$.

54. A hot brick is removed from a kiln and set on the floor to cool. Let t be time in minutes after the brick was removed. The difference, $D(t)$, between the brick's temperature, initially $350°F$, and room temperature, $70°F$, decays exponentially over time at a rate of 3% per minute. The brick's temperature, $H(t)$, is a transformation of $D(t)$. Find a formula for $H(t)$. Compare the graphs of $D(t)$ and $H(t)$, paying attention to the asymptotes.

55. Let $T(d)$ give the average temperature in your hometown on the dth day of last year (so $d = 1$ is January 1, etc.).

(a) Graph $T(d)$ for $1 \leq d \leq 365$.
(b) Give a possible value for each of the following: $T(6); T(100); T(215); T(371)$.
(c) What is the relationship between $T(d)$ and $T(d + 365)$? Explain.
(d) If you graph $w(d) = T(d + 365)$ on the same axes as $T(d)$, how would the two graphs compare?
(e) Do you think the function $T(d) + 365$ has any practical significance? Explain.

56. Let $f(t)$ be the odometer reading in miles on Joe's car at the start of day t after the car was built. On the morning of the 400th day of the car's life, when the odometer reads 3000 miles, Joe starts a long trip. Find formulas for the following functions.

(a) $h(t)$, the odometer reading at the start of day t of the trip.
(b) $k(t)$, the number of miles driven during the first t days of the trip.

57. Let $H(t)$ be the thermometer reading (Celsius) of a person t hours after onset of an illness. Normal body temperature is $37°C$. Find a formula for the fever, the number $f(t)$ of degrees greater than normal, after t hours.

58. Let $f(x) = e^x$ and $g(x) = 5e^x$. If $g(x) = f(x - h)$, find h.

6.2 REFLECTIONS AND SYMMETRY

In Section 6.1 we saw that a horizontal shift of the graph of a function results from a change to the input of the function (specifically, adding or subtracting a constant inside the function's parentheses). A vertical shift corresponds to an outside change.

In this section we consider the effect of reflecting a function's graph about the x or y-axis. A reflection about the x-axis corresponds to an outside change to the function's formula; a reflection about the y-axis corresponds to an inside change.

A Formula for a Reflection

Figure 6.12 shows the graph of a function $y = f(x)$ whose values are in Table 6.8. Note that we do not need an explicit formula for f.

Figure 6.12: A graph of the function $y = f(x)$

Table 6.8   *Values of the function* $y = f(x)$

x	y
-3	1
-2	2
-1	4
0	8
1	16
2	32
3	64

Figure 6.13 shows a vertical reflection of the graph of f about the x-axis, giving the graph of $y = g(x)$. Figure 6.14 shows a horizontal reflection of the graph of f about the y-axis, giving $y = h(x)$. Figure 6.15 shows a horizontal reflection of the graph of f about the y-axis followed by a vertical reflection about the x-axis, giving $y = k(x)$.

Figure 6.13: Reflection about x-axis: $y = g(x)$

Figure 6.14: Reflection about y-axis: $y = h(x)$

Figure 6.15: Reflection about y- and x-axes: $y = k(x)$

Example 1   Use the graphs in Figures 6.13 to 6.15 to find formulas in terms of f for

(a) $y = g(x)$ (b) $y = h(x)$ (c) $y = k(x)$.

Solution   (a) Figure 6.13 shows the graph of f reflected in the x-axis, giving the graph of $g(x)$. Values of $g(x)$ are in Table 6.9.

Table 6.9   *Values of the functions* $g(x)$ *and* $f(x)$ *from Figure 6.13*

x	-3	-2	-1	0	1	2	3
$g(x)$	-1	-2	-4	-8	-16	-32	-64
$f(x)$	1	2	4	8	16	32	64

Notice that under reflection in the x-axis,
The point $(2, 32)$ becomes $(2, -32)$,
The point $(3, 64)$ becomes $(3, -64)$, etc.
Thus, when a point is reflected vertically about the x-axis, the x-value stays fixed, while the y-value changes sign. That is, for a given x-value,

$$y\text{-value of } g \text{ is the negative of } y\text{-value of } f.$$

Algebraically, this means

$$g(x) = -f(x).$$

234

(b) Figure 6.14 shows the graph of f reflected in the y-axis, giving the graph of $h(x)$. Values of $h(x)$ are in Table 6.10.

Table 6.10   *Values of the functions $h(x)$ and $f(x)$ from Figure 6.14*

x	-3	-2	-1	0	1	2	3
$h(x)$	64	32	16	8	4	2	1
$f(x)$	1	2	4	8	16	32	64

Notice that under reflection in the y-axis,
The point $(2, 32)$ becomes $(-2, 32)$,
The point $(3, 64)$ becomes $(-3, 64)$, etc.

Thus, when a point is reflected horizontally about the y-axis, the y-value remains fixed, while the x-value changes sign. This means

$$h(x) = f(-x).$$

(c) The graph of the function $y = k(x)$ results from a horizontal reflection of the graph of f about the y-axis, followed by a vertical reflection about the x-axis. Notice that a horizontal reflection corresponds to multiplying the inputs by -1 and a vertical reflection corresponds to multiplying the outputs by -1. Thus, we have

Vertical reflection across the x-axis
$$k(x) = -f(-x).$$
Horizontal reflection across the y-axis

Let's check a point. If $x = 1$, then the formula $k(x) = -f(-x)$ gives:

$$k(1) = -f(-1) = -4 \qquad \text{since } f(-1) = 4.$$

This result is consistent with the graph, since $(1, -4)$ is on the graph of $k(x)$.

For a function f:
- The graph of $y = -f(x)$ is a reflection of the graph of $y = f(x)$ about the x-axis.
- The graph of $y = f(-x)$ is a reflection of the graph of $y = f(x)$ about the y-axis.

Symmetry About the y-Axis

The graph of $p(x) = x^2$ in Figure 6.16 is *symmetric* about the y-axis. In other words, the part of the graph to the left of the y-axis is the mirror image of the part to the right of the y-axis. Reflecting the graph of $p(x)$ about the y-axis gives the graph of $p(x)$ again.

Figure 6.16: Reflecting the graph of $p(x) = x^2$ about the y-axis does not change its appearance

Symmetry about the y-axis is called *even symmetry*, because power functions with even exponents, such as $y = x^2$, $y = x^4$, $y = x^6$, ... have this property. Since $y = p(-x)$ is a reflection of the graph of p about the y-axis and $p(x)$ has even symmetry, we have

$$p(-x) = p(x).$$

Example 2   For $p(x) = x^2$, check that $p(-2) = p(2)$. Explain what this tells us about the graph of p.

Solution   Let $x = 2$. Then $p(2) = 2^2 = 4$, and $p(-2) = (-2)^2 = 4$, so $p(-2) = p(2)$. This means that the point $(2, 4)$ and its reflection about the y-axis, $(-2, 4)$, are both on the graph of $p(x)$.

Example 3   For the function $p(x) = x^2$, check algebraically that $p(-x) = p(x)$ for all x.

Solution   Substitute $-x$ into the formula for $p(x)$, giving

$$\begin{aligned}
p(-x) &= (-x)^2 = (-x) \cdot (-x) \\
&= x^2 \\
&= p(x).
\end{aligned}$$

Thus, $p(-x) = p(x)$.

In general,

If f is a function, then f is called an **even function** if, for all values of x in the domain of f,

$$f(-x) = f(x).$$

The graph of f is symmetric about the y-axis.

Symmetry About the Origin

Figures 6.17 and 6.18 show the graph of $q(x) = x^3$. Reflecting the graph of q first about the y-axis and then about the x-axis (or vice-versa) gives the graph of q again. This kind of symmetry is called symmetry about the origin, or *odd symmetry*.

In Example 1, we saw that $y = -f(-x)$ is a reflection of the graph of $y = f(x)$ about both the y-axis and the x-axis. Since $q(x) = x^3$ is symmetric about the origin, q is the same function as this double reflection. That is,

$$q(x) = -q(-x), \quad \text{which means that} \quad q(-x) = -q(x).$$

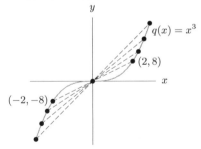

Figure 6.17: If the graph is reflected about the y-axis and then about the x-axis, it does not change

Figure 6.18: If every point on this graph is reflected about the origin, the graph is unchanged

Example 4   For $q(x) = x^3$, check that $q(-2) = -q(2)$. Explain what this tells us about the graph of q.

Solution   Let $x = 2$. Then $q(2) = 2^3 = 8$, and $q(-2) = (-2)^3 = -8$, so $q(-2) = -q(2)$. This means the point $(2, 8)$ and its reflection about the origin, $(-2, -8)$, are both on the graph of q.

Example 5   For the function $q(x) = x^3$, check algebraically that $q(-x) = -q(x)$ for all x.

Solution   We evaluate $q(-x)$, giving

$$q(-x) = (-x)^3 = (-x) \cdot (-x) \cdot (-x)$$
$$= -x^3$$
$$= -q(x).$$

Thus, $q(-x) = -q(x)$.

In general,

> If f is a function, then f is called an **odd function** if, for all values of x in the domain of f,
>
> $$f(-x) = -f(x).$$
>
> The graph of f is symmetric about the origin.

Example 6   Determine whether the following functions are symmetric about the y-axis, the origin, or neither.
(a) $f(x) = |x|$ (b) $g(x) = 1/x$ (c) $h(x) = -x^3 - 3x^2 + 2$

Solution   The graphs of the functions in Figures 6.19, 6.20, and 6.21 are helpful in identifying symmetry.

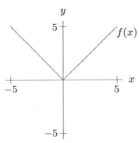

Figure 6.19: The graph of $f(x) = |x|$ appears to be symmetric about the y-axis

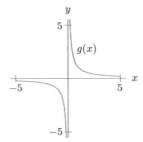

Figure 6.20: The graph of $g(x) = 1/x$ appears to be symmetric about the origin

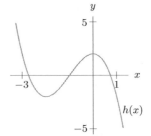

Figure 6.21: The graph of $h(x) = -x^3 - 3x^2 + 2$ is symmetric neither about the y-axis nor about the origin

From the graphs it appears that f is symmetric about the y-axis (even symmetry), g is symmetric about the origin (odd symmetry), and h has neither type of symmetry. However, to be sure, check algebraically.

If $f(-x) = f(x)$, then f has even symmetry. We check by substituting $-x$ in for x:

$$f(-x) = |-x|$$
$$= |x|$$
$$= f(x).$$

Thus, f does have even symmetry.

If $g(-x) = -g(x)$, then g is symmetric about the origin. We check by substituting $-x$ for x:

$$g(-x) = \frac{1}{-x}$$
$$= -\frac{1}{x}$$
$$= -g(x).$$

Thus, g is symmetric about the origin.

The graph of h does not exhibit odd or even symmetry. To confirm, look at an example, say $x = 1$:

$$h(1) = -1^3 - 3 \cdot 1^2 + 2 = -2.$$

Now substitute $x = -1$, giving

$$h(-1) = -(-1)^3 - 3 \cdot (-1)^2 + 2 = 0.$$

Thus $h(1) \neq h(-1)$, so the function is not symmetric about the y-axis. Also, $h(-1) \neq -h(1)$, so the function is not symmetric about the origin.

Combining Shifts and Reflections

We can combine the horizontal and vertical shifts from Section 6.1 with the horizontal and vertical reflections of this section to make more complex transformations of functions.

Example 7   When a yam is taken from a refrigerator at $0°C$ and put into an oven at $150°C$, the yam's temperature rises toward that of the oven.[1] Let $Y(t)$ be the temperature in $°C$ of the yam t minutes after it is put in the oven. Let $D(t) = 150 - Y(t)$ be the temperature difference between the oven and the yam at time t. Figure 6.22 shows a graph of $D(t)$.

(a) Describe the transformations we apply to the graph of $D(t)$ to obtain the graph of $Y(t)$.
(b) Sketch a graph of $Y(t)$.
(c) Explain the significance of the vertical intercept of Y.
(d) Explain the significance of the horizontal asymptote of Y.

Figure 6.22: Temperature difference: Decreasing over time

Figure 6.23: Temperature of the yam, $Y(t) = -D(t) + 150$

[1] In practice, refrigerators keep food slightly above $0°C$—at about 2-3°C—to prevent freezing.

Solution   (a) Writing $Y(t)$ in the form

$$Y(t) = \underbrace{-D(t)}_{\text{Reflect}} + \underbrace{150}_{\text{Shift}}$$

shows that the graph of Y is obtained by reflecting the graph of D about the t-axis and then shifting it vertically up 150 units.

(b) See Figure 6.23.

(c) The vertical intercept is $Y = 0$ because the temperature of the yam when it is first put into the oven is $0°C$.

(d) The horizontal asymptote, $Y = 150$, represents the temperature of the oven. As the yam sits in the oven, its temperature approaches the temperature of the oven.

Exercises and Problems for Section 6.2

Skill Refresher

In Exercises S1–S4, evaluate each function at $x = 3$. Round your answer to 3 decimal places.

S1. $f(x) = e^x$ **S2.** $g(x) = -e^x$

S3. $h(x) = e^{-x}$ **S4.** $k(x) = -e^{-x}$

For each function in Exercises S5–S10, give a formula for the following expressions,

(a) $f(-x)$ (b) $-f(x)$

S5. $f(x) = 2x^2$ **S6.** $f(x) = \dfrac{1}{x}$

S7. $f(x) = 2x^3 - 3$ **S8.** $f(x) = 4x^3 + 9x$

S9. $f(x) = 3x^4 - 2x$ **S10.** $f(x) = \dfrac{3x^3}{x^2 - 1}$

Exercises

1. The graph of $y = f(x)$ contains the point $(2, -3)$. What point must lie on the reflected graph if the graph is reflected

     (a) About the y-axis?   (b) About the x-axis?

2. The graph of $P = g(t)$ contains the point $(-1, -5)$.

     (a) If the graph has even symmetry, which other point must lie on the graph?
     (b) What point must lie on the graph of $-g(t)$?

3. The graph of $H(x)$ is symmetric about the origin. If $H(-3) = 7$, what is $H(3)$?

4. The range of $Q(x)$ is $-2 \le Q(x) \le 12$. What is the range of $-Q(x)$?

In Exercises 5–8, the function $Q(t)$ has domain $t > 0$ and range $-4 \le Q(t) \le 7$. Give the domain and range for the transformation of $Q(t)$.

5. $y = Q(-t)$ 6. $y = -Q(t)$

7. $y = -Q(-t)$ 8. $y = -Q(t - 4)$

9. If the graph of $y = e^x$ is reflected about the x-axis, what is the formula for the resulting graph? Check by graphing both functions together.

10. If the graph of $y = e^x$ is reflected about the y-axis, what is the formula for the resulting graph? Check by graphing both functions together.

11. Complete the following tables using $f(p) = p^2 + 2p - 3$, and $g(p) = f(-p)$, and $h(p) = -f(p)$. Graph the three functions. Explain how the graphs of g and h are related to the graph of f.

p	−3	−2	−1	0	1	2	3
$f(p)$							

p	−3	−2	−1	0	1	2	3
$g(p)$							

p	−3	−2	−1	0	1	2	3
$h(p)$							

12. Graph $y = f(x) = 4^x$ and $y = f(-x)$ on the same set of axes. How are these graphs related? Give an explicit formula for $y = f(-x)$.

13. Graph $y = g(x) = \left(\frac{1}{3}\right)^x$ and $y = -g(x)$ on the same set of axes. How are these graphs related? Give an explicit formula for $y = -g(x)$.

Give a formula and graph for each of the transformations of $m(n) = n^2 - 4n + 5$ in Exercises 14–17.

14. $y = m(-n)$

15. $y = -m(n)$

16. $y = -m(-n)$

17. $y = m(-n) + 3$

Give a formula and graph for each of the transformations of $k(w) = 3^w$ in Exercises 18–21.

18. $y = k(-w)$

19. $y = -k(w)$

20. $y = -k(-w)$

21. $y = -k(w - 2)$

In Exercises 22–25, show that the function is even, odd, or neither.

22. $f(x) = 7x^2 - 2x + 1$

23. $f(x) = 4x^7 - 3x^5$

24. $f(x) = 8x^6 + 12x^2$

25. $f(x) = x^5 + 3x^3 - 2$

Problems

26. (a) Graph the function obtained from $f(x) = x^3$ by first reflecting about the x-axis, then translating up two units. Write a formula for the resulting function.
   (b) Graph the function obtained from f by first translating up two units, then reflecting about the x-axis. Write a formula for the resulting function.
   (c) Are the functions in parts (a) and (b) the same?

27. (a) Graph the function obtained from $g(x) = 2^x$ by first reflecting about the y-axis, then translating down three units. Write a formula for the resulting function.
   (b) Graph the function obtained from g by first translating down three units, then reflecting about the y-axis. Write a formula for the resulting function.
   (c) Are the functions in parts (a) and (b) the same?

28. Using Figure 6.24, evaluate
   (a) $f(-x)$ for $x = -4$
   (b) $-f(x)$ for $x = -6$
   (c) $-f(-x)$ for $x = -4$
   (d) $-f(x + 2)$ for $x = 0$
   (e) $f(-x) + 4$ for $x = -6$

29. (a) If $g(x) = \sqrt[3]{x}$, find a formula for $g(-x)$.
   (b) Graph $y = g(x) = \sqrt[3]{x}$, $y = g(-x)$, and $y = -g(x)$ on the same axes.
   (c) Is $g(x) = \sqrt[3]{x}$ even, odd, or neither?

30. If the graph of a line $y = b + mx$ is reflected about the y-axis, what are the slope and intercepts of the resulting line?

31. Graph $y = \log(1/x)$ and $y = \log x$ on the same axes. How are the two graphs related? Use the properties of logarithms to explain the relationship algebraically.

32. Using Figure 6.25, graph the following transformations of f on separate axes.

   (a) $y = f(x) - 2$
   (b) $y = f(x - 2)$
   (c) $y = -f(x)$
   (d) $y = f(-x)$

Figure 6.24

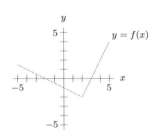

Figure 6.25

33. Using Figure 6.26, match the functions (i)-(v) with a graph (a)-(e).

(i) $y = f(-x)$ (ii) $y = -f(x)$

(iii) $y = f(-x) + 3$ (iv) $y = -f(x - 1)$

(v) $y = -f(-x)$

Figure 6.26

34. In Table 6.11, fill in as many y-values as you can if you know that f is

(a) An even function   (b) An odd function.

Table 6.11

x	-3	-2	-1	0	1	2	3
y	5		-4			-8	

35. Figure 6.27 shows the graph of a function f in the second quadrant. In each of the following cases, sketch $y = f(x)$, given that f is symmetric about

(a) The y-axis. (b) The origin. (c) The line $y = x$.

Figure 6.27

36. For each table, decide whether the function could be symmetric about the y-axis, about the origin, or neither.

(a)

x	-3	-2	-1	0	1	2	3
$f(x)$	6	1	-2	-3	-2	1	6

(b)

x	-3	-2	-1	0	1	2	3
$g(x)$	-8.1	-2.4	-0.3	0	0.3	2.4	8.1

(c)

x	-3	-2	-1	0	1	2	3
$f(x) + g(x)$	-2.1	-1.4	-2.3	-3	-1.7	3.4	14.1

(d)

x	-3	-2	-1	0	1	2	3
$f(x + 1)$	1	-2	-3	-2	1	6	13

37. Let $f(x)$ be an even function, and let $g(x)$ be an odd function. If possible, determine whether each function must be even or odd.

(a) $h(x) = f(x)g(x)$ (b) $k(x) = f(x) + g(x)$

(c) $m(x) = g(f(x))$

38. Let both $f(x)$ and $g(x)$ be odd functions. If possible, determine whether each function must be even or odd.

(a) $h(x) = f(x)g(x)$ (b) $k(x) = f(x) - g(x)$

(c) $m(x) = f(g(x))$

39. A function is called symmetric about the line $y = x$ if interchanging x and y gives the same graph. The simplest example is the function $y = x$. Graph another straight line that is symmetric about the line $y = x$ and give its equation.

40. Show that the graph of the function h is symmetric about the origin, given that

$$h(x) = \frac{1 + x^2}{x - x^3}.$$

41. Comment on the following justification that the function $f(x) = x^3 - x^2 + 1$ is an even function: Because $f(0) = 1 \neq -f(0)$, we know that $f(x)$ is not odd. If a function is not odd, it must be even.

42. Let $f(x)$ be a function that is always increasing and concave down. Determine whether each function is always increasing or always decreasing, and whether each function is always concave up or always concave down.

  (a) $f(-x)$ **(b)** $-f(x)$ **(c)** $-f(-x)$

43. Is it possible for an odd function whose domain is all real numbers to be strictly concave up?

44. Let $f(x) = b + mx$.

  (a) Can $f(x)$ be even? How?
  (b) Can $f(x)$ be odd? How?
  (c) Can $f(x)$ be both odd and even? How?

45. If f is an odd function and defined at $x = 0$, what is the value of $f(0)$? Explain how you can use this result to show that $c(x) = x + 1$ and $d(x) = 2^x$ are not odd.

46. In the first quadrant an even function is increasing and concave down. What can you say about the function's behavior in the second quadrant?

47. Show that the power function $f(x) = x^{1/3}$ is odd. Give a counterexample to the statement that all power functions of the form $f(x) = x^p$ are odd.

48. Graph $s(x) = 2^x + (\frac{1}{2})^x$, $c(x) = 2^x - (\frac{1}{2})^x$, and $n(x) = 2^x - (\frac{1}{2})^{x-1}$. State whether you think these functions are even, odd, or neither. Show that your statements are true using algebra. That is, prove or disprove statements such as $s(-x) = s(x)$.

49. There are functions that are *neither* even nor odd. Is there a function that is *both* even and odd?

50. Some functions are symmetric about the y-axis. Is it possible for a function to be symmetric about the x-axis?

6.3 VERTICAL STRETCHES AND COMPRESSIONS

We have studied translations and reflections of graphs. In this section, we consider vertical stretches and compressions of graphs. As with a vertical translation, a vertical stretch or compression of a function is represented by an outside change to its formula.

Vertical Stretch: An Amplifier

An amplifier takes a weak signal from a recording and transforms it into a stronger signal to power a set of speakers.

Figure 6.28 shows a graph of an audio signal (in volts) as a function of time, t, both before and after amplification. Notice that the wave crests of the amplified signal are 3 times as high as those of the original signal; similarly, the amplified wave troughs are 3 times deeper than the original wave troughs. The amplifier has boosted the strength of the signal by a factor of 3. If f is the original signal function and V is the amplified signal function, then

$$\underbrace{\text{Amplified signal strength at time } t}_{V(t)} = 3 \cdot \underbrace{\text{Original signal strength at time } t}_{f(t)},$$

so we have

$$V(t) = 3 \cdot f(t).$$

This formula tells us that the values of the amplified signal are 3 times the values of the original signal. The graph of V is the graph of f stretched vertically by a factor of 3. As expected, a vertical stretch of the graph of $f(t)$ corresponds to an outside change in the formula,

Notice that the t-intercepts remain fixed under a vertical stretch, because the f-value of these points is 0, which is unchanged when multiplied by 3.

Figure 6.28: An amplifier transforms a weak signal into a signal 3 times as strong

Negative Stretch Factor

What happens if we multiply a function by a negative stretch factor? Figure 6.29 gives a graph of a function $y = f(x)$, together with a graph of $y = -2 \cdot f(x)$. The stretch factor is $k = -2$. We think of $y = -2f(x)$ as a combination of two separate transformations of $y = f(x)$. First, the graph is stretched by a factor of 2, then it is reflected across the x-axis.

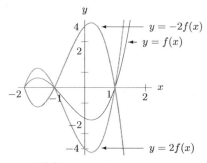

Figure 6.29: The graph of $y = -2f(x)$ is a vertically stretched version of the graph of $y = f(x)$ that has been reflected across the x-axis

Formula for Vertical Stretch or Compression

Generalizing the examples gives the following result:

If f is a function and k is a constant, then the graph of $y = k \cdot f(x)$ is the graph of $y = f(x)$
- Vertically stretched by a factor of k, if $k > 1$.
- Vertically compressed by a factor of k, if $0 < k < 1$.
- Vertically stretched or compressed by a factor $|k|$ and reflected across x-axis, if $k < 0$.

Example 1 A yam is placed in a $150°C$ oven. Table 6.12 gives values of $H = r(t)$, the yam's temperature t minutes after being placed in the oven. Figure 6.30 shows these data points joined by a curve.

(a) Describe the function r in words. What do the data tell you about the yam's temperature?
(b) Make a table of values for $q(t) = 1.5r(t)$. Graph the function q.
(c) How are the functions q and r related? Under what condition might q describe a yam's temperature?

243

Table 6.12 *Temperature of a yam*

t, time (min)	$r(t)$, temperature (°C)
0	0
10	75
20	113
30	131
40	141
50	145
60	148

H, temperature (°C)

Figure 6.30: The temperature of a yam at time t

Solution

(a) The function r is increasing and concave down. The yam starts out at 0°C and warms up quickly at first. Later, the yam heats up more slowly. The temperature levels off at 150°C, the oven's temperature, represented by the horizontal asymptote.

(b) We calculate values of $q(t)$ from values of r. For example, Table 6.12 gives $r(0) = 0$ and $r(10) = 75$. Thus,

$$q(0) = 1.5r(0) = 1.5 \cdot 0 = 0,$$

$$q(10) = 1.5r(10) = 1.5(75) = 112.5 \text{ and so on.}$$

The values for $q(t)$ are 1.5 times as large as the corresponding values for $r(t)$. See Table 6.13. The data are plotted in Figure 6.31.

(c) The graph of q is the graph of r stretched vertically by a factor of $k = 1.5$. The horizontal asymptote of r was $H = 150$, so the horizontal asymptote of q is $H = 1.5 \cdot 150 = 225$. This suggests that the yam has been placed in a 225°C oven instead of a 150°C oven.

Table 6.13 *Values of $q(t) = 1.5r(t)$*

t, time (min)	$q(t)$, temperature (°C)
0	0
10	112.5
20	169.5
30	196.5
40	211.5
50	217.5
60	222

Figure 6.31: Graph of $q(t) = 1.5r(t)$

Stretch Factors and Average Rates of Change

Consider again the graph of the audio signal and its amplification in Figure 6.28. Notice that the amplified signal, V, is increasing on the same intervals as the original signal, f. Similarly, both functions decrease on the same intervals.

Stretching or compressing a function vertically does not change the intervals on which the function increases or decreases. However, the average rate of change of a function, visible in the steepness of the graph, is altered by a vertical stretch or compression.

Example 2 In Example 1, the function $H = r(t)$ gives the temperature (in °C) of a yam placed in a 150°C oven. The function $q(t) = 1.5r(t)$ gives the temperature of the yam placed in a 225°C oven. In both cases, the temperature starts at 0°C. After 10 minutes, $r(10) = 75$°C and $q(10) = 112.5$°C.

(a) For each of the two yams, find the rate of change of temperature over ten-minute intervals from $t = 0$ to $t = 60$.

(b) For each ten-minute interval, what is the relationship between the two values you found in part (a) for the yams?

Solution (a) For the yam with temperature $r(t)$, from $t = 0$ to $t = 10$, we have

$$\begin{matrix}\text{Average rate of change} \\ \text{of temperature, } r\end{matrix} = \frac{\Delta H}{\Delta t} = \frac{r(10) - r(0)}{10 - 0} = \frac{75 - 0}{10} = 7.5°\text{C/min.}$$

Thus, in the 150°C oven, the yam's temperature increased at an average rate of 7.5°C per minute. For the yam with temperature $q(t)$, from $t = 0$ to $t = 10$,

$$\begin{matrix}\text{Average rate of change} \\ \text{of temperature}\end{matrix} = \frac{\Delta H}{\Delta t} = \frac{112.5 - 0}{10} = 11.25°\text{C/min.}$$

Thus, in the 225°C oven, the yam's temperature increased at an average rate of 11.25°C per minute. Similar calculations for other time intervals give the values in Table 6.14.

(b) Notice that $11.25 = 1.5(7.5)$, and each rate of change in the 225°C oven is 1.5 times the corresponding rate of change in the 150°C oven. This reflects the fact that $q(t) = 1.5r(t)$.

Table 6.14 *The average rate of change of yams' temperatures, $r(t)$ and $q(t)$*

Time interval (min)	$0 - 10$	$10 - 20$	$20 - 30$	$30 - 40$	$40 - 50$	$50 - 60$
Average rate of change of r (°C/min)	7.5	3.8	1.8	1	0.4	0.3
Average rate of change of q (°C/min)	11.25	5.7	2.7	1.5	0.6	0.45

In the last example, multiplying a function by a factor of 1.5 had the effect of multiplying the function's average rate of change on each interval by the same factor. More generally, if $g(x) = k \cdot f(x)$, between $x = a$ and $x = b$,

$$\begin{matrix}\text{Average rate of change} \\ \text{of } y = g(x)\end{matrix} = \frac{\Delta y}{\Delta x} = \frac{g(b) - g(a)}{b - a} = \frac{k \cdot f(b) - k \cdot f(a)}{b - a}$$

$$= k \cdot \frac{f(b) - f(a)}{b - a} \quad \text{(factoring out } k)$$

$$= k \cdot \left(\begin{matrix}\text{Average rate of change} \\ \text{of } f\end{matrix}\right).$$

In general, we have the following result:

If $g(x) = k \cdot f(x)$, then on any interval,

Average rate of change of $g = k \cdot$ (Average rate of change of f).

Combining Stretches and Shifts

Stretches and shifts can be combined to give more general transformations of functions.

Example 3 The function $y = f(x)$ is graphed in Figure 6.32. Graph the function $g(x) = -\dfrac{1}{2}f(x+3) - 1$.

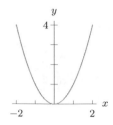

Figure 6.32: Graph of $y = f(x)$

Solution   To combine several transformations, always work from inside the parentheses outward as in Figure 6.33. The graphs corresponding to each step are shown in Figure 6.34. Note that we did not need a formula for f to graph g.

Figure 6.33

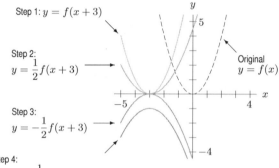

Figure 6.34: The graph of $y = f(x)$ transformed in four steps into $g(x) = -(1/2)f(x+3) - 1$

Exercises and Problems for Section 6.3

Skill Refresher

S1. If $f(x) = x^2$, evaluate each expression below at $x = 6$.

  (a) $2f(x)$ (b) $-\frac{1}{2}f(x)$

  (c) $5f(x) - 3$ (d) $\frac{1}{4}f(x-1)$

S2. Evaluate each expression below at $x = -2$ if $g(x) = \frac{1}{x}$.

  (a) $-4g(x)$ (b) $\frac{2}{3}g(x)$

  (c) $2g(x+5)$ (d) $-\frac{1}{5}g(-x)$

S3. Write a formula for each of the transformations of $f(x) = \sqrt{x}$ given below.

  (a) $y = -\frac{1}{3}f(x)$ (b) $y = 5f(-x)$

  (c) $y = 6f(x-8)$ (d) $y = \frac{1}{4}f(2-x)$

S4. Write a formula for each of the transformations of $p(x) = 3x^2 - 6$ given below.

  (a) $y = 5p(x)$ (b) $y = -\frac{1}{3}p(-x)$

  (c) $y = -2p(x+3)$ (d) $y = \frac{5}{3}p(x-1)$

Exercises

1. Let $y = f(x)$. Write a formula for the transformation that both increases the y-value by a factor of 10 and shifts the graph to the right by 2 units.

2. The graph of the function $g(x)$ contains the point $(5, \frac{1}{3})$. What point must be on the graph of $y = 3g(x + 1)$?

3. The range of the function $C(x)$ is $-1 \leq C(x) \leq 1$. What is the range of $0.25C(x)$?

Exercises 4–7 refer to functions obtained by applying a transformation to $P(n)$, whose domain is $-3 < n \leq 8$ and range is $-6 \leq P(n) < 12$. Find a possible formula for the function in terms of $P(n)$.

4. The domain of $Q(n)$ is $-3 < n \leq 8$ and the range is $-2 \leq Q(n) < 4$.

5. The domain of $R(n)$ is $-3 < n \leq 8$ and the range is $-60 < R(n) \leq 30$.

6. The domain of $S(n)$ is $-8 \leq n < 3$ and the range is $2 \leq S(n) < 20$.

7. The domain of $T(n)$ is $-10 < n \leq 1$ and the range is $-1.5 \leq T(n) < 3$.

In Exercises 8–11, graph and label $f(x)$, $4f(x)$, $-\frac{1}{2}f(x)$, and $-5f(x)$ on the same axes.

8. $f(x) = \sqrt{x}$ **9.** $f(x) = -x^2 + 7x$

10. $f(x) = e^x$ **11.** $f(x) = \ln x$

12. Using Table 6.15, make tables for the following transformations of f on an appropriate domain.

(a) $\frac{1}{2}f(x)$ **(b)** $-2f(x + 1)$ **(c)** $f(x) + 5$
(d) $f(x - 2)$ **(e)** $f(-x)$ **(f)** $-f(x)$

Table 6.15

x	-3	-2	-1	0	1	2	3
$f(x)$	2	3	7	-1	-3	4	8

13. Using Table 6.16, create a table of values for

(a) $f(-x)$ **(b)** $-f(x)$ **(c)** $3f(x)$

(d) Which of these tables from parts (a), (b), and (c) represents an even function?

Table 6.16

x	-4	-3	-2	-1	0	1	2	3	4
$f(x)$	13	6	1	-2	-3	-2	1	6	13

Without a calculator, graph the transformations in Exercises 14–19. Label at least three points.

14. $y = f(x + 3)$ if $f(x) = |x|$

15. $y = f(x) + 3$ if $f(x) = |x|$

16. $y = -g(x)$ if $g(x) = x^2$

17. $y = g(-x)$ if $g(x) = x^2$

18. $y = 3h(x)$ if $h(x) = 2^x$

19. $y = 0.5h(x)$ if $h(x) = 2^x$

20. Using Figure 6.35, match the functions (i)–(v) with a graph (a)–(i).

(i) $y = 2f(x)$ (ii) $y = \frac{1}{3}f(x)$
(iii) $y = -f(x + 1)$ (iv) $y = f(x + 2) + 1$
(v) $y = f(-x)$

Figure 6.35

(a)   (b)

(c)   (d)

(e)   (f)

(g)   (h)

(i)

Problems

21. Describe the effect of the transformation $2f(x+1)$ on the graph of $y = f(x)$.

22. The function $s(t)$ gives the distance (miles) in terms of time (hours). If the average rate of change of $s(t)$ on $0 \le t \le 4$ is 70 mph, what is the average rate of change of $\frac{1}{2}s(t)$ on this interval?

In Problems 23–27, let $f(t) = 1/(1+x^2)$. Graph the function given, labeling intercepts and asymptotes.

23. $y = f(t)$ **24.** $y = f(t-3)$

25. $y = 0.5f(t)$ **26.** $y = -f(t)$

27. $y = f(t+5) - 5$

28. The number of gallons of paint, $n = f(A)$, needed to cover a house is a function of the surface area, in ft^2. Match each story to one expression.

(a) I figured out how many gallons I needed and then bought two extra gallons just in case.
(b) I bought enough paint to cover my house twice.
(c) I bought enough paint to cover my house and my welcome sign, which measures 2 square feet.

(i) $2f(A)$ (ii) $f(A+2)$ (iii) $f(A)+2$

29. The US population in millions is $P(t)$ today and t is in years. Match each statement (I)–(IV) with one of the formulas (a)–(h).

I.   The population 10 years before today.
II. Today's population plus 10 million immigrants.
III. Ten percent of the population we have today.
IV. The population after 100,000 people have emigrated.

(a) $P(t) - 10$ (b) $P(t-10)$ (c) $0.1P(t)$
(d) $P(t) + 10$ (e) $P(t+10)$ (f) $P(t)/0.1$
(g) $P(t) + 0.1$ (h) $P(t) - 0.1$

30. Let $R = P(t)$ be the number of rabbits living in a national park in month t. What do the following expressions represent?

(a) $P(t+1)$ (b) $2P(t)$

31. Suppose $C(t)$ represents the cost in Euros of the first t days of a business trip to France from the United States. Find a formula for $h(t)$, the cost in US dollars for the first t days. During the trip, 1 Euro was equivalent to 1.3 US dollars.

32. Suppose that $f(x)$ is the age in years of the ice x cm below the surface of a glacier in Antarctica. Find the age $g(x)$ for the same ice in centuries.

Graph the transformations of f in Problems 33–37 using Figure 6.36. Label the points corresponding to A and B.

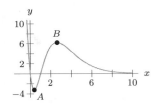

Figure 6.36

33. $y = f(x-3)$ **34.** $y = f(x) - 3$

35. $y = f(-x)/3$ **36.** $y = -2f(x)$

37. Table 6.17 contains values of $f(x)$. Each function in parts (a)–(c) is obtained by applying a single transformation to $f(x)$. The transformation may be a stretch, compression, shift, or reflection. Find a possible formula for each of these functions in terms of f. For example, given the data in Table 6.18, we would say that $g(x) = 3f(x)$.

Table 6.17

x	−6	−4	−2	0	2	4	6
$f(x)$	12	4	−8	−14	−2	0	10

Table 6.18

x	−6	−4	−2	0	2	4	6
$g(x)$	36	12	−24	−42	−6	0	30

(a)

x	−6	−4	−2	0	2	4	6
$h(x)$	6	2	−4	−7	−1	0	5

(b)

x	−6	−4	−2	0	2	4	6
$k(x)$	10	0	−2	−14	−8	4	12

(c)

x	−6	−4	−2	0	2	4	6
$m(x)$	8	0	−12	−18	−6	−4	6

38. Using Figure 6.37, find formulas, in terms of f, for the horizontal and vertical shifts of the graph of f in parts (a)–(c). What is the equation of each asymptote?

Figure 6.37

(a)

(b) (graph)

(c)

39. Using Figure 6.38, find formulas, in terms of f, for the transformations of f in parts (a)–(c).

Figure 6.38

(a)

(b)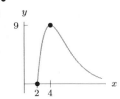

(c) (graph)

40. In Figure 6.39, the point b is labeled on the x-axis. On the y-axis, locate and label the output values:

(a) $f(b)$ (b) $-2f(b)$ (c) $-2f(-b)$

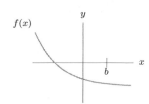

Figure 6.39

41. Figure 6.40 gives a graph of $y = f(x)$. Consider the transformations $y = \frac{1}{2}f(x)$ and $y = 2f(x)$. Which points on the graph of $y = f(x)$ stay fixed under these transformations? Compare the intervals on which all three functions are increasing and decreasing.

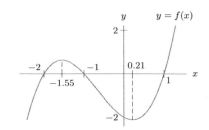

Figure 6.40

The average rate of change of $f(x)$ over the interval $a \le x \le b$ is 28, where a and b denote constants. In Problems 42–44 give the average rate of change over the interval $a \le x \le b$ for each transformation of $f(x)$.

42. $y = 3f(x)$ **43.** $y = -\frac{1}{4}f(x)$ **44.** $y = f(x) + 3$

6.4 HORIZONTAL STRETCHES AND COMPRESSIONS

In Section 6.3, we observed that a vertical stretch of a function's graph corresponds to an outside change in its formula, specifically, multiplication by a stretch factor. Since horizontal changes generally correspond to inside changes, we expect that a horizontal stretch will correspond to a constant multiple of the inputs. This turns out to be the case.

Horizontal Stretch: A Lighthouse Beacon

The beacon in a lighthouse turns once per minute, and its beam sweeps across a beach house. Figure 6.41 gives a graph of $L(t)$, the intensity, or brightness, of the light striking the beach house as a function of time.

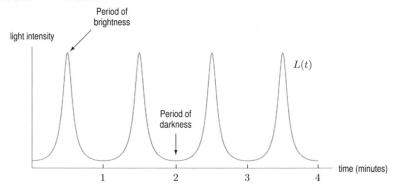

Figure 6.41: Light intensity or brightness, $L(t)$, as a function of time

Now suppose the lighthouse beacon turns twice as fast as before, so that its beam sweeps past the beach house twice instead of once each minute. The periods of brightness now occur twice as often. See Figure 6.42. The graph of $f(t)$, the intensity of light from this faster beacon, is a horizontal squeezing or compression of the original graph of $L(t)$.

If the lighthouse beacon turns at half its original rate, so that its beam sweeps past the beach house once every two minutes instead of once every minute, the periods of brightness occur half as often as originally. Slowing the beacon's speed results in a horizontal stretch of the original graph, illustrated by the graph of $s(t)$, the light intensity of the slow beacon, in Figure 6.43.

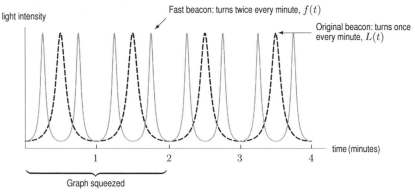

Figure 6.42: Comparing light intensity from the fast beacon, $f(t)$, to light intensity from the original beacon, $L(t)$

Slow beacon: turns once every two minutes, $s(t)$

light intensity

Original beacon: turns once every minute, $L(t)$

time (minutes)

1   2   3   4

Graph stretched

Figure 6.43: Comparing light intensity from the slow beacon, $s(t)$, to light intensity from the original beacon, $L(t)$

Formula for Horizontal Stretch or Compression

How are the formulas for the three light functions related? We expect that multiplying the function's input by a constant will horizontally stretch or compress its graph. The fast beacon corresponds to speeding up by a factor of 2, or multiplying the input by 2. Thus

$$f(t) = L(2t).$$

Similarly for the slow beacon, the input times are multiplied by $1/2$, so

$$s(t) = L(\tfrac{1}{2}t).$$

Generalizing the lighthouse example gives the following result:

If f is a function and k a positive constant, then the graph of $y = f(kx)$ is the graph of f
- Horizontally compressed by a factor of $1/k$ if $k > 1$,
- Horizontally stretched by a factor of $1/k$ if $k < 1$.

If $k < 0$, then the graph of $y = f(kx)$ also involves a horizontal reflection about the y-axis.

Example 1   Values of the function $f(x)$ are in Table 6.19 and its graph is in Figure 6.44. Make a table and a graph of the function $g(x) = f(\tfrac{1}{2}x)$.

Table 6.19   *Values of $f(x)$*

x	$f(x)$
-3	0
-2	2
-1	0
0	-1
1	0
2	-1
3	1

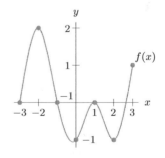

Figure 6.44

Solution To make a table for $g(x) = f(\frac{1}{2}x)$, we substitute values for x. For example, if $x = 4$, then
$$g(4) = f(\tfrac{1}{2} \cdot 4) = f(2).$$
Table 6.19 shows that $f(2) = -1$, so
$$g(4) = f(2) = -1.$$
This result is recorded in Table 6.20. If $x = 6$, since Table 6.19 gives $f(3) = 1$, we have
$$g(6) = f(\tfrac{1}{2} \cdot 6) = f(3) = 1.$$
In Figure 6.45, we see that the graph of g is the graph of f stretched horizontally away from the y-axis. Substituting $x = 0$ gives
$$g(0) = f(\tfrac{1}{2} \cdot 0) = f(0) = -1,$$
so the y-intercept remains fixed (at -1) under a horizontal stretch.

Table 6.20 *Values of* $g(x) = f(\frac{1}{2}x)$

x	$g(x)$
-6	0
-4	2
-2	0
0	-1
2	0
4	-1
6	1

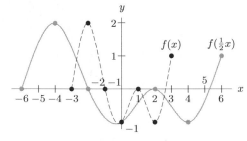

Figure 6.45: The graph of $g(x) = f(\frac{1}{2}x)$ is the graph of $y = f(x)$ stretched away from the y-axis by a factor of 2

Example 1 shows the effect of an inside multiple of $1/2$. We see that the graph of f is stretched by a factor of 2 horizontally from the y-axis. The next example shows the effect on the graph of an inside multiple of 2.

Example 2 Let $f(x)$ be the function in Example 1. Make a table and a graph for the function $h(x) = f(2x)$.

Solution We use Table 6.19 and the formula $h(x) = f(2x)$ to evaluate $h(x)$ at several values of x. For example, if $x = 1$, then
$$h(1) = f(2 \cdot 1) = f(2).$$
Table 6.19 shows that $f(2) = -1$, so $h(1) = -1$. These values are recorded in Table 6.21. Similarly, substituting $x = 1.5$ gives
$$h(1.5) = f(2 \cdot 1.5) = f(3) = 1.$$

Table 6.21 *Values of* $h(x) = f(2x)$

x	$h(x)$
-1.5	0
-1.0	2
-0.5	0
0.0	-1
0.5	0
1.0	-1
1.5	1

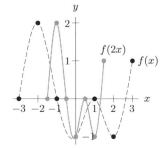

Figure 6.46: The graph of $h(x) = f(2x)$ is the graph of $y = f(x)$ compressed horizontally by a factor of $1/2$

Since $h(0) = f(2 \cdot 0) = f(0)$, the y-intercept remains fixed (at -1). In Figure 6.46 we see that the graph of h is the graph of f compressed by a factor of 1/2 horizontally toward the y-axis.

In Chapter 4, we used the function $P = 263c^{0.009t}$ to model the US population in millions. This function is a transformation of the exponential function $f(t) = e^t$, since we can write

$$P = 263e^{0.009t} = 263f(0.009t).$$

The US population is $f(t) = e^t$ stretched vertically by a factor of 263 and stretched horizontally by a factor of $1/0.009 \approx 111$.

Example 3   Match the functions $f(t) = e^t$, $g(t) = e^{0.5t}$, $h(t) = e^{0.8t}$, $j(t) = e^{2t}$ with the graphs in Figure 6.47.

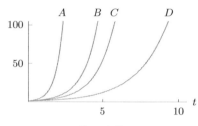

Figure 6.47

Solution   Since the function $j(t) = e^{2t}$ climbs fastest of the four and $g(t) = e^{0.5t}$ climbs slowest, graph A must be j and graph D must be g. Similarly, graph B is f and graph C is h.

Exercises and Problems for Section 6.4

Skill Refresher

In Exercises S1–S4, write a formula for each of the transformations of $f(x) = x^3 - 5$.

S1. $y = f(2x)$ **S2.** $y = 2f(x)$

S3. $y = f\left(-\frac{1}{3}x\right)$ **S4.** $y = \frac{1}{5}f(3x)$

In Exercises S5–S8, write a formula for each of the transformations of $Q(t) = 4e^{6t}$.

S5. $y = Q\left(\frac{1}{3}t\right)$ **S6.** $y = \frac{1}{3}Q(t)$

S7. $y = Q(2t) + 11$ **S8.** $y = 7Q(t - 3)$

Exercises

1. The point $(2, 3)$ lies on the graph of $g(x)$. What point must lie on the graph of $g(2x)$?

2. Describe the effect of the transformation $10f(\frac{1}{10}x)$ on the graph of $f(x)$.

3. Using Table 6.22, make a table of values for $f(\frac{1}{2}x)$ for an appropriate domain.

Table 6.22

x	-3	-2	-1	0	1	2	3
$f(x)$	2	3	7	-1	-3	4	8

4. Fill in all the blanks in Table 6.23 for which you have sufficient information.

Table 6.23

x	-3	-2	-1	0	1	2	3
$f(x)$	-4	-1	2	3	0	-3	-6
$f(\frac{1}{2}x)$							
$f(2x)$							

5. Graph $m(x) = e^x$, $n(x) = e^{2x}$, and $p(x) = 2e^x$ on the same axes and describe how the graphs of $n(x)$ and $p(x)$ compare with that of $m(x)$.

6. Graph $y = h(3x)$ if $h(x) = 2^x$.

In Exercises 7–9, graph and label $f(x)$, $f(\frac{1}{2}x)$, and $f(-3x)$ on the same axes between $x = -2$ and $x = 2$.

7. $f(x) = e^x + x^3 - 4x^2$

8. $f(x) = e^{x+7} + (x-4)^3 - (x+2)^2$

9. $f(x) = \ln(x^4 + 3x^2 + 4)$

10. Using Figure 6.48, match each function to a graph (if any) that represents it:

    (i) $y = f(2x)$ (ii) $y = 2f(2x)$ (iii) $y = f(\frac{1}{2}x)$

(a)
(b)
(c)
(d)
(e)
(f)
(g)
(h)
(i)

Figure 6.48

11. Using Figure 6.49, graph the following functions on separate sets of axes, together with the graph of the original function. Label any intercepts or special points.

    (a) $y = f(3x)$ (b) $y = f(-2x)$ (c) $y = f(\frac{1}{2}x)$

Figure 6.49

Problems

12. For the function $f(p)$ an input of 2 yields an output value of 4. What value of p would you use to have $f(3p) = 4$?

13. The domain of $l(x)$ is $-12 \le x \le 12$ and its range is $0 \le l(x) \le 3$. What are the domain and range of

    (a) $l(2x)$?   (b) $l(\frac{1}{2}x)$?

14. The point (a, b) lies on the graph of $y = f(x)$. If the graph is stretched away from the y-axis by a factor of d (where $d > 1$), and then translated upward by c units, what are the new coordinates for the point?

In Problems 15–16, graph the transformation of f, the function in Figure 6.50.

Figure 6.50

15. $y = -2f(x - 1)$ **16.** $y = f(x/2) - 1$

17. Let $T(d)$ be the temperature of the seawater in the Mariana Trench d meters below the surface. Find a formula for $p(x)$, the temperature x km below the surface.

18. Let $f(t)$ be a man's height in meters when he turns t months old. Find a formula for his height $g(n)$ in centimeters when he turns n years old.

19. Let $A(t)$ be the altitude in meters of a balloonist t minutes after liftoff. Find a formula for

    (a) $f(s)$, the altitude s seconds after liftoff.
    (b) $g(h)$, the altitude h hours after liftoff.

20. Every day I take the same taxi over the same route from home to the train station. The trip is x miles, so the cost for the trip is $f(x)$. Match each story in (a)–(d) to a function in (i)–(iv) representing the amount paid to the driver.

    (a) I received a raise yesterday, so today I gave my driver a five-dollar tip.
    (b) I had a new driver today and he got lost. He drove five extra miles and charged me for it.
    (c) I haven't paid my driver all week. Today is Friday and I'll pay what I owe for the week.
    (d) The meter in the taxi went crazy and showed five times the number of miles I actually traveled.

    (i) $5f(x)$ (ii) $f(x) + 5$
    (iii) $f(5x)$ (iv) $f(x + 5)$

21. A company projects a total profit, $P(t)$ dollars, in year t. Explain the economic meaning of $r(t) = 0.5P(t)$ and $s(t) = P(0.5t)$.

22. Let $A = f(r)$ be the area of a circle of radius r.

    (a) Write a formula for $f(r)$.
    (b) Which expression represents the area of a circle whose radius is increased by 10%? Explain.

      (i) $0.10f(r)$ (ii) $f(r + 0.10)$ (iii) $f(0.10r)$
      (iv) $f(1.1r)$ (v) $f(r) + 0.10$

    (c) By what percent does the area increase if the radius is increased by 10%?

In Problems 23–24, state which graph represents

    (a) $f(x)$ **(b)** $f(-2x)$ **(c)** $f(-\frac{1}{2}x)$ **(d)** $f(2x)$

23.   **24.**

25. Find a formula for the function in Figure 6.52 as a transformation of the function f in Figure 6.51.

Figure 6.51

Figure 6.52

26. This problem investigates the effect of a horizontal stretch on the zeros of a function.

    (a) Graph $f(x) = 4 - x^2$. Mark the zeros of f on the graph.
    (b) Graph and find a formula for $g(x) = f(0.5x)$. What are the zeros of $g(x)$?
    (c) Graph and find a formula for $h(x) = f(2x)$. What are the zeros of $h(x)$?
    (d) Without graphing, what are the zeros of $f(10x)$?

27. In Figure 6.53, the point c is labeled on the x-axis. On the y-axis, locate and label output values:

(a) $g(c)$ (b) $2g(c)$ (c) $g(2c)$

Figure 6.53

The function $f(x)$ has domain $-6 \leq x \leq 2$, and the average rate of change of $f(x)$ over the interval $-6 \leq x \leq 2$ is -3. For each transformation of $f(x)$ in Problems 28–31,

(a) State the domain of the function.

(b) Give the average rate of change of the function over its new domain found in part (a).

28. $g(x) = f(2x)$

29. $h(x) = f\left(\dfrac{1}{4}x\right)$

30. $k(x) = f(x + 2)$

31. $m(x) = f(-x)$

32. Figure 6.54 shows the graphs of $f(x)$ and $g(x)$. It is claimed that $f(x)$ is a horizontal stretch of $g(x)$. If that could be true, find the stretch. If that could not be true, explain.

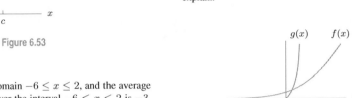

Figure 6.54

6.5 COMBINING TRANSFORMATIONS

In Sections 6.1–6.4, vertical and horizontal transformations were applied to graphs of functions. In this section we see what happens when several transformations are applied in succession.

In arithmetic, the result of a calculation depends on the order in which operations are performed. For example, adding 3 to 5 and then doubling the result gives a different result than doubling 5 and then adding 3 to the result, that is, $(5 + 3) \cdot 2 \neq 5 \cdot 2 + 3$.

The same is true when we apply a sequence of transformations to a function. For example, if we apply a horizontal shift followed by a horizontal stretch, we may get a different result than if we first applied the horizontal stretch followed by the horizontal shift.

Multiple Inside Changes

Inside changes lead to horizontal transformations. We see the effect of reversing the order of shifts and stretches (or compressions).

Example 1   Figure 6.55 shows the graph of a function g.

(a) Graph the function that is obtained by first shifting the graph of g horizontally right by 6 units and then compressing horizontally by a factor of $1/3$. Give a formula for this function.

(b) Graph the function that is obtained by first compressing the graph of g horizontally by a factor of $1/3$ and then shifting horizontally right by 6 units. Give a formula for this function.

(c) Compare the graphs in your answers to parts (a) and (b). How are they related?

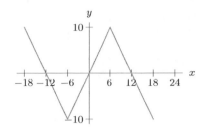

Figure 6.55: Graph of $y = g(x)$

Solution   (a) The first step is to shift the graph of g right by 6, giving the graph of an intermediate function, $w(x) = g(x - 6)$. The next step is to compress this graph by $1/3$, giving the graph of

$$y = w(3x) \qquad \text{compress intermediate graph by } 1/3$$
$$= g(3x - 6) \quad \text{since } w(x) = g(x - 6).$$

Notice that we do not really care about the intermediate function, w, beyond its role as the first step in the process. See Figure 6.56. A formula for the final result is $y = g(3x - 6)$.

(b) Here, the first step is to compress the graph of g horizontally by a factor of $1/3$, giving the graph of an intermediate function $v(x) = g(3x)$. The next step is to shift this graph to the right by 6, giving the graph of

$$y = v(x - 6) \qquad \text{shift intermediate graph right by } 6$$
$$= g\left(3(x - 6)\right). \quad \text{since } v(x) = g(3x)$$

Notice we only use the intermediate function, v, to keep track of the first step. See Figure 6.57. A formula for the final result is $y = g(3(x - 6))$.

Figure 6.56: Graph of $y = g(3x - 6)$

Figure 6.57: Graph of $y = g(3(x - 6))$

(c) The final graphs in part (a) and (b) are the same shape and size, each extending 12 units in the x-direction and from -10 to 10 in the y-direction. However, they are in different positions. The graph in part (a) extends from -4 to 8, while the graph in part (b) extends from 0 to 12.

Example 1 shows that applying transformations in different orders can give different results. When we apply a horizontal shift and then a horizontal stretch or compression, the function is usually expressed in the the form $y = f(Bx - h)$, for example $y = g(3x - 6)$ in part (a). However, when we reverse the order and first apply a horizontal stretch or compression followed by a horizontal shift, the function is usually expressed in the form $y = f(B(x - h))$, for example $y = g(3(x - 6))$

in part (b). In this section we usually rewrite transformations to apply the stretch/compression first, and then the shift. To achieve this result, we write the inside changes in the form

$$y = f(B(x - h)).$$

Then the horizontal stretch/compression factor is $1/|B|$ and the horizontal shift is h units.

Example 2   (a) Rewrite the function $y = f(2x - 6)$ in the form $y = f(B(x - h))$.
(b) Use the result to describe the graph of $y = f(2x - 6)$ as the result of first applying a horizontal stretch or compression to the graph of f and then applying a horizontal shift. What is the stretch/compression factor? What is the shift?

Solution   (a) We have $f(2x - 6) = f(2(x - 3))$.
(b) Thus, the graph of $y = f(2x - 6)$ can be obtained from the graph of $y = f(x)$ by first horizontally compressing it by a factor of $1/2$ and then shifting horizontally right by $h = 3$ units.

Multiple Outside Changes

We now see how two outside changes interact. Outside transformations lead to vertical transformations; first we see the effect of reversing the order of vertical shifts and vertical stretches (or compressions).

Example 3   (a) The graph of a function is obtained from the graph of $y = f(x)$ by first stretching vertically by a factor of 3 and then shifting upward by 2. Give a formula for the function in terms of f.
(b) The graph of a function is obtained from the graph of $y = f(x)$ by first shifting upward by 2 and then stretching vertically by a factor of 3. Give a formula for the function in terms of f.
(c) Are the results of parts (a) and (b) the same? If not, how are they related?

Solution   (a) Stretching the graph of f vertically by a factor of 3 gives the intermediate function

$$y = 3f(x);$$

shifting this function upward by 2 gives the result

$$y = 3f(x) + 2.$$

(b) Shifting upward by 2 gives the intermediate function

$$y = f(x) + 2;$$

stretching this function vertically by a factor of 3 gives the result

$$y = 3(f(x) + 2).$$

(c) The two functions are not the same. Since $y = 3(f(x) + 2) = 3f(x) + 6$, the two graphs are the same shape, but translated vertically by 4, the difference in the two shifts.

For outside changes, to apply the stretch/compression first, we write the function in the form

$$y = Af(x) + k.$$

Then the vertical stretch/compression factor is $|A|$ and the vertical shift is k.

Ordering Horizontal and Vertical Transformations

For transformations involving multiple inside and outside changes, it does not matter whether we do the inside changes first, or the outside changes. However, the order of the horizontal changes matters, as does the order of the vertical changes. We can follow the effect of a sequence of transformations on the graph by writing the function in the following form:

For nonzero constants A, B, h and k, the graph of the function

$$y = Af(B(x - h)) + k$$

is obtained by applying the transformations to the graph of $f(x)$ in the following order:
- Horizontal stretch/compression by a factor of $1/|B|$
- Horizontal shift by h units
- Vertical stretch/compression by a factor of $|A|$
- Vertical shift by k units

If $A < 0$, follow the vertical stretch/compression by a reflection about the x-axis.
If $B < 0$, follow the horizontal stretch/compression by a reflection about the y-axis.

Example 4 illustrates the use of these steps to graph multiple inside and outside changes.

Example 4   Figure 6.58 shows the graph of a function f.

(a) Put the function $r(x) = -\frac{1}{3}(f(2x - 8) + 3)$ in the form $y = Af(B(x - h)) + k$ and determine the values for constants A, B, h, and k.

(b) Express r as the result of applying a list of transformations to f, specifying the order in which the transformations are applied. Sketch a graph of r using the graph of f.

Figure 6.58: Graph of $y = f(x)$

Solution   (a) Expanding on the outside and factoring on the inside, we have

$$r(x) = -\frac{1}{3}f(2x - 8) - 1 = -\frac{1}{3}f\left(2(x - 4)\right) - 1,$$

so $A = -1/3, B = 2, h = 4$, and $k = -1$.

(b) See Figure 6.59. To find the graph of r, we carry out these steps:
- Horizontally compress the graph of f by $1/|B| = 1/2$.
- Horizontally shift the resulting graph to the right by $h = 4$.

- Vertically compress the resulting graph by $|A| = 1/3$ and reflect the graph about the x-axis.
- Vertically shift the resulting graph by $k = -1$.

Figure 6.59: Graph of $y = -\frac{1}{3}(f(2x - 8) + 3)$

In Section 3.2 we found it useful to express a quadratic function in vertex form. In the next example, we revisit this idea in the context of transformations.

Example 5

(a) Let $y = 5(x + 2)^2 + 7$. Determine the values of $A, B, h,$ and k when y is put in the form $y = Af(B(x - h)) + k$ with $f(x) = x^2$. List the transformations applied to $f(x) = x^2$ to give $y = 5(x + 2)^2 + 7$.

(b) Using your answers in part (a), sketch a graph of $y = 5(x + 2)^2 + 7$, labeling the vertex.

Solution

(a) If $f(x) = x^2$, we see $y = 5(x + 2)^2 + 7 = 5f(x + 2) + 7$, so $A = 5$, $B = 1$, $h = -2$, and $k = 7$. Based on the values of these constants, we carry out these steps:

- Horizontal shift 2 to the left of the graph of $f(x) = x^2$.
- Vertical stretch of the resulting graph by a factor of 5.
- Vertical shift of the resulting graph up by 7.

Since $B = 1$, there is no horizontal compression, stretch, or reflection.

(b) Figure 6.60 shows the result of applying this sequence of transformations to the graph of f.

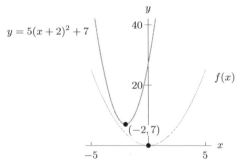

Figure 6.60: Graphs of $y = x^2$ and $y = 5(x + 2)^2 + 7$

260

Exercises and Problems for Section 6.5

Skill Refresher

In Exercises S1–S4, solve for the constant h.

S1. $4x + 12 = 4(x - h)$ **S2.** $\frac{1}{5}t - 10 = \frac{1}{5}(t - h)$

S3. $-3z + 10 = -3(z - h)$ **S4.** $-\frac{1}{9}x - 4 = -\frac{1}{9}(x - h)$

S5. Let $f(x) = \sqrt[3]{x}$. Evaluate each expression at $x = 1$.

  (a) $f(8x) - 3$ **(b)** $8f(x - 3)$
  (c) $8f(x) - 3$ **(d)** $8(f(x) - 3)$
  (e) $f(8(x - 3))$ **(f)** $f(8x - 3)$

S6. Write a formula for each transformations of $Q(t) = e^t$.

  (a) $y = -7Q(t - 4)$ **(b)** $y = -7Q(t) - 4$

  (c) $y = -7(Q(t) - 4)$ **(d)** $y = Q(-7t) - 4$

  (e) $y = Q(-7(t - 4))$ **(f)** $y = \frac{1}{4}Q(-7t + 2) - 4$

In Exercises S7–S10, rewrite as $y = Af(B(x - h)) + k$ and give values for A, B, h, and k.

S7. $y = f(-2x) + 9$ **S8.** $y = -f(2x - 6) + 9$

S9. $y = 6f\left(-\frac{1}{3}x - 9\right)$

S10. $y = -5\left(f(-x - 7) + 2\right)$

Exercises

1. Describe $y = f(3x - 2)$ as the result of first applying a stretch or compression and then applying a shift to f.

2. Describe $y = 5(g(x) - 8)$ as the result of first applying a stretch or compression and then applying a shift to g.

3. $(6, -9)$. For each of the following functions, find a point on its graph:

  (a) $g(2x) - 5$ **(b)** $3g(x) + 1$
  (c) $-(g(\frac{1}{3}(x + 4)) - 8)$ **(d)** $\frac{1}{2}g(-5x - 15) - 8$

4. Table 6.24 gives values of x and $f(x)$. Supply the values of each function shown. In some cases, there may not be enough information to fill in a box.

Table 6.24

x	-2	-1	0	1	2
$f(x)$	-3	-4	2	0	5
$2f(x) + 3$					
$f(x - 1) + 1$					
$f(x + 2) - 1$					
$3f(2x + 2) - 1$					

5. Table 6.25 gives values of function v. Create a table giving five values of the function $w(t) = 40 - 2v(-0.5t)$.

Table 6.25

t	0	1	2	3	4
$v(t)$	20	17	16	19	23

6. Figure 6.61 shows the graph of $f(x) = |x|$. Graph each transformation of $f(x)$:

  (a) $g(x) = f(x) + 1$ **(b)** $h(x) = f(x + 1)$
  (c) $j(x) = f(2x + 1) - 3$ **(d)** $k(x) = \frac{1}{2}f(2x - 4) + 1$
  (e) $m(x) = -\frac{1}{2}f(4x + 12) - 3$

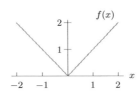

Figure 6.61

7. Figure 6.62 shows the graph of $f(x) = 2^x$. Graph each transformation of $f(x)$:

  (a) $f(3x + 6)$ **(b)** $f(-\frac{1}{2}x - 1)$
  (c) $0.4f(-x + 1) - 2$ **(d)** $-f(\frac{1}{2}x + 4) + 1$

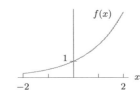

Figure 6.62

8. Using Figure 6.63, graph the following functions.

(a) $y = -f(x) + 2$ (b) $y = 2f(x)$

(c) $y = f(x - 3)$ (d) $y = -\dfrac{1}{2}f(x + 1) - 3$

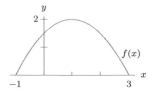

Figure 6.63

9. Using Figure 6.64, sketch $y = 2f(0.5x) + 20$.

Figure 6.64

In Exercises 10–11, use Figure 6.65 to graph the function.

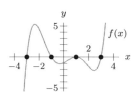

Figure 6.65

10. $y = -2f(-0.5x)$ **11.** $h(x) = f(2x - 1)$

12. Using Figure 6.66, graph each of the following functions on separate sets of axes, together with the graph of the original function. Label intercepts and asymptotes.

(a) $y = 3f(x)$ (b) $y = f(x - 1)$

(c) $y = f(x) - 1$ (d) $y = -2f(x)$

(e) $y = \frac{1}{2}f(x + 2) - 1$ (f) $y = -f(-x)$

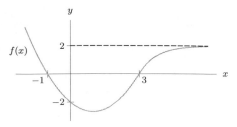

Figure 6.66

13. The graph of v has a horizontal asymptote at $y = -4$ and a vertical asymptote at $t = 5$. Give the asymptotes of $w(t) = 3 - 0.5v(-2t)$.

14. The function $p(t)$ has domain $1 \leq t \leq 12$ and range $-40 < p \leq 160$. What is the new domain and range of

(a) $p(\frac{1}{5}t + 4)$?   (b) $-\frac{1}{10}p(2t) + 50$?

In Exercises 15–16, sketch and label graphs of the functions using Figure 6.67. Briefly describe the relationship between your graph and the graph of f.

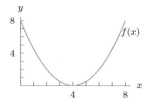

Figure 6.67

15. $h(x) = f(2x + 6)$.   **16.** $q(x) = f\left(2(x + 6)\right)$.

Problems

17. Figure 6.68 shows the graph of a function f.

    (a) Graph the function that is obtained by first shifting the graph of f vertically upward by 3 units and then stretching it vertically by a factor of 2.

    (b) Graph the function that is obtained by first stretching the graph of f vertically by a factor of 2 and then shifting up vertically by 3 units.

    (c) Compare your answers in parts (a) and (b).

Figure 6.68

18. Is $y = f(2x - 6)$ the function obtained from f by a horizontal compression by a factor of $1/2$ followed by a horizontal shift of 6 units to the right? Explain why or why not.

19. Is the function $y = 5(g(x) - 2)$ obtained from g by a vertical stretch by a factor of 5 followed by a vertical shift of 2 units downward? If not, what vertical shift is needed?

20. The *Heaviside step function*, $H(x)$, is defined as follows:

$$H(x) = 1 \text{ for } x \geq 0$$
$$H(x) = 0 \text{ for } x < 0.$$

Graph the Heaviside function, then sketch graphs of the following transformations of H:

    (a) $y = H(x) - 2$ **(b)** $y = H(x + 2)$

    (c) $y = -3H(-x) + 4$

21. The graph of g is found by shifting the graph of f to the left by 4 units, then reflecting it vertically across the x-axis, then shifting it up by 2 units, then finally stretching it vertically by a factor of 3. Find a formula for g in terms of f.

22. The graph of g is the graph of f shifted right by 3 units, then reflected vertically across the x-axis, then shifted down by 2 units, then stretched vertically by a factor of 2. Find a formula for g in terms of f.

23. The graph of g is found by shifting the graph of f up by 2 units and left by 3 units. The graph of h is found by reflecting the graph of g horizontally, then reflecting it vertically and stretching it vertically by a factor of 2. Find a formula for h in terms of f.

In Problems 24–25, the points $(-12, 20)$, $(0, 6)$, $(36, -2)$ lie on the graph of f.

24. List three points on the graph of $g(x) = 10 - 2f(-3x)$.

25. The graph of f is found by shifting the graph of h to the left by 3 units, then stretching it vertically by a factor of 2, then shifting it up by 6 units. Find three points on the graph of h.

26. Use shifts, reflections, and vertical stretches to graph each parabola without a calculator. Then write each equation in standard form:

    (a) $y = (x + 3)^2 - 4$ **(b)** $y = -2(x + 1)^2 + 3$

27. Sketch $y = 160 - 4f(-x/10)$ if $f(x) = 20 \cdot 2^x$.

28. Let $h(t) = t^2$. Parts (a)–(c) investigate the effects of changing the order of horizontal transformations.

    (a) Give a formula in vertex form for the quadratic function obtained by first shifting the function $h(t)$ to the right 6 units and then compressing horizontally by a factor of $1/2$.

    (b) Give a formula in vertex form for the quadratic function obtained by first compressing the function $h(t)$ horizontally by a factor of $1/2$ and then shifting to the right 6 units.

    (c) If you first horizontally compress $h(t)$ by a factor of $1/2$, by how much and in what direction would you next need to shift horizontally in order to get the same result as in part (a)?

29. Which (if any) of the following transformations of f is not the same as the others?

    (a) Shift f up by 3, then stretch it vertically by a factor of 2, then reflect it vertically.

    (b) Reflect f vertically, then shift it down by 3, then stretch it vertically by a factor of 2.

    (c) Stretch f vertically by a factor of 2, then shift it up by 6, then reflect it vertically.

    (d) Reflect f vertically, then stretch it vertically by a factor of 2, then shift it down by 6.

30. Let $f(x) = e^x$ and $g(x) = 5e^{x-2}$. If $g(x) = kf(x)$, find k.

31. The log function has the property that the graph resulting from a horizontal stretch can also be obtained by a vertical shift.

    (a) Graph $f(x) = \log x$ and $g(x) = \log(10x)$ and determine the vertical shift.

    (b) Explain how you could have predicted the answer to part (a) from the properties of logarithms.

    (c) If $h(x) = \log(ax)$, what is the vertical shift k making $h(x) = \log(x) + k$?

32. Applying a horizontal stretch by a factor of k (where k is a constant such that $k > 1$) to $f(x) = \ln x$ is equivalent to applying what shift to f? Give both the amount and the direction of the shift.

33. Shifting $g(x) = e^x$ to the right k units (where k is a constant such that $k > 0$) is equivalent to applying what stretch or compression to g? Be sure you describe the amount and direction of the stretch or compression needed.

34. **(a)** The point $(-2, 5)$ lies on the graph of $y = r(x)$. What are the coordinates of the transformed point on the graph of $y = 3(r(x) + 2)$?
(b) Express the function $y = 3(r(x) + 2)$ as the result of first applying a vertical stretch or compression and then applying a vertical shift to the function r. What is the stretch/compression? What is the shift?

35. **(a)** Describe the graph of $y = 2f(x) + 8$ as the result of applying a stretch or compression to the graph of f, then applying a shift.
(b) Now describe this graph as the result of applying a shift to the graph of f, then applying a stretch or compression.

36. **(a)** Describe the graph of $y = f\left(\frac{1}{3}x + 4\right)$ as the result of applying a stretch or compression to f, then applying a shift.
(b) Describe this graph as the result of applying a shift to f, then applying a stretch or compression.

37. The function $d(t)$ graphed in Figure 6.69 gives the winter temperature in °F at a high school, t hours after midnight.

(a) Describe in words the heating schedule for this building during the winter months.
(b) Graph $c(t) = 142 - d(t)$.
(c) Explain why c might describe the cooling schedule for summer months.

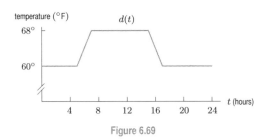

Figure 6.69

38. Let $D(t)$ denote the depth, in meters, of the water at a fixed location in a bay t hours from noon. Find a formula for each function below by applying transformation(s) to $D(t)$.

(a) $f(t)$, the depth of the tide in kilometers.

(b) $g(x)$, the depth of the tide in kilometers x minutes from noon.
(c) $j(x)$, the depth of the tide in kilometers x minutes from 2 pm.

39. Let f be defined by the graph in Figure 6.70. Find formulas (in terms of f) for the following transformations of f and sketch a graph of each. Show that these transformations lead to different outcomes.

(a) First shift the graph of f upward by 3 units, then reflect it across the x-axis.
(b) First reflect the graph of f across the x-axis. Then, shift it upward by 3 units.

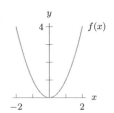

Figure 6.70

40. **(a)** Graph $h(x) = -2x^2 - 8x - 8$.
(b) Compare the graphs of $h(x)$ and $f(x) = x^2$. How are these two graphs related? Be specific.

For Problems 41–42, find a formula for the family of functions obtained from $f(x)$ by: **(a)** Stretching vertically **(b)** Stretching vertically and shifting horizontally. Compare the graph of a typical member of the family and the graph of $f(x)$. Include intercepts and asymptotes in your discussion. Are the two families the same?

41. $f(x) = x$

42. $f(x) = 2^x$

In Problems 43–45, you are given that $g(x) = r \cdot f(sx) + j$, where r, s, j are constants.

43. For the linear function $f(x) = b + mx$, is g also linear? If so, write g in the form $g(x) = B + Mx$ and state the values of B and M.

44. For the exponential function $f(x) = ae^{kx}$, is g also exponential? If so, write g in the form $g(x) = Ae^{Kx}$ and state the values of A and K.

45. For the quadratic function $f(x) = a(x - h)^2 + k$, is g also quadratic? If so, write g in the form $g(x) = A(x - H)^2 + K$ and state the values of A, H, and K.

CHAPTER SUMMARY

- **Vertical and Horizontal Shifts**
  Vertical: $y = g(x) + k$.
  Upward if $k > 0$; downward if $k < 0$.
  Horizontal: $y = g(x + k)$.
  Left if $k > 0$; right if $k < 0$.

- **Reflections**
  Across x-axis: $y = -f(x)$.
  Across y-axis: $y = f(-x)$.

- **Symmetry**
  About y-axis: $f(-x) = f(x)$; even function.
  About the origin: $f(-x) = -f(x)$; odd function.

- **Stretches and Compressions**
  Vertical: $y = kf(x)$. Stretch if $|k| > 0$; compress if

$0 < |k| < 1$; reflect across x-axis if $k < 0$.
Horizontal: $y = f(kx)$. Compress if $|k| > 0$; stretch if
$0 < |k| < 1$; reflect across y-axis if $k < 0$.

- **Combining Transformations**
  Standard form: $y = Af(B(x - h)) + k$.
  Order of changes to graph of f:
  Horizontal stretch/compression by a factor of $1/|B|$
  Horizontal shift by h units
  Vertical stretch/compression by a factor of $|A|$
  Vertical shift by k units
  If $A < 0$, reflect about the x-axis.
  If $B < 0$, reflect about the y-axis.

REVIEW EXERCISES AND PROBLEMS FOR CHAPTER SIX

Exercises

1. Suppose $x = 2$. Determine the value of the input of the function f in each of the following expressions:

   (a) $f(2x)$ (b) $f(\frac{1}{2}x)$ (c) $f(x+3)$ (d) $f(-x)$

2. Determine the value of x in each of the following expressions that leads to an input of 2 to the function f:

   (a) $f(2x)$ (b) $f(\frac{1}{2}x)$ (c) $f(x+3)$ (d) $f(-x)$

3. The point $(2, 5)$ is on the graph of $y = f(x)$. Give the coordinates of one point on the graph of each of the following functions.

   (a) $y = f(x - 4)$ (b) $y = f(x) - 4$
   (c) $y = f(4x)$ (d) $y = 4f(x)$

4. The point $(-3, 4)$ is on the graph of $y = g(x)$. Give the coordinates of one point on the graph of each of the following functions.

   (a) $y = g(\frac{1}{3}x)$ (b) $y = \frac{1}{3}g(x)$
   (c) $y = g(-3x)$ (d) $y = -g(3x)$

Are the functions in Exercises 5–10 even, odd, or neither?

5. $a(x) = \dfrac{1}{x}$ **6.** $m(x) = \dfrac{1}{x^2}$

7. $e(x) = x + 3$ **8.** $p(x) = x^2 + 2x$

9. $b(x) = |x|$ **10.** $q(x) = 2^{x+1}$

11. Let $f(x) = 1 - x$. Evaluate and simplify:

   (a) $f(2x)$ (b) $f(x + 1)$ (c) $f(1 - x)$
   (d) $f(x^2)$ (e) $f(1/x)$ (f) $f(\sqrt{x})$

12. Fill in all the blanks in Table 6.26 for which you have sufficient information.

Table 6.26

x	-3	-2	-1	0	1	2	3
$f(x)$	-4	-1	2	3	0	-3	-6
$f(-x)$							
$-f(x)$							
$f(x) - 2$							
$f(x - 2)$							
$f(x) + 2$							
$f(x + 2)$							
$2f(x)$							
$-f(x)/3$							

265

Problems

In Problems 13–14, use Figure 6.71 to sketch the function.

Figure 6.71

13. $y = f(x + 2) + 2$ **14.** $y = -2f(-x)$

In Problems 15–16, use Figure 6.71 to find a possible formula for the transformation of f shown.

15.

16.

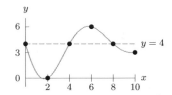

17. The function $f(x)$ contains the point $(-3, 1)$. The function $g(x)$ is obtained by applying a single transformation to the graph of $f(x)$ such that $g(x)$ contains the point $(3, 1)$. Describe the transformation that is applied to $f(x)$ in order to get the function $g(x)$ if

    (a) $g(x)$ is obtained by applying only one reflection to the graph of $f(x)$.

    (b) $g(x)$ is obtained by applying only one shift to the graph of $f(x)$.

18. Let $D(p)$ be the number of iced cappuccinos sold each week by a coffeehouse when the price is p cents.

    (a) What does the expression $D(225)$ represent?

    (b) Do you think that $D(p)$ is an increasing function or a decreasing function? Why?

    (c) What does the following equation tell you about p?
       $D(p) = 180$

    (d) The coffeehouse sells n iced cappuccinos when they charge the average price in their area, t cents. Thus, $D(t) = n$. What is the meaning of the following expressions: $D(1.5t)$, $1.5D(t)$, $D(t+50)$, $D(t)+50$?

19. Without a calculator, match each of the functions (a)–(f) with one of the graphs (I)–(VI).

    (a) $y = e^x$ **(b)** $y = e^{5x}$ **(c)** $y = 5e^x$

    (d) $y = e^{x+5}$ **(e)** $y = e^{-x}$ **(f)** $y = e^x + 5$

20. The graph in Figure 6.72 gives the number of hours of daylight in Charlotte, North Carolina on day d of the year, where $d = 0$ is January 1. Graph the number of hours of daylight in Buenos Aires, Argentina, which is as far south of the equator as Charlotte is north. [Hint: When it is summer in the Northern Hemisphere, it is winter in the Southern Hemisphere.]

Figure 6.72

21. During a hurricane, a brick breaks loose from the top of a chimney, 38 feet above the ground. As the brick falls, its distance from the ground after t seconds is given by:

$$d(t) = -16t^2 + 38.$$

(a) Find formulas for $d(t) - 15$ and $d(t - 1.5)$.

(b) On the same axes, graph $d(t)$, $d(t) - 15$, $d(t - 1.5)$.

(c) Suppose $d(t)$ represents the height of a brick which began to fall at noon. What might $d(t) - 15$ represent? $d(t - 1.5)$?

(d) Using algebra, determine when the brick hits the ground:

   (i) If $d(t)$ represents the distance of the brick from the ground,

   (ii) If $d(t) - 15$ represents the distance of the brick from the ground.

(e) Use one of your answers in part (d) to determine when the brick hits the ground if $d(t - 1.5)$ represents its distance above the ground at time t.

The functions graphed in Problems 22–23 are transformations of some basic function. Give a possible formula for each one.

22.

23.

In Problems 24–25, use Figure 6.73 to find a formula for the transformations of $h(x)$.

Figure 6.73

24.

25.

Problems 26–30 use Table 6.27 which gives the total cost, $C = f(n)$, for a carpenter to build n wooden chairs.

Table 6.27

n	0	10	20	30	40	50
$f(n)$	5000	6000	6800	7450	8000	8500

26. Evaluate the following expressions. Explain in everyday terms what they mean.

(a) $f(10)$ **(b)** $f(x)$ if $x = 30$

(c) z if $f(z) = 8000$ **(d)** $f(0)$

27. Find approximate values for p and q if $f(p) = 6400$ and $q = f(26)$.

28. Let $d_1 = f(30) - f(20)$, $d_2 = f(40) - f(30)$, and $d_3 = f(50) - f(40)$.

(a) Evaluate d_1, d_2 and d_3.

(b) What do these numbers tell you about the carpenter's cost of building chairs?

29. Graph $f(n)$. Label the quantities you found in Problems 26–28 on your graph.

30. The carpenter currently builds k chairs per week.

(a) What do the following expressions represent?

   (i) $f(k + 10)$ (ii) $f(k) + 10$

   (iii) $f(2k)$ (iv) $2f(k)$

(b) If the carpenter sells his chairs at 80% above cost, plus an additional 5% sales tax, write an expression for his gross income (including sales tax) each week.

31. In Figure 6.74, the value of d is labeled on the x-axis. Locate the following quantities on the y-axis:

(a) $g(d)$ **(b)** $g(-d)$ **(c)** $-g(-d)$

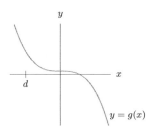

Figure 6.74

32. In Figure 6.75, the values c and d are labeled on the x-axis. On the y-axis, locate the following quantities:

(a) $h(c)$ (b) $h(d)$

(c) $h(c+d)$ (d) $h(c)+h(d)$

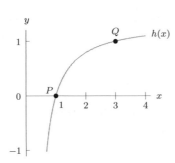

Figure 6.75

In Problems 33–35, use Figure 6.76 to find a formula for the graphs in terms of h.

Figure 6.76

33.

34.

35.

For Problems 36–37 use the graph of $y = f(x)$ in Figure 6.77.

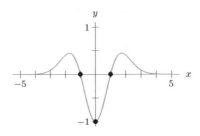

Figure 6.77

36. Graph $y = 2 - f(x-2)$.

37. Find a formula in terms of f for the graph in Figure 6.78.

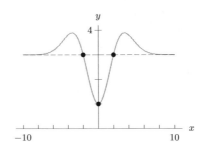

Figure 6.78

38. Gwendolyn, a pleasant parabola, was taking a peaceful nap when her dream turned into a nightmare: she dreamt that a low-flying pterodactyl was swooping toward her. Startled, she flipped over the horizontal axis, darted up (vertically) by three units, and to the left (horizontally) by two units. Finally she woke up and realized that her equation was $y = (x-1)^2 + 3$. What was her equation before she had the bad dream?

39. Suppose $w = j(x)$ is the average daily quantity of water (in gallons) required by an oak tree of height x feet.

(a) What does the expression $j(25)$ represent? What about $j^{-1}(25)$?

(b) What does the following equation tell you about v: $j(v) = 50$. Rewrite this statement in terms of j^{-1}.

(c) Oak trees are on average z feet high and a tree of average height requires p gallons of water. Represent this fact in terms of j and then in terms of j^{-1}.

(d) Using the definitions of z and p from part (c), what do the following expressions represent?

$$j(2z), \quad 2j(z), \quad j(z + 10), \quad j(z) + 10,$$
$$j^{-1}(2p), \quad j^{-1}(p + 10), \quad j^{-1}(p) + 10.$$

Table 6.28 gives values of $T = f(d)$, the average temperature (in °C) at a depth d meters in a borehole in Belleterre, Quebec. The functions in Problems 40–45 describe boreholes near Belleterre. Construct a table of values for each function and describe in words what it tells you about the borehole.[2]

Table 6.28

d, depth (m)	25	50	75	100
T, temp (°C)	5.5	5.2	5.1	5.1
d, depth (m)	125	150	175	200
T, temp (°C)	5.3	5.5	5.75	6

40. $g(d) = f(d) - 3$

41. $h(d) = f(d + 5)$

42. $m(d) = f(d - 10)$

43. $n(d) = 1.5f(d)$

44. $p(d) = f(0.8d)$

45. $q(d) = 1.5f(d) + 2$

CHECK YOUR UNDERSTANDING

Are the statements in Problems 1–23 true or false? Give an explanation for your answer.

1. If $g(x) = f(x) + 3$ then the graph of $g(x)$ is a vertical shift of the graph of f.

2. If $g(t) = f(t - 2)$ then the graph of $g(t)$ can be obtained by shifting the graph of f two units to the left.

3. If $g(x) = f(x) + k$ and k is negative, the graph of $g(x)$ is the same as the graph of f, but shifted down.

4. Vertical and horizontal shifts are called translations.

5. The reflection of $y = x^2$ across the x-axis is $y = -x^2$.

6. If $f(x)$ is an odd function, then $f(x) = f(-x)$.

7. The graphs of odd functions are symmetric about the y-axis.

8. The graph of $y = -f(x)$ is the reflection of the graph of $y = f(x)$ across the x-axis.

9. The graph of $y = f(-x)$ is the reflection of the graph of $y = f(x)$ across the y-axis.

10. If the graph of a function f is symmetric about the y-axis then $f(x) = f(-x)$.

11. Figure 6.79 suggests that $g(x) = f(x + 2) + 1$.

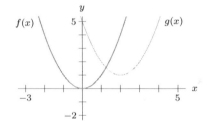

Figure 6.79

12. If $g(x) = x^2 + 4$ then $g(x - 2) = x^2$.

13. For any function f, we have $f(x + k) = f(x) + k$.

14. Figure 6.80 could be the graph of $f(x) = |x - 1| - 2$.

Figure 6.80

---

[2]Hugo Beltrami of St. Francis Xavier University and David Chapman of the University of Utah posted this data at http://esrc.stfx.ca/borehole/node3.html, accessed December 20, 2005.

Chapter Ten

COMPOSITIONS, INVERSES, AND COMBINATIONS OF FUNCTIONS

Contents

10.1 COMPOSITION OF FUNCTIONS

Recall that composition of functions was introduced in Section 2.4.

> The function $f(g(t))$ is said to be a **composition** of f with g. The function $f(g(t))$ is defined by using the output of the function g as the input to f.

The composite function $f(g(t))$ is only defined for values in the domain of g whose $g(t)$ values are in the domain of f.

For example, recall the London Eye Ferris wheel example from Section 7.1. We wished to find the height on the Ferris wheel at a particular time. If $H = f(\theta)$ represents the height on the Ferris wheel (in feet) as a function of angular position (in degrees) and $\theta = g(t)$ represents the angular position as a function of time (in minutes), then the composition of f with g gives a function $H = f(g(t))$ that represents the height on the Ferris wheel as a function of time.

Formulas for Composite Functions

A therapeutic drug has the side effect of raising a patient's heart rate. The relation between Q, the amount of drug in the patient's body (in milligrams), and r, the patient's heart rate (in beats per minute), is given by the formula

$$r = f(Q) = 60 + 0.2Q.$$

Over time, the level of the drug in the patient's bloodstream falls. The drug level as a function of time t, in hours since the initial injection, is

$$Q = g(t) = 250(0.8)^t.$$

Since heart rate depends on the drug level and drug level depends on time, the heart rate also depends on time. To find a formula for heart rate as a function of time, we use the function $g(t)$ as the input to f. Thus,

$$r = f(\underbrace{\text{input}}_{g(t)}) = 60 + 0.2(\underbrace{\text{input}}_{g(t)}),$$

so

$$r = f(g(t)) = 60 + 0.2g(t).$$

Substituting the formula for $g(t)$ gives

$$r = h(t) = f(g(t)) = 60 + 0.2 \cdot \underbrace{250(0.8)^t}_{g(t)}$$

so

$$r = h(t) = 60 + 50(0.8)^t.$$

Notice that the units of the input in this composite function are hours (the same units as the input in the inside function g), and the units of the output of the composite function are beats per minute (the same units as the output of the outside function f).

So far we have considered examples of two functions composed together, but there is no limit on the number of functions that can be composed. Functions can even be composed with themselves.

Example 1   Let $p(x) = \sin x + 1$ and $q(x) = x^2 - 3$. Find a formula in terms of x for $w(x) = p(p(q(x)))$.

Solution   We work from inside the parentheses outward. First we find $p(q(x))$, and then input the result to p.

$$w(x) = p(p(q(x)))$$
$$= p(p(x^2 - 3))$$
$$= p(\underbrace{\sin(x^2 - 3) + 1}_{\text{Input for } p})$$
$$= \sin(\sin(x^2 - 3) + 1) + 1. \qquad \text{\small Because } p(\text{Input}) = \sin(\text{Input}) + 1$$

Composition of Functions Defined by Tables

Often we do not have a formula for a function, but we can arrange the values of the function we do know in a table. In the next example, we compose functions that are defined using tables.

Example 2   Complete Table 10.1. Assume that $f(x)$ is invertible.

Table 10.1

x	$f(x)$	$g(x)$	$g(f(x))$
0	2	3	2
1	3	1	3
2	1		

Solution   We will first look at $g(f(2))$. From the table we see that $f(2) = 1$. Therefore, we have $g(f(2)) = g(1)$. Since $g(1) = 1$, we can fill in the entry for $g(f(2))$ the following way: $g(f(2)) = g(1) = 1$.

To find $g(2)$, we have to use information about $g(f(x))$. We first need to find a value of x such that $f(x) = 2$. That means that we are looking for $f^{-1}(2)$. From the table we see that $f^{-1}(2) = 0$, or equivalently, $f(0) = 2$. Therefore, $g(2) = g(f(0))$. From the table we see that $g(f(0)) = 2$. Thus, $g(2) = 2$.

Composition of Functions Defined by Graphs

So far we have composed functions defined by tables and formulas. We can also compose functions defined by graphs.

Example 3   Let u and v be two functions defined by the graphs in Figure 10.1. Evaluate:

(a) $v(u(-1))$ (b) $u(v(5))$ (c) $v(u(0)) + u(v(4))$

Figure 10.1: Evaluate the composition of functions u and v defined by their graphs

273

Solution

(a) To evaluate $v(u(-1))$, start with $u(-1)$. From Figure 10.1, we see that $u(-1) = 1$. Thus,
$$v(u(-1)) = v(1).$$

From the graph we see that $v(1) = 2$, so
$$v(u(-1)) = 2.$$

(b) Since $v(5) = -2$, we have $u(v(5)) = u(-2) = 0$.

(c) Since $u(0) = 0$, we have $v(u(0)) = v(0) = 3$.

Since $v(4) = -1$, we have $u(v(4)) = u(-1) = 1$.

Thus $v(u(0)) + u(v(4)) = 3 + 1 = 4$.

Decomposition of Functions

Sometimes we reason backward to find the functions that went into a composition. This process is called *decomposition*.

Example 4 Let $h(x) = f(g(x)) = e^{x^2+1}$. Find possible formulas for $f(x)$ and $g(x)$.

Solution

In the formula $h(x) = e^{x^2+1}$, the expression $x^2 + 1$ is in the exponent. We can take the inside function to be $g(x) = x^2 + 1$. This means that we can write
$$h(x) = e^{\underbrace{x^2 + 1}_{g(x)}} = e^{g(x)}.$$

Then the outside function is $f(x) = e^x$. We check that composing f and g gives h:
$$f(g(x)) = f(x^2 + 1) = e^{x^2+1} = h(x).$$

There are many possible solutions to Example 4. For example, we might choose $f(x) = e^{x+1}$ and $g(x) = x^2$. Then
$$f(g(x)) = e^{g(x)+1} = e^{x^2+1} = h(x).$$

Alternatively, we might choose $f(x) = e^{x^2+1}$ and $g(x) = x$. Although this satisfies the condition that $h(x) = f(g(x))$, it is not very useful, because f is the same as h. This kind of decomposition is referred to as *trivial*. Another example of a trivial decomposition of $h(x)$ is $f(x) = x$ and $g(x) = e^{x^2+1}$.

We saw in Example 1 that we can compose more than two functions. Similarly, it may be possible to decompose a function into more than two simpler functions.

Example 5 Let $p(z) = \sin^2(\ln z)$. Decompose $p(z)$ into three simpler functions by giving formulas for $f(z)$, $g(z)$, and $h(z)$ where
$$p(z) = f(g(h(z))).$$

Solution

We work from inside the parentheses outward. In the formula $p(z) = \sin^2(\ln z)$, we have the expression $\ln z$ inside the $\sin^2$ function. In the formula $p(z) = f(g(h(z)))$, the innermost function is $h(z)$. Thus, we let
$$h(z) = \ln z.$$

In the formula $p(z) = \sin^2(\ln z)$, the operation $\sin^2$ applied to the innermost expression $\ln z$ means we first take the sin of $\ln z$ and then square the result. In other words, $p(z) = (\sin(\ln z))^2$. Thus, we let

$$g(\text{Input}) = \sin(\text{Input})$$
$$g(z) = \sin z.$$

So we have

$$g(h(z)) = g(\ln z) = \sin(\ln z).$$

Finally, since $p(z) = \sin^2(\ln z) = (\sin(\ln z))^2$, we square the expression $\sin(\ln z)$ and let

$$f(\text{Input}) = \text{Input}^2$$
$$f(z) = z^2.$$

To check, we compute

$$\begin{aligned} f(g(h(z))) &= f(g(\ln z)) &&\text{Since } h(z) = \ln z \\ &= f(\underbrace{\sin(\ln z)}_{\text{Input for } f}) &&\text{Since } g(\ln z) = \sin(\ln z) \\ &= \sin^2(\ln z). &&\text{Since } f(\sin(\ln z)) = (\sin(\ln z))^2 \end{aligned}$$

Exercises and Problems for Section 10.1

Exercises

In Exercises 1–2, find and simplify for $f(x) = 2^x$ and $g(x) = \dfrac{x}{x+1}$.

1. $f(g(x))$

2. $g(f(x))$

3. Let $f(x) = \sin 4x$ and $g(x) = \sqrt{x}$. Find formulas for $f(g(x))$ and $g(f(x))$.

4. Let $m(x) = 3 + x^2$ and $n(x) = \tan x$. Find formulas for $m(n(x))$ and $n(m(x))$.

5. Find a formula in terms of x for the function $w(x) = p(p(x))$, where $p(x) = 2x + 1$.

6. Use Table 10.2 to construct a table of values for $r(x) = p(q(x))$.

Table 10.2

x	0	1	2	3	4	5
$p(x)$	1	0	5	2	3	4
$q(x)$	5	2	3	1	4	8

7. Let p and q be the functions in Exercise 6. Construct a table of values for $s(x) = q(p(x))$.

In Exercises 8–13, let $f(x) = 3x^2$, $g(x) = 9x - 2$, $m(x) = 4x$, and $r(x) = \sqrt{3x}$. Find and simplify the composite function.

8. $r(g(x))$

9. $f(r(x))$

10. $r(f(x))$

11. $g(f(x))$

12. $g(m(f(x)))$

13. $f(m(g(x)))$

In Exercises 14–18, identify the function $f(x)$.

14. $h(x) = e^{f(x)} = e^{\sin x}$

15. $j(x) = \sqrt{f(x)} = \sqrt{\ln(x^2 + 4)}$

16. $k(x) = \sin(f(x)) = \sin(x^3 + 3x + 1)$

17. $l(x) = (f(x))^2 = \cos^2 2x$

18. $m(x) = \ln f(x) = \ln(5 + 1/x)$

Problems

In Problems 19–22, give a practical interpretation in words of the function.

19. $f(h(t))$, where $A = f(r)$ is the area of a circle of radius r and $r = h(t)$ is the radius of the circle at time t.

20. $k(g(t))$, where $L = k(H)$ is the length of a steel bar at temperature H and $H = g(t)$ is temperature at time t.

21. $R(Y(q))$, where R gives a farmer's revenue as a function of corn yield per acre, and Y gives the corn yield as a function of the quantity, q, of fertilizer.

22. $t(f(H))$, where $t(v)$ is the time of a trip at velocity v, and $v = f(H)$ is velocity at temperature H.

23. Suppose $u(v(x)) = \dfrac{1}{x^2 - 1}$ and $v(u(x)) = \dfrac{1}{(x-1)^2}$. Find possible formulas for $u(x)$ and $v(x)$.

In Problems 24–27, suppose that $f(x) = g(h(x))$. Find possible formulas for $g(x)$ and $h(x)$ (There may be more than one possible answer. Assume $g(x) \neq x$ and $h(x) \neq x$.)

24. $f(x) = (x+3)^2$

25. $f(x) = \sqrt{1 + \sqrt{x}}$

26. $f(x) = 9x^2 + 3x$

27. $f(x) = \dfrac{1}{x^2 + 8x + 16}$

28. Complete Table 10.3 given that $h(x) = f(g(x))$.

Table 10.3

x	$f(x)$	$g(x)$	$h(x)$
0	1	2	5
1	9	0	
2		1	

29. Complete the table given $h(x) = g(f(x))$.

x	$f(x)$	$g(x)$	$h(x)$
0	2		
1		0	0
2		3	2
3	0		1
4	3	2	4

30. Complete Table 10.4 given that $w(t) = v(u(t))$.

Table 10.4

t	u	v	w
0	2	3	—
1	—	—	2
2	1	1	4
3	—	2	0
4	0	0	—

In Problems 31–33, let $x > 0$ and $k(x) = e^x$. Find a possible formula for $f(x)$.

31. $k(f(x)) = e^{2x}$

32. $f(k(x)) = e^{2x}$

33. $k(f(x)) = x$

In Problems 34–37, find a simplified formula for the difference quotient

$$\frac{f(x+h) - f(x)}{h}.$$

34. $f(x) = x^2 + x$

35. $f(x) = \sqrt{x}$

36. $f(x) = \dfrac{1}{x}$

37. $f(x) = 2^x$

38. Using Figure 10.2, estimate the following:

(a) $f(g(2))$ (b) $g(f(2))$ (c) $f(f(3))$ (d) $g(g(3))$

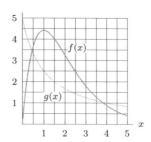

Figure 10.2

39. Use Figure 10.3 to calculate the following:

    (a) $f(f(1))$ **(b)** $g(g(1))$

    (c) $f(g(2))$ **(d)** $g(f(2))$

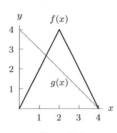

Figure 10.3

40. Use Figure 10.3 to find all solutions to the equations:

    (a) $f(g(x)) = 0$ **(b)** $g(f(x)) = 0$

41. Let $f(x)$ and $g(x)$ be the functions in Figure 10.3.

    (a) Graph the functions $f(g(x))$ and $g(f(x))$.

    (b) On what interval(s) is $f(g(x))$ increasing?

    (c) On what interval(s) is $g(f(x))$ increasing?

In Problems 42–45, use the information from Figures 10.4 and 10.5 to graph the functions.

Figure 10.4   Figure 10.5

42. $f(g(x))$ **43.** $g(f(x))$ **44.** $f(f(x))$ **45.** $g(g(x))$

46. Find $f(f(1))$ for

$$f(x) = \begin{cases} 2 & \text{if } x \le 0 \\ 3x + 1 & \text{if } 0 < x < 2 \\ x^2 - 3 & \text{if } x \ge 2 \end{cases}$$

47. If $s(x) = 5 + \dfrac{1}{x+5} + x$, $k(x) = x + 5$, and $s(x) = v(k(x))$, what is $v(x)$?

48. Let $f(x) = 12 - 4x$, $g(x) = 1/x$, and $h(x) = \sqrt{x-4}$. Find the domain of the functions:

    (a) $g(f(x))$ **(b)** $h(f(x))$

Decompose the functions in Problems 49–54 into $u(v(x))$ for given u or v.

49. $y = \dfrac{1+x^2}{2+x^2}$ given that

    (a) $v(x) = x^2$ **(b)** $v(x) = x^2 + 1$

50. $y = e^{-\sqrt{x}}$ given that

    (a) $u(x) = e^x$ **(b)** $v(x) = \sqrt{x}$

51. $y = \sqrt{1 - x^3}$ given that

    (a) $u(x) = \sqrt{1 + x^3}$ **(b)** $v(x) = x^3$

52. $y = 2^{x+1}$ given that

    (a) $u(x) = 2x$ **(b)** $v(x) = -x$

53. $y = \sin^2 x$ given that

    (a) $u(x) = x^2$ **(b)** $v(x) = x^2$

54. $y = e^{2\cos x}$ given that

    (a) $u(x) = e^x$ **(b)** $v(x) = \cos x$

55. (a) Use Table 10.5 and Figure 10.6 to calculate:

    (i) $f(g(4))$ (ii) $g(f(4))$

    (iii) $f(f(0))$ (iv) $g(g(0))$

    (b) Solve $g(g(x)) = 1$ for x.

Table 10.5

x	0	1	2	3	4	5
$f(x)$	2	5	3	4	1	0

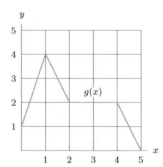

Figure 10.6

56. You have two money machines, both of which increase any money inserted into them. The first machine doubles your money. The second adds five dollars. The money that comes out is described by $d(x) = 2x$ in the first case and $a(x) = x + 5$ in the second, where x is the number of dollars inserted. The machines can be hooked up so that the money coming out of one machine goes into the other. Find formulas for each of the two possible composition machines. Is one machine more profitable than the other?

57. Let $p(t) = 10(0.01)^t$ and $q(t) = \log t^2$. Solve the equation $q(p(t)) = 0$ for t.

58. Let $f(t) = \sin t$ and $g(t) = 3t - \pi/4$. Solve the equation $f(g(t)) = 1$ for t in the interval $0 \leq t \leq 2\pi/3$.

59. Let $f(x) = \sqrt{x}$ and $g(x) = x^2$. Calculate the domain of $f(g(x))$ and the domain of $g(f(x))$.

60. The graphs for $y = f(x)$ and $y = g(x)$ are shown in Figure 10.7.

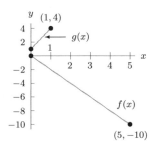

Figure 10.7

(a) Write an equation for $f(x)$.

(b) State the domain and range of $f(x)$.
(c) Write an equation for $g(x)$.
(d) State the domain and range of $g(x)$.
(e) Write an equation for $h(x) = f(g(x))$.
(f) State the domain and range of $h(x)$.
(g) Draw the graph of $h(x)$.

61. Letting $r(x) = 3x^3 - 4x^2$, find $q(x)$ given that
$$q(r(x)) = \frac{8^{x^3}}{16^{x^2}}.$$

In Problems 62–63, find a simplified formula for g given that
$$f(x) = \frac{x+1}{x+3}.$$

62. $g(x) = f(h(x))$ where $h(x) = 3x^2 - 1$.

63. $f(x) = g(x) + \dfrac{2x+4}{x+3}$.

64. Which of the following statements must be true in order for the point $(2, 5)$ to be on the graph of $h(x) = g(f(x))$?

(a) The domain of f includes 2.
(b) The domain of g includes 2.
(c) The range of f includes 5.
(d) The range of g includes 5.
(e) The function g is invertible.

65. Which of the following statements must be true in order for $h(x) = g(f(x))$ to be defined for all x?

(a) The domain of f is all x.
(b) The domain of g is all x.
(c) The range of f is all y.
(d) The range of g is all y.
(e) The range of f is within the domain of g.

10.2 INVERTIBILITY AND PROPERTIES OF INVERSE FUNCTIONS

Inverse functions were introduced in Section 2.4. In Section 5.1, we defined the logarithm as the inverse function of the exponential function. In Section 8.4, we defined the arccosine as the inverse of cosine. We now study inverse functions in general.

Definition of Inverse Function

Recall that the statement $f^{-1}(50) = 20$ means that $f(20) = 50$. In fact, the values of f^{-1} are determined in just this way. In general,

Suppose $Q = f(t)$ is a function with the property that each value of Q determines exactly one value of t. Then f has an **inverse function**, f^{-1}, and

$$f^{-1}(Q) = t \quad \text{if and only if} \quad Q = f(t).$$

If a function has an inverse, it is said to be **invertible**.

The definitions of the logarithm and of the inverse cosine have the same form as the definition of f^{-1}. Since $y = \log x$ is the inverse function of $y = 10^x$, we have

$$x = \log y \quad \text{if and only if} \quad y = 10^x,$$

and since $y = \cos^{-1} t$ is the inverse function of $y = \cos t$,

$$t = \cos^{-1} y \quad \text{if and only if} \quad y = \cos t.$$

Example 1 Find a solution to the equation $\sin x = 0.8$ using an inverse function.

Solution A solution is $x = \sin^{-1}(0.8)$. A calculator (set in radians) gives $x = \sin^{-1}(0.8) \approx 0.927$.

Finding a Formula for an Inverse Function

As we have seen in Section 2.4, it is sometimes possible to find a formula for an inverse function f^{-1} from a formula for f.

Example 2 Suppose you deposit $500 into a savings account that pays 4% interest compounded annually. The balance, in dollars, in the account after t years is given by $B = f(t) = 500(1.04)^t$.

(a) Find a formula for $t = f^{-1}(B)$.
(b) What does the inverse function represent in terms of the account?

Solution (a) To find a formula for f^{-1}, we solve for t in terms of B:

$$B = 500(1.04)^t$$

$$\frac{B}{500} = (1.04)^t$$

$$\log\left(\frac{B}{500}\right) = t \log 1.04 \qquad \text{Taking logs of both sides}$$

$$t = \frac{\log(B/500)}{\log 1.04}.$$

Thus, a formula for the inverse function is

$$t = f^{-1}(B) = \frac{\log(B/500)}{\log 1.04}.$$

(b) The function $t = f^{-1}(B)$ gives the number of years for the balance to grow to $\$B$.

In the previous example the variables of the function $B = f(t)$ had contextual meaning, so the inverse function was written as $t = f^{-1}(B)$. In abstract mathematical examples, a function $y = f(x)$ will often have its inverse function written with x as the independent variable.

Example 3 Find the inverse of the function

$$f(x) = \frac{3x}{2x + 1}.$$

Solution First, we solve the equation $y = f(x)$ for x:

$$y = \frac{3x}{2x+1}$$
$$2xy + y = 3x$$
$$2xy - 3x = -y$$
$$x(2y - 3) = -y$$
$$x = \frac{-y}{2y-3} = \frac{y}{3-2y}.$$

As before, we write $x = f^{-1}(y) = \dfrac{y}{3-2y}$.

Since y is now the independent variable, by convention we rewrite the inverse function with x as the independent variable. We have

$$f^{-1}(x) = \frac{x}{3-2x}.$$

Noninvertible Functions: Horizontal Line Test

Not every function has an inverse function. A function $Q = f(t)$ has no inverse if it returns the same Q-value for two different t-values. When that happens, the value of t cannot be uniquely determined from the value of Q.

For example, if $q(x) = x^2$ then $q(-3) = 9$ and $q(+3) = 9$. This means that we cannot say what the value $q^{-1}(9)$ would be. (Is it $+3$ or -3?) Thus, q is not invertible. In Figure 10.8, notice that the horizontal line $y = 9$ intersects the graph of $q(x) = x^2$ at two different points: $(-3, 9)$ and $(3, 9)$. This corresponds to the fact that the function q returns $y = 9$ for two different x-values, $x = +3$ and $x = -3$.

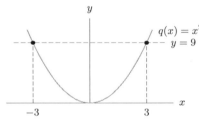

Figure 10.8: The graph of $q(x) = x^2$ fails the horizontal line test

We have the following general result:

> **The Horizontal Line Test** If there is a horizontal line that intersects a function's graph in more than one point, then the function does not have an inverse. If every horizontal line intersects a function's graph at most once, then the function has an inverse.

Evaluating an Inverse Function Graphically

Finding a formula for an inverse function can be difficult. However, this does not mean that the inverse function does not exist. Even without a formula, it may be possible to find values of the inverse function.

Example 4   Let $u(x) = x^3 + x + 1$. Explain why a graph suggests the function u is invertible. Assuming u has an inverse, estimate $u^{-1}(4)$.

Solution   To show that u is invertible, we could try to find a formula for u^{-1}. To do this, we would solve the equation $y = x^3 + x + 1$ for x. Unfortunately, this is difficult. However, the graph in Figure 10.9 suggests that u passes the horizontal line test and therefore that u is invertible. To estimate $u^{-1}(4)$, we find an x-value such that

$$x^3 + x + 1 = 4.$$

In Figure 10.9, the graph of $y = u(x)$ and the horizontal line $y = 4$ intersect at the point $x \approx 1.213$. Thus, tracing along the graph, we estimate $u^{-1}(4) \approx 1.213$.

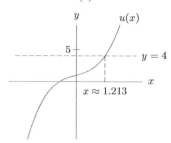

Figure 10.9: The graph of $u(x)$ passes the horizontal line test.
Since $u(1.213) \approx 4$, we have $u^{-1}(4) \approx 1.213$

In Example 4, even without a formula for u^{-1}, we can approximate $u^{-1}(a)$ for any value of a.

Example 5   Let $P(x) = 2^x$.

(a) Show that P is invertible.
(b) Find a formula for $P^{-1}(x)$.
(c) Sketch the graphs of P and P^{-1} on the same axes.
(d) What are the domain and range of P and P^{-1}?

Solution   (a) Since P is an exponential function with base 2, it is always increasing, and therefore passes the horizontal line test. (See the graph of P in Figure 10.10.) Thus, P has an inverse function.

(b) To find a formula for $P^{-1}(x)$, we solve for x in the equation

$$2^x = y.$$

We take the log of both sides to get

$$\log 2^x = \log y$$
$$x \log 2 = \log y$$
$$x = P^{-1}(y) = \frac{\log y}{\log 2}.$$

Thus, we have a formula for P^{-1} with y as the input. To graph P and P^{-1} on the same axes, we write P^{-1} as a function of x:

$$P^{-1}(x) = \frac{\log x}{\log 2} = \frac{1}{\log 2} \cdot \log x = 3.322 \log x.$$

(c) Table 10.6 gives values of $P(x)$ for $x = -3, -2, \ldots, 3$. Interchanging the columns of Table 10.6 gives Table 10.7 for $P^{-1}(x)$. We use these tables to sketch Figure 10.10.

Table 10.6   *Values of* $P(x) = 2^x$

x	$P(x) = 2^x$
−3	0.125
−2	0.25
−1	0.5
0	1
1	2
2	4
3	8

Table 10.7   *Values of* $P^{-1}(x)$

x	$P^{-1}(x)$
0.125	−3
0.25	−2
0.5	−1
1	0
2	1
4	2
8	3

Figure 10.10: The graphs of $P(x) = 2^x$ and its inverse are symmetrical across the line $y = x$

(d) The domain of P, an exponential function, is all real numbers, and its range is all positive numbers. The domain of P^{-1}, a logarithmic function, is all positive numbers and its range is all real numbers.

The Graph, Domain, and Range of an Inverse Function

In Figure 10.10, we see that the graph of P^{-1} is the mirror-image of the graph of P across the line $y = x$. In general, this is true if the x- and y-axes have the same scale. To understand why this occurs, consider how a function is related to its inverse.

If f is an invertible function with, for example, $f(2) = 5$, then $f^{-1}(5) = 2$. Thus, the point $(2, 5)$ is on the graph of f and the point $(5, 2)$ is on the graph of f^{-1}. Generalizing, if (a, b) is any point on the graph of f, then (b, a) is a point on the graph of f^{-1}. Figure 10.11 shows how reflecting the point (a, b) across the line $y = x$ gives the point (b, a). Consequently, the graph of f^{-1} is the reflection of the graph of f across the line $y = x$.

Notice that outputs from a function are inputs to its inverse function. Similarly, outputs from the inverse function are inputs to the original function. This is expressed in the statement $f^{-1}(b) = a$ if and only if $f(a) = b$, and also in the fact that we can obtain a table for f^{-1} by interchanging the columns of a table for f. Consequently, the domain and range for f^{-1} are obtained by interchanging the domain and range of f. In other words,

---

Graph of f^{-1} is reflection of graph of f across the line $y = x$.

Domain of f^{-1} = Range of f and   Range of f^{-1} = Domain of f.

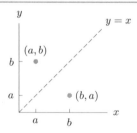

Figure 10.11: The reflection of the point (a, b) across the line $y = x$ is the point (b, a)

As we saw in Example 5, the function P has all real numbers as its domain and all positive numbers as its range; the function P^{-1} has all positive numbers as its domain and all real numbers as its range.

A Property of Inverse Functions

The fact that Tables 10.6 and 10.7 contain the same values, but with the columns switched, reflects the special relationship between the values of $P(x)$ and $P^{-1}(x)$. For the function in Example 5

$$P^{-1}(2) = 1 \quad \text{and} \quad P(1) = 2 \quad \text{so} \quad P^{-1}(P(1)) = 1,$$

and

$$P^{-1}(0.25) = -2 \quad \text{and} \quad P(-2) = 0.25 \quad \text{so} \quad P^{-1}(P(-2)) = -2.$$

This result holds for any input x, so in general,

$$P^{-1}(P(x)) = x.$$

In addition, $P(P^{-1}(2)) = 2$ and $P(P^{-1}(0.25)) = 0.25$, and for any x

$$P(P^{-1}(x)) = x.$$

Similar reasoning holds for any other invertible function, suggesting the general result:

> If $y = f(x)$ is an invertible function and $y = f^{-1}(x)$ is its inverse, then
> - $f^{-1}(f(x)) = x$ for all values of x for which $f(x)$ is defined,
> - $f(f^{-1}(x)) = x$ for all values of x for which $f^{-1}(x)$ is defined.

This property tell us that composing a function and its inverse function returns the original value as the end result. We can use this property to decide whether two functions are inverses.

Example 6　(a) Check that $f(x) = \dfrac{x}{2x+1}$ and $f^{-1}(x) = \dfrac{x}{1-2x}$ are inverse functions of each other.

(b) Graph f and f^{-1} on axes with the same scale. What are the domains and ranges of f and f^{-1}?

Solution　(a) To check that these functions are inverses, we compose

$$f^{-1}(f(x)) = \frac{f(x)}{1 - 2f(x)} = \frac{\dfrac{x}{2x+1}}{1 - 2\left(\dfrac{x}{2x+1}\right)}$$

$$= \frac{\dfrac{x}{2x+1}}{\dfrac{2x+1}{2x+1} - \dfrac{2x}{2x+1}}$$

$$= \frac{\dfrac{x}{2x+1}}{\dfrac{1}{2x+1}}$$

$$= x.$$

Similarly, you can check that $f(f^{-1}(x)) = x$.

(b) The graphs of f and f^{-1} in Figure 10.12 are symmetric about the line $y = x$.

Figure 10.12: The graph of $f(x) = x/(2x + 1)$ and the inverse $f^{-1}(x) = x/(1 - 2x)$

The function $f(x) = x/(2x + 1)$ is undefined at $x = -1/2$, so its domain consists of all real numbers except $-1/2$. Figure 10.12 suggests that f has a horizontal asymptote at $y = 1/2$ which it does not cross and that its range is all real numbers except $1/2$.

Because the inverse function $f^{-1}(x) = x/(1 - 2x)$ is undefined at $x = 1/2$, its domain is all real numbers except $1/2$. Note that this is the same as the range of f. The graph of f^{-1} appears to have a horizontal asymptote which it does not cross at $y = -1/2$, suggesting that its range is all real numbers except $-1/2$. Note that this is the same as the domain of f.

The ranges of the functions f and f^{-1} can be confirmed algebraically.

Restricting the Domain

A function that fails the horizontal line test is not invertible. For this reason, the function $f(x) = x^2$ does not have an inverse function. However, by considering only part of the graph of f, we can eliminate the duplication of y-values. Suppose we consider the half of the parabola with $x \geq 0$. See Figure 10.13. This part of the graph does pass the horizontal line test because there is only one (positive) x-value for each y-value in the range of f.

Figure 10.13

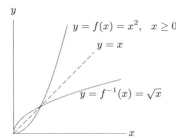

Figure 10.14

We can find an inverse for $f(x) = x^2$ on its restricted domain,[1] $x \geq 0$. Using the fact that $x \geq 0$ and solving $y = x^2$ for x gives

$$x = \sqrt{y}.$$

Thus a formula for the inverse function is

$$x = f^{-1}(y) = \sqrt{y}.$$

Rewriting the formula for f^{-1} with x as the input, we have

$$f^{-1}(x) = \sqrt{x}.$$

The graphs of f and f^{-1} are shown in Figure 10.14. Note that the domain of f is the the range of f^{-1}, and the domain of f^{-1} ($x \geq 0$) is the range of f.

---

[1]Technically, changing the domain results in a new function, but we will continue to call it $f(x)$.

In Section 8.4 we restricted the domains of the sine, cosine, and tangent functions in order to define their inverse functions:

$$y = \sin^{-1} x \quad \text{if and only if} \quad x = \sin y \quad \text{and} \quad -\frac{\pi}{2} \leq y \leq \frac{\pi}{2}$$

$$y = \cos^{-1} x \quad \text{if and only if} \quad x = \cos y \quad \text{and} \quad 0 \leq y \leq \pi$$

$$y = \tan^{-1} x \quad \text{if and only if} \quad x = \tan y \quad \text{and} \quad -\frac{\pi}{2} < y < \frac{\pi}{2}.$$

The graphs of each of the inverse trigonometric functions are shown in Figures 10.15-10.17. Note the symmetry about the line $y = x$ for each trigonometric function and its inverse.

| Figure 10.15 | Figure 10.16 | Figure 10.17 |

In each case, the restricted domain of the function is the range of the inverse function. In addition, the domain of the inverse is the range of the original function. For example,

$$y = \sin x \quad \text{has restricted domain } -\frac{\pi}{2} \leq x \leq \frac{\pi}{2} \quad \text{and} \quad \text{range} \quad -1 \leq y \leq 1$$

$$y = \sin^{-1} x \quad \text{has domain} \quad -1 \leq x \leq 1 \quad \text{and} \quad \text{range} \quad -\frac{\pi}{2} \leq y \leq \frac{\pi}{2}.$$

Exercises and Problems for Section 10.2

Exercises

In Exercises 1–6, use a graph to decide whether or not the function is invertible.

1. $y = x^6 + 2x^2 - 10$

2. $y = x^4 - 6x + 12$

3. $y = e^{x^2}$

4. $y = \cos(x^3)$

5. $y = |x|$

6. $y = x + \ln x$

In Exercises 7–14, check that the functions are inverses.

7. $f(x) = \frac{x}{4} - \frac{3}{2}$ and $g(t) = 4\left(t + \frac{3}{2}\right)$

8. $f(x) = 1 + 7x^3$ and $f^{-1}(x) = \sqrt[3]{\frac{x-1}{7}}$

9. $g(x) = 1 - \frac{1}{x-1}$ and $g^{-1}(x) = 1 + \frac{1}{1-x}$

10. $h(x) = \sqrt{2x}$ and $k(t) = \frac{t^2}{2}$, for $x, t \geq 0$

11. $f(x) = e^{x+1}$ and $f^{-1}(x) = \ln x - 1$

12. $f(x) = e^{2x}$ and $f^{-1}(x) = \frac{\ln x}{2}$

13. $f(x) = e^{x/2}$ and $f^{-1}(x) = 2\ln x$

14. $f(x) = \ln(x/2)$ and $f^{-1}(x) = 2e^x$

In Exercises 15–31, find a formula for the inverse function. Assume these functions are defined on domains on which they are invertible.

15. $f(x) = x + 5$

16. $g(x) = 1 - x$

17. $h(x) = \sqrt{x}$

18. $j(x) = \frac{1}{x}$

19. $f(x) = 3x - 7$

20. $k(x) = \frac{x}{x-1}$

21. $l(x) = \sqrt{1 - 2x^2}$

22. $m(x) = \dfrac{1}{x} - x$

23. $n(x) = (1 + x^2)^2$

24. $o(x) = 1/(1 + \dfrac{1}{x})$

25. $j(x) = \sqrt{1 + \sqrt{x}}$

26. $h(x) = \dfrac{2x + 1}{3x - 2}$

27. $k(x) = \dfrac{3 - \sqrt{x}}{\sqrt{x} + 2}$

28. $g(x) = \dfrac{\ln x - 5}{2\ln x + 7}$

29. $h(x) = \log\left(\dfrac{x + 5}{x - 4}\right)$

30. $f(x) = \cos\sqrt{x}$

31. $g(x) = 2^{\sin x}$

32. Check that the functions $R = f(T) = 150 + 5T$ and $T = f^{-1}(R) = \frac{1}{5}R - 30$ satisfy the identities

$$f^{-1}(f(T)) = T \quad \text{and} \quad f(f^{-1}(R)) = R.$$

Problems

33. If $P = f(t)$ gives the population of a city, in thousands, as a function of time, t, in years, what does $f^{-1}(P)$ represent? What are its units?

34. If $C = f(q)$ gives the cost, in dollars, to manufacture q items, what does $f^{-1}(C)$ represent? What are its units?

35. Let $R = f(T) = 150 + 5T$ give the resistance of a circuit element as a function of temperature.

   (a) Find a formula for $T = f^{-1}(R)$.
   (b) Make a table of values showing values of f. Make another table showing values of f^{-1}. Explain the relationship between the tables.

36. The police can determine the speed a car was traveling from the length of the skid marks it leaves. The function they use is $S = f(L) = 2\sqrt{(5L)}$ where S is speed (mph) and L is the length of the skid marks (feet).

   (a) If skid marks of length 125 feet are measured, what was the speed of the car?
   (b) Find a formula for the inverse function.
   (c) If the car had been traveling at 80 mph, how long would the skid marks be?

37. Let $f(x) = 5^x$.

   (a) Evaluate $f(3)$ and $f^{-1}(1/25)$ exactly.
   (b) Approximate the value of $f^{-1}(10)$.

38. Let $P = f(t) = 37.8(1.044)^t$ be the population of a town (in thousands) in year t.

   (a) Describe the town's population in words.
   (b) Evaluate $f(50)$. What does this quantity tell you about the population?
   (c) Find a formula for $f^{-1}(P)$ in terms of P.
   (d) Evaluate $f^{-1}(50)$. What does this quantity tell you about the population?

39. Figure 10.18 defines the function f. Rank the following quantities in order from least to greatest:

$$0, f(0), f^{-1}(0), 3, f(3), f^{-1}(3).$$

Figure 10.18

40. Let $C = f(q) = 200 + 0.1q$ give the cost in dollars to manufacture q kg of a chemical. Find and interpret $f^{-1}(C)$.

41. Let $P = f(t) = 10e^{0.02t}$ give the population in millions at time t in years. Find and interpret $f^{-1}(P)$.

42. The noise level, N, of a sound in decibels is given by

$$N = f(I) = 10\log\left(\dfrac{I}{I_0}\right),$$

where I is the intensity of the sound and I_0 is a constant. Find and interpret $f^{-1}(N)$.

43. A research facility on the Isle of Shoals has 800 gallons of fresh water for a two-month period.

   (a) There are 7 members of the research team and each is allotted 2 gallons of water per day for cooking and drinking. Find a formula for $f(t)$, the amount of fresh water left on the island after t days has elapsed.
   (b) Evaluate and interpret the following expressions:

     (i) $f(0)$ (ii) $f^{-1}(0)$
     (iii) t if $f(t) = \dfrac{1}{2}f(0)$ (iv) $800 - f(t)$

44. The rating, r, of an earthquake of intensity I is given by $r = f(I) = \log(I/I_0)$, where I_0 is a constant. Find and interpret $f^{-1}(r)$.

45. Let $f(x) = e^x$ and $g(x) = \ln x$.

   (a) Find $f(g(x))$ and $g(f(x))$. What can you conclude about the relationship between these two functions?

   (b) Graph $f(x)$ and $g(x)$ together on axes with the same scales. What is the line of symmetry of the graph?

46. Let $p(t) = 10^t$ and $q(t) = \log t$.

   (a) Find $p(q(t))$ and $q(p(t))$. What can you conclude about the relationship between these two functions?

   (b) Graph $p(t)$ and $q(t)$ together on axes with the same scales. What is the line of symmetry of the graph?

47. Table 10.8 gives the number N of cows in a herd.

   (a) Find an exponential function that approximates the data.

   (b) Find the inverse function of the function in part (a).

   (c) When do you predict that the herd will contain 400 cows?

Table 10.8

t (years)	0	1	2
$N = P(t)$ (cows)	150	165	182

48. There is a linear relationship between the number of units, $N(x)$, of a product that a company sells and the amount of money, x, spent on advertising. If the company spends \$25,000 on advertising, it sells 400 units, and for each additional \$5,000 spent, it sells 20 units more.

   (a) Calculate and interpret $N(20{,}000)$.

   (b) Find a formula for $N(x)$ in terms of x.

   (c) Give interpretations of the slope and the x- and y-intercepts of $N(x)$ if possible.

   (d) Calculate and interpret $N^{-1}(500)$.

   (e) An internal audit reveals that the profit made by the company on the sale of 10 units of its product, before advertising costs have been accounted for, is \$2,000. What are the implications regarding the company's advertising campaign? Discuss.

49. A hot brick is removed from a kiln at $200°C$ above room temperature. Over time, the brick cools off. After 2 hours have elapsed, the brick is $20°C$ above room temperature. Let t be the time in hours since the brick was removed from the kiln. Let $y = H(t)$ be the difference between the brick's and the room's temperature at time t. Assume that $H(t)$ is an exponential function.

   (a) Find a formula for $H(t)$.

   (b) How many degrees does the brick's temperature drop during the first quarter hour? During the next quarter hour?

   (c) Find and interpret $H^{-1}(y)$.

   (d) How much time elapses before the brick's temperature is $5°C$ above room temperature?

   (e) Interpret the physical meaning of the horizontal asymptote of $H(t)$.

50. The *quadratic mean* (or RMS) of x and the constant A is given by $f(x) = 0.5(x^2 + A^2)^{0.5}$. Assuming $x \geq 0$, find a formula for $f^{-1}(x)$.

51. The *harmonic mean* of x and the constant A is given by $f(x) = 0.5(x^{-1} + A^{-1})^{-1}$. Find a formula for $f^{-1}(x)$.

52. Values of f and g are in Table 10.9. Based on this table:

   (a) Is $f(x)$ invertible? If not, explain why; if so, construct a table of values of $f^{-1}(x)$ for all values of x for which $f^{-1}(x)$ is defined.

   (b) Answer the same question as in part (a) for $g(x)$.

   (c) Make a table of values for $h(x) = f(g(x))$, with $x = -3, -2, -1, 0, 1, 2, 3$.

   (d) Explain why you cannot define a function $j(x)$ by the formula $j(x) = g(f(x))$.

Table 10.9

x	-3	-2	-1	0	1	2	3
$f(x)$	9	7	6	-4	-5	-8	-9
$g(x)$	3	1	3	2	-3	-1	3

Problems 53–54 involve the *Lambert W function*,[2] defined by $W(x) = f^{-1}(x)$ where $f(x) = xe^x$ with $x \geq -1$. Since $f\left(f^{-1}(x)\right) = x$, this means $W(x)e^{W(x)} = x$.

53. Find three points on the graph of W by finding $f(-1)$, $f(0)$, and $f(1)$.

54. Given that $W(10) = 1.746$, find a solution to the equation $te^{2t} = 5$.

55. Suppose $P = f(t)$ is the population (in thousands) in year t, and that $f(7) = 13$ and $f(12) = 20$,

   (a) Find a formula for $f(t)$ assuming f is exponential.

   (b) Find a formula for $f^{-1}(P)$.

   (c) Evaluate $f(25)$ and $f^{-1}(25)$. Explain what these expressions mean in terms of population.

---

[2] See http://en.wikipedia.org/wiki/Lambert%27s_W_function, accessed April 30, 2008.

56. A gymnast at Ringling Bros. and Barnum & Bailey Circus is fired straight up in the air from a cannon. While she is in the air, a trampoline is moved into the spot where the cannon was. Figure 10.19 is a graph of the gymnast's height, h, as a function of time, t.

(a) Approximately what is her maximum height?

(b) Approximately when does she land on the trampoline?

(c) Restrict the domain of $h(t)$ so that $h(t)$ has an inverse. That is, pick a piece of the graph on which $h(t)$ does have an inverse. Graph this new restricted function.

(d) Change the story to go with your graph in part (c).

(e) Graph the inverse of the function in part (c). Explain in your story why it makes sense that the inverse is a function.

height (m)

36

$h(t)$

time (sec)

6

Figure 10.19

57. A 100-ml solution contains 99% alcohol and 1% water. Let $y = C(x)$ be the concentration of alcohol in the solution after x ml of alcohol are removed, so

$$C(x) = \frac{\text{Amount of alcohol}}{\text{Amount of solution}}.$$

(a) What is $C(0)$?

(b) Find a formula in terms of x for $C(x)$.

(c) Find a formula in terms of y for $C^{-1}(y)$.

(d) Explain the physical significance of $C^{-1}(y)$.

58. (a) How much alcohol do you think should be removed from the 99% solution in Problem 57 in order to obtain a 98% solution? (Make a guess.)

(b) Express the exact answer to part (a) using the function C^{-1} you found in Problem 57.

(c) Determine the exact answer to part (a). Are you surprised by your result?

The predicted pulse in beats per minute (bpm) of a healthy person fifteen minutes after consuming q milligrams of caffeine is given by $r = f(q)$. The amount of caffeine in a serving of coffee is q_c, and $r_c = f(q_c)$. Assume that f is an increasing function for non-toxic levels of caffeine. What do the statements in Problems 59–64 tell you about caffeine and a person's pulse?

59. $f(2q_c)$ **60.** $f^{-1}(r_c + 20)$

61. $2f^{-1}(r_c) + 20$ **62.** $f(q_c) - f(0)$

63. $f^{-1}(r_c + 20) - q_c$ **64.** $f^{-1}(1.1f(q_c))$

10.3 COMBINATIONS OF FUNCTIONS

Like numbers, functions can be combined using addition, subtraction, multiplication, and division.

The Difference of Two Functions Defined by Formulas: A Measure of Prosperity

We can define new functions as the sum or difference of two functions. In Chapter 4, we discussed Thomas Malthus, who predicted widespread food shortages because he believed that human populations increase exponentially, whereas the food supply increases linearly. We considered a country with population $P(t)$ million in year t. The population is initially 2 million and grows at the rate of 4% per year, so

$$P(t) = 2(1.04)^t.$$

Let $N(t)$ be the number of people (in millions) that the country can feed in year t. The annual food supply is initially adequate for 4 million people and it increases by enough for an additional 0.5 million people every year. Thus

$$N(t) = 4 + 0.5t.$$

This country first experiences shortages in about 78 years. (See Figure 10.20.) When is it most prosperous?

Figure 10.20: Predicted population, $P(t)$, and number of people who can be fed, $N(t)$, over a 100-year period

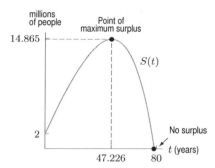

Figure 10.21: Surplus graphed using the formula $S(t) = 4 + 0.5t - 2(1.04)^t$

The answer depends on how we decide to measure prosperity. We could measure prosperity in one of the following ways:

- By the food surplus—that is, the amount of food the country has over and above its needs. This surplus food could be warehoused or exported in trade.

- By the per capita food supply—that is, how much food there is per person. (The term *per capita* means per person, or literally, "per head.") This indicates the portion of the country's wealth each person might enjoy.

First, we choose to measure prosperity in terms of food surplus, $S(t)$, in year t, where

$$S(t) = \underbrace{\text{Number of people that can be fed}}_{N(t)} - \underbrace{\text{Number of people living in the country}}_{P(t)}$$

so

$$S(t) = N(t) - P(t).$$

For example, to determine the surplus in year $t = 25$, we evaluate

$$S(25) = N(25) - P(25).$$

Since $N(25) = 4 + 0.5(25) = 16.5$ and $P(25) = 2(1.04)^{25} \approx 5.332$, we have

$$S(25) \approx 16.5 - 5.332 = 11.168.$$

Thus, in year 25 the food surplus could feed 11.168 million additional people.

We use the formulas for N and P to find a formula for S:

$$S(t) = \underbrace{N(t)}_{4+0.5t} - \underbrace{P(t)}_{2(1.04)^t},$$

so

$$S(t) = 4 + 0.5t - 2(1.04)^t.$$

A graph of S is shown in Figure 10.21. The maximum surplus occurs sometime during the 48th year. In that year, there is surplus food sufficient for an additional 14.865 million people.

The Sum and Difference of Two Functions Defined by Graphs

How does the graph of the surplus function S, shown in Figure 10.21, relate to the graphs of N and P in Figure 10.20? Since

$$S(t) = N(t) - P(t),$$

the value of $S(t)$ is represented graphically as the vertical distance between the graphs of $N(t)$ and $P(t)$. See Figure 10.22. Figure 10.23 shows the surplus plotted against time.

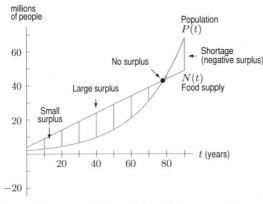

Figure 10.22: Surplus, $S(t) = N(t) - P(t)$, as vertical distance between $N(t)$ and $P(t)$ graphs

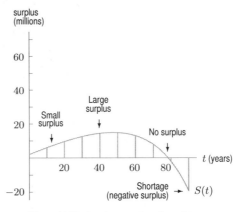

Figure 10.23: Surplus as a function of time

From year $t = 0$ to $t \approx 78.320$, the food supply is more than the population needs. Therefore the surplus, $S(t)$, is positive on this time interval. At time $t = 78.320$, the food supply is exactly sufficient for the population, so $S(t) = 0$, resulting in the horizontal intercept $t = 78.320$ on the graph of $S(t)$ in Figure 10.23. For times $t > 78.320$, the food supply is less than the population needs. Therefore the surplus is negative, representing a food shortage.

In the next example we consider a sum of two functions.

Example 1   Let $f(x) = x$ and $g(x) = \dfrac{1}{x}$. By adding vertical distances on the graphs of f and g, sketch

$$h(x) = f(x) + g(x) \quad \text{for } x > 0.$$

Solution   The graphs of f and g are shown in Figure 10.24. For each value of x, we add the vertical distances that represent $f(x)$ and $g(x)$ to get a point on the graph of $h(x)$. Compare the graph of $h(x)$ to the values shown in Table 10.10.

Table 10.10   *Adding function values*

x	$\frac{1}{4}$	$\frac{1}{2}$	1	2	4
$f(x) = x$	$\frac{1}{4}$	$\frac{1}{2}$	1	2	4
$g(x) = 1/x$	4	2	1	$\frac{1}{2}$	$\frac{1}{4}$
$h(x) = f(x) + g(x)$	$4\frac{1}{4}$	$2\frac{1}{2}$	2	$2\frac{1}{2}$	$4\frac{1}{4}$

Note that as x increases, $g(x)$ decreases toward zero, so the values of $h(x)$ get closer to the values of $f(x)$. On the other hand, as x approaches zero, $h(x)$ gets closer to $g(x)$.

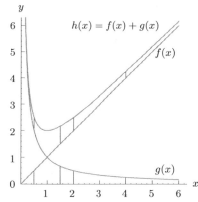

Figure 10.24: Graph of $h(x) = f(x) + g(x)$ constructed by adding vertical distances under f and g

Factoring a Function's Formula into a Product

It is often useful to be able to express a given function as a product of functions.

Example 2   Find exactly all the zeros of the function

$$p(x) = 2^x \cdot 6x^2 - 2^x \cdot x - 2^{x+1}.$$

Solution   We could approximate the zeros by finding the points where the graph of the function p crosses the x-axis. Unfortunately, these solutions are not exact. Alternatively, we can express p as a product. Using the fact that

$$2^{x+1} = 2^x \cdot 2^1 = 2 \cdot 2^x,$$

we rewrite the formula for p as

$$
\begin{aligned}
p(x) &= 2^x \cdot 6x^2 - 2^x x - 2 \cdot 2^x \\
&= 2^x(6x^2 - x - 2) && \text{Factoring out } 2^x \\
&= 2^x(2x + 1)(3x - 2). && \text{Factoring the quadratic}
\end{aligned}
$$

Thus p is the product of the exponential function 2^x and two linear functions. Since p is a product, it equals zero if one or more of its factors equals zero. But 2^x is never equal to 0, so $p(x)$ equals zero if and only if one of the linear factors is zero:

$$
\begin{aligned}
(2x + 1) = 0 \qquad & \text{or } (3x - 2) = 0 \\
x = -\frac{1}{2} \qquad & \qquad x = \frac{2}{3}.
\end{aligned}
$$

The Quotient of Functions Defined by Formulas and Graphs: Prosperity

Now let's think about our second proposed measure of prosperity, the per capita food supply, $R(t)$. With this definition of prosperity

$$R(t) = \frac{\text{Number of people that can be fed}}{\text{Number of people living in the country}} = \frac{N(t)}{P(t)}.$$

For example,

$$R(25) = \frac{N(25)}{P(25)} = \frac{16.5}{5.332} \approx 3.1.$$

This means that in year 25, everybody in the country could, on average, have more than three times as much food as he or she needs. The formula for $R(t)$ is

$$R(t) = \frac{N(t)}{P(t)} = \frac{4 + 0.5t}{2(1.04)^t}.$$

From the graph of R in Figure 10.25, we see that the maximum per capita food supply occurs during the 18th year. Notice this maximum prosperity prediction is different from the one made using the surplus function $S(t)$.

However, both prosperity models predict that shortages begin after time $t = 78.320$. This is not a coincidence. The food surplus model predicts shortages when $S(t) = N(t) - P(t) < 0$, or $N(t) < P(t)$. The per capita food supply model predicts shortages when $R(t) < 1$, meaning that the amount of food available per person is less than the amount necessary to feed 1 person. Since $R(t) = \frac{N(t)}{P(t)} < 1$ is true only when $N(t) < P(t)$, the same condition leads to shortages.

Figure 10.25: Per capita food supply,
$R(t) = \frac{N(t)}{P(t)}$

The Quotient of Functions Defined by Tables: Per Capita Crime Rate

Table 10.11 gives the number of violent crimes committed in two cities between 2005 and 2010. It appears that crime in both cities is on the rise and that there is less crime in City B than in City A.

Table 10.11   *Number of violent crimes committed each year in two cities*

Year	2005	2006	2007	2008	2009	2010
t, years since 2005	0	1	2	3	4	5
Crimes in City A	793	795	807	818	825	831
Crimes in City B	448	500	525	566	593	652

Table 10.12 gives the population for these two cities from 2005 to 2010. The population of City A is larger than that of City B and both cities are growing.

Table 10.12 *Population of the two cities*

Year	2005	2006	2007	2008	2009	2010
t, years since 2000	0	1	2	3	4	5
Population of City A	61,000	62,100	63,220	64,350	65,510	66,690
Population of City B	28,000	28,588	29,188	29,801	30,427	31,066

Can we attribute the growth in crime in both cities to the population growth? Can we attribute the larger number of crimes in City A to its larger population? To answer these questions, we consider the per capita crime rate in each city.

Let's define $N_A(t)$ to be the number of crimes in City A during year t (where $t = 0$ means 2005). Similarly, let's define $P_A(t)$ to be the population of City A in year t. Then the per capita crime rate in City A, $r_A(t)$, is given by

$$r_A(t) = \frac{\text{Number of crimes in year } t}{\text{Number of people in year } t} = \frac{N_A(t)}{P_A(t)}.$$

We have defined a new function, $r_A(t)$, as the quotient of $N_A(t)$ and $P_A(t)$. For example, the data in Tables 10.11 and 10.12 shows that the per capita crime rate for City A in year $t = 0$ is

$$r_A(0) = \frac{N_A(0)}{P_A(0)} = \frac{793}{61,000} = 0.0130 \text{ crimes per person.}$$

Similarly, the per capita crime rate for the year $t = 1$ is

$$r_A(1) = \frac{N_A(1)}{P_A(1)} = \frac{795}{62,100} = 0.0128 \text{ crimes per person.}$$

Thus, the per capita crime rate in City A actually decreased from 0.0130 crimes per person in 2005 to 0.0128 crimes per person in 2006.

Example 3
(a) Make a table of values for $r_A(t)$ and $r_B(t)$, the per capita crime rates of Cities A and B.
(b) Use the table to decide which city is more dangerous.

Solution
(a) Table 10.13 gives values of $r_A(t)$ for $t = 0, 1, \ldots, 5$. The per capita crime rate in City A declined between 2005 and 2010 despite the fact that the total number of crimes rose during this period. Table 10.13 also gives values of $r_B(t)$, the per capita crime rate of City B, defined by

$$r_B(t) = \frac{N_B(t)}{P_B(t)},$$

where $N_B(t)$ is the number of crimes in City B in year t and $P_B(t)$ is the population of City B in year t. For example, the per capita crime rate in City B in year $t = 0$ is

$$r_B(0) = \frac{N_B(0)}{P_B(0)} = \frac{448}{28,000} = 0.016 \text{ crimes per person.}$$

Table 10.13 *Values of $r_A(t)$ and $r_B(t)$, the per capita violent crime rates of Cities A and B*

Year	2005	2006	2007	2008	2009	2010
t, years since 2005	0	1	2	3	4	5
$r_A(t) = N_A(t)/P_A(t)$	0.0130	0.0128	0.01276	0.01271	0.01259	0.01246
$r_B(t) = N_B(t)/P_B(t)$	0.01600	0.01749	0.01799	0.01899	0.01949	0.02099

    (b) From Table 10.13, we see that between 2005 and 2010, City A has a lower per capita crime rate than City B. The crime rate of City A is decreasing, whereas the crime rate of City B is increasing. Thus, even though Table 10.11 indicates that there are more crimes committed in City A, Table 10.13 tells us that City B is, in some sense, more dangerous. Table 10.13 also tells us that, even though the number of crimes is rising in both cities, City A is getting safer, while City B is getting more dangerous.

Exercises and Problems for Section 10.3

Exercises

In Exercises 1–6, find the following functions.

(a) $f(x) + g(x)$ (b) $f(x) - g(x)$
(c) $f(x)g(x)$ (d) $f(x)/g(x)$

1. $f(x) = x + 1$ $g(x) = 3x^2$
2. $f(x) = x^2 + 4$ $g(x) = x + 2$
3. $f(x) = x + 5$ $g(x) = x - 5$
4. $f(x) = x^2 + 4$ $g(x) = x^2 + 2$
5. $f(x) = x^3$ $g(x) = x^2$
6. $f(x) = \sqrt{x}$ $g(x) = x^2 + 2$

In Exercises 7–12, find simplified formulas using

$$u(x) = 2x - 1, \quad v(x) = 1 - x, \quad \text{and} \quad w(x) = \frac{1}{x}.$$

7. $f(x) = u(x) + v(x)$
8. $g(x) = v(x)w(x)$
9. $h(x) = 2u(x) - 3v(x)$
10. $j(x) = \dfrac{u(x)}{w(x)}$

11. $k(x) = (v(x))^2$
12. $l(x) = u(x) - v(x) - w(x)$

In Exercises 13–16, let $u(x) = e^x$ and $v(x) = 2x + 1$. Find a simplified formula for the function.

13. $f(x) = u(x)v(x)$ 14. $g(x) = u(x)^2 + v(x)^2$

15. $h(x) = (v(u(x)))^2$ 16. $k(x) = v(u(x)^2)$

Find formulas for the functions in Exercises 17–22. Let $f(x) = \sin x$ and $g(x) = x^2$.

17. $f(x) + g(x)$ 18. $g(x)f(x)$

19. $f(x)/g(x)$ 20. $f(g(x))$

21. $g(f(x))$ 22. $1 - (f(x))^2$

Problems

23. Use Table 10.14 to make tables of values for $x = -1, 0, 1, 2, 3, 4$ for the following functions.

(a) $h(x) = f(x) + g(x)$ (b) $j(x) = 2f(x)$

(c) $k(x) = (g(x))^2$ (d) $m(x) = g(x)/f(x)$

Table 10.14

x	−1	0	1	2	3	4
$f(x)$	−4	−1	2	5	8	11
$g(x)$	4	1	0	1	4	9

24. Let $f(x) = x + 1$ and $g(x) = x^2 - 1$. In parts (a)–(e), write a formula in terms of $f(x)$ and $g(x)$ for the function. Then evaluate the formula for $x = 3$. Write a formula in terms of x for each function. Check your formulas for $x = 3$.

(a) $h(x)$ is the sum of $f(x)$ and $g(x)$.
(b) $j(x)$ is the difference between $g(x)$ and twice $f(x)$.
(c) $k(x)$ is the product of $f(x)$ and $g(x)$.
(d) $m(x)$ is the ratio of $g(x)$ to $f(x)$.
(e) $n(x)$ is defined by $n(x) = (f(x))^2 - g(x)$.

25. Let $f(t)$ be the number of men and $g(t)$ be the number of women in Canada in year t. Let $h(t)$ be the average income, in Canadian dollars, of women in Canada in year t.

(a) Find the function $p(t)$, which gives the number of people in Canada in year t.
(b) Find the total amount of money $m(t)$ earned by Canadian women in year t.

Evaluate the expressions in Problems 26–27 using Figures 10.26 and 10.27, giving estimates if necessary.

Figure 10.26

Figure 10.27

26. $f(g(65))$

27. $v(50)$ where $v(x) = g(x)f(x)$

28. Let $f(x) = \dfrac{1}{x+1}$. Find and simplify $f\left(\dfrac{1}{x}\right) + \dfrac{1}{f(x)}$.

29. Use Table 10.15 to make tables of values for the following functions.

(a) $f(x) = r(x) + t(x)$ (b) $g(x) = 4 - 2s(x)$
(c) $h(x) = r(x)t(x)$ (d) $j(x) = \dfrac{r(x) - t(x)}{s(x)}$

(e) $k(x) = r(x)^2$ (f) $l(x) = r(x) + s(x)t(x)$

Table 10.15

x	-2	-1	0	1	2	3
$r(x)$	4	5	6	7	8	9
$s(x)$	-2	2	-2	2	-2	2
$t(x)$	8	5	7	-3	2	13

30. Find formulas for H and h given that:

$$F(x) = \cos x \qquad f(x) = -\sin x$$
$$G(x) = \sqrt{x} \qquad g(x) = \frac{1}{2\sqrt{x}}$$
$$H(x) = F(G(x)) ; \quad h(x) = f(G(x)) \cdot g(x).$$

31. Judging from Figure 10.28, sketch a graph of $h(x) = f(x)g(x)$. [Hint: Note where $g(x) = 0$ and $g(x) = 1$.]

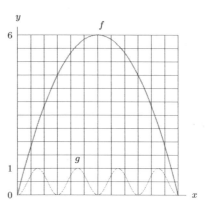

Figure 10.28

Create tables for the functions in Problems 32–33 based on Table 10.16.

Table 10.16

x	0	1	2	3	4	5
$v(x)$	4	3	3	5	4	4
$w(x)$	2	1	3	4	0	5

32. $p(x) = v(x)w(x)$ **33.** $q(x) = w^{-1}(v(x))$

34. In 1961 and 1962, large amounts of the radioactive isotope carbon-14 were produced by tests of nuclear bombs.[3] If t is years since 1963, the amount of carbon-14, as a percent in excess of the normal level, is given by

$$C(t) = 108(e^{-0.1t} - e^{-0.7t}).$$

(a) Graph the function.
(b) Approximately when was the level of carbon-14 the highest?
(c) What happens to the level of carbon-14 in the long run?

35. An average of 50,000 people visit Riverside Park each day in the summer. The park charges $15.00 for admission. Consultants predict that for each $1.00 increase in the entrance price, the park would lose an average of 2500 customers per day. Express the daily revenue from ticket sales as a function of the number of $1.00 price increases. What ticket price maximizes the revenue from ticket sales?

36. Graph $h(x) = f(x) + g(x)$ using Figure 10.29.

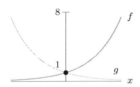

Figure 10.29

37. Use Figure 10.30 to graph $h(x) = g(x) - f(x)$. On the graph of $h(x)$, label the points whose x-coordinates are $x = a$, $x = b$, and $x = c$. Label the y-intercept.

Figure 10.30

38. Table 10.17 gives the upper household income limits for the twentieth and the lower household income limits of the ninety-fifth percentiles t years after 2000.[4] For instance, $P_{20}(5) = 19,178$ tells us that in 2005 the maximum income for a household in the poorest 20% of all households was $19,178. Let $f(t) = P_{95}(t) - P_{20}(t)$ and $g(t) = P_{95}(t)/P_{20}(t)$.

(a) Make tables of values for f and g.
(b) Describe in words what f and g tell you about household income.

Table 10.17

t (yrs)	0	1	2
$P_{20}(t)$ ($)	17,920	17,970	17,916
$P_{95}(t)$ ($)	145,220	150,449	150,002

t (yrs)	3	4	5
$P_{20}(t)$ ($)	17,984	18,486	19,178
$P_{95}(t)$ ($)	154,120	157,152	166,000

39. Sketch two linear functions whose product is the function f graphed in Figure 10.31(a). Explain why this is not possible for the function q graphed in Figure 10.31(b).

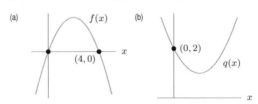

Figure 10.31

40. Judging from Figure 10.32, sketch a graph of $h(x) = g(x) - f(x)$. (Hint: Note where $g(x) = f(x)$.)

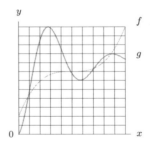

Figure 10.32

---

[3] Adapted from William Bolton, *Patterns in Physics* (New York: McGraw-Hill, 1974).
[4] US Census Bureau, www.census.gov/hhes/www/income/histinc/h01ar.html, accessed November 18, 2009.

41. Find simplified formulas for H and h given that:

$$F(x) = e^{-x^2} \qquad f(x) = -2xe^{-x^2}$$
$$G(x) = x^4 \qquad g(x) = 4x^3$$
$$H(x) = \frac{F(x)}{G(x)} \qquad h(x) = \frac{f(x)G(x) - F(x)g(x)}{(G(x))^2}.$$

42. At the Mauna Loa Observatory, measurements of CO_2 levels (ppm) in the atmosphere reveal a slow exponential increase due to deforestation and burning of fossil fuels, and a periodic seasonal variation.

   (a) In 1960, the average CO_2 level was 316.75 parts per million and was rising by 0.4% per year. Write the average annual CO_2 level as an exponential function of time, t, in years since 1960.

   (b) Each year, the CO_2 level oscillates once between 3.25 ppm above and 3.25 ppm below the average level. Write a sinusoidal function for the seasonal variation in CO_2 levels in terms of time, t.

   (c) Graph the sum of your functions in parts (a) and (b).

43. Table 10.18 gives data on strawberry production from 2004 through 2008,[5] where t is in years since 2004. Let $f_{CA}(t)$, $f_{FL}(t)$, and $f_{US}(t)$ be the harvested area in year t for strawberries grown in California, Florida, and the US overall, respectively. Likewise, let $g_{CA}(t)$, $g_{FL}(t)$, and $g_{US}(t)$ give the yield in thousands of pounds per acre for these three regions.

   (a) Let $h_{CA}(t) = f_{CA}(t) \cdot g_{CA}(t)$. Create a table of values for $h_{CA}(t)$ for $0 \leq t \leq 4$. Describe in words what $h_{CA}(t)$ tells you about strawberry production.

   (b) Let $p(t)$ be the fraction of all US strawberries (by weight) grown in Florida and California in year t. Find a formula for $p(t)$ in terms of f_{CA}, f_{FL}, f_{US}. Use Table 10.18 to make a table of values for $p(t)$.

Table 10.18

	Harvested area (acres)			Yield (1000 lbs per acre)		
t	CA	FL	US total	CA	FL	US total
0	33,200	7,100	51,400	59.0	23.0	43.1
1	34,300	7,300	52,200	60.0	24.5	44.5
2	35,800	7,300	53,460	59.0	28.0	45.0
3	35,500	6,600	52,180	60.5	32.0	46.9
4	37,600	6,900	54,470	60.5	26.0	46.5

44. In Figure 10.33, the line l_2 is fixed and the point P moves along l_2. Define $f(\theta)$ as the y-coordinate of P.

   (a) Find a formula for $f(\theta)$ if $0 < \theta < \pi/2$. [Hint: Use the equation for l_2.]

   (b) Graph $y = f(\theta)$ on the interval $-\pi \leq \theta \leq \pi$.

   (c) How does the y-coordinate of P change as θ changes? Is $y = f(\theta)$ periodic?

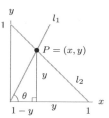

Figure 10.33

45. Let $f(x) = kx^2 + B$ and $g(x) = C^{2x}$ and

$$h(x) = kx^2 C^{2x} + BC^{2x} + C^{2x}.$$

Suppose $f(3) = 7$ and $g(3) = 5$. Evaluate $h(3)$.

In Problems 46–52, you hire either Ace Construction or Space Contractors to build office space. Let $f(x)$ be the average total cost in dollars of building x square feet of office space, as estimated by Ace. Let $h(x)$ be the total number of square feet of office space you can build with x dollars, as estimated by Space.

46. Describe in words what the following statement tells you: $f(2000) = 200,000$.

47. Let $g(x) = f(x)/x$. Using the information from Problem 46, evaluate $g(2000)$, and describe in words what $g(2000)$ represents. [Hint: Think about the units.]

48. Ace tells you that, due to the economies of scale, "Building twice as much office space always costs less than twice as much." Express this statement symbolically, in terms of f and x. [Hint: If you are building x square feet, how do you represent the cost? How would you represent twice the cost? How do you represent the cost of building twice as many square feet?]

49. Suppose that $q > p$ and $p > 1$. Assuming that the contractor's statement in Problem 48 is correct, rank the following in increasing order, using inequality signs: $f(p)$, $g(p)$, $f(q)$, $g(q)$.

50. What does the statement $h(200,000) = 1500$ tell you?

51. Let $j(x)$ be the average cost in dollars per square foot of office space as estimated by Space Contractors. Give a formula for $j(x)$. (Your formula will have $h(x)$ in it.)

52. Research reveals that $h(f(x)) < x$ for every value of x you check. Explain the implications of this statement. [Hint: Which company seems more economical?]

[5] usda.mannlib.cornell.edu/usda/nass/NoncFruitNu//2000s/2009/NoncFruiNu-07-08-2009.pdf, accessed November 27, 2009.

CHAPTER SUMMARY

- **Composition of Functions**
  Notation: $h(t) = f(g(t))$.
  Domain and range; Decomposition.
- **Inverse Functions**
  Definition: $f^{-1}(Q) = t$ if and only if $Q = f(t)$.
  Invertibility; horizontal line test.

Domain and range of an inverse function.
Restricting domain of a function to construct an inverse.
Graph of an inverse function.
$f^{-1}(f(x)) = x$ and $f(f^{-1}(x)) = x$.

- **Combinations of Functions**
  Sums, differences, products, quotients of functions.

REVIEW EXERCISES AND PROBLEMS FOR CHAPTER TEN

Exercises

1. Let $h(x) = 2^x$ and $k(x) = x^2$. Find formulas for $h(k(x))$ and $k(h(x))$.

Find formulas for the functions in Exercises 2–7 and simplify.
Let $f(x) = x^2 + 1$, $g(x) = \dfrac{1}{x-3}$, and $h(x) = \sqrt{x}$.

2. $f(g(x))$ **3.** $g(f(x))$ **4.** $f(h(x))$

5. $h(f(x))$ **6.** $g(g(x))$ **7.** $g(f(h(x)))$

8. Using Tables 10.19 and 10.20, complete Table 10.21:

Table 10.19

x	$f(x)$
0	0
$\pi/6$	$1/2$
$\pi/4$	$\sqrt{2}/2$
$\pi/3$	$\sqrt{3}/2$
$\pi/2$	1

Table 10.20

y	$g(y)$
0	$\pi/2$
$1/4$	π
$\sqrt{2}/4$	0
$1/2$	$\pi/3$
$\sqrt{2}/2$	$\pi/4$
$3/4$	0
$\sqrt{3}/2$	$\pi/6$
1	0

Table 10.21

x	$g(f(x))$
0	
$\pi/6$	
$\pi/4$	
$\pi/3$	
$\pi/2$	

9. For each of the following functions, use a graph to decide whether or not the function is invertible.

(a) $y = e^{x^2}$ (b) $y = \cos(x^3)$ (c) $y = x + \ln x$

Find the inverses of the functions in Exercises 10–22.

10. $h(x) = 12x^3$ **11.** $h(x) = \dfrac{x}{2x+1}$

12. $k(x) = 3 \cdot e^{2x}$ **13.** $g(x) = e^{3x+1}$

14. $n(x) = \log(x-3)$ **15.** $h(x) = \ln(1-2x)$

16. $h(x) = \dfrac{\sqrt{x}}{\sqrt{x}+1}$ **17.** $g(x) = \dfrac{x-2}{2x+3}$

18. $f(x) = \sqrt{\dfrac{4-7x}{4-x}}$ **19.** $f(x) = \dfrac{\sqrt{x}+3}{11-\sqrt{x}}$

20. $f(x) = \ln\left(1 + \dfrac{1}{x}\right)$ **21.** $s(x) = \dfrac{3}{2+\log x}$

22. $q(x) = \ln(x+3) - \ln(x-5)$

In Exercises 23–28, state whether the function is invertible. If so, give a formula for the inverse function.

23. $f(x) = 6x^2 - 2x - 3$ **24.** $q(x) = 3x^3 - 2$

25. $m(x) = 3x^3 - 2x^2 + 5x$ **26.** $p(x) = 5x^5 + 4$

27. $r(x) = e^x - 7$ **28.** $b(x) = \sqrt[3]{x} - 2$

29. Check that $h^{-1}(h(x)) = x$ if $h(x) = \sqrt{\dfrac{1-x}{x}}$ for $0 < x \leq 1$ and $h^{-1}(x) = \dfrac{1}{x^2+1}$ for $x \geq 0$.

30. Suppose $f(x) = \dfrac{x}{2x+1}$. Find a formula for $f^{-1}(x)$.

In Exercises 31–36, find simplified formulas if $f(x) = e^x$, $g(x) = 2x - 1$, and $h(x) = \sqrt{x}$.

31. $g(f(x))$ **32.** $g(x)f(x)$ **33.** $g(g(x))$

34. $f(g(h(x)))$ **35.** $f(g(x))h(x)$ **36.** $(f(h(x)))^2$

37. Find formulas for the following functions, given that

$$f(x) = x^2 + x, \qquad g(x) = 2x - 3. \qquad h(x) = \frac{x}{1-x}.$$

(a) $f(2x)$ (b) $g(x^2)$ (c) $h(1-x)$

(d) $(f(x))^2$ (e) $g^{-1}(x)$ (f) $(h(x))^{-1}$

(g) $f(x) \cdot g(x)$ (h) $h(f(x))$

In Exercises 38–40, find simplified formulas if $u(x) = \dfrac{1}{1+x^2}$, $v(x) = e^x$, and $w(x) = \ln x$.

38. $v(x)/u(x)$ **39.** $u(v(x)) \cdot w(v(x))$

40. $\dfrac{w(2+h) - w(2)}{h}$

In Exercises 41–46, find a simplified formula for the function. Let $m(x) = 3x^2 - x$, $n(x) = 2x$, and $o(x) = \sqrt{x+2}$.

41. $f(x) = m(x) + n(x)$ **42.** $g(x) = (o(x))^2$

43. $h(x) - n(x)o(x)$ **44.** $i(x) = m(o(x))n(x)$

45. $j(x) = (m(x))/n(x)$

46. $k(x) = m(x) - n(x) - o(x)$

In Exercises 47–50 find simplified formulas if $f(x) = x^{3/2}$, $g(x) = \dfrac{(3x-1)^2}{4}$, and $h(x) = \tan 2x$.

47. $f(x)h(x)$ **48.** $\dfrac{h(x)}{f(g(x))}$

49. $h(g(x)) - f(9x)$ **50.** $h(x/2) \cos x$

Problems

51. Complete Table 10.22 if $r(t) = q(p(t))$.

Table 10.22

t	$p(t)$	$q(t)$	$r(t)$
0	4	??	??
1	??	2	1
2	??	??	0
3	2	0	4
4	1	5	??
5	0	1	3

52. Complete Table 10.23, Table 10.24, and Table 10.25 given that $h(x) = g(f(x))$. Assume that different values of x lead to different values of $f(x)$.

Table 10.23

x	$f(x)$
-2	4
-1	
0	
1	5
2	1

Table 10.24

x	$g(x)$
1	
2	1
3	2
4	0
5	-1

Table 10.25

x	$h(x)$
-2	
-1	1
0	2
1	
2	-2

Decompose the functions in Problems 53–60 into two new functions, u and v, where v is the inside function, $u(x) \neq x$, and $v(x) \neq x$.

53. $f(x) = \sqrt{3 - 5x}$ **54.** $g(x) = \sin(x^2)$

55. $h(x) = \sin^2 x$ **56.** $k(x) = e^{\sin x} + \sin x$

57. $F(x) = (2x + 5)^3$ **58.** $G(x) = \dfrac{2}{1 + \sqrt{x}}$

59. $H(x) = 3^{2x-1}$ **60.** $J(x) = 8 - 2|x|$

61. Using your knowledge of the absolute value function, explain in a few sentences the relationship between the graph of $y = |\sin x|$ and the graph of $y = \sin x$.

62. Graph the following functions for $-2\pi \leq x \leq 2\pi$.

(a) $f(x) = \sin x$ (b) $g(x) = |\sin x|$

(c) $h(x) = \sin |x|$ (d) $i(x) = |\sin |x||$

(e) Do any two of these functions have identical graphs? If so, explain why this makes sense.

63. Suppose $p(x) = (1/x) + 1$ and $q(x) = x - 2$.

(a) Let $r(x) = p(q(x))$. Find a formula for $r(x)$ and simplify it.

(b) Write formulas for $s(x)$ and $t(x)$ such that $p(x) = s(t(x))$, where $s(x) \neq x$ and $t(x) \neq x$.

(c) Let a be different from 0 and -1. Find a simplified expression for $p(p(a))$.

64. Let $f(x) = \frac{1}{x}$ and $g(x) = \sin x$. Calculate the domain of $f(g(x))$ and the domain of $g(f(x))$.

65. Suppose that $h(x) = f(g(x))$, and that f is invertible. Complete the following table.

x	$f(x)$	$g(x)$	$h(x)$
0	9	1	
1	0		1
2	1	0	

In Problems 66–67, a population is given by the formula $P = f(t) = 20 + 0.4t$ where P is the number of people (in thousands) and t is the number of years since 1985.

66. Evaluate the following quantities. Explain in words what each tells you about the population.

(a) $f(25)$ (b) $f^{-1}(25)$

(c) Show how to estimate $f^{-1}(25)$ from a graph of f.

67. (a) Find a formula for $t = f^{-1}(P)$.

(b) Construct tables of values for both functions for values of t from $t = 0$ years to $t = 20$ years, using five-year intervals.

68. Let $P = f(t) = 14 \cdot 2^{t/12}$ give the size in 1000s of an animal population in year t.

(a) Find $f^{-1}(P)$.

(b) Evaluate $f^{-1}(24)$. Say what this tells you about the population.

69. If $t = g(v)$ represents the time in hours it takes to drive to the next town at velocity v mph, what does $g^{-1}(t)$ represent? What are its units?

70. Let $f(x) = e^x$. Solve each of the following equations exactly for x.

(a) $(f(x))^{-1} = 2$ (b) $f^{-1}(x) = 2$

(c) $f(x^{-1}) = 2$

71. Simplify the expression $\cos^2(\arcsin t)$, using the property that inverses "undo" each other.

Solve the equations in Problems 72–77 exactly. Use an inverse function when appropriate.

72. $7\sin(3x) = 2$

73. $2^{x+5} = 3$

74. $x^{1.05} = 1.09$

75. $\ln(x+3) = 1.8$

76. $\dfrac{2x+3}{x+3} = 8$

77. $\sqrt{x + \sqrt{x}} = 3$

78. Let $Q = f(t) = 20(0.96)^{t/3}$ be the number of grams of a radioactive substance remaining after t years.

(a) Describe the behavior of the radioactive substance as a function of time.

(b) Evaluate $f(8)$. Explain the meaning of this quantity in practical terms.

(c) Find a formula for $f^{-1}(Q)$ in terms of Q.

(d) Evaluate $f^{-1}(8)$. Explain the meaning of this quantity in practical terms.

79. (a) What is the formula for the area of a circle in terms of its radius?

(b) Graph this function for the domain all real numbers.

(c) What domain actually applies in this situation? On separate axes, graph the function for this domain.

(d) Find the inverse of the function in part (c).

(e) Graph the inverse function on the domain you gave in part (c) on the same axes used in part (c).

(f) If area is a function of the radius, is radius a function of area? Explain carefully.

80. A company believes there is a linear relationship between the consumer demand for its products and the price charged. When the price was \$3 per unit, the quantity demanded was 500 units per week. When the unit price was raised to \$4, the quantity demanded dropped to 300 units per week. Let $D(p)$ be the quantity per week demanded by consumers at a unit price of \$$p$.

(a) Estimate and interpret $D(5)$.

(b) Find a formula for $D(p)$ in terms of p.

(c) Calculate and interpret $D^{-1}(5)$.

(d) Give an interpretation of the slope of $D(p)$ in terms of demand.

(e) Currently, the company can produce 400 units every week. What should the price of the product be if the company wants to sell all 400 units?

(f) If the company produced 500 units per week instead of 400 units per week, would its weekly revenues increase, and if so, by how much?

81. Use Figure 10.34.

(a) Evaluate $f(g(a))$.

(b) Evaluate $g(f(c))$.

(c) Evaluate $f^{-1}(b) - g^{-1}(b)$.

(d) For what positive value(s) of x is $f(x) \le g(x)$?

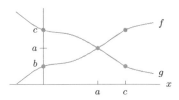

Figure 10.34

82. Use Table 10.26 to make tables of values for the following functions.

(a) $n(x) = f(x) + g(x)$
(b) $p(x) = 2f(x)g(x) - f(x)$
(c) $q(x) = g(x)/f(x)$

Table 10.26

x	1	2	3	4
$f(x)$	3	4	1	2
$g(x)$	2	1	4	3

For Problems 83–87, let

$$p(x) = 2x - 3 \qquad q(x) = \sqrt{x} - 3$$
$$r(x) = \frac{2x - 1}{2x + 1} \qquad s(x) = (x - 1)^2$$

83. Find and simplify $p(q(x))$.

84. Find and simplify $r^{-1}(x)$.

85. Solve for x exactly: $p(x) = r(x)$.

86. Find $u(x)$ given that $q(x) = p(u(x))$.

87. Graph and label $p(s(x))$.

88. Let $f(x) = e^x$. For each of the following, use the rules of logarithms and exponents (if possible) to find the exact solution to each equation. If this is not possible, use a graph to find an approximate solution.

(a) $f(3x) + f(3x) = 1$ (b) $f(x) + f(3x) = 1$
(c) $f(3x)f(3x) = 2$ (d) $f(x)f(3x) = 2$

89. Let $u(x) = \sin x$, $v(x) = \cos x$, and $w(x) = x^2$.

(a) Let $f(x) = \sin^2 x$. Is $f(x)$ equal to $u(u(x))$ or to $(u(x))^2$? Justify your answer.
(b) Let $p(x) = \sin(\cos^2 x)$. Circle all of the following functions that are equal to $p(x)$.
   (i) $u(x)(v(x))^2$
   (ii) $u((v(x))^2)$
   (iii) $u(w(v(x)))$
   (iv) $u(x)w(v(x))$
(c) Calculate each of the following and simplify as far as possible.
   (i) $(u(x) + v(x))^2$
   (ii) $(u(x))^2 + (v(x))^2$
   (iii) $u(x^2) + v(x^2)$

Using Figures 10.35 and 10.36, graph the functions in Problems 90–93.

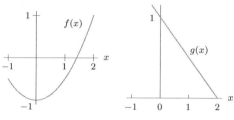

Figure 10.35   Figure 10.36

90. $f(x) - g(x)$ **91.** $f(g(x))$

92. $g(f(x))$ **93.** $g(f(x - 2))$

94. Using Figure 10.37, match the functions (a)–(g) and graphs (I)–(IV). There may be some functions whose graphs are not shown.

Figure 10.37

(a) $y = -f(x)$ (b) $y = f(-x)$
(c) $y = f(-x) - 2$ (d) $y = f^{-1}(x)$
(e) $y = -f^{-1}(x)$ (f) $y = f(x + 1)$
(g) $y = -(f(x) - 2)$

95. (a) On the same set of axes, graph $f(x) = (x-4)^2 - 2$ and $g(x) = -(x-2)^2 + 8$.

(b) Make a table of values for f and g for $x = 0, 1, 2, ..., 6$.

(c) Make a table of values for $y = f(x) - g(x)$ for $x = 0, 1, 2, ..., 6$.

(d) On your graph, sketch the vertical line segment of length $f(x) - g(x)$ for each integer value of x from 0 to 6. Check that the segment lengths agree with the values from part (c).

(e) Plot the values from your table for the function $y = f(x) - g(x)$ on your graph.

(f) Simplify the formulas for $f(x)$ and $g(x)$ in part (a). Find a formula for $y = f(x) - g(x)$.

(g) Use part (f) to graph $y = f(x) - g(x)$ on the same axes as f and g. Does the graph pass through the points you plotted in part (e)?

96. Figure 10.38 shows a weight attached to the end of a spring that is hanging from the ceiling. The weight is pulled down from the ceiling and then released. The weight oscillates up and down, but over time, friction decreases the magnitude of the vertical oscillations. Which of the following functions could describe the distance of the weight from the ceiling, d, as a function of time, t?

(i) $d = 2 + \cos t$ (ii) $d = 2 + e^{-t} \cos t$

(iii) $d = 2 + \cos(e^t)$ (iv) $d = 2 + e^{\cos t}$

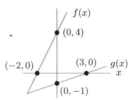

Figure 10.38

97. (a) Find possible formulas for the functions in Figure 10.39.

(b) Let $h(x) = f(x) \cdot g(x)$. Graph $f(x)$, $g(x)$ and $h(x)$ on the same set of axes.

Figure 10.39

98. Use Figure 10.40 to graph $c(x) = a(x) \cdot b(x)$. [Hint: There is not enough information to determine formulas for a and b but you can use the method of Problem 97.]

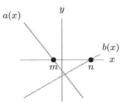

Figure 10.40

99. Use Figure 10.41 to graph the following functions.

(a) $y = g(x) - 3$ **(b)** $y = g(x) + x$

Figure 10.41

100. Describe the similarities and differences between the graphs of $y = \sin(1/x)$ and $y = 1/\sin x$.

101. Is the following statement true or false? If $f(x) \cdot g(x)$ is an odd function, then both $f(x)$ and $g(x)$ are odd functions. Explain your answer.

In Problems 102–103, find a simplified formula for g given that $f(x) = x^2 + 5x + 6$.

102. $g(f(x)) = 64 \cdot 2^{x^2} \cdot 32^x$

103. $f(x) = g(x)h(x)$ where $h(x) = 2x + 6$.

104. Assume that $f(x) = 3 \cdot 9^x$ and that $g(x) = 3^x$.

(a) If $f(x) = h(g(x))$, find a formula for $h(x)$.

(b) If $f(x) = g(j(x))$, find a formula for $j(x)$.

302

105. In calculus, it is often necessary to write functions in the form $y = f(G(x)) \cdot g(x)$. Do this for the following functions, giving formulas for f, g, and G. There may be more than one possible answer.

(a) $y = 6xe^{3x^2}$ (b) $y = -\dfrac{\sin\left(\sqrt{x}\right)}{2\sqrt{x}}$

106. Currency traders often move investments from one country to another in order to make a profit. Table 10.27 gives exchange rates for US dollars, Japanese yen, and the European Union's euro.[6] In November, 2009, for example, 1 US dollar purchases 89.1823 Japanese yen or 0.6686 European euro. Similarly, 1 European euro purchases 133.39 Japanese yen or 1.4957 US dollars. Suppose

$f(x) = $ Number of yen one can buy with x dollars

$g(x) = $ Number of euros one can buy with x dollars

$h(x) = $ Number of euros one can buy with x yen

(a) Find formulas for f, g, and h.
(b) Evaluate and interpret in terms of currency: $h(f(1000))$.

Table 10.27 *Exchange rate for US dollars, Japanese yen and euros, November 18, 2009*

Amount invested	Dollars purchased	Yen purchased	Euros purchased
1 dollar	1.0000	89.1823	0.6686
1 yen	0.01121	1.0000	0.007496
1 euro	1.4957	133.39	1.0000

107. Letting $h(x) = f(x) + g(x)$, say which of the following statements must be true. Briefly explain your reasoning.

(a) If f and g have the same domain, so does h.
(b) If f and g have the same range, so does h.
(c) If f and g lack zeros, so does h.
(d) Where defined, $\dfrac{\Delta h}{\Delta x} = \dfrac{\Delta f}{\Delta x} + \dfrac{\Delta g}{\Delta x}$.

108. (a) Is the sum of two even functions even, odd, or neither? Justify your answer.
(b) Is the sum of two odd functions even, odd, or neither? Justify your answer.
(c) Is the sum of an even and an odd function even, odd, or neither? Justify your answer.

In Problems 109–112, let $f(x)$ be an increasing function and let $g(x)$ be a decreasing function. Are the following functions increasing, decreasing, or is it impossible to tell? Explain.

109. $f(f(x))$ **110.** $g(f(x))$

111. $f(x) + g(x)$ **112.** $f(x) - g(x)$

113. For a positive integer x, let $f(x)$ be the remainder obtained by dividing x by 3. For example, $f(6) = 0$, because 6 divided by 3 equals 2 with a remainder of 0. Likewise, $f(7) = 1$, because 7 divided by 3 equals 2 with a remainder of 1.

(a) Evaluate $f(8)$, $f(17)$, $f(29)$, $f(99)$.
(b) Find a formula for $f(3x)$.
(c) Is $f(x)$ invertible?
(d) Find a formula in terms of $f(x)$ for $f(f(x))$.
(e) Does $f(x + y)$ necessarily equal $f(x) + f(y)$?

114. Suppose that f, g, and h are invertible and that

$$f(x) = g(h(x)).$$

Find a formula for $f^{-1}(x)$ in terms of g^{-1} and h^{-1}.

115. The von Bertalanffy growth model predicts the mean length L of fish of age t (in years):[7]

$$L = f(t) = L_\infty \left(1 - e^{-k(t+t_0)}\right), \text{ for constant } L_\infty, k, t_0.$$

Find a formula for f^{-1}. Describe in words what f^{-1} tells you about fish. What is the domain of f^{-1}?

CHECK YOUR UNDERSTANDING

Let $f(x) = \dfrac{1}{x}$, $g(x) = \sqrt{x}$, and $h(x) = x - 5$. Are the statements in Problems 1–10 true or false? Give an explanation for your answer.

1. $f(4) + g(4) = (f + g)(8)$.

2. $\dfrac{h(x)}{f(x)} = \dfrac{x-5}{x}$.

3. $f(4) + g(4) = 2\frac{1}{4}$.

4. $f(g(x))$ is defined for all x.

---

[6]www.x-rates.com, accessed November 18, 2009. Currency exchange rates fluctuate constantly.
[7]Per Sparre, *Introduction to Tropical Fish Stock Assessment*, Danish Institute for Fisheries Research, and Siebren C. Venema, FAO Fisheries Department, available at www.fao.org/docrep/W5449E/w5449e00.htm., accessed November 2001.

5. $g(f(x)) = \sqrt{\dfrac{1}{x}}$.

6. $f(x)g(x) = f(g(x))$.

7. $2f(2) = g(1)$.

8. $f(1)g(1)h(1) = -4$.

9. $\dfrac{f(3) + g(3)}{h(3)} = \dfrac{\frac{1}{3} + \sqrt{3}}{-2}$.

10. $4h(2) = h(8)$.

Are the statements in Problems 11–37 true or false? Give an explanation for your answer.

11. If $f(x) = x^2$ and $g(x) = \sqrt{x+3}$. Then $f(g(x))$ is defined for all x.

12. If $f(x) = x^2$ and $g(x) = \sqrt{x+3}$. Then $f(g(6)) = 9$.

13. In general $f(g(x)) = g(f(x))$.

14. The formula for the area of a circle is $A = \pi r^2$ and the formula for the circumference of a circle is $C = 2\pi r$. Then the area of a circle as a function of the circumference is $A = \dfrac{C^2}{2\pi}$.

15. If $f(x) = x^2 + 2$ then $f(f(1)) = 11$.

16. If $h(x) = f(g(x))$, $h(2) = 1\frac{1}{4}$ and $g(2) = \frac{1}{2}$ then $f(x)$ might be equal to $x^2 + 1$.

17. If $f(x) = \dfrac{1}{x}$ then $f(x+h) = \dfrac{1}{x} + \dfrac{1}{h}$.

18. If $f(x) = x^2 + x$, then $\dfrac{f(x+h) - f(x)}{h} = 2x + h$.

19. If $f(x) = x^2$ and $g(x) = \sin x$ then $f(g(x)) = x^2 \sin x$.

20. If $f(x)$ and $g(x)$ are linear, then $f(g(x))$ is linear.

21. If $f(x)$ and $g(x)$ are quadratic, then $f(g(x))$ is quadratic.

22. There is more than one way to write $h(x) = 3(x^2 + 1)^3$ as a composition $h(x) = f(g(x))$.

23. The composition $f(g(x))$ is never the same as the composite $g(f(x))$.

24. If f and g are both increasing, then $h(x) = f(g(x))$ is also increasing.

25. The functions f and g given in Tables 10.28 and 10.29 satisfy $g(f(2)) = f(g(3))$.

Table 10.28

t	1	2	3	4
$f(t)$	3	1	2	4

Table 10.29

x	1	2	3	4
$g(x)$	3	4	1	2

26. If f is increasing and invertible, then f^{-1} is decreasing.

27. If there is a vertical line that intersects a graph in more than one point, then the graph does not represent a function.

28. Every function has an inverse.

29. If $g(3) = g(5)$, then g is not invertible.

30. If no horizontal line intersects the graph of a function in more than one point, then the function has an inverse.

31. Most quadratic functions have an inverse.

32. All linear functions of the form $f(x) = mx + b, m \neq 0$ have inverses.

33. The following table describes y as a function of x.

Table 10.30

x	1	2	3	4	5	6
y	3	4	7	8	5	3

34. The table in Problem 33 describes a function from x to y that is invertible.

35. The graph in Figure 10.42 is the graph of a function.

Figure 10.42

36. The function graphed in Figure 10.42 is invertible.

37. For an invertible function g, it is always true that $g^{-1}(g(x)) = x$.

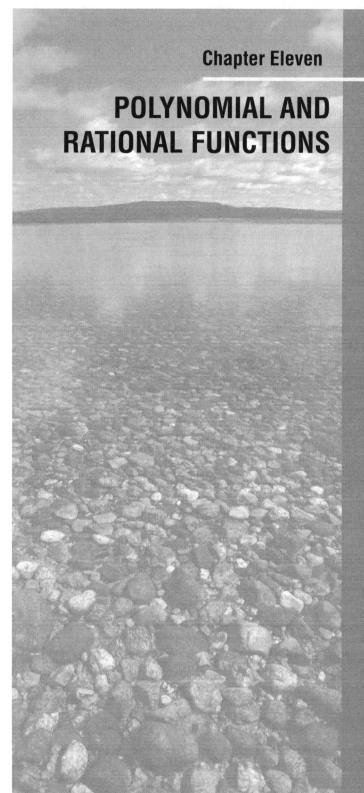

Chapter Eleven

POLYNOMIAL AND RATIONAL FUNCTIONS

Contents

11.1 POWER FUNCTIONS

Proportionality and Power Functions

The following two examples introduce proportionality and power functions.

Example 1 The area, A, of a circle is proportional to the square of its radius, r:

$$A = \pi r^2.$$

Example 2 The weight, w, of an object is inversely proportional to the square of the object's distance, d, from the earth's center:[1]

$$w = \frac{k}{d^2} = kd^{-2}.$$

For an object with weight 44 pounds on the surface of the earth, which is about 3959 miles from the earth's center, we get the data listed in Table 11.1 and graphed in Figure 11.1.

Table 11.1 *Weight of an object, w, inversely proportional to the square of the object's distance, d, from the earth's center*

d, miles	$w = f(d)$, lbs
4000	43.3
5000	27.8
6000	19.2
7000	14.1
8000	10.8

Figure 11.1: Weight, w, inversely proportional to the square of the object's distance, d, from the earth's center

---

A quantity y is **(directly) proportional to a power** of x if

$$y = kx^n, \qquad k \text{ and } n \text{ are constants.}$$

A quantity y is **inversely proportional** to x^n if

$$y = \frac{k}{x^n}, \qquad k \text{ and } n \text{ are constants.}$$

---

[1] There is a distinction between mass and weight. For example, astronauts in orbit may be weightless, but they still have mass.

The functions in Examples 1 and 2 are power functions. Generalizing, we define:

> A **power function** is a function of the form
>
> $$f(x) = kx^p, \qquad \text{where } k \text{ and } p \text{ are constants.}$$

Example 3   Which of the following functions are power functions? For each power function, state the value of the constants k and p in the formula $y = kx^p$.

(a) $f(x) = 13\sqrt[3]{x}$ (b) $g(x) = 2(x+5)^3$ (c) $u(x) = \sqrt{\dfrac{25}{x^3}}$ (d) $v(x) = 6 \cdot 3^x$

Solution   The functions f and u are power functions; the functions g and v are not.

(a) The function $f(x) = 13\sqrt[3]{x}$ is a power function because we can write its formula as

$$f(x) = 13x^{1/3}.$$

Here, $k = 13$ and $p = 1/3$.

(b) Although the value of $g(x) = 2(x+5)^3$ is proportional to the cube of $x+5$, it is *not* proportional to a power of x. We cannot write $g(x)$ in the form $g(x) = kx^p$; thus, g is not a power function.

(c) We can rewrite the formula for $u(x) = \sqrt{25/x^3}$ as

$$u(x) = \frac{\sqrt{25}}{\sqrt{x^3}} = \frac{5}{(x^3)^{1/2}} = \frac{5}{x^{3/2}} = 5x^{-3/2}.$$

Thus, u is a power function. Here, $k = 5$ and $p = -3/2$.

(d) Although the value of $v(x) = 6 \cdot 3^x$ is proportional to a power of 3, the power is not a constant— it is the variable x. In fact, $v(x) = 6 \cdot 3^x$ is an exponential function, not a power function. Notice that $y = 6 \cdot x^3$ is a power function. However, $6 \cdot x^3$ and $6 \cdot 3^x$ are quite different.

The Effect of the Power p

We now study functions whose constant of proportionality is $k = 1$ so that we can focus on the effect of the power p.

Graphs of the Special Cases $y = x^0$ and $y = x^1$

The power functions corresponding to $p = 0$ and $p = 1$ are both linear. The graph of $y = x^0 = 1$ is a horizontal line through the point $(1, 1)$. The graph of $y = x^1 = x$ is a line through the origin with slope $+1$.

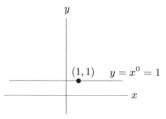

Figure 11.2: Graph of $y = x^0 = 1$

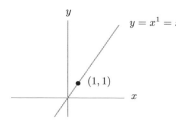

Figure 11.3: Graph of $y = x^1 = x$

Positive Integer Powers: $y = x^3$, x^5, x^7 ... and $y = x^2$, x^4, x^6 ...

The graphs of all power functions with p a positive even integer have the same characteristic $\bigcup$-shape and are symmetric about the y-axis. For instance, the graphs of $y = x^2$ and $y = x^4$ in Figure 11.4 are similar in shape, although the graph of $y = x^4$ is flatter near the origin and steeper away from the origin than the graph of $y = x^2$.

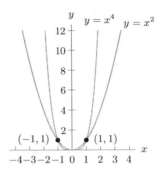

Figure 11.4: Graphs of positive even powers of x are $\bigcup$-shaped

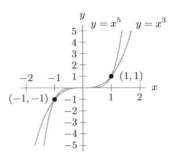

Figure 11.5: Graphs of positive odd powers of x are "chair-shaped"

The graphs of power functions with p a positive odd integer resemble the side view of a chair and are symmetric about the origin. Figure 11.5 shows the graphs of $y = x^3$ and $y = x^5$. The graph of $y = x^5$ is flatter near the origin and steeper far from the origin than the graph of $y = x^3$.

Negative Integer Powers: $y = x^{-1}$, x^{-3}, x^{-5}, ... and $y = x^{-2}$, x^{-4}, x^{-6}, ...

For negative powers, if we rewrite

$$y = x^{-1} = \frac{1}{x}$$

and

$$y = x^{-2} = \frac{1}{x^2},$$

then it is clear that as $x > 0$ increases, the denominators increase and the functions decrease. The graphs of power functions with odd negative powers, $y = x^{-3}$, x^{-5}, ..., resemble the graph of $y = x^{-1} = 1/x$. The graphs of even integer powers, $y = x^{-4}$, x^{-6}, ..., are similar in shape to the graph of $y = x^{-2} = 1/x^2$. See Figures 11.6 and 11.7.

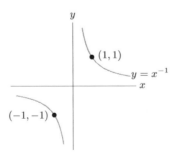

Figure 11.6: Graph of $y = x^{-1} = 1/x$

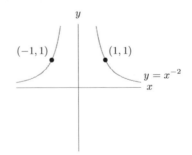

Figure 11.7: Graph of $y = x^{-2} = 1/x^2$

We see in Figures 11.6 and 11.7 that $y = 0$ is a horizontal asymptote and $x = 0$ is a vertical asymptote for the graphs of $y = 1/x$ and $y = 1/x^2$.

Numerically, the values of $1/x$ and $1/x^2$ can be made as close to zero as we like by choosing a sufficiently large x (positive or negative). See Table 11.2 for positive values of x. Graphically, this means that the curves $y = 1/x$ and $y = 1/x^2$ get closer and closer to the x-axis for large values of x. We write $y \to 0$ as $x \to \pm\infty$. Using limit notation, we see

$$\lim_{x \to \infty} \left(\frac{1}{x}\right) = 0, \quad \lim_{x \to -\infty} \left(\frac{1}{x}\right) = 0 \quad \text{and} \quad \lim_{x \to \infty} \left(\frac{1}{x^2}\right) = 0, \quad \lim_{x \to -\infty} \left(\frac{1}{x^2}\right) = 0.$$

Table 11.2 *Values of x^{-1} and x^{-2} approach zero as x grows large*

x	0	10	20	30	40	50
$y = 1/x$	Undefined	0.1	0.05	0.033	0.025	0.02
$y = 1/x^2$	Undefined	0.01	0.0025	0.0011	0.0006	0.0004

On the other hand, as x gets close to zero, the values of $1/x$ and $1/x^2$ get very large. See Table 11.3. Graphically, this means that the curves $y = 1/x$ and $y = 1/x^2$ get very close to the y-axis as x gets close to zero. From Figure 11.6, we see that[2]

$$\lim_{x \to 0^+} \left(\frac{1}{x}\right) = \infty \quad \text{and} \quad \lim_{x \to 0^-} \left(\frac{1}{x}\right) = -\infty.$$

From Figure 11.7, we see that

$$\lim_{x \to 0} \left(\frac{1}{x^2}\right) = \infty.$$

Table 11.3 *Values of x^{-1} and x^{-2} grow large as x approaches zero from the positive side*

x	0.1	0.05	0.01	0.001	0.0001	0
$y = 1/x$	10	20	100	1000	10,000	Undefined
$y = 1/x^2$	100	400	10,000	1,000,000	100,000,000	Undefined

Graphs of Positive Fractional Powers: $y = x^{1/2}, x^{1/3}, x^{1/4}, \ldots$

Figure 11.8 shows the graphs of $y = x^{1/2}$ and $y = x^{1/4}$. These graphs have the same shape, although $y = x^{1/4}$ is steeper near the origin and flatter away from the origin than $y = x^{1/2}$. The same can be said about the graphs of $y = x^{1/3}$ and $y = x^{1/5}$ in Figure 11.9. In general, if n is a positive integer, then the graph of $y = x^{1/n}$ resembles the graph of $y = x^{1/2}$ if n is even; if n is odd, the graph resembles the graph of $y = x^{1/3}$.

Notice that the graphs of $y = x^{1/2}$ and $y = x^{1/3}$ bend in a direction opposite to that of the graphs of $y = x^2$ and x^3. For example, the graph of $y = x^2$ is concave up, but the graph of $y = x^{1/2}$ is concave down. However, all these functions become infinitely large as x increases.

---

[2]Some authors say that these limits do not exist.

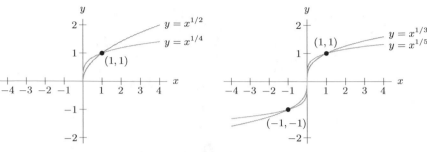

Figure 11.8: The graphs of $y = x^{1/2}$ and $y = x^{1/4}$ Figure 11.9: The graphs of $y = x^{1/3}$ and $y = x^{1/5}$

Example 4   From geometry, we know that the radius of a sphere is directly proportional to the cube root of its volume. In this example, we use that proportionality relationship. If a sphere of radius 18.2 cm has a volume of 25,252.4 cm³, what is the radius of a sphere whose volume is 30,000 cm³?

Solution   Since the radius of the sphere is proportional to the cube root of its volume, we know that

$$r = kV^{1/3}, \qquad \text{for } k \text{ constant.}$$

We also know that $r = 18.2$ cm when $V = 25,252.4$ cm³; therefore

$$18.2 = k(25,252.4)^{1/3},$$

giving

$$k = \frac{18.2}{(25,252.4)^{1/3}} \approx 0.620.$$

Thus, when $V = 30,000$, we get $r = 0.620(30,000)^{1/3} \approx 19.3$, so the radius of the sphere is approximately 19.3 cm.

To compare the proportionality constant in Example 4 with that given by geometry, notice that since

$$V = \frac{4}{3}\pi r^3,$$

we have

$$r = \left(\frac{3}{4\pi}V\right)^{1/3} = \left(\frac{3}{4\pi}\right)^{1/3} V^{1/3}.$$

Thus, the constant of proportionality is $(3/(4\pi))^{1/3} = 0.620$, as before.

Finding the Formula for a Power Function

As is the case for linear and exponential functions, the formula of a power function can be found using two points on its graph.

Example 5   Water is leaking out of a container with a hole in the bottom. Torricelli's Law states that at any instant, the velocity v with which water escapes from the container is a power function of d, the depth of the water at that moment. When $d = 9$ feet, then $v = 24$ ft/sec; when $d = 1/4$ foot, then $v = 4$ ft/sec. Express v as a function of d.

Solution   Torricelli's Law tells us that $v = kd^p$, where k and p are constants. Since $v = 24$ when $d = 9$ we have $24 = k9^p$ and since $v = 4$ when $d = 1/4$ we have $4 = k(1/4)^p$. Taking the ratio gives

$$\frac{24}{4} = \frac{k9^p}{k(1/4)^p}$$
$$6 = 36^p.$$

Since $36^{1/2} = 6$, we must have $p = 1/2$, so $v = kd^{1/2}$. Substituting $v = 24$ and $d = 9$ gives

$$24 = k9^{1/2},$$

so $k = 8$. Therefore we have $v = 8d^{1/2}$. *Note*: Torricelli's Law is often written in the form $v = \sqrt{2gd}$, where $g = 32$ ft/sec^2 is the acceleration due to gravity.

Exercises and Problems for Section 11.1

Skill Refresher

Simplify the expressions in Exercises S1–S4.

S1. $\sqrt{36t^2}$

S2. $\left(3x\sqrt{x^3}\right)^2$

S3. $(0.1)^2\left(4xy^2\right)^2$

S4. $7\left(5w^{1/2}\right)\left(2w^{1/3}\right)$

In Exercises S5–S6, solve for x.

S5. $\dfrac{10x^5}{x^2} = 2$

S6. $5x^{-2} = 500$

Are the statements in Exercises S7–S10 true or false?

S7. $t^3t^4 = t^{12}$

S8. $(p^3)^8 = p^{11}$

S9. $\dfrac{m^8}{2m^2} = \dfrac{1}{2}m^4$

S10. $5z^{-4} = \dfrac{1}{5z^4}$

Exercises

Are the functions in Exercises 1–6 power functions? If so, write the function in the form $f(x) = kx^p$.

1. $g(x) = \dfrac{(-x^3)^3}{6}$

2. $R(t) = \dfrac{4}{\sqrt{16t}}$

3. $f(x) = 4(x+7)^2$

4. $T(s) = (6s^{-2})(es^{-3})$

5. $h(x) = 22(7^x)^2$

6. $K(w) = \dfrac{w^4}{4\sqrt{w^3}}$

7. Write $y = 3\left(\dfrac{2}{5\sqrt{7x}}\right)^4$ in the form $y = ax^p$ and state the values of a and p.

8. Write $y = \sqrt{\pi(2x)^3}$ in the form $y = ax^p$ and state the values of a and p.

Do the power functions in Exercises 9–12 appear to have odd, even, or fractional powers?

9. x

10. x

11. x

12. x

In Exercises 13–14, find a power function through the two points.

13. $(1,3)$ $(4,13)$ **14.** $(7,8)$ $(1,0.7)$

In Exercises 15–16, find possible formulas for the power functions with the properties given.

15. $f(1) = \frac{3}{2}$ and $f(2) = \frac{3}{8}$

16. $g\left(-\frac{1}{5}\right) = 25$ and $g(2) = -\frac{1}{40}$

17. Suppose c is directly proportional to the square of d. If $c = 45$ when $d = 3$, find the constant of proportionality and write the formula for c as a function of d. Use your formula to find c when $d = 5$.

18. Suppose c is inversely proportional to the square of d. If $c = 45$ when $d = 3$, find the constant of proportionality and write the formula for c as a function of d. Use your formula to find c when $d = 5$.

19. If y is directly proportional to x, and $y = 6$ when $x = 4$, find the constant of proportionality, write a formula for y in terms of x, and find x when $y = 8$.

20. If y is inversely proportional to x, and $y = 6$ when $x = 4$, find the constant of proportionality, write a formula for y in terms of x, and find x when $y = 8$.

In Exercises 21–24, find possible formulas for the power functions.

21.

x	2	3	4	5
$f(x)$	12	27	48	75

22.

x	-6	-2	3	4
$g(x)$	36	4/3	$-9/2$	$-32/3$

23.

x	0	1	2	3
$j(x)$	0	2	16	54

24.

x	-2	$-1/2$	1/4	4
$h(x)$	$-1/2$	-8	-32	$-1/8$

25. Find **(a)** $\lim\limits_{x \to \infty} x^{-4}$ **(b)** $\lim\limits_{x \to -\infty} 2x^{-1}$

26. Find **(a)** $\lim\limits_{t \to \infty} (t^{-3} + 2)$ **(b)** $\lim\limits_{y \to -\infty} (5 - 7y^{-2})$

Problems

27. Compare the graphs of $y = x^2$, $y = x^4$, and $y = x^6$. Describe the similarities and differences.

28. Describe the behavior of $y = x^{-10}$ and $y = -x^{10}$ as

(a) $x \to 0$ **(b)** $x \to \infty$ **(c)** $x \to -\infty$

29. Describe the behavior of $y = x^{-3}$ and $y = x^{1/3}$ as

(a) $x \to 0$ from the right **(b)** $x \to \infty$

30. (a) Figure 11.10 shows $g(x)$, a mystery power function. If you learn that the point $(-1, 3)$ lies on its graph, do you have enough information to write a formula for $g(x)$?

(b) If you are told that the point $(1, -3)$ also lies on the graph, what new deductions can you make?

(c) If the point $(2, -96)$ lies on the graph g, in addition to the points already given, state three other points that also lie on it.

$g(x)$

Figure 11.10

31. Figure 11.11 shows the power function $y = c(t)$. Is $c(t) = 1/t$ the only possible formula for c? Could there be others?

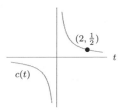

Figure 11.11

32. (a) Match the functions $x, x^2, x^3, x^{1/2}, x^{1/3}, x^{3/2}$ with the graphs in Figure 11.12. Justify your choice.
   (b) What is the relationship between the concavity of $y = x^2$ and $y = x^{1/2}$? Between the concavity of $y = x^3$ and $y = x^{1/3}$ for $x > 0$? Explain why this happens.

Figure 11.12

Problems 33–34 refer to the power functions f, g, w, v graphed in Figure 11.13. All four graphs contain the point $(1, 1)$.

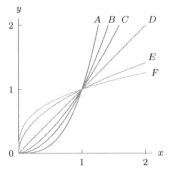

Figure 11.13

33. Rank the four functions in order of p, the power, from least to greatest.

34. For which (if any) of the four functions is the power p odd?

35. For the power function $F(x) = kx^n$, let $f(x) = nkx^{n-1}$. Find f given that $F(x) = \dfrac{1}{\sqrt[3]{7x}}$.

36. For the power function $f(x) = kx^n$, let $F(x) = \dfrac{kx^{n+1}}{n+1}$. Find F given that $f(x) = \dfrac{\sqrt[5]{x^2}}{4}$.

37. The cost of denim fabric is directly proportional to the amount that you buy. Let $C(x)$ be the cost, in dollars, of x yards of denim fabric.

   (a) Write a formula for the cost, $C(x)$, in terms of x. Your answer will contain a constant, k.
   (b) A particular type of denim costs $28.50 for 3 yards. Find k and rewrite the formula for $C(x)$ using it.
   (c) Graph $C(x)$.
   (d) How much does it cost to buy 5.5 yards of denim?

38. Three ounces of broiled ground beef contains 245 calories.[3] Is the number of calories directly or inversely proportional to the number of ounces? Explain your reasoning and write a formula for the proportion. How many calories are there in 4 ounces of broiled hamburger?

39. The circulation time of a mammal—that is, the average time it takes for all the blood in the body to circulate once and return to the heart—is governed by the equation

$$t = 17.4m^{1/4},$$

where m is the body mass of the mammal in kilograms, and t is the circulation time in seconds.[4]

   (a) Complete Table 11.4, which shows typical body masses in kilograms for various mammals.[5]
   (b) If the circulation time of one mammal is twice that of another, what is the relationship between their body masses?

---

[3] *The World Almanac Book of Facts*, 1999, p. 718.
[4] K. Schmidt-Nielsen, *Scaling, Why is Animal Size so Important?* (Cambridge: CUP, 1984).
[5] R. McNeill Alexander, *Dynamics of Dinosaurs and Other Extinct Giants* (New York: Columbia University Press, 1989).

Table 11.4

Animal	Body mass (kg)	Circulation time (sec)
Blue whale	91000	
African elephant	5450	
White rhinoceros	3000	
Hippopotamus	2520	
Black rhinoceros	1170	
Horse	700	
Lion	180	
Human	70	

40. In 2004, Agutter and Wheatley[6] reported

> The relationship between body mass, M, and standard metabolic rate, B, among living organisms remains controversial, though it is widely accepted that in many cases B is approximately proportional to the three-quarters power of M.

(a) Write a function that represents this relationship.

(b) The average mass of an African forest elephant is 4.6 metric tons[7] and that of a typical mouse is 20 grams. Use part (a) to determine how many times greater the metabolic rate of an elephant is than that of a mouse. (1 metric ton = 1,000,000 grams.)

41. The musical pitch, P, of a guitar string can be varied by changing its density, ρ. The pitch is inversely proportional to the square root of the density, so a string that is denser produces a lower pitch. Write an expression for the pitch in terms of the density.

42. A 30-second commercial during Super Bowl XLIV in 2010 cost advertisers up to $3 million. For the first Super Bowl in 1967, an advertiser could have purchased approximately 34.439 minutes of advertising time for the same amount of money.[8]

(a) Assuming that cost is proportional to time, find the cost of advertising, in dollars/second, during the 1967 and 2010 Super Bowls.

(b) How many times more expensive was Super Bowl advertising in 2010 than in 1967?

43. Driving at 55 mph, it takes approximately 3.5 hours to drive from Long Island to Albany, NY. Is the time the drive takes directly or inversely proportional to the speed? Explain your reasoning and write a formula for the proportion. To get to Albany in 3 hours, how fast would you have to drive?

44. Ship designers usually construct scale models before building a real ship. The formula that relates the speed u to the hull length l of a ship is

$$u = k\sqrt{l},$$

where k is a positive constant. This constant k varies depending on the ship's design, but scale models of a real ship have the same k as the real ship after which they are modeled.[9]

(a) How fast should a scale model with hull length 4 meters travel to simulate a real ship with hull length 225 meters traveling 9 meters/sec?

(b) A new ship is to be built whose speed is to be 10% greater than the speed of an existing ship with the same design. What is the relationship between the hull lengths of the new ship and the existing ship?

45. A volcano erupts in a powerful explosion. The sound from the explosion is heard in all directions for many hundreds of kilometers. The speed of sound is about 340 meters per second.

(a) Fill in Table 11.5 showing the distance, d, that the sound of the explosion has traveled at time t. Write a formula for d as a function of t.

(b) How long after the explosion will a person living 200 km away hear the explosion?

(c) Fill in Table 11.5 showing the land area, A, over which the explosion can be heard as a function of time. Write a formula for A as a function of t.

(d) The average population density around the volcano is 31 people per square kilometer. Write a formula for P as function of t, where P is the number of people who have heard the explosion at time t.

(e) Graph the function $P = f(t)$. How long will it take until 1 million people have heard the explosion?

Table 11.5

Time, t	5 sec	10 sec	1 min	5 min
Distance, d (km)				
Area, A (km^2)				

[6]P. S. Agutter and D. N. Wheatley, (2004) Metabolic scaling: consensus or controversy? *Theor. Biol. Med. Mod.* 1:13, PMID: 15546492

[7]www.pbs.org/wnet/nature/elephants/life.html, accessed June 14, 2010.

[8]www.dailfinance.com/2009/09/20/cbs-super-bowl-ad-sales-slip-behind-last-years-pace, accessed November 27, 2009.

[9]R. McNeill Alexander, *Dynamics of Dinosaurs and Other Extinct Giants* (New York: Columbia University Press, 1989).

46. Two oil tankers crash in the Pacific Ocean. The spreading oil slick has a circular shape, and the radius of the circle is increasing at 200 meters per hour.

    (a) Express the radius of the spill, r, as a power function of time, t, in hours since the crash.

    (b) Express the area of the spill, A, as a power function of time, t.

    (c) Clean-up efforts begin 7 hours after the spill. How large an area is covered by oil at that time?

47. In a microwave oven, cooking time is inversely proportional to the amount of power used. It takes 6.5 minutes to heat a frozen dinner at 750 watts.

    (a) Write a formula for the cooking time, t, as a function of power level, w.

    (b) Fill in Table 11.6 with the cooking times needed to heat the frozen dinner at various power levels.

    (c) Graph the function $t = f(w)$.

    (d) If it takes 2 minutes to heat a rhubarb crumble at 250 watts, how long will it take at 500 watts?

Table 11.6

Power, w (watts)	250	300	500	650
Time, t (mins)				

48. An average hailstone is a sphere of radius 0.3 centimeter. Severe thunderstorms can produce hailstones of radius 0.95 centimeter. The largest hailstone found in the US had radius 7.05 centimeters. Table 11.7 gives the masses of these hailstones in grams.[10]

    (a) Using the data given, check that mass, m, is proportional to the cube of the radius, r.

    (b) Find the constant of proportionality and write m as a function of r.

    (c) The largest recorded hailstone was found in India in 1939 and weighed 3.4 kilograms. What was its radius?

    (d) Calculate the density of ice in grams per cubic centimeter. [Hint: Density is mass per unit volume.]

Table 11.7

Radius, r (cm)	0.3	0.95	7.05
Mass, m (gm)	0.058	1.835	750

49. The following questions involve the behavior of the power function $y = x^{-p}$, for p a positive integer. If a distinction between even and odd values of p is significant, the significance should be indicated.

    (a) What is the domain of $y = x^{-p}$? What is the range?

    (b) What symmetries does the graph of $y = x^{-p}$ have?

    (c) What is the behavior of $y = x^{-p}$ as $x \to 0$?

    (d) What is the behavior of $y = x^{-p}$ for large positive values of x? For large negative values of x?

50. Let $f(x) = 16x^4$ and $g(x) = 4x^2$.

    (a) If $f(x) = g(h(x))$, find a possible formula for $h(x)$, assuming $h(x) \le 0$ for all x.

    (b) If $f(x) = j(2g(x))$, find a possible formula for $j(x)$, assuming $j(x)$ is a power function.

51. Consider the power function $y = t(x) = k \cdot x^{p/3}$ where p is any integer, $p \ne 0$.

    (a) For what values of p does $t(x)$ have domain restrictions? What are those restrictions?

    (b) What is the range of $t(x)$ if p is even? If p is odd?

    (c) What symmetry does the graph of $t(x)$ exhibit if p is even? If p is odd?

11.2 POLYNOMIAL FUNCTIONS

A *polynomial function* is a sum of power functions whose exponents are nonnegative integers. We use what we learned about power functions to study polynomials.

Example 1   You make five separate deposits of $1000 each into a savings account, one deposit per year, beginning today. What annual interest rate gives a balance in the account of $6000 five years from today? (Assume the interest rate is constant over these five years.)

Solution   Let r be the annual interest rate. Our goal is to determine what value of r gives you $6000 in five years. In year $t = 0$, you make a $1000 deposit. One year later, you have $1000 plus the interest earned on that amount. At that time, you add another $1000.

    To picture how this works, imagine the account pays 5% annual interest, compounded annually. Then, after one year, your balance would be

[10]C. Donald Ahrens, *Essentials of Meteorology* (Wadsworth: Belmont, CA, 1998).

$$\text{Balance} = (100\% \text{ of Initial deposit}) + (5\% \text{ of Initial deposit}) + \text{Second deposit}$$

$$= 105\% \text{ of } \underbrace{\text{Initial deposit}}_{\$1000} + \underbrace{\text{Second deposit}}_{\$1000}$$

$$= 1.05(1000) + 1000.$$

Let x represent the annual growth factor, $1 + r$. For example, if the account paid 5% interest, then $x = 1 + 0.05 = 1.05$. We write the balance after one year in terms of x:

$$\text{Balance after one year} = 1000x + 1000.$$

After two years, you would have earned interest on the first-year balance. This gives

$$\text{Balance after earning interest} = \underbrace{(1000x + 1000)}_{\text{First-year balance}}x = 1000x^2 + 1000x.$$

The third $1000 deposit brings your balance to

$$\text{Balance after two years} = 1000x^2 + 1000x + \underbrace{1000.}_{\text{Third deposit}}$$

A year's worth of interest on this amount, plus the fourth $1000 deposit, brings your balance to

$$\text{Balance after three years} = \underbrace{(1000x^2 + 1000x + 1000)}_{\text{Second-year balance}}x + \underbrace{1000}_{\text{Fourth deposit}}$$

$$= 1000x^3 + 1000x^2 + 1000x + 1000.$$

The pattern is this: Each of the $1000 deposits grows to $1000x^n$ by the end of its nth year in the bank. Thus,

$$\text{Balance after five years} = 1000x^5 + 1000x^4 + 1000x^3 + 1000x^2 + 1000x.$$

If the interest rate is chosen correctly, then the balance will be $6000 in five years. This gives us

$$1000x^5 + 1000x^4 + 1000x^3 + 1000x^2 + 1000x = 6000.$$

Dividing by 1000 and moving the 6 to the left side, we have the equation

$$x^5 + x^4 + x^3 + x^2 + x - 6 = 0.$$

Solving this equation for x determines how much interest we must earn. Using a computer or calculator, we find where the graph of $Q(x) = x^5 + x^4 + x^3 + x^2 + x - 6$ crosses the x-axis. Figure 11.14 shows that this occurs at $x \approx 1.0614$. Since $x = 1 + r$, this means $r = 0.0614$. So the account must earn 6.14% annual interest[11] for the balance to be $6000 at the end of five years.

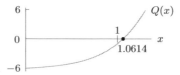

Figure 11.14: Finding where $Q(x)$ crosses the x-axis, for $x \geq 0$

You may wonder if Q crosses the x-axis more than once. For $x \geq 0$, graphing Q on a larger scale suggests that Q increases for all values of x and crosses the x-axis only once. For $x > 1$,

---

[11]This is 6.14% interest per year, compounded annually.

we expect Q to be an increasing function, because larger values of x indicate higher interest rates and therefore larger values of $Q(x)$. Having crossed the axis once, the graph of Q does not "turn around" to cross it again.

The function $Q(x) = x^5 + x^4 + x^3 + x^2 + x - 6$ is the sum of power functions; Q is called a *polynomial*. (Note that the expression -6 can be written as $-6x^0$, so it, too, is a power function.)

A General Formula for the Family of Polynomial Functions

The general formula for a polynomial function can be written as

$$p(x) = a_n x^n + a_{n-1} x^{n-1} + \ldots + a_1 x + a_0,$$

where n is called the *degree* of the polynomial and a_n is the *leading coefficient*. For example, the function

$$g(x) = 3x^2 + 4x^5 + x - x^3 + 1,$$

is a polynomial of degree 5 because the term with the highest power is $4x^5$. It is customary to write a polynomial with the powers in decreasing order from left to right:

$$g(x) = 4x^5 - x^3 + 3x^2 + x + 1.$$

The function g has one other term, $0 \cdot x^4$, which we don't bother to write down. The values of g's coefficients are $a_5 = 4, a_4 = 0, a_3 = -1, a_2 = 3, a_1 = 1$, and $a_0 = 1$. In summary:

The general formula for the family of polynomial functions can be written as

$$p(x) = a_n x^n + a_{n-1} x^{n-1} + \ldots + a_1 x + a_0,$$

where n is a positive integer called the **degree** of p and where $a_n \neq 0$.
- Each power function $a_i x^i$ in this sum is called a **term**.
- The constants $a_n, a_{n-1}, \ldots, a_0$ are called **coefficients**.
- The term a_0 is called the **constant term**. The term with the highest power, $a_n x^n$, is called the **leading term**.
- To write a polynomial in **standard form**, we arrange its terms from highest power to lowest power, going from left to right.

Like the power functions from which they are built, polynomials are defined for all values of x. Except for polynomials of degree zero (whose graphs are horizontal lines), the graphs of polynomials do not have horizontal or vertical asymptotes; they are smooth and unbroken. The shape of the graph depends on its degree; typical graphs are shown in Figure 11.15.

Quadratic ($n = 2$)   Cubic ($n = 3$)   Quartic ($n = 4$)   Quintic ($n = 5$)

Figure 11.15: Graphs of typical polynomials of degree n

The Long-Run Behavior of Polynomial Functions

We have seen that, as x grows large, $y = x^2$ increases fast, $y = x^3$ increases faster, and $y = x^4$ increases faster still. In general, power functions with larger positive powers eventually grow much faster than those with smaller powers. This tells us about the behavior of polynomials for large x. For instance, consider the polynomial $g(x) = 4x^5 - x^3 + 3x^2 + x + 1$. Provided x is large enough, the value of the term $4x^5$ is much larger than the value of the other terms combined. For example, if $x = 100$,

$$4x^5 = 4(100)^5 = 40{,}000{,}000{,}000,$$

and the other terms in $g(x)$ are

$$-x^3 + 3x^2 + x + 1 = -(100)^3 + 3(100)^2 + 100 + 1$$
$$= -1{,}000{,}000 + 30{,}000 + 100 + 1 = -969{,}899.$$

Therefore $p(100) = 39{,}999{,}030{,}101$, which is approximately equal to the value of the $4x^5$ term. In general, if x is large enough, the most important contribution to the value of a polynomial p is made by the leading term; we can ignore the lower power terms.

> When viewed on a large enough scale, the graph of the polynomial $p(x) = a_n x^n + a_{n-1} x^{n-1} + \cdots + a_1 x + a_0$ looks like the graph of the power function $y = a_n x^n$. This behavior is called the **long-run behavior** of the polynomial. Using limit notation, we write
>
> $$\lim_{x \to \infty} p(x) = \lim_{x \to \infty} a_n x^n \quad \text{and} \quad \lim_{x \to -\infty} p(x) = \lim_{x \to -\infty} a_n x^n.$$

Example 2   Find a window in which the graph of $f(x) = x^3 + x^2$ resembles the power function $y = x^3$.

Solution   Figure 11.16 gives the graphs of $f(x) = x^3 + x^2$ and $y = x^3$. On this scale, f does not look like a power function. On the larger scale in Figure 11.17, the graph of f resembles the graph of $y = x^3$. On this larger scale, the "bumps" in the graph of f are too small to be seen. On an even larger scale, as in Figure 11.18, the graph of f is indistinguishable from the graph of $y = x^3$.

Figure 11.16: On this scale, $f(x) = x^3 + x^2$ does not look like a power function

Figure 11.17: On this scale, $f(x) = x^3 + x^2$ resembles the power function $y = x^3$

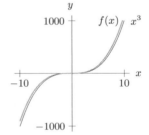

Figure 11.18: On this scale, $f(x) = x^3 + x^2$ is nearly indistinguishable from $y = x^3$

Zeros of Polynomials

The *zeros* of a polynomial p are values of x for which $p(x) = 0$. The zeros are also the x-intercepts, because they tell us where the graph of p crosses the x-axis. Factoring can sometimes be used to find the zeros of a polynomial; however, the graphical method of Example 1 can always be used. In addition, the long-run behavior of the polynomial can give us clues as to how many zeros (if any) there may be.

Example 3   Given the polynomial

$$q(x) = 3x^6 - 2x^5 + 4x^2 - 1,$$

where $q(0) = -1$, is there a reason to expect a solution to the equation $q(x) = 0$? If not, explain why not. If so, how do you know?

Solution   The equation $q(x) = 0$ must have at least two solutions. We know this because on a large scale, q looks like the power function $y = 3x^6$. (See Figure 11.19.) The function $y = 3x^6$ takes on large positive values as x grows large (either positive or negative). Since the graph of q is smooth and unbroken, it must cross the x-axis at least twice to get from $q(0) = -1$ to the positive values it attains as $x \to \infty$ and $x \to -\infty$.

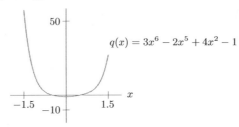

Figure 11.19: Graph must cross x-axis at least twice since $q(0) = -1$ and $q(x)$ looks like $3x^6$ for large x

A sixth-degree polynomial such as q in Example 3 can have as many as six real zeros. We consider the zeros of a polynomial in more detail in Section 11.3.

Exercises and Problems for Section 11.2

Exercises

Are the functions in Exercises 1–6 polynomials? If so, of what degree?

1. $y = 5^x - 2$

2. $y = 5 + x$

3. $y = 4x^2 + 2$

4. $y = 7t^6 - 8t + 7.2$

5. $y = 4x^4 - 3x^3 + 2e^x$

6. $y = 4x^2 - 7\sqrt{x^9} + 10$

For the polynomials in Exercises 7–9, state the degree, the number of terms, and describe the long-run behavior.

7. $y = 2x^3 - 3x + 7$

8. $y = 1 - 2x^4 + x^3$

9. $y = (x + 4)(2x - 3)(5 - x)$

10. Find

(a) $\lim\limits_{x \to \infty} (3x^2 - 5x + 7)$ (b) $\lim\limits_{x \to -\infty} (7x^2 - 9x^3)$

Problems

11. Estimate the zeros of $f(x) = x^4 - 3x^2 - x + 2$.

12. Estimate the minimum value of $g(x) = x^4 - 3x^3 - 8$.

13. Compare the graphs of $f(x) = x^3 + 5x^2 - x - 5$ and $g(x) = -2x^3 - 10x^2 + 2x + 10$ on a window that shows all intercepts. How are the graphs similar? Different? Discuss.

14. Let $u(x) = -\frac{1}{5}(x - 3)(x + 1)(x + 5)$ and $v(x) = -\frac{1}{5}x^2(x - 5)$.

(a) Graph u and v for $-10 \leq x \leq 10$, $-10 \leq y \leq 10$. How are the graphs similar? How are they different?

(b) Compare the graphs of u and v on the window $-20 \leq x \leq 20$, $-1600 \leq y \leq 1600$, the window $-50 \leq x \leq 50$, $-25{,}000 \leq y \leq 25{,}000$, and the window $-500 \leq x \leq 500$, $-25{,}000{,}000 \leq y \leq 25{,}000{,}000$. Discuss.

15. Find the equation of the line through the y-intercept of $y = x^4 - 3x^5 - 1 + x^2$ and the x-intercept of $y = 2x - 4$.

16. Let $f(x) = \left(\dfrac{1}{50,000}\right) x^3 + \left(\dfrac{1}{2}\right) x$.

   (a) For small values of x, which term of f is more important? Explain your answer.

   (b) Graph $y = f(x)$ for $-10 \le x \le 10$, $-10 \le y \le 10$. Is this graph linear? How does the appearance of this graph agree with your answer to part (a)?

   (c) How large a value of x is required for the cubic term of f to be equal to the linear term?

17. Find four different viewing windows on which $f(x) = (x+2)(x-1)(x-3)^2$ resembles graphs (a)–(d).

(a)

(b)

(c)

(d)

In Problems 18–21, find a viewing window on which the graph of $f(x) = x^3 + x^2$ resembles the plot.

18.

19.

20.

21.

22. The polynomial function $f(x) = x^3 + x + 1$ is invertible—that is, this function has an inverse.

   (a) Graph $y = f(x)$. Explain how you can tell from the graph that f is invertible.

   (b) Find $f(0.5)$ and an approximate value for $f^{-1}(0.5)$.

23. If $f(x) = x^2$ and $g(x) = (x+2)(x-1)(x-3)$, find all x for which $f(x) < g(x)$.

24. In calculus, we often consider pairs of polynomials. If $F(x) = 3x^4 - 4x^3 + 5x - 4$, find a_4, a_3, a_2, a_1, a_0. Then use these values to construct the cubic polynomial

$$f(x) = 4a_4 x^3 + 3a_3 x^2 + 2a_2 x + a_1.$$

25. The town of Liddleville was founded in 1890. Its population y (in hundreds) was modeled, for t in years since 1890, by

$$y = 1 - 0.58t + 4.89t^2 - 1.872t^3 + 0.247t^4 - 0.0111t^5.$$

   (a) Graph the function for $0 \le t \le 8$, $-2 \le y \le 12$.

   (b) What was the population of Liddleville when it was founded?

   (c) When did the population of Liddleville reach zero? Give the year and the month.

   (d) What was the largest population of Liddleville after 1890? When did Liddleville reach that population? Give the month and year.

   (e) What population was predicted for 1898? Comment.

26. (a) The total cost, in millions of dollars, of producing x thousand units of an item is $C(x) = 4(x-1)^2 + 4$. Graph $C(x)$.

   (b) The revenue (in millions of dollars) from selling x thousand units of the item is $R(x) = 10x$. What does this tell you about the price of each unit?

   (c) Profit is revenue minus cost. For what values of x does the firm make a profit? Break even? Lose money?

27. Let V represent the volume in liters of air in the lungs during a 5-second respiratory cycle. If t is time in seconds, V is given by

$$V = 0.1729t + 0.1522t^2 - 0.0374t^3.$$

   (a) Graph this function for $0 \le t \le 5$.

   (b) What is the maximum value of V on this interval? What is its practical significance?

   (c) Explain the practical significance of the t- and V-intercepts on the interval $0 \le t \le 5$.

28. The volume, V, in milliliters, of 1 kg of water as a function of temperature T is given, for $0 \leq T \leq 30°C$, by:

$$V = 999.87 - 0.06426T + 0.0085143T^2 - 0.0000679T^3.$$

(a) Graph V.

(b) Describe the shape of your graph. Does V increase or decrease as T increases? Does the graph curve upward or downward? What does the graph tell us about how the volume varies with temperature?

(c) At what temperature does water have the maximum density? How does that appear on your graph? (Density = Mass/Volume. In this problem, the mass of the water is 1 kg.)

29. Let f and g be polynomial functions. Are the following compositions also polynomial functions? Explain your answer.

$$f(g(x)) \qquad \text{and} \qquad g(f(x))$$

30. **(a)** Suppose $f(x) = ax^2 + bx + c$. What must be true about the coefficients if f is an even function?

(b) Suppose $g(x) = ax^3 + bx^2 + cx + d$. What must be true about the coefficients if g is an odd function?

31. Let g be a polynomial function of degree n, where n is a positive odd integer. For each of the following statements, write *true* if the statement is always true, *false* otherwise. If the statement is false, give an example that illustrates why it is false.

(a) g is an odd function.

(b) g has an inverse.

(c) $\lim\limits_{x \to \infty} g(x) = \infty$.

(d) If $\lim\limits_{x \to -\infty} g(x) = -\infty$, then $\lim\limits_{x \to \infty} g(x) = \infty$.

32. Let $f(x) = x - \dfrac{x^3}{6} + \dfrac{x^5}{120}$.

(a) Graph $y = f(x)$ and $y = \sin x$ for $-2\pi \leq x \leq 2\pi$, $-3 \leq y \leq 3$.

(b) The graph of f resembles the graph of $\sin x$ on a small interval. Based on your graphs from part (a), give the approximate interval.

(c) Your calculator uses a function similar to f in order to evaluate the sine function. How reasonable an approximation does f give for $\sin(\pi/8)$?

(d) Explain how you could use the function f to approximate the value of $\sin \theta$, where $\theta = 18$ radians. [Hint: Use the fact that the sine function is periodic.]

33. For certain x-values, the function $f(x) = 1/(1 + x)$ can be well-approximated by the polynomial

$$p(x) = 1 - x + x^2 - x^3 + x^4 - x^5.$$

(a) Show that $p(0.5) \approx f(0.5) = 2/3$. To how many decimal places do $p(0.5)$ and $f(0.5)$ agree?

(b) Calculate $p(1)$. How well does $p(1)$ approximate $f(1)$?

(c) Graph $p(x)$ and $f(x)$ together on the same set of axes for $-1 \leq x \leq 1$. Based on your graph, for what range of values of x does $p(x)$ appear to give a good estimate for $f(x)$?

34. Table 11.8 gives v, the speed of sound (in m/sec) in water as a function of the temperature T (in °C).[12]

(a) An approximate linear formula for v is given by $v = 1402.385 + 5.038813T$. Over what temperature range does this formula agree with the values in Table 11.8 to within $1°C$?

(b) The formula in part (a) can be improved by adding the quadratic term $-5.799136 \cdot 10^{-2}T^2$. Repeat part (a) using this adjusted formula.

(c) The formula in part (b) can be further improved by adding the cubic term $3.287156 \cdot 10^{-4}T^3$. Repeat part (a) using this adjusted formula.

(d) The speed of sound in water at $50°C$ is 1542.6 m/s. If we want to improve our formula still further by adding a quartic (fourth-degree) term, should this term be positive or negative?

Table 11.8

T	0	5	10	15	20	25	30
v	1402.4	1426.2	1447.3	1466.0	1482.4	1496.7	1509.2

11.3 THE SHORT-RUN BEHAVIOR OF POLYNOMIALS

The long-run behavior of a polynomial is determined by its leading term. However, polynomials with the same leading term may have very different short-run behaviors.

Example 1   Compare the graphs of the polynomials f, g, and h given by

$$f(x) = x^4 - 4x^3 + 16x - 16, \quad g(x) = x^4 - 4x^3 - 4x^2 + 16x, \quad h(x) = x^4 + x^3 - 8x^2 - 12x.$$

[12]Data from the Marczak formula at the UK National Physical Laboratory: www.npl.co.uk, accessed 2001.

Solution   Each of these functions is a fourth-degree polynomial, and each has x^4 as its leading term. Thus, all their graphs resemble the graph of x^4 on a large scale. See Figure 11.20.

However, on a smaller scale, the functions look different. See Figure 11.21. Two of the graphs go through the origin while the third does not. The graphs also differ from one another in the number of bumps each one has and in the number of times each one crosses the x-axis. Thus, polynomials with the same leading term look similar on a large scale, but may look dissimilar on a small scale.

Figure 11.20: On a large scale, the polynomials f, g, and h resemble the power function $y = x^4$

Figure 11.21: On a smaller scale, the polynomials f, g, and h look quite different from one another

Factored Form, Zeros, and the Short-Run Behavior of a Polynomial

To predict the long-run behavior of a polynomial, we use the highest-power term. To determine the zeros and the short-run behavior of a polynomial, we write it in factored form with as many linear factors as possible.

Example 2   Investigate the short-run behavior of the third-degree polynomial $u(x) = x^3 - x^2 - 6x$.

(a) Rewrite $u(x)$ as a product of linear factors.
(b) Find the zeros of $u(x)$.
(c) Describe the graph of $u(x)$. Where does it cross the x-axis? the y-axis? Where is $u(x)$ positive? Negative?

Solution   (a) By factoring out an x and then factoring the quadratic, $x^2 - x - 6$, we rewrite $u(x)$ as

$$u(x) = x^3 - x^2 - 6x = x(x^2 - x - 6) = x(x - 3)(x + 2).$$

Thus, we have expressed $u(x)$ as the product of three linear factors, x, $x - 3$, and $x + 2$.

(b) The polynomial equals zero if and only if at least one of its factors is zero. We solve the equation:

$$x(x - 3)(x + 2) = 0,$$

giving

$$x = 0, \quad \text{or} \quad x - 3 = 0, \quad \text{or} \quad x + 2 = 0,$$

so

$$x = 0, \quad \text{or} \quad x = 3, \quad \text{or} \quad x = -2.$$

These are the zeros, or x-intercepts, of u. To check, evaluate $u(x)$ for these x-values; you should get 0. There are no other zeros.

(c) To describe the graph of u, we give the x- and y-intercepts, and the long-run behavior.

The factored form, $u(x) = x(x - 3)(x + 2)$, shows that the graph crosses the x-axis at $x = 0, 3, -2$. The graph of u crosses the y-axis at $u(0) = 0^3 - 0^2 - 6 \cdot 0 = 0$; that is, at $y = 0$. For large values of x, the graph of $y = u(x)$ resembles the graph of its leading term, $y = x^3$. Figure 11.22 shows where u is positive and where u is negative.

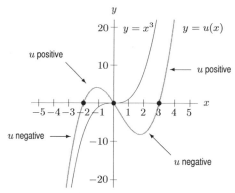

Figure 11.22: The graph of $u(x) = x^3 - x^2 - 6x$ has zeros at $x = -2, 0$, and 3. Its long-run behavior resembles $y = x^3$

In Example 2, each linear factor produced a zero of the polynomial. Now suppose that we do not know the polynomial p, but we do know that it has zeros at $x = 0, -12, 31$. Then we know that the factored form of the polynomial must include the factors $(x - 0)$ or x, and $(x - (-12))$ or $(x + 12)$, and $(x - 31)$. It may include other factors too. In summary:

Suppose p is a polynomial. If the formula for p has a **linear factor**, that is, a factor of the form $(x - k)$, then p has a zero at $x = k$.

Conversely, if p has a **zero** at $x = k$, then p has a linear factor of the form $(x - k)$.

The Number of Factors, Zeros, and Bumps

The number of linear factors is always less than or equal to the degree of a polynomial. For example, a fourth-degree polynomial can have no more than four linear factors. This makes sense because if we had another factor in the product and multiplied out, the highest power of x would be greater than four. Since each zero corresponds to a linear factor, the number of zeros is less than or equal to the degree of the polynomial.

Between any two consecutive zeros of a polynomial, there is at least one bump. For example, in Figure 11.22, the function is zero at $x = 0$ and negative at $x = 1$, and must change direction to come back up and cross the x-axis at $x = 3$. Using calculus, it can be shown that any third-degree polynomial has no more than two bumps. In general:

The graph of an nth-degree polynomial has at most n zeros and turns at most $(n - 1)$ times.

Multiple Zeros

The functions $s(x) = (x - 4)^2$ and $t(x) = (x + 1)^3$ are both polynomials in factored form. Each is a horizontal shift of a power function. We refer to the zeros of s and t as *multiple zeros*, because in each case the factor contributing the value of $y = 0$ occurs more than once. For instance, we say that $x = 4$ is a *double zero* of s, since

$$s(x) = (x - 4)^2 = \underbrace{(x - 4)(x - 4)}_{\text{Occurs twice}}.$$

Likewise, we say that $x = -1$ is a *triple zero* of t, since

$$t(x) = (x + 1)^3 = \underbrace{(x + 1)(x + 1)(x + 1)}_{\text{Occurs three times}}.$$

The graphs of s and t in Figures 11.23 and 11.24 show typical behavior near multiple zeros.

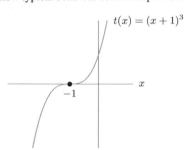

Figure 11.23: Double zero at $x = 4$

Figure 11.24: Triple zero at $x = -1$

In general:

If p is a polynomial with a repeated linear factor, then p has a **multiple zero**.

- If the factor $(x - k)$ occurs an even number of times, the graph of $y = p(x)$ does not cross the x-axis at $x = k$, but "bounces" off the x-axis at $x = k$. (See Figure 11.23.)
- If the factor $(x - k)$ occurs an odd number of times, the graph of $y = p(x)$ crosses the x-axis at $x = k$, but it looks flattened there. (See Figure 11.24.)

Example 3 Describe in words the zeros of the 4th-degree polynomials $f(x)$, $g(x)$, and $h(x)$, in Figure 11.25.

Figure 11.25: Three 4th-degree polynomials

Solution The graph suggests that f has a single zero at $x = -2$. The flattened appearance near $x = 2$ suggests that f has a multiple zero there. Since the graph crosses the x-axis at $x = 2$ (instead of bouncing off it), this zero must occur an odd number of times. Since f is 4th degree, f has at most 4 factors, so there must be a triple zero at $x = 2$.

The graph of g has four single zeros. The graph of h has two single zeros (at $x = 0$ and $x = 3$) and a double zero at $x = -2$. The multiplicity of the zero at $x = -2$ is not higher than two because h is of degree $n = 4$.

Finding the Formula for a Polynomial from its Graph

The graph of a polynomial often enables us to find a possible formula for the polynomial.

Example 4 Find a possible formula for the polynomial function f graphed in Figure 11.26.

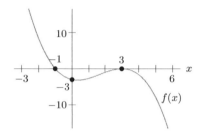

Figure 11.26: Features of the graph lead to a possible formula for this polynomial

Solution Based on its long-run behavior, f is of odd degree greater than or equal to 3. The polynomial has zeros at $x = -1$ and $x = 3$. We see that $x = 3$ is a multiple zero of even power, because the graph bounces off the x-axis here instead of crossing it. Therefore, we try the formula

$$f(x) = k(x + 1)(x - 3)^2$$

where k represents a stretch factor. The shape of the graph shows that k must be negative.

To find k, we use the fact that $f(0) = -3$, so

$$f(0) = k(0 + 1)(0 - 3)^2 = -3,$$

which gives

$$9k = -3 \quad \text{so} \quad k = -\frac{1}{3}.$$

Thus, $f(x) = -\frac{1}{3}(x + 1)(x - 3)^2$ is a possible formula for this polynomial.

The formula for f we found in Example 4 is the polynomial of least degree we could have chosen. However, there are other polynomials, such as $y = -\frac{1}{27}(x + 1)(x - 3)^4$, with the same overall behavior as the function shown in Figure 11.26.

Exercises and Problems for Section 11.3

Exercises

In Exercises 1–4, find the zeros of the functions.

1. $y = x^3 + 7x^2 + 12x$

2. $y = (x^2 + 2x - 7)(x^3 + 4x^2 - 21x)$

3. $y = 7(x + 3)(x - 2)(x + 7)$

4. $y = a(x + 2)(x - b)$, where a, b are nonzero constants

5. Use the graph of $h(x)$ in Figure 11.21 on page 448 to determine the factored form of
$$h(x) = x^4 + x^3 - 8x^2 - 12x.$$

6. Use the graph of $g(x)$ in Figure 11.21 on page 448 to determine the factored form of
$$g(x) = x^4 - 4x^3 - 4x^2 + 16x.$$

7. Use the graph of $f(x)$ in Figure 11.21 on page 448 to determine the factored form of
$$f(x) = x^4 - 4x^3 + 16x - 16.$$

8. Factor $f(x) = 8x^3 - 4x^2 - 60x$ completely, and determine the zeros of f.

9. Find a possible formula for a polynomial with zeros at (and only at) $x = -2, 2, 5$, a y-intercept at $y = 5$, and long-run behavior of $y \to -\infty$ as $x \to \pm\infty$.

Without a calculator, graph the polynomials in Exercises 10–11. Label all the x-intercepts and y-intercepts.

10. $f(x) = -5(x^2 - 4)(25 - x^2)$

11. $g(x) = 5(x - 4)(x^2 - 25)$

Problems

12. **(a)** Let $f(x) = (2x - 1)(3x - 1)(x - 7)(x - 9)$. What are the zeros of this polynomial?
    (b) Is it possible to find a viewing window that shows all of the zeros and all of the the turning points of f?
    (c) Find two separate viewing windows that together show all the zeros and all the turning points of f.

13. **(a)** Experiment with various viewing windows to determine the zeros of $f(x) = 2x^4 + 9x^3 - 7x^2 - 9x + 5$. Then write f in factored form.
    (b) Find a single viewing window that clearly shows all of the turning points of f.

14. Let $p(x) = x^4 + 10x^3 - 68x^2 + 102x - 45$. By experimenting with various viewing windows, determine the zeros of p and use this information to write $p(x)$ in factored form.

15. Without using a calculator, decide which of the equations A–E best describes the polynomial in Figure 11.27.

    A $y = (x + 2)(x + 1)(x - 2)(x - 3)$
    B $y = x(x + 2)(x + 1)(x - 2)(x - 3)$
    C $y = -\frac{1}{2}(x + 2)(x + 1)(x - 2)(x - 3)$
    D $y = \frac{1}{2}(x + 2)(x + 1)(x - 2)(x - 3)$
    E $y = -(x + 2)(x + 1)(x - 2)(x - 3)$

Figure 11.27

In Problems 16–21, find a possible formula for each polynomial with the given properties.

16. f has degree ≤ 2, $f(0) = 0$ and $f(1) = 1$.

17. f has degree ≤ 2, $f(0) = f(1) = f(2) = 1$.

18. f has degree ≤ 2, $f(0) = f(2) = 0$ and $f(3) = 3$.

19. f is third degree with $f(-3) = 0$, $f(1) = 0$, $f(4) = 0$, and $f(2) = 5$.

20. g is fourth degree, g has a double zero at $x = 3$, $g(5) = 0$, $g(-1) = 0$, and $g(0) = 3$.

21. Least possible degree through the points $(-3, 0)$, $(1, 0)$, and $(0, -3)$.

22. Which of these functions have inverses that are functions? Discuss.
    (a) $f(x) = (x - 2)^3 + 4$.
    (b) $g(x) = x^3 - 4x^2 + 2$.

In Problems 23–32, give a possible formula for the polynomial.

23.

24.

25.

Note appearance near origin

26.

27.

28.

29.

30.

31.

32.

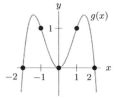

For Problems 33–38, find the real zeros (if any) of the polynomials.

33. $y = 4x^2 - 1$

34. $y = x^4 + 6x^2 + 9$

35. $y = (x^2 - 8x + 12)(x - 3)$

36. $y = x^2 + 5x + 6$

37. $y = 4x^2 + 1$

38. $y = ax^2(x^2 + 4)(x + 3)$, where a is a nonzero constant.

39. Suppose the polynomial

$$f(x) = (x - 5)^2(x - 3)^2(x - 1)(x - r)(x + 3)^s \cdot g(x)$$

is an even function. What can you say about the constants r, s and the second-degree polynomial function $g(x)$?

40. Find at least two different third-degree polynomials having zeros at $x = -1$ and $x = 2$ (and nowhere else), and y-intercept at $y = 3$.

41. An open-top box is to be constructed from a 6-in by 8-in rectangular sheet of tin by cutting out squares of equal size at each corner, then folding up the resulting flaps. Let x denote the length of the side of each cut-out square. Assume negligible thickness.

   (a) Find a formula for the volume of the box as a function of x.
   (b) For what values of x does the formula from part (a) make sense in the context of the problem?
   (c) Sketch a graph of the volume function.
   (d) What, approximately, is the maximum volume of the box?

42. You wish to pack a cardboard box inside a wooden crate. In order to have room for the packing materials, you need to leave a 0.5-ft space around the front, back, and sides of the box, and a 1-ft space around the top and bottom of the box. If the cardboard box is x feet long, $(x + 2)$ feet wide, and $(x - 1)$ feet deep, find a formula in terms of x for the amount of packing material needed.

43. Take an 8.5- by 11-inch piece of paper and cut out four equal squares from the corners. Fold up the sides to create an open box. Find the dimensions of the box that has maximum volume.

44. Give the domain for $g(x) = \ln\left((x - 3)^2(x + 2)\right)$.

45. Given that a, b, and c are constants, $a < b < c$, state the domain of

$$y = \sqrt{(x - a)(x - b)(x - c)}.$$

[Hint: Graph $y = (x - a)(x - b)(x - c)$.]

46. Consider the function $a(x) = x^5 + 2x^3 - 4x$.

(a) Without using a calculator or computer, what can you say about the graph of a?

(b) Use a calculator or a computer to determine the zeros of this function to three decimal places.

(c) Explain why you think that you have all the possible zeros.

(d) What are the zeros of $b(x) = 2x^5 + 4x^3 - 8x$? Does your answer surprise you?

47. In each of the following cases, find a possible formula for the polynomial f.

(a) Suppose f has zeros at $x = -2$, $x = 3$, $x = 5$ and a y-intercept of 4.

(b) In addition to the properties in part (a), suppose f has the following long-run behavior: As $x \to \pm\infty$, $y \to -\infty$. [Hint: Assume f has a double zero.]

(c) In addition to the properties in part (a), suppose f

has the following long-run behavior: As $x \to \pm\infty$, $y \to +\infty$.

48. The following statements about $f(x)$ are true:

- $f(x)$ is a polynomial function
- $f(x) = 0$ at exactly four different values of x
- $f(x) \to -\infty$ as $x \to \pm\infty$

For each of the following statements, write *true* if the statement must be true, *never true* if the statement is never true, or *sometimes true* if it is sometimes true and sometimes not true.

(a) $f(x)$ is an odd function

(b) $f(x)$ is an even function

(c) $f(x)$ is a fourth-degree polynomial

(d) $f(x)$ is a fifth-degree polynomial

(e) $f(-x) \to -\infty$ as $x \to \pm\infty$

(f) $f(x)$ is invertible

11.4 RATIONAL FUNCTIONS

The Average Cost of Producing a Therapeutic Drug

A pharmaceutical company wants to begin production of a new drug. The total cost C, in dollars, of making q grams of the drug is given by the linear function

$$C(q) = 2{,}500{,}000 + 2000q.$$

The fact that $C(0) = 2{,}500{,}000$ tells us that the company spends \$2,500,000 before it starts making the drug. This quantity is known as the *fixed cost* because it does not depend on how much of the drug is made. It represents the cost for research, testing, and equipment. In addition, the slope of C tells us that each gram of the drug costs an extra \$2000 to make. This quantity is known as the *variable cost* per unit. It represents the additional cost, in labor and materials, to make an additional gram of the drug.

The fixed cost of \$2.5 million is large compared to the variable cost of \$2000 per gram. This means that it is impractical for the company to make a small amount of the drug. For instance, the total cost for 10 grams is

$$C(10) = 2{,}500{,}000 + 2000 \cdot 10 = 2{,}520{,}000,$$

which works out to an average cost of \$252,000 per gram. The company would probably never sell such an expensive drug.

However, as larger quantities of the drug are manufactured, the initial expenditure of \$2.5 million seems less significant. The fixed cost averages out over a large quantity. For example, if the company makes 10,000 grams of the drug,

$$\text{Average cost} = \frac{\text{Cost of producing 10,000 grams}}{10{,}000} = \frac{2{,}500{,}000 + 2000 \cdot 10{,}000}{10{,}000} = 2250,$$

or \$2250 per gram of drug produced.

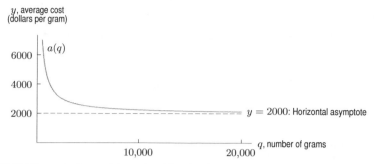

Figure 11.28: The graph of $y = a(q)$, a rational function, has a horizontal asymptote at $y = 2000$ and a vertical asymptote at $q = 0$

We define the average cost, $a(q)$, as the cost per gram to produce q grams of the drug:

$$a(q) = \frac{\text{Average cost of}}{\text{producing } q \text{ grams}} = \frac{\text{Total cost}}{\text{Number of grams}} = \frac{C(q)}{q} = \frac{2{,}500{,}000 + 2000q}{q}.$$

Figure 11.28 gives a graph of $y = a(q)$ for $q > 0$. The horizontal asymptote reflects the fact that for large values of q, the value of $a(q)$ is close to 2000. This is because, as more of the drug is produced, the average cost gets closer to \$2000 per gram. See Table 11.9.

The vertical asymptote of $y = a(q)$ is the y-axis, which tells us that the average cost per gram is very large if a small amount of the drug is made. This is because the initial \$2.5 million expenditure is averaged over very few units. We saw that producing only 10 grams costs a staggering \$252,000 per gram.

Table 11.9   *As quantity q increases, the average cost $a(q)$ draws closer to \$2000 per gram*

Quantity, q	Total cost, $C(q) = 2{,}500{,}000 + 2000q$	Average cost, $a(q) = C(q)/q$
10,000	$2{,}500{,}000 + 20{,}000{,}000 = 22{,}500{,}000$	2250
50,000	$2{,}500{,}000 + 100{,}000{,}000 = 102{,}500{,}000$	2050
100,000	$2{,}500{,}000 + 200{,}000{,}000 = 202{,}500{,}000$	2025
500,000	$2{,}500{,}000 + 1{,}000{,}000{,}000 = 1{,}002{,}500{,}000$	2005

What is a Rational Function?

The formula for $a(q)$ is the ratio of the polynomial $2{,}500{,}000 + 2000q$ and the polynomial q. Since $a(q)$ is given by the ratio of two polynomials, $a(q)$ is an example of a *rational function*. In general:

> If r can be written as the ratio of polynomial functions $p(x)$ and $q(x)$, that is, if
>
> $$r(x) = \frac{p(x)}{q(x)},$$
>
> then r is called a **rational function**. (We assume that $q(x)$ is not the constant polynomial $q(x) = 0$.)

The Long-Run Behavior of Rational Functions

In the long run, every rational function behaves like a power function. For example, consider

$$f(x) = \frac{6x^4 + x^3 + 1}{-5x + 2x^2}.$$

Since the long-run behavior of a polynomial is determined by its highest-power term, for large x the numerator behaves like $6x^4$ and the denominator behaves like $2x^2$. The long-run behavior of f is

$$f(x) = \frac{6x^4 + x^3 + 1}{-5x + 2x^2} \approx \frac{6x^4}{2x^2} = 3x^2,$$

so

$$\lim_{x \to \pm\infty} f(x) = \lim_{x \to \pm\infty} (3x^2) = \infty.$$

See Figure 11.29.

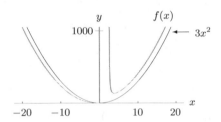

Figure 11.29: In the long run, the graph of $f(x)$ looks like the graph of $3x^2$

In general, if r is any rational function, then for large enough values of x,

$$r(x) = \frac{a_n x^n + a_{n-1} x^{n-1} + \cdots + a_0}{b_m x^m + b_{m-1} x^{m-1} + \cdots + b_0} \approx \frac{a_n x^n}{b_m x^m} = \frac{a_n}{b_m} x^{n-m}.$$

This means that on a large scale r resembles the function $y = \left(\dfrac{a_n}{b_m}\right) x^{n-m}$, which is a power function of the form $y = kx^p$, where $k = a_n/b_m$ and $p = n - m$. In summary:

For x of large enough magnitude (either positive or negative), the graph of the rational function r looks like the graph of a power function. If $r(x) = p(x)/q(x)$, then the **long-run behavior** of $y = r(x)$ is given by

$$y = \frac{\text{Leading term of } p}{\text{Leading term of } q}.$$

Using limits, we write

$$\lim_{x \to \pm\infty} \frac{p(x)}{q(x)} = \lim_{x \to \pm\infty} \frac{\text{Leading term of } p}{\text{Leading term of } q}.$$

Note that this limit, if it exists, gives the horizontal asymptote of $r(x)$.

Example 1   For positive x, describe the long-run behavior of the rational function

$$r(x) = \frac{x + 3}{x + 2}.$$

Solution   If x is a large positive number, then

$$r(x) = \frac{\text{Big number} + 3}{\text{Same big number} + 2} \approx \frac{\text{Big number}}{\text{Same big number}} = 1.$$

For example, if $x = 100$, we have

$$r(x) = \frac{103}{102} = 1.0098\ldots \approx 1.$$

If $x = 10,000$, we have

$$r(x) = \frac{10,003}{10,002} = 1.00009998\ldots \approx 1,$$

For large positive x-values, $r(x) \approx 1$. Thus, for large enough values of x, the graph of $y = r(x)$ looks like the line $y = 1$, its horizontal asymptote. We write $\lim_{x \to \infty} r(x) = 1$. See Figure 11.30. However, for $x > 0$, the graph of r is above the line since the numerator is larger than the denominator.

Figure 11.30: For large positive values of x, the graph of $r(x) = (x + 3)/(x + 2)$ looks like the horizontal line $y = 1$

Example 2   For positive x, describe the positive long-run behavior of the rational function

$$g(x) = \frac{3x + 1}{x^2 + x - 2}.$$

Solution   The leading term in the numerator is $3x$ and the leading term in the denominator is x^2. Thus for large enough values of x,

$$g(x) \approx \frac{3x}{x^2} = \frac{3}{x},$$

so

$$\lim_{x \to \infty} g(x) = \lim_{x \to \infty} \left(\frac{3}{x} \right) = 0.$$

Figure 11.31 shows the graphs of $y = g(x)$ and $y = 3/x$. For large values of x, the two graphs are nearly indistinguishable. Both graphs have a horizontal asymptote at $y = 0$.

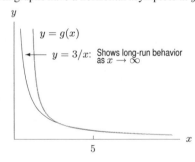

Figure 11.31: For large enough values of x, the function g looks like the function $y = 3x^{-1}$

What Causes Asymptotes?

The graphs of rational functions often behave differently from the graphs of polynomials. Polynomial graphs (except constant functions) cannot level off to a horizontal line as the graphs of rational functions can. In Example 1, the numerator and denominator are approximately equal for large x, producing the horizontal asymptote $y = 1$. In Example 2, the denominator grows faster than the numerator, driving the quotient toward zero.

The rapid rise (or fall) of the graph of a rational function near its vertical asymptote is due to the denominator becoming small (close to zero). It is tempting to assume that any function that has a denominator has a vertical asymptote. However, this is not true. To have a vertical asymptote, the denominator must equal zero. For example, suppose that

$$r(x) = \frac{1}{x^2 + 3}.$$

The denominator is always greater than 3; it is never 0. We see from Figure 11.32 that r does not have a vertical asymptote.

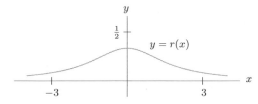

Figure 11.32: The rational function $r(x) = 1/(x^2 + 3)$ has no vertical asymptote

Exercises and Problems for Section 11.4

Skill Refresher

For Exercises S1–S4, perform the operations. Express answers in reduced form.

S1. $\dfrac{6}{y} + \dfrac{7}{y^3}$

S2. $\dfrac{13}{x-1} + \dfrac{14}{2x-2}$

S3. $\dfrac{\frac{1}{x} - \frac{2}{x^2}}{\frac{2x-4}{x^5}}$

S4. $\dfrac{9}{x^2 + 5x + 6} + \dfrac{12}{x+3}$

S5. $\dfrac{5}{(x-2)^2(x+1)} - \dfrac{18}{(x-2)}$

In Exercises S6–S9, simplify, if possible.

S6. $\dfrac{1/(x+y)}{x+y}$

S7. $\dfrac{(w+2)/2}{w+2}$

S8. $\dfrac{a^2 - b^2}{a^2 + b^2}$

S9. $\dfrac{x^{-1} + x^{-2}}{1 - x^{-2}}.$

Exercises

Are the functions in Exercises 1–7 rational functions? If so, write them in the form $p(x)/q(x)$, the ratio of polynomials.

1. $f(x) = \dfrac{x+2}{x^2 - 1}$

2. $f(x) = \dfrac{4^x + 3}{3^x - 1}$

3. $f(x) = \dfrac{x^2}{2} + \dfrac{1}{x}$

4. $f(x) = \dfrac{x^4 + 3^x - x^2}{x^3 - 2}$

5. $f(x) = \dfrac{\sqrt{x} + 1}{x + 1}$

6. $f(x) = \dfrac{x^3}{2x^2} + \dfrac{1}{6}$

7. $f(x) = \dfrac{9x - 1}{4\sqrt{x} + 7} + \dfrac{5x^3}{x^2 - 1}$

Evaluate the limits in Exercises 8–11.

8. $\lim\limits_{x \to \infty} \left(2x^{-3} + 4\right)$

9. $\lim\limits_{x \to \infty} \left(3x^{-2} + 5x + 7\right)$

10. $\lim\limits_{x \to \infty} \dfrac{4x + 3x^2}{4x^2 + 3x}$

11. $\lim\limits_{x \to -\infty} \dfrac{3x^2 + x}{2x^2 + 5x^3}$

Find the horizontal asymptote, if it exists, of the functions in Exercises 12–14.

12. $h(x) = 3 - \dfrac{1}{x} + \dfrac{x}{x+1}$

13. $f(x) = \dfrac{1}{1 + \dfrac{1}{x}}$

14. $g(x) = \dfrac{(1-x)(2+3x)}{2x^2 + 1}$

15. Compare and discuss the long-run behaviors of the following functions:

$$f(x) = \frac{x^2 + 1}{x^2 + 5}, \quad g(x) = \frac{x^3 + 1}{x^2 + 5}, \quad h(x) = \frac{x+1}{x^2 + 5}.$$

Problems

16. Find a formula for $f^{-1}(x)$ given that

$$f(x) = \frac{4 - 3x}{5x - 4}.$$

17. Give examples of rational functions with even symmetry, odd symmetry, and neither. How does the symmetry of $f(x) = p(x)/q(x)$ depend on the symmetry of $p(x)$ and $q(x)$?

18. Let $r(x) = p(x)/q(x)$, where p and q are polynomials of degrees m and n, respectively. What conditions on m and n ensure that the following statements are true?

    (a) $\displaystyle\lim_{x \to \infty} r(x) = 0$

    (b) $\displaystyle\lim_{x \to \infty} r(x) = k$, with $k \neq 0$.

19. Let t be the time in weeks. At time $t = 0$, organic waste is dumped into a pond. The oxygen level in the pond at time t is given by

$$f(t) = \frac{t^2 - t + 1}{t^2 + 1}.$$

Assume $f(0) = 1$ is the normal level of oxygen.

    (a) Graph this function.

    (b) Describe the shape of the graph. What is the significance of the minimum for the pond?

    (c) What eventually happens to the oxygen level?

    (d) Approximately how many weeks must pass before the oxygen level returns to 75% of its normal level?

20. A small printing house agrees to publish a book of poems illustrated by the author. The printing house plans to recover its investment of \$80,000 and make a profit of \$40,000. The price of the book will depend on the number of copies they expect to sell.

    (a) Fill in the table with the price per copy for each projected sales figure.

Number of copies sold	1000	2000	4000	6000
Price per copy				

    (b) Give a formula for the price per copy, p, as a function of projected sales, s.

    (c) Graph the function $p = f(s)$.

21. Bronze is an alloy, or mixture, of copper and tin. The alloy initially contains 3 kg copper and 9 kg tin. You add x kg of copper to this 12 kg of alloy. The concentration of copper in the alloy is a function of x:

$$f(x) = \text{Concentration of copper} = \frac{\text{Total amount of copper}}{\text{Total amount of alloy}}.$$

    (a) Find a formula for f in terms of x, the amount of copper added.

    (b) Evaluate the following expressions and explain their significance for the alloy:

        (i) $f(\frac{1}{2})$ **(ii)** $f(0)$ **(iii)** $f(-1)$

        (iv) $f^{-1}(\frac{1}{2})$ **(v)** $f^{-1}(0)$

    (c) Graph $f(x)$ for $-5 \leq x \leq 5$, $-0.25 \leq y \leq 0.5$. Interpret the intercepts in the context of the alloy.

    (d) Graph $f(x)$ for $-3 \leq x \leq 100$, $0 \leq y \leq 1$. Describe the appearance of your graph for large x-values. Does the appearance agree with what you expect to happen when large amounts of copper are added to the alloy?

22. A chemist is studying the properties of a bronze alloy (mixture) of copper and tin. She begins with 2 kg of an alloy that is one-half tin. Keeping the amount of copper constant, she adds small amounts of tin to the alloy. Letting x be the total amount of tin added, define

$$C(x) = \text{Concentration of tin} = \frac{\text{Total amount of tin}}{\text{Total amount of alloy}}.$$

    (a) Find a formula for $C(x)$.

    (b) Evaluate $C(0.5)$ and $C(-0.5)$. Explain the physical significance of these quantities.

    (c) Graph $y = C(x)$, labeling all interesting features. Describe the physical significance of the features you have labeled.

23. The population of Mathville has been increasing since 2010 when it was 12,000. If the population t years after 2010 is

$$P(t) = 20 \left(\frac{4t + 3}{2t + 5} \right) \text{ thousand,}$$

when will the population of Mathville reach 20,000? When will it reach 50,000?

24. A car is driven for 60 miles. The first 10 miles are through a large city at a speed of 40 mph; once out of the city a speed of V mph is maintained.

(a) Calculate the average speed for the 60-mile trip.

(b) If you want to average 60 mph for the trip, how fast need you go during the last 50 miles?

25. An alcohol solution consists of 5 gallons of pure water and x gallons of alcohol, $x > 0$. Let $f(x)$ be the ratio of the volume of alcohol to the total volume of liquid. [Note that $f(x)$ is the concentration of the alcohol in the solution.]

(a) Find a possible formula for $f(x)$.

(b) Evaluate and interpret $f(7)$ in the context of the mixture.

(c) What is the zero of f? Interpret your result in the context of the mixture.

(d) Find an equation for the horizontal asymptote of f. Explain its significance in the context of the mixture.

26. The total cost $C(n)$ for a producer to manufacture n units of a good is given by

$$C(n) = 5000 + 50n.$$

The average cost of producing n units is $a(n) = C(n)/n$.

(a) Evaluate and interpret the economic significance of:

   (i) $C(1)$ (ii) $C(100)$

   (iii) $C(1000)$ (iv) $C(10000)$

(b) Evaluate and interpret the economic significance of:

   (i) $a(1)$ (ii) $a(100)$

   (iii) $a(1000)$ (iv) $a(10000)$

(c) Based on part (b), what trend do you notice in the values of $a(n)$ as n gets large? Explain this trend in economic terms.

27. Figure 11.33 shows the cost function, $C(n)$, from Problem 26, and a line, l, that passes through the origin.

(a) What is the slope of line l?

(b) How does line l relate to $a(n_0)$, the average cost of producing n_0 units (as defined in Problem 26)?

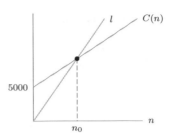

Figure 11.33

28. Typically, the average cost of production (as defined in Problem 26) decreases as the level of production increases. Is this always the case for the goods whose total cost function is graphed in Figure 11.34? Use the result of Problem 27 and explain your reasoning.

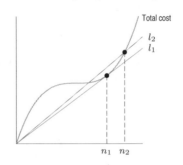

Figure 11.34

29. It costs a company $30,000 to begin production of a good, plus $3 for every unit of the good produced. Let x be the number of units produced by the company.

(a) Find a formula for $C(x)$, the total cost for the production of x units of the good.

(b) Find a formula for the company's average cost per unit, $a(x)$.

(c) Graph $y = a(x)$ for $0 < x \le 50{,}000$, $0 \le y \le 10$. Label the horizontal asymptote.

(d) Explain in economic terms why the graph of a has the long-run behavior that it does.

(e) Explain in economic terms why the graph of a has the vertical asymptote that it does.

(f) Find a formula for $a^{-1}(y)$. Give an economic interpretation of $a^{-1}(y)$.

(g) The company makes a profit if the average cost of its good is less than $5 per unit. Find the minimum number of units the company can produce and make a profit.

30. Find a rational function of the form

$$R(x) = \frac{1}{1 + cx}$$

whose values equal those of $f(x) = e^x$ at $x = 0$ and $x = 1$. Plot and compare your approximation on the interval $(0, 1)$ and comment on the result.

11.5 THE SHORT-RUN BEHAVIOR OF RATIONAL FUNCTIONS

The short-run behavior of a polynomial can often be determined from its factored form. The same is true of rational functions. If r is a rational function given by

$$r(x) = \frac{p(x)}{q(x)}, \qquad p, q \text{ polynomials,}$$

then the short-run behaviors of p and q tell us about the short-run behavior of r.

The Zeros and Vertical Asymptotes of a Rational Function

A fraction is equal to zero if and only if its numerator equals zero (and its denominator does not equal zero). Thus, the rational function $r(x) = p(x)/q(x)$ has a zero wherever p has a zero, provided q does not have a zero there.

Just as we can find the zeros of a rational function by looking at its numerator, we can find the vertical asymptotes by looking at its denominator. A rational function is large wherever its denominator is small. This means that r has a vertical asymptote wherever its denominator has a zero, provided its numerator does not also have a zero there.

Example 1 Find the zeros and vertical asymptotes of the rational function $r(x) = \dfrac{x+3}{x+2}$.

Solution We see that $r(x) = 0$ if

$$\frac{x+3}{x+2} = 0.$$

This ratio equals zero only if the numerator is zero (and the denominator is not zero), so

$$x + 3 = 0$$
$$x = -3.$$

The only zero of r is $x = -3$. To check, note that $r(-3) = 0/(-1) = 0$. The denominator has a zero at $x = -2$, so the graph of $r(x)$ has a vertical asymptote there. Note that as x approaches -2 from the left $r(x)$ tends toward $-\infty$ and as x approaches -2 from the right $r(x)$ tends toward ∞.

Example 2 Graph $r(x) = \dfrac{25}{(x+2)(x-3)^2}$, showing all the important features.

Solution Since the numerator of this function is never zero, r has no zeros, meaning that the graph of r never crosses the x-axis. The graph of r has vertical asymptotes at $x = -2$ and $x = 3$ because this is where the denominator is zero. What does the graph of r look like near its asymptote at $x = -2$?

At $x = -2$, the numerator is 25 and the value of the factor $(x - 3)^2$ is $(-2 - 3)^2 = 25$. Thus, near $x = -2$,

$$r(x) = \frac{25}{(x + 2)(x - 3)^2} \approx \frac{25}{(x + 2)(25)} = \frac{1}{x + 2}.$$

So, near $x = -2$, the graph of r looks like the graph of $y = 1/(x + 2)$. Note that the graph of $y = 1/(x + 2)$ is the graph of $y = 1/x$ shifted to the left by 2 units. We see that

$$\lim_{x \to -2^-} r(x) = -\infty \quad \text{and} \quad \lim_{x \to -2^+} r(x) = \infty.$$

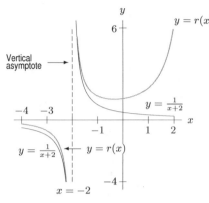

Figure 11.35: The rational function r resembles the shifted power function $1/(x + 2)$ near the asymptote at $x = -2$

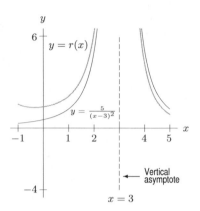

Figure 11.36: The rational function r resembles the shifted power function $5/(x - 3)^2$ near the asymptote at $x = 3$

What does the graph of r look like near its vertical asymptote at $x = 3$? Near $x = 3$, the numerator is 25 and value of the factor $(x + 2)$ is approximately $(3 + 2) = 5$. Thus, near $x = 3$,

$$r(x) \approx \frac{25}{(5)(x - 3)^2} = \frac{5}{(x - 3)^2}.$$

Near $x = 3$, the graph of r looks like the the graph of $y = 5/(x - 3)^2$. We see that

$$\lim_{x \to 3} r(x) = \infty.$$

The graph of $y = 5/(x - 3)^2$ is the graph of $y = 5/x^2$ shifted to the right 3 units. Since

$$r(0) = \frac{25}{(0 + 2)(0 - 3)^2} = \frac{25}{18} \approx 1.4,$$

the graph of r crosses the y-axis at $25/18$. The long-run behavior of r is given by the ratio of the leading term in the numerator to the leading term in the denominator. The numerator is 25, and if we multiply out the denominator, we see that its leading term is x^3. Thus, the long-run behavior of r is given by $y = 25/x^3$, which has a horizontal asymptote at $y = 0$. See Figure 11.37. We see that

$$\lim_{x \to \pm\infty} r(x) = 0.$$

336

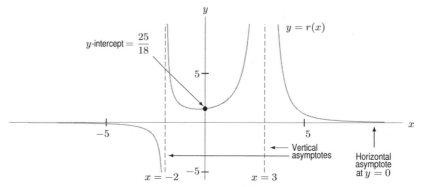

Figure 11.37: A graph of the rational function $r(x) = \dfrac{25}{(x+2)(x-3)^2}$, showing intercepts and asymptotes

The Graph of a Rational Function

We can now summarize what we have learned about the graphs of rational functions.

If r is a rational function given by $r(x) = \dfrac{p(x)}{q(x)}$, where p and q are polynomials with different zeros, then:

- The **long-run behavior** and **horizontal asymptote** (if any) of r are given by the ratio of the leading terms of p and q.

- The **zeros** of r are the same as the zeros of the numerator, p.

- The graph of r has a **vertical asymptote** at each of the zeros of the denominator, q.

If p and q have zeros at the same x-values, the rational function may behave differently. See the discussion about holes in graphs on page 465.

Can a Graph Cross an Asymptote?

The graph of a rational function never crosses a vertical asymptote. However, the graphs of some rational functions cross their horizontal asymptotes. The difference is that a vertical asymptote occurs where the function is undefined, so there can be no y-value there, whereas a horizontal asymptote represents the limiting value of the function as $x \to \pm\infty$. There is no reason that the function cannot take on this limiting y-value for some finite x-value. For example, the graph of $r(x) = \dfrac{x^2 + 2x - 3}{x^2}$ crosses the line $y = 1$, its horizontal asymptote; the graph does not cross the vertical asymptote, the y-axis. See Figure 11.38.

Figure 11.38: A rational function can cross its horizontal asymptote

Rational Functions as Transformations of Power Functions

The average cost function on page 455 can be written as

$$a(q) = \frac{2{,}500{,}000 + 2000q}{q} = 2{,}500{,}000q^{-1} + 2000.$$

Thus, the graph of a is the graph of the power function $y = 2{,}500{,}000q^{-1}$ shifted up 2000 units. Many rational functions can be viewed as translations of power functions.

Finding a Formula for a Rational Function from its Graph

The graph of a rational function can give a good idea of its formula. Zeros of the function correspond to factors in the numerator and vertical asymptotes correspond to factors in the denominator.

Example 3   Find a possible formula for the rational function, $g(x)$, graphed in Figure 11.39.

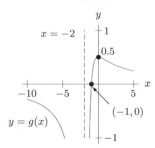

Figure 11.39: The graph of $y = g(x)$, a rational function

Solution   From the graph, we see that g has a zero at $x = -1$ and a vertical asymptote at $x = -2$. This means that the numerator of g has a zero at $x = -1$ and the denominator of g has a zero at $x = -2$. The zero of g does not seem to be a multiple zero because the graph crosses the x-axis instead of bouncing and does not have a flattened appearance. Thus, we conclude that the numerator of g has one factor of $(x + 1)$.

The values of $g(x)$ have the same sign on both sides of the vertical asymptote. Thus, the behavior of g near its vertical asymptote is more like the behavior of $y = 1/(x + 2)^2$ than like $y = 1/(x + 2)$. We conclude that the denominator of g has a factor of $(x + 2)^2$. This suggests

$$g(x) = k \cdot \frac{x + 1}{(x + 2)^2},$$

where k is a stretch factor. To find the value of k, use the fact that $g(0) = 0.5$. So

$$0.5 = k \cdot \frac{0 + 1}{(0 + 2)^2}$$

$$0.5 = k \cdot \frac{1}{4}$$

$$k = 2.$$

Thus, a possible formula for g is $g(x) = \dfrac{2(x + 1)}{(x + 2)^2}$.

When Numerator and Denominator Have the Same Zeros: Holes

The rational function $h(x) = \dfrac{x^2 + x - 2}{x - 1}$ is undefined at $x = 1$ because the denominator equals zero at $x = 1$. However, the graph of h does not have a vertical asymptote at $x = 1$ because the numerator of h also equals zero at $x = 1$. At $x = 1$,

$$h(1) = \frac{x^2 + x - 2}{x - 1} = \frac{1^2 + 1 - 2}{1 - 1} = \frac{0}{0},$$

and this ratio is undefined. What does the graph of h look like? Factoring the numerator of h gives

$$h(x) = \frac{(x - 1)(x + 2)}{x - 1} = \frac{x - 1}{x - 1}(x + 2).$$

For any $x \neq 1$, we can cancel $(x - 1)$ top and bottom and rewrite the formula for h as

$$h(x) = x + 2, \qquad \text{provided } x \neq 1.$$

Thus, the graph of h is the line $y = x + 2$ except at $x = 1$, where h is undefined. The line $y = x + 2$ contains the point $(1, 3)$, but the graph of h does not. Therefore, we say that the graph of h has a *hole* in it at the point $(1, 3)$. See Figure 11.40.

Figure 11.40: The graph of $y = h(x)$ is the line $y = x + 2$, except at the point $(1, 3)$, where it has a hole

Exercises and Problems for Section 11.5

Exercises

For the rational functions in Exercises 1–4, find all zeros and vertical asymptotes and describe the long-run behavior, then graph the function.

1. $y = \dfrac{x - 4}{x^2 - 9}$

2. $y = \dfrac{x^2 - 4}{x - 9}$

3. $y = \dfrac{x + 3}{x + 5}$

4. $y = \dfrac{x + 3}{(x + 5)^2}$

In Exercises 5–8, what are the x-intercepts, y-intercepts, and horizontal and vertical asymptotes (if any)?

5. $h(x) = \dfrac{x^2 - 4}{x^3 + 4x^2}$

6. $k(x) = \dfrac{x(4 - x)}{x^2 - 6x + 5}$

7. $f(x) = \dfrac{x - 2}{x - 4}$

8. $g(x) = \dfrac{x^2 - 9}{x^2 + 9}$

9. Let $G(x) = \dfrac{2x}{x+4}$.

   (a) Complete Table 11.10 for x-values close to -4. What happens to the values of $G(x)$ as x approaches -4 from the left? From the right?

Table 11.10

x	-5	-4.1	-4.01	-4	-3.99	-3.9	-3
$G(x)$							

   (b) Complete Tables 11.11 and 11.12. What happens to the values of $G(x)$ as x takes very large positive values? As x takes very large negative values?

Table 11.11

x	5	10	100	1000
$G(x)$				

Table 11.12

x	-5	-10	-100	-1000
$G(x)$				

   (c) Without a calculator, graph $y = G(x)$. Give equations for the horizontal and vertical asymptotes.

10. Let $g(x) = \dfrac{1}{(x+2)^2}$.

   (a) Complete Table 11.13 for x-values close to -2. What happens to the values of $g(x)$ as x approaches -2 from the left? From the right?

Table 11.13

x	-3	-2.1	-2.01	-2	-1.99	-1.9	-1
$g(x)$							

   (b) Complete Tables 11.14 and 11.15. What happens to the values of $g(x)$ as x takes very large positive values? As x takes very large negative values?

Table 11.14

x	5	10	100	1000
$g(x)$				

Table 11.15

x	-5	-10	-100	-1000
$g(x)$				

   (c) Without a calculator, graph $y = g(x)$. Give equations for the horizontal and vertical asymptotes.

Problems

Graph the functions in Problems 11–12 without a calculator.

11. $y = 2 + \dfrac{1}{x}$

12. $y = \dfrac{2x^2 - 10x + 12}{x^2 - 16}$

In Problems 13–14, estimate the one-sided limits:

(a) $\displaystyle\lim_{x \to a^+} f(x)$ **(b)** $\displaystyle\lim_{x \to a^-} f(x)$

13. $f(x) = \dfrac{x}{5-x}$ with $a = 5$

14. $f(x) = \dfrac{5-x}{(x-2)^2}$ with $a = 2$

15. Without a calculator, match the functions (a)–(f) with their graphs in (i)–(vi) by finding the zeros, asymptotes, and end behavior for each function.

   (a) $y = \dfrac{-1}{(x-5)^2} - 1$ **(b)** $y = \dfrac{x-2}{(x+1)(x-3)}$

   (c) $y = \dfrac{2x+4}{x-1}$ **(d)** $y = \dfrac{1}{x+1} + \dfrac{1}{x-3}$

   (e) $y = \dfrac{1-x^2}{x-2}$ **(f)** $y = \dfrac{1-4x}{2x+2}$

(i)

(ii)

(iii)

(iv)

(v)

(vi)

16. Let $f(x) = x^2 - 4$, $g(x) = x^2 + 4$, and $h(x) = x + 5$. Without a calculator, match the functions in (a)–(f) to the descriptions in (i)–(viii). Some of the functions may match none of the descriptions.

(a) $y = \dfrac{f(x)}{g(x)}$ (b) $y = \dfrac{g(x)}{f(x)}$ (c) $y = \dfrac{h(x)}{f(x)}$

(d) $y = f(\dfrac{1}{x})$ (e) $y = \dfrac{g(x)}{h(x)}$ (f) $y = \dfrac{h(x^2)}{h(x)}$

(g) $y = \dfrac{1}{g(x)}$ (h) $y = f(x)\cdot g(x)$

(i) Horizontal asymptote at $y = 0$ and one zero at $x = -5$.

(ii) No horizontal asymptote, no zeros, and a vertical asymptote at $x = -5$.

(iii) Zeros at $x = -5$, $x = -2$, and $x = 2$.

(iv) No zeros, a horizontal asymptote at $y = 0$, and a vertical asymptote at $x = -5$.

(v) Two zeros, no vertical asymptotes, and a horizontal asymptote at $y = 1$.

(vi) No zeros, no vertical asymptotes, and a horizontal asymptote at $y = 1$.

(vii) Horizontal asymptote at $y = -4$.

(viii) No horizontal asymptotes, two zeros, and a vertical asymptote at $x = -5$.

In Problems 17–18,

(a) Estimate $\lim\limits_{x\to\infty} f(x)$ and $\lim\limits_{x\to-\infty} f(x)$.

(b) What does the vertical asymptote tell you about limits?

17.

18.

19. Suppose that n is a constant and that $f(x)$ is a function defined when $x = n$. Complete the following sentences.

(a) If $f(n)$ is large, then $\dfrac{1}{f(n)}$ is ...

(b) If $f(n)$ is small, then $\dfrac{1}{f(n)}$ is ...

(c) If $f(n) = 0$, then $\dfrac{1}{f(n)}$ is ...

(d) If $f(n)$ is positive, then $\dfrac{1}{f(n)}$ is ...

(e) If $f(n)$ is negative, then $\dfrac{1}{f(n)}$ is ...

20. (a) Use the results of Problem 19 to graph $y = 1/f(x)$ given the graph of $y = f(x)$ in Figure 11.41.

(b) Find a possible formula for the function in Figure 11.41. Use this formula to check your graph for part (a).

Figure 11.41

21. Use the graph of f in Figure 11.42 to graph

(a) $y = -f(-x) + 2$ (b) $y = \dfrac{1}{f(x)}$

Figure 11.42

Problems 22–24 show a transformation of $y = 1/x$.

(a) Find a possible formula for the graph.

(b) Write the formula from part (a) as the ratio of two linear polynomials.

(c) Find the coordinates of the intercepts of the graph.

22.

23.

24.

Each of the functions in Problems 25–27 is a transformation of $y = 1/x^p$. For each function, determine p, describe the transformation in words, and graph the function, labeling any intercepts and asymptotes.

25. $f(x) = \dfrac{1}{x - 3} + 4$

26. $g(x) = -\dfrac{1}{(x - 2)^2} - 3$

27. $h(x) = \dfrac{1}{x - 1} + \dfrac{2}{1 - x} + 2$

Problems 28–31 give values of transformations of either $y = 1/x$ or $y = 1/x^2$. In each case

(a) Determine if the values are from a transformation of $y = 1/x$ or $y = 1/x^2$. Explain your reasoning.

(b) Find a possible formula for the function.

28.

x	y
-1000	1.000001
-100	1.00001
-10	1.01
10	1.01
100	1.0001
1000	1.000001

29.

x	y
1.5	-1.5
1.9	-9.5
1.95	-19.5
2	Undefined
2.05	20.5
2.1	10.5
2.5	2.5

30.

x	y
2.7	12.1
2.9	101
2.95	401
3	Undefined
3.05	401
3.1	101
3.3	12.1

31.

x	y
-1000	0.499
-100	0.490
-10	0.400
10	0.600
100	0.510
1000	0.501

32. Cut four equal squares from the corners of a $8.5'' \times 11''$ piece of paper. Fold up the sides to create an open box. Find the dimensions of the box with the maximum volume per surface area.

Find possible formulas for the functions in Problems 33–38.

33.

34.

35.

36.

37.

38.

39. The graph of $f(x) = \dfrac{18 - 11x + x^2}{x - 2}$ is a line with a hole in it. What is the equation of the line? What are the coordinates of the hole?

40. The graph of $g(x) = \dfrac{x^3 + 5x^2 + x + 5}{x + 5}$ is a parabola with a hole in it. What is the equation of the parabola? What are the coordinates of the hole?

41. Write a formula for a function, $h(x)$, whose graph is identical to the graph of $y = x^3$, except that the graph of h has a hole at $(2, 8)$. Express the formula as a ratio of two polynomials

In Problems 42–44, find a possible formula for the rational functions.

42. This function has zeros at $x = 2$ and $x = 3$. It has a vertical asymptote at $x = 5$. It has a horizontal asymptote of $y = -3$.

43. The graph of $y = g(x)$ has two vertical asymptotes: one at $x = -2$ and one at $x = 3$. It has a horizontal asymptote of $y = 0$. The graph of g crosses the x-axis once, at $x = 5$.

44. The graph of $y = h(x)$ has two vertical asymptotes: one at $x = -2$ and one at $x = 3$. It has a horizontal asymptote of $y = 1$. The graph of h touches the x-axis once, at $x = 5$.

11.6 COMPARING POWER, EXPONENTIAL, AND LOG FUNCTIONS

In preceding chapters, we encountered exponential and logarithmic functions. In this section, we compare the long- and short-run behaviors of these functions and power functions.

Comparing Power Functions

For power functions $y = kx^p$ for large x, the higher the power of x, the faster the function climbs. See Figure 11.43. Not only are the higher powers larger, but they are *much* larger. This is because if $x = 100$, for example, 100^5 is one hundred times as big as 100^4, which is one hundred times as big as 100^3. As x gets larger (written as $x \to \infty$), any positive power of x grows much faster than all lower powers of x. We say that, as $x \to \infty$, higher powers of x *dominate* lower powers.

As x approaches zero (written $x \to 0$), the situation is reversed. Figure 11.44 is a close-up view near the origin. For x between 0 and 1, x^3 is bigger than x^4, which is bigger than x^5. (Try $x = 0.1$ to confirm this.) For values of x near zero, smaller powers dominate.

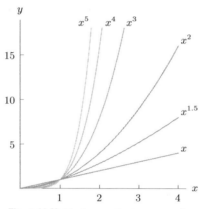

Figure 11.43: For large x: Large powers of x dominate

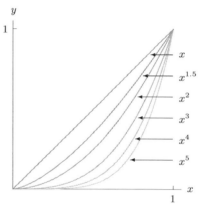

Figure 11.44: For $0 \leq x \leq 1$: Small powers of x dominate

In Chapter 6 we saw the effect of k on the graph of $f(x) = kx^p$. The coefficient k stretches or compresses the graph vertically; if k is negative, the graph is reflected across the x-axis. How does the value of k affect the long-term growth rate of $f(x) = kx^p$? Is the growth of a power function affected more by the size of the coefficient or by the size of the power?

Example 1   Let $f(x) = 100x^3$ and $g(x) = x^4$ for $x > 0$. Compare the long-term behavior of these two functions using graphs.

Solution   For $x < 10$, Figure 11.45 suggests that f is growing faster than g and that f dominates g. Eventually, however, the fact that g has a higher power than f asserts itself. In Figure 11.46, we see that $g(x)$ has caught up to $f(x)$ at $x = 100$. In Figure 11.47, we see that for $x > 100$, values of g are larger than values of f.

Could the graphs of f and g intersect again for some value of $x > 100$? To show that this cannot be the case, solve the equation $g(x) = f(x)$:

$$x^4 = 100x^3$$
$$x^4 - 100x^3 = 0$$
$$x^3(x - 100) = 0.$$

Since the only solutions to this equation are $x = 0$ and $x = 100$, the graphs of f and g do not cross for $x > 100$.

Figure 11.45: On this interval, f climbs faster than g

Figure 11.46: On this interval, g catches up to f

Figure 11.47: On this interval, g ends up far ahead of f

When comparing power functions with positive coefficients, higher powers dominate.

Comparing Exponential Functions and Power Functions

Both power functions and exponential functions can increase at phenomenal rates. For example, Table 11.16 shows values of $f(x) = x^4$ and $g(x) = 2^x$.

Table 11.16   *The exponential function $g(x) = 2^x$ eventually grows faster than the power function $f(x) = x^4$*

x	0	5	10	15	20
$f(x) = x^4$	0	625	10,000	50,625	160,000
$g(x) = 2^x$	1	32	1024	32,768	1,048,576

Despite the impressive growth in the value of the power function $f(x) = x^4$, in the long run $g(x) = 2^x$ grows faster. By the time $x = 20$, the value of $g(20) = 2^{20}$ is over six times as large as $f(20) = 20^4$. Figure 11.48 shows the exponential function $g(x) = 2^x$ catching up to $f(x) = x^4$.

But what about a more slowly growing exponential function? After all, $y = 2^x$ increases at a 100% growth rate. Figure 11.49 compares $y = x^4$ to the exponential function $y = 1.005^x$. Despite the fact that this exponential function creeps along at a 0.5% growth rate, at around $x = 7000$, it overtakes the power function. In summary,

---

Any positive increasing exponential function eventually grows faster than *any* power function.

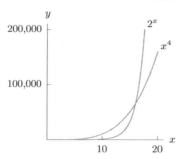

Figure 11.48: The exponential function $y = 2^x$ dominates the power function $y = x^4$

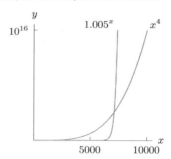

Figure 11.49: The exponential function $y = 1.005^x$ dominates the power function $y = x^4$

Decreasing Exponential Functions and Decreasing Power Functions

Just as an increasing exponential function eventually outpaces any increasing power function, an exponential decay function wins the race toward the x-axis. In general:

> *Any* positive decreasing exponential function eventually approaches the horizontal axis faster than any positive decreasing power function.

For example, let's compare the long-term behavior of the decreasing exponential function $y = 0.5^x$ with the decreasing power function $y = x^{-2}$. By rewriting

$$y = 0.5^x = \left(\frac{1}{2}\right)^x = \frac{1}{2^x} \quad \text{and} \quad y = x^{-2} = \frac{1}{x^2}$$

we can see the comparison more easily. In the long run, the smallest of these two fractions is the one with the largest denominator. The fact that 2^x is eventually larger than x^2 means that $1/2^x$ is eventually smaller than $1/x^2$.

Figure 11.50 shows $y = 0.5^x$ and $y = x^{-2}$. Both graphs have the x-axis as a horizontal asymptote. As x increases, the exponential function $y = 0.5^x$ approaches the x-axis faster than the power function $y = x^{-2}$. Figure 11.51 shows what happens for large values of x. The exponential function approaches the x-axis so rapidly that it becomes invisible compared to $y = x^{-2}$.

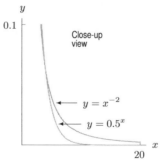

Figure 11.50: Graphs of $y = x^{-2}$ and $y = 0.5^x$

Figure 11.51: Graphs of $y = x^{-2}$ and $y = 0.5^x$

Comparing Log and Power Functions

Power functions like $y = x^{1/2}$ and $y = x^{1/3}$ grow quite slowly. However, they grow rapidly in comparison to log functions. In fact:

Any positive increasing power function eventually grows more rapidly than $y = \log x$ and $y = \ln x$.

For example, Figure 11.52 shows the graphs of $y = x^{1/2}$ and $y = \log x$. The fact that exponential functions grow so fast should alert you to the fact that their inverses, the logarithms, grow very slowly. See Figure 11.53.

Figure 11.52: Graphs of $y = x^{1/2}$ and $y = \log x$

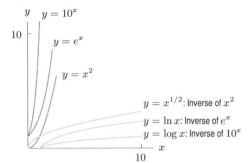

Figure 11.53: Graphs of $y = 10^x$, $y = e^x$, $y = x^2$, $y = x^{1/2}$, $y = \ln x$, and $y = \log x$

Exercises and Problems for Section 11.6

Exercises

Can the formulas in Exercises 1–6 be written in the form of an exponential function or a power function? If not, explain why the function does not fit either form.

1. $p(x) = (5^x)^2$

2. $q(x) = 5^{(x^2)}$

3. $m(x) = 3(3x + 1)^2$

4. $n(x) = 3 \cdot 2^{3x+1}$

5. $r(x) = 2 \cdot 3^{-2x}$

6. $s(x) = \dfrac{4}{5x^{-3}}$

7. Without a calculator, match the following functions with the graphs in Figure 11.54.

(i) $y = x^5$ (ii) $y = x^2$ (iii) $y = x$ (iv) $y = x^3$

Figure 11.54

8. Without a calculator, match the following functions with the graphs in Figure 11.55.

(i) $y = x^5$ (ii) $y = x^2$ (iii) $y = x$ (iv) $y = x^3$

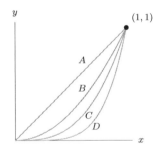

Figure 11.55

9. Let $f(x) = 3^x$ and $g(x) = x^3$.

(a) Complete the following table of values:

x	-3	-2	-1	0	1	2	3
$f(x)$							
$g(x)$							

(b) Describe the long-run behaviors of f and g as $x \to -\infty$ and as $x \to +\infty$.

Problems

14. The functions $y = x^{-3}$ and $y = 3^{-x}$ both approach zero as $x \to \infty$. Which function approaches zero faster? Support your conclusion numerically.

15. The functions $y = x^{-3}$ and $y = e^{-x}$ both approach zero as $x \to \infty$. Which function approaches zero faster? Support your conclusion numerically.

16. Let $f(x) = x^x$. Is f a power function, an exponential function, both, or neither? Discuss.

In Problems 17–19, find a possible formula for f if f is

(a) Linear   **(b)** Exponential   **(c)** Power function.

17. $f(1) = 18$ and $f(3) = 1458$

18. $f(1) = 16$ and $f(2) = 128$

19. $f(-1) = \frac{3}{4}$ and $f(2) = 48$

20. Data from four functions are in Tables 11.17–11.20. One function is linear, one is logarithmic, and the other two are power functions (one cubic and one quadratic). Find a formula for each function, and explain how you made your choices.

Table 11.17

x	$j(x)$
1.8	1.75
2.2	3.19
2.6	5.27
3.0	8.10
3.4	11.79

Table 11.18

x	$k(x)$
2.8	0.36
3.0	0.60
3.2	0.84
3.4	1.08
3.6	1.32

Table 11.19

x	$m(x)$
0.2	-0.699
0.6	-0.222
1.0	0.00
1.4	0.146
1.8	0.255

Table 11.20

x	$z(x)$
-4.0	6.4
-2	1.6
0	0
2	1.6
4	6.4

21. Match the graphs in Figure 11.56 with the functions $y = kx^{9/16}$, $y = kx^{3/8}$, $y = kx^{5/7}$, $y = kx^{3/11}$.

In Exercises 10–13, which function dominates as $x \to \infty$?

10. $y = ax^3$, $y = bx^2$, $a, b > 0$

11. $y = 7(0.99)^x$, $y = 6x^{35}$

12. $y = 4e^x$, $y = 2x^{50}$

13. $y = 50x^{1.1}$, $y = 1000x^{1.08}$

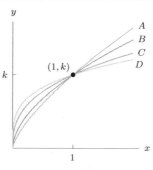

Figure 11.56

22. (a) Match the functions $f(x) = x^2$, $g(x) = 2x^2$, and $h(x) = x^3$ to their graphs in Figure 11.57.

(b) Do graphs A and B intersect for $x > 0$? If so, for what value(s) of x? If not, explain how you know.

(c) Do graphs C and A intersect for $x > 0$? If so, for what value(s) of x? If not, explain how you know.

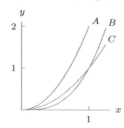

Figure 11.57

23. In Figure 11.58, find the values of m, t, and k.

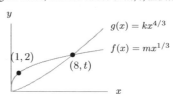

Figure 11.58

24. **(a)** Given $t(x) = x^{-2}$ and $r(x) = 40x^{-3}$, find v such that $t(v) = r(v)$.

   (b) For $0 < x < v$, which is greater, $t(x)$ or $r(x)$?

   (c) For $x > v$, which is greater, $t(x)$ or $r(x)$?

What is the long-run behavior of the functions in Problems 25–36?

25. $y = \dfrac{x^2 + 5}{x^8}$

26. $y = \dfrac{5 - t^2}{(7 + t + \sqrt{t})t^5}$

27. $y = \dfrac{2^t + 7}{5^t + 9}$

28. $y = \dfrac{3^{-t}}{4^t + 7}$

29. $y = \dfrac{x(x + 5)(x - 7)}{4 + x^2}$

30. $y = \dfrac{2^x + 3}{x^2 + 5}$

31. $y = \dfrac{\ln x}{\sqrt{x} + 5}$

32. $y = \dfrac{e^t + t^2}{\ln |t|}$

33. $y = \dfrac{e^x - e^{-x}}{2}$

34. $y = \dfrac{e^x - e^{-x}}{e^x + e^{-x}}$

35. $y = \dfrac{e^x + 5}{x^{100} + 50}$

36. $y = \dfrac{e^{2t}}{e^{3t} + 5}$

37. Table 11.21 gives approximate values for three functions, f, g, and h. One is exponential, one is trigonometric, and one is a power function. Determine which is which and find possible formulas for each.

Table 11.21

x	-2	-1	0	1	2
$f(x)$	4	2	4	6	4
$g(x)$	20.0	2.5	0.0	-2.5	-20.0
$h(x)$	1.33	0.67	0.33	0.17	0.08

38. A woman opens a bank account with an initial deposit of $1000. At the end of each year thereafter, she deposits an additional $1000.

   (a) The account earns 6% annual interest, compounded annually. Complete Table 11.22.

   (b) Does the balance of this account grow linearly, exponentially, or neither? Justify your answer.

Table 11.22

Years elapsed	Start-of-year balance	End-of-year deposit	End-of-year interest
0	$1000.00	$1000	$60.00
1	$2060.00	$1000	$123.60
2	$3183.60	$1000	
3		$1000	
4		$1000	
5		$1000	

39. The annual percentage rate (APR) paid by the account in Problem 38 is r, where r does not necessarily equal 6%. Define $p_n(r)$ as the balance of the account after n years have elapsed. (For example, $p_2(0.06) = \$3183.60$, because, according to Table 11.22, the balance after 2 years is $3183.60 if the APR is 6%.)

   (a) Find formulas for $p_5(r)$ and $p_{10}(r)$.

   (b) What is APR if the woman in Problem 38 has $10,000 in 5 years?

40. Values of f and g are in Table 11.23 and 11.24. One function is of the form $y = a \cdot d^{p/q}$ with $p > q$; the other is of the form $y = b \cdot d^{p/q}$ with $p < q$. Which is which? How can you tell?

Table 11.23

d	2	2.2	2.4	2.6	2.8
$f(d)$	151.6	160.5	169.1	177.4	185.5

Table 11.24

d	10	10.2	10.4	10.6	10.8
$g(d)$	7.924	8.115	8.306	8.498	8.691

11.7 FITTING EXPONENTIALS AND POLYNOMIALS TO DATA

In Section 1.6 we used linear regression to find the equation for a line of best fit for a set of data. In this section, we fit an exponential or a power function to a set of data.

The Spread of AIDS

The data in Table 11.25 give the total number of deaths in the US from AIDS from 1981 to 1996. Figure 11.59 suggests that a linear function may not give the best possible fit for these data.

Table 11.25   *US deaths from AIDS,*
1981–96

t	N	t	N
1	159	9	90039
2	622	10	121577
3	2130	11	158193
4	5635	12	199287
5	12607	13	243923
6	24717	14	292586
7	41129	15	340957
8	62248	16	375904

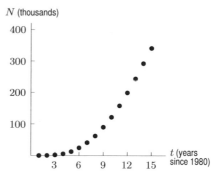

Figure 11.59: US deaths from AIDS, 1981–96

Fitting an Exponential

We first fit an exponential function to the data[13] in Table 11.25

$$N = ae^{kt},$$

where N is the total number of deaths t years after 1980.

Using exponential regression on a calculator or computer, we obtain[14]

$$N \approx 630e^{0.47t}.$$

Figure 11.60 shows how the graph of this formula fits the data points.

Fitting a Power Function

Now we fit the AIDS data with a power function of the form

$$N = at^p,$$

where a and p are constants. Some scientists have suggested that a power function may be a better model for the growth of AIDS than an exponential function.[15] Using power function regression on a calculator or a computer, we obtain

$$N \approx 107t^{3.005}.$$

Figure 11.60 shows the graph of this power function with the data.

Which Function Best Fits the Data?

Both the exponential function

$$N = 630e^{0.47t}$$

and the power function

$$N = 107t^{3.005}$$

---

[13]*HIV/AIDS Surveillance Report*, Year-end Edition, Vol. 9, No. 2, Table 13, US Department of Health and Human Services, Centers for Disease Control and Prevention, Atlanta. 2000–2004 data from *HIV/AIDS Surveillance Report*, Vol. 16, at www.cdc.gov/hiv/stats/hastlink.htm, accessed January 15, 2006. Data does not include 450 people whose dates of death are unknown.

[14]Calculator and computer answers for exponential regression may vary slightly due to different algorithms used.

[15]Stirling A. Colgate, E. Ann Stanley, James M. Hyman, Scott P. Layne, and Alifford Qualls, "Risk behavior-based model of the cubic growth of acquired immunodeficiency syndrome in the United States," *Proc. Natl. Acad. Sci. USA*, Vol. 86, June 1989, Population Biology.

fit the AIDS data reasonably well. By visual inspection alone, the power function arguably provides the better fit. If we fit a linear function to the original data we get

$$N = -97311 + 25946t.$$

Even this linear function gives a possible fit for $t \geq 4$, that is, for 1984 to 1996. (See Figure 11.60.)

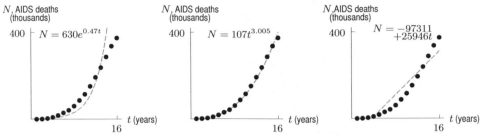

Figure 11.60: The AIDS data since 1981 together with an exponential model, a power-function model, and a linear model

Despite the fact that all three functions fit the data reasonably well up to 1996, it's important to realize that they give wildly different predictions for the future. If we use each model to estimate the total number of AIDS deaths by the year 2010 (when $t = 30$), the exponential model gives

$$N = 630e^{(0.47)30} \approx 837{,}322{,}467, \quad \text{about triple the current US population;}$$

the power model gives

$$N = 107(30)^{3.005} \approx 2{,}938{,}550, \quad \text{or about 1\% of the current population;}$$

and the linear model gives

$$N = -97311 + 25946 \cdot 30 = 681{,}069, \quad \text{or about 0.22\% of the current population.}$$

Which function is the best predictor of the future? To explore this question, let us add some more recent data to our previous data on AIDS deaths. See Table 11.26.

Table 11.26 *US deaths from AIDS, 1997–2007*

t	N
17	406,444
18	424,841
19	442,013
20	457,258
21	462,653
22	501,669
23	524,060
24	529,113
25	553,173
26	568,737
27	583,298

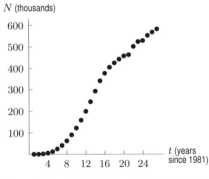

Figure 11.61: US deaths from AIDS, 1981–2007

When data from the entire period from 1981 to 2007 are plotted together (see Figure 11.61), we see that the rate of increase of AIDS deaths reaches a peak sometime around 1995 and then begins to taper off. Since none of the three types of functions we have used to model AIDS deaths exhibit this type of behavior, some other type of function is needed to describe the number of AIDS deaths accurately over the entire 26-year period.

This example illustrates that while a certain type of function may fit a set of data over a short period of time, care must be taken when using a mathematical model to make predictions about the future. An understanding of the processes leading to the data is crucial in answering any long-term question.

Exercises and Problems for Section 11.7

Exercises

1. Find a formula for the power function $f(x)$ such that $f(1) = 1$ and $f(2) = c$.

2. Find a formula for an exponential function $h(x)$.

x	2	3	4	5
$h(x)$	4.5948	7.4744	10.5561	13.7973

3. Find a formula for the power function $g(x)$.

x	2	3	4	5
$g(x)$	4.5948	7.4744	10.5561	13.7973

4. Table 11.27 shows the Maine lobster catch[16] (in millions of pounds) from 1970 to 2000.

   (a) With t in years since 1965, use a calculator or computer to fit the data with

     (i) A power function of the form $y = at^b$.

     (ii) A quadratic function of the form $y = at^2 + bt + c$.

   (b) Discuss which function is a better fit.

Table 11.27

Year	1970	1975	1980	1985	1990	1995	2000
t	5	10	15	20	25	30	35
Lobster	17	19	22	20	27	36	56

5. Students in the School of Forestry & Environmental Studies at Yale University collected data measuring sassafras trees. Table 11.28 lists the diameter at breast height (dbh, in cm) and the total dry weight (w, in gm) of different trees.[17]

   (a) Find a power function that fits the data.

   (b) Predict the total weight of a tree with a dbh of 20 cm.

(c) If a tree has a total dry weight of 100,000 gm, what is its expected dbh?

Table 11.28

dbh	5	23.4	11.8	16.7	4.2	5.6
w	5,353	169,290	30,696	76,730	3,436	5,636
dbh	3.8	4.3	6.5	21.9	17.7	25.5
w	14,983	2,098	7,364	177,596	100,848	171,598

6. Anthropologists suggest that the relationship between the body weight and brain weight of primates can be modeled with a power function. Table 11.29 lists various body weights and the corresponding brain weights of different primates.[18]

   (a) Using Table 11.29, find a power function that gives the brain weight, Q (in mg), as a function of the body weight, b (in gm).

   (b) The erythrocebus (Patas monkey) has a body weight of 7800 gm. Estimate its brain weight.

Table 11.29

b	6667	960	6800	9500	1088
Q	56,567	18,200	110,525	120,100	20,700
b	2733	3000	6300	1500	665
Q	78,250	58,200	96,400	31,700	25,050

In Exercises 7–12, find an equation for y in terms of x.

7.

8.

---

[16] Adapted from *The New York Times*, p. 16, May 31, 2001.

[17] www.yale.edu/fes519b/totoket/allom/allom.htm, accessed December 15, 2002.

[18] mac-huwis.lut.ac.uk/~wis/lectures/primate-adaptation/10PrimateBrains.pdf, accessed December 15, 2002.

9.

10.

11.

12.

Problems

13. **(a)** Find a linear function that fits the data in Table 11.30. How good is the fit?

(b) The data in the table was generated using the power function $y = 5x^3$. Explain why (in this case) a linear function gives such a good fit to a power function. Does the fit remain good for other values of x?

Table 11.30

x	2.00	2.01	2.02	2.03	2.04	2.05
y	40.000	40.603	41.212	41.827	42.448	43.076

14. An analog radio dial can be measured in millimeters from left to right. Although the scale of the dial can be different from radio to radio, Table 11.31 gives typical measurements.

(a) Which radio band data appear linear? Graph and connect the data points for each band.

(b) Which radio band data appear exponential?

(c) Find a possible formula for the FM station number in terms of x.

(d) Find a possible formula for the AM station number in terms of x.

Table 11.31

x, millimeters	5	15	25	35	45	55
FM (mhz)	88	92	96	100	104	108
AM (khz/10)	53	65	80	100	130	160

15. A tube of soil is held horizontally and wetted at one end. The distance, x, which the water has reached from the end by time t is given by

$$x = at^b,$$

where a and b are constants that vary with the sample of soil. The data for such an experiment is given in Table 11.32.[19] For this soil it is known that $b \approx 0.4$. What value for a makes this a reasonable model?

Table 11.32 *Movement of wetting front*

Time (minutes)	0	1	2	4	8
Distance (cm)	0	3.7	4.5	6.0	8.0
Time (minutes)	16	32	64	128	256
Distance (cm)	10.6	13.8	18.6	24.3	32.0

16. In this problem you will fit a quartic polynomial to the AIDS data.

(a) With N as the total number of AIDS deaths in the US t years after 1980, use a calculator or computer to fit the data in Table 11.25 on page 475 with a polynomial of the form

$$N = at^4 + bt^3 + ct^2 + dt + e.$$

(b) Graph the data and your quartic for $0 \leq t \leq 16$. Comment on the fit.

(c) Graph the data and your quartic for $0 \leq t \leq 30$. Comment on the predictions made by this model.

17. The managers of a furniture store have compiled data showing the weekly demand for recliners at various prices.

(a) In Table 11.33, fill in the revenue generated by selling the number of recliners at the corresponding price.

(b) Find the quadratic function that best fits the data.

(c) According to the function you found, what price should the store charge for their recliners to maximize revenue? What is the maximum revenue?

Table 11.33

Recliner price ($)	399	499	599	699	799
Demand (recliners)	62	55	47	40	34
Revenue ($)					

[19] Adapted from I. A. Guerrini, "An example of motion in a course of physics for agriculture," *The Physics Teacher*, February 1984, 102–103.

18. The population of Armenia,[20] the smallest of the former Soviet republics, is shown from 2006 to 2010 in Table 11.34.

    (a) Does the function giving the population as a function of time appear to be increasing or decreasing? Concave up or concave down?

    (b) Find a power function that approximates this data with time, t, in years since 2005.

    (c) Using your function, estimate the population in 2012. Have you used interpolation or extrapolation?

Table 11.34

Year	2006	2007	2008	2009	2010
Pop. (millions)	2.976	2.972	2.969	2.967	2.967

19. Cellular telephone use has increased over the past two decades. Table 11.35 gives the number of cellular telephone subscriptions, in thousands, from 1985 to 2007.[21]

    (a) Fit an exponential function to this data with time in years since 1985.

    (b) Based on your model, by what percent was the number of cell subscribers increasing each year?

    (c) In the long run, what do you expect of the rate of growth? What does this mean in terms of the shape of the graph?

Table 11.35

Year	1985	1990	1995	2000	2005	2007
Subscriptions	340	5283	33786	109478	207896	255396

20. The use of one-way pagers declined as cell phones became more popular.[22] The number of users is given in Table 11.36 and plotted in Figure 11.62, along with a quadratic regression function.

    (a) How well does the graph of the quadratic function fit the data?

    (b) Find a cubic regression function. Does it fit better?

Table 11.36

Year	1990	1991	1992	1993	1994	1995
Users, millions	10	12	15	19	25	32
Year	1996	1997	1998	1999	2000	
Users, millions	38	43	44	43	37	

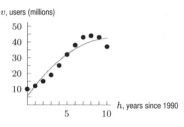

Figure 11.62

21. Table 11.37 gives the estimated population, in thousands, of the American colonies from 1650 to 1770.[23]

    (a) Make a scatterplot of the data using $t = 0$ to represent the year 1650.

    (b) Fit an exponential function to the data.

    (c) Explain the meaning of the parameters in your model.

    (d) Use your function to predict the population in 1750. Is it high or low?

    (e) According to the US Census Bureau[24], the US population in 1800 was 5,308,483. Use your function to make a prediction for 1800. Is it high or low?

Table 11.37

Year	1650	1670	1690	1700
Population	50.4	111.9	210.4	250.9
Year	1720	1740	1750	1770
Population	466.2	905.6	1170.8	2148.1

22. The US Census Bureau began recording census data in 1790. Table 11.38 gives the population of the US in millions from 1790 to 1860.[25]

    (a) With t = 0 representing the number of years since 1790, fit an exponential function to the data.

    (b) The 1800 census value is 5.3 million. Find the population predicted by your function for 1800. Problem 21 gave a prediction of 5.5 million using the data for 1650 to 1750. Using the two data sets, explain the difference in predicted values.

    (c) Use your function to project the population of the US in 2010. Is this prediction reasonable?

---

[20]http://www.census.gov/ipc/www/idb/country.php, accessed May 29, 2010.

[21]*World Almanac and Book of Facts*, 2009, p. 406.

[22]*The New York Times*, p. 16, April 11, 2002.

[23]*The World Almanac and Book of Facts, 2002*, New York, NY, p. 376.

[24]http://www.census.gov/, accessed January 15, 2003.

[25]http://www.census.gov/, accessed January 15, 2003.

Table 11.38

Year	1790	1800	1810	1820
Population	3.929	5.308	7.240	9.638
Year	1830	1840	1850	1860
Population	12.861	17.063	23.192	31.443

23. Table 11.39 gives N, the number of transistors per integrated circuit chip, t years after 1970.[26]

    (a) Plot N vs t and fit an exponential curve to the data.
    (b) According to the formula of your curve of best fit, approximately how often does the number of transistors double?

    Table 11.39

Chip name	t	N
4004	1	2,300
8008	2	2,500
8080	4	4,500
8086	8	29,000
Intel286	12	134,000
Intel386	15	275,000
Intel486	19	1,200,000
Pentium	23	3,100,000
Pentium II	27	7,500,000
Pentium III	29	9,500,000
Pentium 4	30	42,000,000
Itanium	31	25,000,000
Itanium 2	33	220,000,000
Itanium 2 (9MB cache)	34	592,000,000
Dual Core Itanium	36	1,720,000,000
Xeon 7460	38	1,900,000,000
Xeon 7500	39	2,300,000,000

24. The US export of edible fishery produce, in thousands of metric tons, is shown in Table 11.40.[27] With t in years since 1935, fit the data with a function of the form

    (a) $y = at^b$ (b) $y = ab^t$ (c) $y = at^2 + bt + c$

    (d) Discuss the reliability for estimating 2010 exports with each function.

Table 11.40

Year	1940	1945	1950	1955	1960	1965	1970
Fish export	66	62	55	50	31	50	73
Year	1975	1980	1985	1990	1995	2000	2005
Fish export	109	275	305	883	929	982	1329

25. The data in Table 11.40 show a big jump in fish exports between 1985 and 1990. This suggests fitting a piecewise defined function. With t in years since 1935, fit a quadratic function to the data from

    (a) 1940 to 1985   (b) 1990 to 2005

    (c) Write a piecewise defined function using parts (a) and (b). Graph the function and the data.

26. (a) Using the data in Table 11.25 on page 475, plot $\ln N$ against t. If the original data were exponential, the points would lie on a line.
    (b) Fit a line to the graph from part (a).
    (c) From the equation of the line, obtain the formula for N as an exponential function of t.

27. (a) Let $N = at^p$, with a, p constant. Explain why if you plot $\ln N$ against $\ln t$, you get a line.
    (b) To decide if a function of the form $N = at^p$ fits some data, you plot $\ln N$ against $\ln t$. Explain why this plot is useful.

28. (a) Using the data in Table 11.25 on page 475, plot $\ln N$ against $\ln t$. If a power function fitted the original data, the points would lie on a line.
    (b) Fit a line to the graph from part (a).
    (c) From the equation of the line, obtain the formula for N as a power function of t.

29. According to the US Census Bureau, the 2008 mean income by age is as given in Table 11.41.[28]

    (a) Choose the best type of function to fit the data: linear, exponential, power, or quadratic.
    (b) Using a mid-range age value for each interval, find an equation to fit the data.
    (c) Interpolation estimates incomes for ages within the range of the data. Predict the income of a 37-year-old.
    (d) Extrapolation estimates incomes outside the range of data. Use your function to predict the income of a 10-year-old. Is it reasonable?

Table 11.41

Age	Mean income, dollars
15 to 24	14,268
25 to 34	36,146
35 to 44	47,520
45 to 54	49,570
55 to 64	46,408
65 to 74	33,286
75+ years	24,396

[26]The Intel Corporation, www.intel.com/museum/archives/history_docs/mooreslaw.htm, intel.com, www.geek.com.

[27]www.st.nmfs.gov/st1/trade/trade2001.pdf, accessed December 15, 2002 and www.st.nmfs.gov/st1/trade/documents/TRADE2005.pdf, accessed July 25, 2006.

[28]www.census.gov/hhes/www/income/histinc/p10ar.html, accessed November 27, 2009.

30. German physicist Arnd Leike of the University of Munich won the 2002 Ig Nobel prize in Physics for experiments with beer foam conducted with his students.[29] The data in Table 11.42 give the height (in cm) of beer foam after t seconds for three different types of beer, Erdinger Weissbier, Augustinerbräu München, and Budweiser Budvar. The heights are denoted h_e, h_a, and h_b, respectively.

(a) Plot these points and fit exponential functions to them. Give the equations in the form $h = h_0 e^{-t/\tau}$.

(b) What does the value of h_0 tell you for each type of beer? What does the value of τ tell you for each type of beer?

Table 11.42

t	h_e	h_a	h_b	t	h_e	h_a	h_b
0	17.0	14.0	14.0	120	10.7	6.0	7.0
15	16.1	11.8	12.1	150	9.7	5.3	6.2
30	14.9	10.5	10.9	180	8.9	4.4	5.5
45	14.0	9.3	10.0	210	8.3	3.5	4.5
60	13.2	8.5	9.3	240	7.5	2.9	3.5
75	12.5	7.7	8.6	300	6.3	1.3	2.0
90	11.9	7.1	8.0	360	5.2	0.7	0.9
105	11.2	6.5	7.5				

31. Table 11.43 gives the development time t (in days) for eggs of the pea weevil (*Bruchus pisorum*) at temperature H (°C).[30]

(a) Plot these data and fit a power function.

(b) Ecologists define the development rate $r = 1/t$ where t is the development time. Plot r against H, and fit a linear function.

(c) At a certain temperature, the value of r drops to 0 and pea weevil eggs will not develop. What is this temperature according to the model from part (a)? Part (b)? Which model's prediction do you think is more reasonable?

Table 11.43

H, °C	10.7	14.4	16.2	18.1	21.4	23.7	24.7	26.9
t, days	38.0	19.5	15.6	9.6	9.5	7.3	4.5	4.5

32. In this problem, we will determine whether or not the compact disc data from Table 5.8 on page 210 can be well modeled using a power function of the form $l = kc^p$, where l and c give the number of LPs and CDs (in millions) respectively, and where k and p are constant.

(a) Based on the plot of the data in Figure 5.24 on page 210, what do you expect to be true about the sign of the power p?

(b) Fit a power function to the data. One data point may have to be omitted. Which point and why?

(c) Let $y = \ln l$ and $x = \ln c$. Find a linear formula for y in terms of x by making substitutions in the equation $l = kc^p$.

(d) Transform the data in Table 5.8 to create a table comparing $x = \ln c$ and $y = \ln l$. What data point must be omitted?

(e) Plot your transformed data from part (d). Based on your plot, do you think a power function gives a good fit to the data? Explain.

33. In 1619, Kepler published his third law, which relates D, the distance of a planet from the Sun, to P, the period of the planet—the time it takes for the planet to orbit the Sun. Kepler conjectured that $P = kD^{3/2}$, where k is a constant that he determined empirically from experimental data. Table 11.44 represents modern observational data. Does this model fit the data? What is your estimate for k? What is the final form of Kepler's law?

Table 11.44 *The period and distance of a planet from the Sun*

Planet	Distance (kms $\times 10^6$)	Period (days)
Mercury	57.9	88
Venus	108.2	225
Earth	149.6	365
Mars	227.9	687
Jupiter	778.3	4329
Saturn	1427.0	10753
Uranus	2870.0	30660
Neptune	4497.0	60150
Pluto	5900.0	90670

---

[29]http://ignobel.com/ig/ig-pastwinners.html. The Ig Nobel prize is a spoof of the Nobel prize and honors researchers whose achievements "cannot or should not be reproduced." The data here is taken from *Demonstration of the Exponential Decay Law Using Beer Froth*, Arnd Leike, *European Journal of Physics*, vol. 23, January 2002, pp. 21-26.

[30]From website created by A. Sharov, http://www.ento.vt.edu/~sharov/PopEcol/lec8/quest8.html, accessed November, 2001. The site attributes the data to Smith, A. M., 1992, *Environ. Entomol.* 21:314-321.

CHAPTER SUMMARY

- **Proportionality**
  Direct and indirect.

- **Power Functions**
  $y = kx^p$.

- **Polynomials**
  General formula:

  $$p(x) = a_n x^n + a_{n-1} x^{n-1} + \cdots + a_1 x + a_0$$

  All terms have non-negative, integer exponents. Leading term $a_n x^n$; coefficients $a_0, \ldots, a_n$; degree n.
  Long-run behavior: Like $y = a_n x^n$.
  Short-run behavior: Zeros corresponding to each factor; multiple zeros.

- **Rational Functions**
  Ratio of polynomials: $r(x) = \dfrac{p(x)}{q(x)}$.
  Long-run behavior: Horizontal asymptote of $r(x)$:
    Given by ratio of highest-degree terms.
  Short-run behavior: Vertical asymptote of $r(x)$:
    At zeros of $q(x)$ (if $p(x) \neq 0$).
  Short-run behavior: Zeros of $r(x)$:
    At zeros of $p(x)$ (if $q(x) \neq 0$).
  Using limits to understand short- and long-run behavior.

- **Comparing Functions**
  Exponential functions eventually dominate power functions. Power functions eventually dominate logs.

- **Fitting Exponentials and Polynomials to Data**

REVIEW EXERCISES AND PROBLEMS FOR CHAPTER ELEVEN

Exercises

In Exercises 1–4, does the function represent proportionality to a power of the independent variable? That is, can the function be written in the form $y = kx^p$ for the variables given in the problem? If so, identify the constant, k, and the power, p.

1. $y = \dfrac{\frac{1}{3}}{2x^7}$

2. $y = \dfrac{6}{-2/x^5}$

3. $z = 5(3)^x$

4. $C = 2q^3 - 5$

In Exercises 5–8, is y a power function of x? If so, write it in the form $y = kx^p$.

5. $y = 6x^3 + 2$

6. $3y = 9x^2$

7. $y - 9 = (x + 3)(x - 3)$

8. $y = 4(x-2)(x+2) + 16$

Does the power function in Exercises 9–14 appear to have an odd power, an even power, or a power between 0 and 1?

9.

10.

11.

12.

13.

14.

15. State the values of k and p if $r(x) = 2\sqrt[3]{7x}\,\sqrt[5]{x^2}$ is written in the form kx^p.

16. Find a possible formula for the power function $f(t)$ given that $f(3) = 5$ and $f(5) = 3$.

17. Show that the function $y = (x^2 - 4)(x^2 - 2x - 3)$ is a polynomial. What is its degree?

Describe in words the long-run behavior as $x \to \infty$ of the functions in Exercises 18–21. What power function does each resemble?

18. $y = 16x^3 - 4023x^2 - 2$

19. $y = 4x^4 - 2x^2 + 3$

20. $y = 5x^2/x^{3/2} + 2$

21. $y = 3x^3 + 2x^2/x^{-7} - 7x^5 + 2$

In Exercises 22–23, find the zeros of the functions.

22. $y = 3x^5 + 7x + 1$ **23.** $y = 2x^2 - 3x - 3$

Are the functions in Exercises 24–25 rational functions? If so, write them in the form $p(x)/q(x)$, the ratio of polynomials.

24. $f(x) = \dfrac{x^2}{x-3} - \dfrac{5}{x-3}$ **25.** $f(x) = \dfrac{x^2+4}{e^x}$

In Exercises 26–27, which function dominates as $x \to \infty$?

26. $y = 12x^3, \quad y = 7/x^{-4}$

27. $y = 4/e^{-x}, \quad y = 17x^{43}$

28. Find

(a) $\displaystyle \lim_{x \to \infty} \frac{x(x^2-4)}{5+5x^3}$ (b) $\displaystyle \lim_{x \to -\infty} \frac{3x(x-1)(x-2)}{5-6x^4}$

29. Find

(a) $\displaystyle \lim_{x \to \infty} \frac{2x+1}{x-5}$ (b) $\displaystyle \lim_{x \to -\infty} \frac{2+5x}{6x+3}$

30. For each of the following functions, state whether it is even, odd, or neither.

(a) $f(x) = x^2 + 3$ (b) $g(x) = x^3 + 3$

(c) $h(x) = 5/x$ (d) $j(x) = |x-4|$

(e) $k(x) = \log x$ (f) $l(x) = \log(x^2)$

(g) $m(x) = 2^x + 2$ (h) $n(x) = \cos x + 2$

Problems

31. It is claimed that Figure 11.63 is the graph of a power function kx^p. If it is, estimate k and p. If it is not, explain why.

Figure 11.63

32. (a) One of the graphs in Figure 11.64 is $y = x^n$ and the other is $y = x^{1/n}$, where n is a positive integer. Which is which? How do you know?

(b) What are the coordinates of point A?

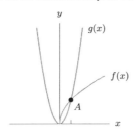

Figure 11.64

33. Without a calculator, match each graph (i)–(iv) with a function in Table 11.45.

Table 11.45

(A) $y = 0.5\sin(2x)$	(J) $y = 2\sin(0.5x)$
(B) $y = -\ln x$	(K) $y = \ln(x-1)$
(C) $y = 10(0.6)^x$	(L) $y = 2e^{-0.2x}$
(D) $y = 2\sin(2x)$	(M) $y = 1/(x-6)$
(E) $y = \ln(-x)$	(N) $y = (x-2)/(x^2-9)$
(F) $y = -15(3.1)^x$	(O) $y = 1/(x^2-4)$
(G) $y = 0.5\sin(0.5x)$	(P) $y = x/(x-3)$
(H) $y = \ln(x+1)$	(Q) $y = (x-1)/(x+3)$
(I) $y = 7(2.5)^x$	(R) $y = 1/(x^2+4)$

34. Without a calculator, match each graph (i)–(viii) with a function in Table 11.46.

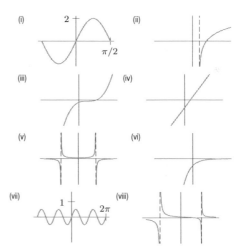

Table 11.46

(A) $y = 0.5\sin(2x)$	(M) $y = (x+3)/(x^2-4)$
(B) $y = 2\sin(2x)$	(N) $y = (x^2-4)/(x^2-1)$
(C) $y = 0.5\sin(0.5x)$	(O) $y = (x+1)^3 - 1$
(D) $y = 2\sin(0.5x)$	(P) $y = -2x - 4$
(E) $y = (x-2)/(x^2-9)$	(Q) $y = 3e^{-x}$
(F) $y = (x-3)/(x^2-1)$	(R) $y = -3e^{x}$
(G) $y = (x-1)^3 - 1$	(S) $y = -3e^{-x}$
(H) $y = 2x - 4$	(T) $y = 3e^{-x^2}$
(I) $y = -\ln x$	(U) $y = 1/(4-x^2)$
(J) $y = \ln(-x)$	(V) $y = 1/(x^2+4)$
(K) $y = \ln(x+1)$	(W) $y = (x+1)^3 + 1$
(L) $y = \ln(x-1)$	(X) $y = 2(x+2)$

41.

42.

43.

44.

Find possible polynomial formulas in Problems 35–44.

35.

36.

37.

38.

39.

40.

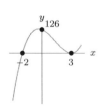

Problems 45–47 show a transformation of $y = 1/x^2$.

(a) Find a formula for the graph.

(b) Write the formula from part (a) as the ratio of two polynomials.

(c) Find the coordinates of any intercepts of the graph.

45.

46.

47.

48. Suppose that $g(2) = 24$ and $g(4) = 96$. Find a formula for g, assuming g is:

   (a) A power function.
   (b) A linear function.
   (c) An exponential function.

49. Let $f(x) = x^2 + 5x + 6$ and $g(x) = x^2 + 1$.

   (a) What are the zeros of f and g?
   (b) Let $r(x) = f(x)/g(x)$. Graph r. Does r have zeros? Vertical asymptotes? What is its long-run behavior as $x \to \pm\infty$?
   (c) Let $s(x) = g(x)/f(x)$. If you graph s in the window $-10 \le x \le 10$, $-10 \le y \le 10$, it appears to have a zero near the origin. Does it? Does s have a vertical asymptote? What is its long-run behavior?

50. Let $f(x) = (x-3)^2$, $g(x) = x^2 - 4$, $h(x) = x+1$, and $j(x) = x^2 + 1$. Without a calculator, match the functions described in (a)–(f) to the functions in (i)–(vi). Some of the descriptions may have no matching function or more than one matching function.

   (i) $p(x) = \dfrac{f(x)}{g(x)}$ (ii) $q(x) = \dfrac{h(x)}{g(x)}$

   (iii) $r(x) = f(x)h(x)$ (iv) $s(x) = \dfrac{g(x)}{j(x)}$

   (v) $t(x) = \dfrac{1}{h(x)}$ (vi) $v(x) = \dfrac{j(x)}{f(x)}$

   (a) Two zeros, no vertical asymptotes, and a horizontal asymptote.
   (b) Two zeros, no vertical asymptote, and no horizontal asymptote.
   (c) One zero, one vertical asymptote, and a horizontal asymptote.
   (d) One zero, two vertical asymptotes, and a horizontal asymptote.
   (e) No zeros, one vertical asymptote, and a horizontal asymptote at $y = 1$.
   (f) No zeros, one vertical asymptote, and a horizontal asymptote at $y = 0$.

51. Suppose f is a polynomial function of degree n, where n is a positive even integer. For each of the following statements, write *true* if the statement is always true, *false* otherwise. If the statement is false, give an example that illustrates why it is false.

   (a) f is an even function.
   (b) f has an inverse.
   (c) f cannot be an odd function.
   (d) If $f(x) \to +\infty$ as $x \to +\infty$, then $f(x) \to -\infty$ as $x \to -\infty$.

52. **(a)** Sketch a graph of $f(x) = x^4 - 17x^2 + 36x - 20$ for $-10 \le x \le 10$, $-10 \le y \le 10$.
   (b) Your graph should appear to have a vertical asymptote at $x = -5$. Does f actually have a vertical asymptote here? Explain.
   (c) How many zeros does f have? Can you find a window in which all of the zeros of f are clearly visible?
   (d) Write the formula of f in factored form.
   (e) How many turning points does the graph of f have? Can you find a window in which all the turning points of f are clearly visible? Explain.

In Problems 53–56, find a possible formula for the rational functions.

53. This function has zeros at $x = -3$ and $x = 2$, and vertical asymptotes at $x = -5$ and $x = 7$. It has a horizontal asymptote of $y = 1$.

54. The graph of $y = f(x)$ has one vertical asymptote, at $x = -1$, and a horizontal asymptote at $y = 1$. The graph of f crosses the y-axis at $y = 3$ and crosses the x-axis once, at $x = -3$.

55.

56.

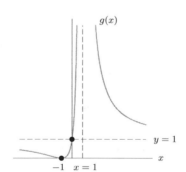

Find possible formulas for the polynomials and rational functions in Problems 57–60.

57. The zeros of f are $x = -3$, $x = 2$, and $x = 5$, and the y-intercept is $y = -6$.

58. This function has zeros at $x = -3$, $x = 2$, $x = 5$, and a double zero at $x = 6$. It has a y-intercept of 7.

59. The polynomial $h(x) = 7$ at $x = -5, -1, 4$, and the y-intercept is 3. [Hint: Visualize h as a vertically shifted version of another polynomial.]

60. The graph of w intercepts the graph of $v(x) = 2x + 5$ at $x = -4, 1, 3$ and has a y-intercept of 2. [Hint: Let $w(x) = p(x) + v(x)$ where p is another polynomial.]

61. On a map, $1/2$ inch represents 5 miles. Is the map distance between two locations directly or inversely proportional to the actual distance that separates the two locations? Explain your reasoning and write a formula for the proportion. How far apart are two towns if the distance between these two towns on the map is 3.25 inches?

62. When a guitar string is plucked, the frequency of the note produced can be adjusted by varying the length of the string. The frequency is inversely proportional to the length, so a longer string results in a lower frequency, while a shorter string results in a higher frequency. Is the length of the string directly proportional or inversely proportional to the frequency?

63. A person's weight, w, on a planet of radius d is given by

$$w = kd^{-2}, \quad k > 0,$$

where the constant k depends on the masses of the person and the planet.

(a) A man weighs 180 lb on the surface of the earth. How much does he weigh on the surface of a planet whose mass is the same the earth's, but whose radius is three times as large? One-third as large?

(b) What fraction of the earth's radius must an equally massive planet have if, on this planet, the weight of the man in part (a) is one ton?

64. One of Kepler's three laws of planetary motion states that the square of the period, P, of a body orbiting the sun is proportional to the cube of its average distance, d, from the sun. The earth has a period of 365 days and its distance from the sun is approximately 93,000,000 miles.

(a) Find P as a function of d.

(b) The planet Jupiter has an average distance from the sun of 483,000,000 miles. How long in earth days is a Jupiter year?

65. The town of Smallsville was founded in 1900. Its population y (in hundreds) is given by the equation

$$y = -0.1x^4 + 1.7x^3 - 9x^2 + 14.4x + 5,$$

where x is the number of years since 1900. Use a the graph in the window $0 \leq x \leq 10$, $-2 \leq y \leq 13$.

(a) What was the population of Smallsville when it was founded?

(b) When did Smallsville become a ghost town (nobody lived there anymore)? Give the year and the month.

(c) What was the largest population of Smallsville after 1905? When did Smallsville reach that population? Again, include the month and year. Explain your method.

66. Let $C(x)$ be a firm's total cost, in millions of dollars, for producing a quantity of x thousand units of an item.

(a) Graph $C(x) = (x - 1)^3 + 1$.

(b) Let $R(x)$ be the revenue to the firm (in millions of dollars) for selling a quantity x thousand units of the good. Suppose $R(x) = x$. What does this tell you about the price of each unit?

(c) Profit equals revenue minus cost. For what values of x does the firm make a profit? Break even? Lose money?

67. Allometry is the study of the relative size of different parts of a body as a consequence of growth.[31] The simplest model of allometry is one in which it is assumed that the sizes of two parts x and y are related by a power law of the form

$$y = kx^p,$$

where k and p are positive constants. This equation is often called the *allometric equation*.

(a) Let x be the length of a fish and y be its weight. If L is a typical unit of length, then L^3 is a typical unit of volume. Show that the assumptions that the length x of a fish is proportional to L, and that its weight y is proportional to its volume and therefore to L^3, lead to the equation $y = kx^3$.

(b) Table 11.47 relates the weight y of plaice[32] to its length x. (Plaice is a type of fish.) If $y = kx^3$, what do you expect to happen if you calculate x^3/y for each of the entries in the table? Do this, and estimate the proportionality constant, k.

(c) With this choice of k, plot the function $y = kx^3$ and the data in Table 11.47. Is the function a reasonable model?

[31] J. S. Huxley, *Problems of Relative Growth* (Dover, 1972).
[32] Adapted from R. J. H. Beverton and S. J. Holt, "On the Dynamics of Exploited Fish Populations," *Fishery Investigations*, Series II, 19, 1957.

Table 11.47

Length (cm)	33.5	34.5	35.5	36.5	37.5	38.5
Weight (gm)	332	363	391	419	455	500
Length (cm)	39.5	40.5	41.5	42.5	43.5	
Weight (gm)	538	574	623	674	724	

68. The thrust, T, delivered by a ship's propeller is proportional[33] to the square of the propeller rotation speed, R, times the fourth power of the propeller diameter, D.

   (a) Write a formula for T in terms of R and D.

   (b) What happens to the thrust if the propeller speed is doubled?

   (c) What happens to the thrust if the propeller diameter is doubled?

   (d) If the propeller diameter is increased by 50%, by how much can the propeller speed be reduced to deliver the same thrust?

69. A function that is not a polynomial can often be approximated by a polynomial. For example, for certain x-values, the function $f(x) = e^x$ can be approximated by the fifth-degree polynomial

$$p(x) = 1 + x + \frac{x^2}{2} + \frac{x^3}{6} + \frac{x^4}{24} + \frac{x^5}{120}.$$

   (a) Show that $p(1) \approx f(1) = e$. How good is the estimate?

   (b) Calculate $p(5)$. How well does $p(5)$ approximate $f(5)$?

(c) Graph $p(x)$ and $f(x)$ together on the same set of axes. Based on your graph, for what range of values of x does $p(x)$ give a good estimate for $f(x)$?

70. The resolution, $r\%$, of a gamma ray telescope depends on the energy v (in millions of electron volts, or MeVs) of the detected gamma rays.[34] The smaller the value of r, the better the telescope is at distinguishing two gamma ray photons of slightly different energies, and the more detailed observations that can be made. Table 11.48 gives values of r for gamma rays at different energies.

   (a) Plot the data in Table 11.48, with r on the vertical axis.

   (b) Based on this data, is the telescope better able to distinguish between high-energy photons or low-energy photons?

   (c) Fit both power and exponential functions to the data, and give their formulas. Which appears to give the better fit?

   (d) The telescope is predicted to grow rapidly worse and worse at distinguishing photons as the energy level drops toward 0 MeV. Which curve, power or exponential, is most consistent with this prediction?

Table 11.48

v, MeV	0.5	0.7	0.9	1.3	1.8	4.0	4.4
r, %	16.0	13.5	12.0	8.5	7.0	4.5	4.0

CHECK YOUR UNDERSTANDING

Are the statements in Problems 1–47 true or false? Give an explanation for your answer.

1. All quadratic functions are power functions.

2. The function $y = 3 \cdot 2^x$ is a power function.

3. Let $g(x) = x^p$. If p is a positive, even integer, then the graph of g passes through the point $(-1, 1)$.

4. Let $g(x) = x^p$. If p is a positive, even integer, then the graph of g is symmetric about the y-axis.

5. Let $g(x) = x^p$. If p is a positive, even integer, then the graph of g is concave up.

6. The graph of $f(x) = x^{-1}$ passes through the origin.

7. The graph of $f(x) = x^{-2}$ has the x-axis as its only asymptote.

8. If $f(x) = x^{-1}$ then $f(x)$ approaches $+\infty$ as x approaches zero.

9. As x grows very large, the values of $f(x) = x^{-1}$ approach zero.

10. The function 2^x eventually grows faster than x^b for any b.

11. The function $f(x) = x^{0.5}$ eventually grows faster than $g(x) = \ln x$.

12. We have $2^x \geq x^2$ on the interval $0 \leq x \leq 4$.

13. The function $f(x) = x^{-3}$ approaches the x-axis faster than $g(x) = e^{-x}$ as x grows very large.

---

[33]Thomas C. Gillner, *Modern Ship Design* (US Naval Institute Press, 1972).

[34]E. Aprile, et al., *The LXeGRIT Compton Status and Future Prospects*, posted at http://arxiv.org as arXiv:astro-ph/0212005v2, accessed December 4, 2002.

14. The function $f(x) = 3^x$ is an example of a power function.

15. The function $y = 3x$ is an example of a power function.

16. Every quadratic function is a polynomial function.

17. The power of the first term of a polynomial is its degree.

18. Far from the origin, the graph of a polynomial looks like the graph of its highest-power term.

19. A zero of a polynomial p is the value $p(0)$.

20. The zeros of a polynomial are the x-coordinates where its graph intersects the x-axis.

21. The y-intercept of a polynomial $y = p(x)$ can be found by evaluating $p(0)$.

22. For very large x-values $f(x) = 1000x^3 + 345x^2 + 17x + 394$ is less than $g(x) = 0.01x^4$.

23. If $y = f(x)$ is a polynomial of degree n, where n is a positive even number, then f has an inverse.

24. If $y = f(x)$ is a polynomial of degree n, where n is a positive odd number, then f has an inverse.

25. If $p(x)$ is a polynomial and $x - a$ is a factor of p, then $x = a$ is a zero of p.

26. A polynomial of degree n cannot have more than n zeros.

27. The polynomial in Figure 11.65 has a multiple zero at $x = -2$.

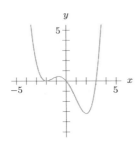

Figure 11.65

28. The polynomial in Figure 11.65 has a multiple zero at $x = 0$.

29. A rational function is the quotient of two polynomials. We assume the denominator is not equal to zero.

30. The function $f(x) = \dfrac{1}{x}$ is a rational function.

31. In order to determine the long-run behavior of a rational function, it is sufficient to consider only the ratio of the highest-power term in the numerator to the highest-power term in the denominator.

32. As x grows through large positive values, $y = \dfrac{x + 18}{x + 9}$ approaches $y = 2$.

33. As x grows through large positive values, $y = \dfrac{2x + 125}{x^2 - 1}$ approaches $y = 0$.

34. As x grows through large positive values, $y = \dfrac{x^3 + 4x^2 - 16x + 12}{4x^3 - 16x + 1}$ has an asymptote at $y = 4$.

35. As x grows through large positive values, $y = \dfrac{1 - 4x^2}{x^2 + 1}$ approaches $y = 0$.

36. As x grows through large positive values, $y = \dfrac{5x}{x + 1}$ approaches $y = -5$.

37. As x grows through large positive values, $y = \dfrac{3x^4 - 6x^3 + 10x^2 - 16x + 7}{-3x + x^2}$ behaves like $y = -x^3$.

38. As x decreases through large negative values, $f(x) = \dfrac{x^3 - 7x^2 + 28x + 76}{-x^2 - 101x + 72}$ approaches positive infinity.

39. A fraction is equal to zero if and only if its numerator equals zero and its denominator does not.

40. The zeros of a function $y = f(x)$ are the values of x that make $y = 0$.

41. The function $f(x) = \dfrac{x + 4}{x - 3}$ has a zero at $x = -4$.

42. The rational function $y = \dfrac{x + 2}{x^2 - 4}$ has a zero at $x = -2$.

43. The rational function $g(w) = \dfrac{12}{(w - 2)(w + 3)}$ has exactly two zeros.

44. If $p(x)$ and $q(x)$ have no zeros in common, then the rational function $r(x) = \dfrac{p(x)}{q(x)}$ has an asymptote at each of the zeros of $p(x)$.

45. In general, the rational function $r(x) = \dfrac{p(x)}{q(x)}$ must have at least one zero.

46. Rational functions can never cross an asymptote.

47. The rational function $g(w) = \dfrac{3w - 3}{(w - 12)(w + 4)}$ has a vertical asymptote at $w = 1$.

SKILLS REFRESHER FOR CHAPTER 11: ALGEBRAIC FRACTIONS

Algebraic fractions are combined in the same way as numeric fractions according to the following rules:

Add numerators when denominators are equal: $\dfrac{a}{c} + \dfrac{b}{c} = \dfrac{a+b}{c}$

Find a common denominator: $\dfrac{a}{b} + \dfrac{c}{d} = \dfrac{a \cdot d}{b \cdot d} + \dfrac{b \cdot c}{b \cdot d} = \dfrac{ad + bc}{bd}$

Multiply numerators and denominators for a product: $\dfrac{a}{b} \cdot \dfrac{c}{d} = \dfrac{ac}{bd}$

To divide by a fraction, multiply by its reciprocal: $\dfrac{a/b}{c/d} = \dfrac{a}{b} \cdot \dfrac{d}{c} = \dfrac{ad}{bc}$

The sign of a fraction is changed by changing the sign of the numerator or the denominator (but not both):

$$-\frac{a}{b} = \frac{-a}{b} = \frac{a}{-b}$$

We assume that no denominators are zero, since we cannot divide by zero; that is, $a/0$ is not defined.

We can simplify a fraction in which either the numerator or denominator is itself a fraction as follows:

$$\frac{a/b}{c} = \frac{a/b}{c/1} = \frac{a}{b} \cdot \frac{1}{c} = \frac{a}{bc} \quad \text{and} \quad \frac{a}{b/c} = \frac{a/1}{b/c} = \frac{a}{1} \cdot \frac{c}{b} = \frac{ac}{b}.$$

Example 1   Perform the indicated operations and express the answers as a single fraction.

(a) $\dfrac{4}{x^2+1} - \dfrac{1-x}{x^2+1}$

(b) $\dfrac{M}{M^2-2M-3} + \dfrac{1}{M^2-2M-3}$

(c) $\dfrac{-H^2P}{17} \cdot \dfrac{\left(PH^{1/3}\right)^2}{K^{-1}}$

(d) $\dfrac{2z/w}{w(w-3z)}$

Solution   (a) $\dfrac{4}{x^2+1} - \dfrac{1-x}{x^2+1} = \dfrac{4-(1-x)}{x^2+1} = \dfrac{3+x}{x^2+1}$

(b) $\dfrac{M}{M^2-2M-3} + \dfrac{1}{M^2-2M-3} = \dfrac{M+1}{(M^2-2M-3)} = \dfrac{M+1}{(M+1)(M-3)} = \dfrac{1}{M-3}$ if $M \neq -1$.

(c) $\dfrac{-H^2P}{17} \cdot \dfrac{\left(PH^{1/3}\right)^2}{K^{-1}} = \dfrac{-H^2P\left(P^2H^{2/3}\right)}{17K^{-1}} = -\dfrac{H^{8/3}P^3K}{17}$

(d) $\dfrac{2z/w}{w(w-3z)} = \dfrac{2z}{w} \cdot \dfrac{1}{w(w-3z)} = \dfrac{2z}{w^2(w-3z)}$

Example 2   Simplify the following expressions, giving your answer as a single fraction.

(a) $2x^{-1/2} + \dfrac{\sqrt{x}}{3}$

(b) $2\sqrt{t+3} + \dfrac{1-2t}{\sqrt{t+3}}$

Solution

(a) $2x^{-1/2} + \dfrac{\sqrt{x}}{3} = \dfrac{2}{\sqrt{x}} + \dfrac{\sqrt{x}}{3} = \dfrac{2 \cdot 3 + \sqrt{x}\sqrt{x}}{3\sqrt{x}} = \dfrac{6+x}{3\sqrt{x}} = \dfrac{6+x}{3x^{1/2}}.$

(b) $2\sqrt{t+3} + \dfrac{1-2t}{\sqrt{t+3}} = \dfrac{2\sqrt{t+3}}{1} + \dfrac{1-2t}{\sqrt{t+3}}$

$\qquad\qquad = \dfrac{2\sqrt{t+3}\sqrt{t+3} + 1 - 2t}{\sqrt{t+3}}$

$\qquad\qquad = \dfrac{2(t+3) + 1 - 2t}{\sqrt{t+3}}$

$\qquad\qquad = \dfrac{7}{\sqrt{t+3}} = \dfrac{7}{(t+3)^{1/2}}.$

Finding a Common Denominator

We can multiply (or divide) both the numerator and denominator of a fraction by the same nonzero number without changing the fraction's value. This is equivalent to multiplying by a factor of $+1$. We are using this rule when we add or subtract fractions with different denominators. For example, to add $\dfrac{x}{3a} + \dfrac{1}{a}$, we multiply $\dfrac{1}{a} \cdot \dfrac{3}{3} = \dfrac{3}{3a}$. Then

$$\frac{x}{3a} + \frac{1}{a} = \frac{x}{3a} + \frac{3}{3a} = \frac{x+3}{3a}.$$

Example 3 Perform the indicated operations:

(a) $3 - \dfrac{1}{x-1}$

(b) $\dfrac{2}{x^2+x} + \dfrac{x}{x+1}$

Solution

(a) $3 - \dfrac{1}{x-1} = 3\dfrac{(x-1)}{(x-1)} - \dfrac{1}{x-1} = \dfrac{3(x-1)-1}{x-1} = \dfrac{3x-3-1}{x-1} = \dfrac{3x-4}{x-1}$

(b) $\dfrac{2}{x^2+x} + \dfrac{x}{x+1} = \dfrac{2}{x(x+1)} + \dfrac{x}{x+1} = \dfrac{2}{x(x+1)} + \dfrac{x(x)}{(x+1)(x)} = \dfrac{2+x^2}{x(x+1)}.$

Note: We can multiply (or divide) the numerator and denominator by the same nonzero number because this is the same as multiplying by a factor of $+1$, and multiplying by a factor of 1 does not change the value of the expression. However, we cannot perform any other operation that would change the value of the expression. For example, we cannot add the same number to the numerator and denominator of a fraction nor can we square both, take the logarithm of both, etc., without changing the fraction.

Reducing Fractions: Canceling

We can reduce a fraction when we have the same (nonzero) factor in both the numerator and the denominator. For example,

$$\frac{ac}{bc} = \frac{a}{b} \cdot \frac{c}{c} = \frac{a}{b} \cdot 1 = \frac{a}{b}.$$

Example 4   Reduce the following fractions (if possible).

(a) $\dfrac{2x}{4y}$

(b) $\dfrac{2+x}{2+y}$

(c) $\dfrac{5n-5}{1-n}$

(d) $\dfrac{x^2(4-2x)-(4x-x^2)2x}{x^4}$

Solution   (a) $\dfrac{2x}{4y}=\dfrac{2}{2}\cdot\dfrac{x}{2y}=\dfrac{x}{2y}$

(b) $\dfrac{2+x}{2+y}$ cannot be reduced further.

(c) $\dfrac{5n-5}{1-n}=\dfrac{5(n-1)}{(-1)(n-1)}=-5$

(d)

$$\frac{x^2(4-2x)-\left(4x-x^2\right)2x}{x^4}=\frac{x^2(4-2x)-(4-x)2x^2}{x^4}$$

$$=\frac{(4-2x)-2(4-x)}{x^2}\left(\frac{x^2}{x^2}\right)$$

$$=\frac{4-2x-8+2x}{x^2}=\frac{-4}{x^2}.$$

Complex Fractions

A *complex fraction* is a fraction whose numerator or denominator (or both) contains one or more fractions. To simplify a complex fraction, we change the numerator and denominator to single fractions and then divide.

Example 5   Write the following as simple fractions in reduced form.

(a) $\dfrac{\dfrac{1}{x+h}-\dfrac{1}{x}}{h}$

(b) $\dfrac{a+b}{a^{-2}-b^{-2}}$

Solution   (a) $\dfrac{\dfrac{1}{x+h}-\dfrac{1}{x}}{h}=\dfrac{\dfrac{x-(x+h)}{x(x+h)}}{h}=\dfrac{\dfrac{-h}{x(x+h)}}{\dfrac{h}{1}}=\dfrac{-h}{x(x+h)}\cdot\dfrac{1}{h}=\dfrac{-1}{x(x+h)}\dfrac{(h)}{(h)}=\dfrac{-1}{x(x+h)}$

(b) $\dfrac{a+b}{a^{-2}-b^{-2}}=\dfrac{a+b}{\dfrac{1}{a^2}-\dfrac{1}{b^2}}=\dfrac{a+b}{\dfrac{b^2-a^2}{a^2b^2}}=\dfrac{a+b}{1}\cdot\dfrac{a^2b^2}{b^2-a^2}=\dfrac{(a+b)(a^2b^2)}{(b+a)(b-a)}=\dfrac{a^2b^2}{b-a}$

Splitting Expressions

We can reverse the rule for adding fractions to split up an expression into two fractions,

$$\frac{a+b}{c}=\frac{a}{c}+\frac{b}{c}.$$

Example 6 Split $\dfrac{3x^2 + 2}{x^3}$ into two reduced fractions.

Solution $\dfrac{3x^2 + 2}{x^3} = \dfrac{3x^2}{x^3} + \dfrac{2}{x^3} = \dfrac{3}{x} + \dfrac{2}{x^3}$

Sometimes we can alter the form of the fraction even further if we can create a duplicate of the denominator within the numerator. This technique is useful when graphing some rational functions. For example, we may rewrite the fraction $\dfrac{x+3}{x-1}$ by creating a factor of $(x-1)$ within the numerator. To do this, we write

$$\frac{x+3}{x-1} = \frac{x-1+1+3}{x-1}$$

which can be written as

$$\frac{(x-1)+4}{x-1}.$$

Then, splitting this fraction, we have

$$\frac{x+3}{x-1} = \frac{x-1}{x-1} + \frac{4}{x-1} = 1 + \frac{4}{x-1}.$$

Note: It is not possible to split a sum that occurs in the denominator of a fraction. For example,

$$\frac{a}{b+c} \text{ does not equal } \frac{a}{b} + \frac{a}{c}.$$

Exercises to Skills Review for Chapter 11

For Exercises 1–30, perform the operations. Express answers in reduced form.

1. $\dfrac{3}{5} + \dfrac{4}{7}$

2. $\dfrac{7}{10} - \dfrac{2}{15}$

3. $\dfrac{1}{2x} - \dfrac{2}{3}$

4. $\dfrac{6}{7y} + \dfrac{9}{y}$

5. $\dfrac{-2}{yz} + \dfrac{4}{z}$

6. $\dfrac{-2z}{y} + \dfrac{4}{y}$

7. $\dfrac{2}{x^2} - \dfrac{3}{x}$

8. $\dfrac{3/4}{7/20}$

9. $\dfrac{5/6}{15}$

10. $\dfrac{3/x}{x^2/6}$

11. $\dfrac{3/x}{6/x^2}$

12. $\dfrac{14}{x-1} + \dfrac{13}{2x-2}$

13. $\dfrac{4z}{x^2 y} - \dfrac{3w}{xy^4}$

14. $\dfrac{10}{y-2} + \dfrac{3}{2-y}$

15. $\dfrac{8y}{y-4} + \dfrac{32}{y-4}$

16. $\dfrac{8y}{y-4} + \dfrac{32}{4-y}$

17. $\dfrac{8}{3x^2 - x - 4} - \dfrac{9}{x+1}$

18. $\dfrac{15}{(x-3)^2(x+5)} + \dfrac{7}{(x-3)(x+5)^2}$

19. $\dfrac{3}{x-4} - \dfrac{2}{x+4}$

20. $\dfrac{x^2}{x-1} - \dfrac{1}{1-x}$

21. $\dfrac{1}{2r+3} + \dfrac{3}{4r^2 + 6r}$

22. $u + a + \dfrac{u}{u+a}$

23. $\dfrac{1}{\sqrt{x}} - \dfrac{1}{(\sqrt{x})^3}$

24. $\dfrac{1}{e^{2x}} + \dfrac{1}{e^x}$

25. $\dfrac{a+b}{2} \cdot \dfrac{8x+2}{b^2 - a^2}$

26. $\dfrac{0.07}{M} + \dfrac{3}{4}M^2$

27. $\dfrac{1}{r_1} + \dfrac{1}{r_2} + \dfrac{1}{r_3}$

28. $\dfrac{8y}{y-4} - \dfrac{32}{y-4}$

29. $\dfrac{a}{a^2 - 9} + \dfrac{1}{a - 3}$

30. $\dfrac{x^3}{x - 4} \Big/ \dfrac{x^2}{x^2 - 2x - 8}$

43. $\dfrac{6l^2 + 3l - 4}{3l^4}$

44. $\dfrac{7 + p}{p^2 + 11}$

45. $\dfrac{\frac{1}{3}x - \frac{1}{2}}{2x}$

46. $\dfrac{t^{-1/2} + t^{1/2}}{t^2}$

In Exercises 31–40, simplify, if possible.

31. $\dfrac{\dfrac{1}{(x + h)^2} - \dfrac{1}{x^2}}{h}$

32. $\dfrac{a^{-2} + b^{-2}}{a^2 + b^2}$

33. $\dfrac{4 - (x + h)^2 - (4 - x^2)}{h}$

34. $\dfrac{b^{-1}(b - b^{-1})}{b + 1}$.

In Exercises 47–52, rewrite in the form $1 + (A/B)$.

47. $\dfrac{x - 2}{x + 5}$

48. $\dfrac{q - 1}{q - 4}$

49. $\dfrac{R + 1}{R}$

50. $\dfrac{3 + 2u}{2u + 1}$

35. $\dfrac{1 - a^{-2}}{1 + a^{-1}}$.

36. $p - \dfrac{q}{\dfrac{p}{q} + \dfrac{q}{p}}$

51. $\dfrac{\cos x + \sin x}{\cos x}$

52. $\dfrac{1 + e^x}{e^x}$

37. $\dfrac{\dfrac{3}{xy} - \dfrac{5}{x^2 y}}{\dfrac{6x^2 - 7x - 5}{x^4 y^2}}$

38. $\dfrac{\dfrac{1}{x}\left(3x^2\right) - (\ln x)(6x)}{(3x^2)^2}$

Are the statements in Exercises 53–58 true or false?

53. $\dfrac{a + c}{a} = 1 + c$

54. $\dfrac{rs - s}{s} = r - 1$

39. $\dfrac{2x(x^3 + 1)^2 - x^2(2)(x^3 + 1)(3x^2)}{[(x^3 + 1)^2]^2}$

40. $\dfrac{\frac{1}{2}(2x - 1)^{-1/2}(2) - (2x - 1)^{1/2}(2x)}{(x^2)^2}$

55. $\dfrac{y}{y + z} = 1 + \dfrac{y}{z}$

56. $\dfrac{2u^2 - w}{u^2 - w} = 2$

In Exercises 41–46, split into a sum or difference of reduced fractions.

57. $\dfrac{x^2 yz}{2x^2 y} = \dfrac{z}{2}$

41. $\dfrac{26x + 1}{2x^3}$

42. $\dfrac{\sqrt{x} + 3}{3\sqrt{x}}$

58. $x^{5/3} - 3x^{2/3} = \dfrac{x^2 - 3x}{x^{1/3}}$

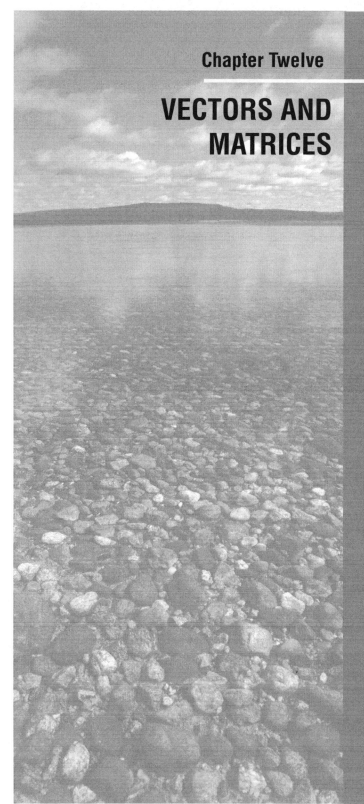

Chapter Twelve

VECTORS AND MATRICES

Contents

12.1 VECTORS

Distance Versus Displacement

If you start at home and walk 3 miles east and then 4 miles north, you have walked a total of 7 miles. However, your distance from home is not 7 miles, but $5 = \sqrt{3^2 + 4^2}$ miles, by the Pythagorean Theorem. See Figure 12.1. As this example illustrates, there is a distinction between *distance* and *displacement*. Distance is a number that measures separation, while displacement consists of separation and direction. For example, walking 3 miles north and walking 3 miles east give different displacements, but both correspond to a distance of 3 miles.

Figure 12.1: After walking 3 miles east then 4 miles north, your distance from home is 5 miles

Adding Displacements Using Triangles

Displacements are added by treating them as arrows called *vectors*. The length of each arrow indicates the magnitude of the displacement, while the orientation of the arrow (which way the arrow points) indicates the direction. To add two displacements, join the tail of the second arrow to the head of the first arrow. Together, the arrows form two sides of a triangle whose third side represents their sum. The sum is the *net displacement* resulting from the two displacements.

Example 1 A person leaves her home and walks 5 miles due east and then 3 miles northeast. How far has she walked? How far away from home is she? What is her net displacement?

Solution In Figure 12.2, the first arrow is 5 units long because she walks 5 miles, while the second arrow is 3 units long and at an angle of $45°$ to the first. The length of the third side, x, of the triangle can be found by the Law of Cosines:

$$x^2 = 5^2 + 3^2 - 2 \cdot 5 \cdot 3 \cos 135°$$
$$= 34 - 30 \left(-\frac{\sqrt{2}}{2} \right)$$
$$= 55.213.$$

This gives $x = \sqrt{55.213} = 7.431$ miles for the distance from home to destination, which is less than the total distance walked ($5 + 3 = 8$ miles). To specify her net displacement we use the angle θ in Figure 12.2. We find θ using the Law of Sines:

$$\frac{\sin \theta}{3} = \frac{\sin 135°}{7.431},$$

giving

$$\sin \theta = 3 \cdot \frac{\sqrt{2}/2}{7.431} = 0.285.$$

Taking the arcsin of both sides, we obtain $\theta = \sin^{-1}(0.285) = 16.588°$. Thus, the net displacement is 7.431 miles in a direction $16.588°$ north of east.

Figure 12.2: A person walks 5 miles east and then 3 miles northeast

The Order of Addition Does Not Affect the Sum

When two displacements are added, the sum is independent of the order in which the two arrows are joined. For example, in Figure 12.3 the 5-mile displacement followed by the 3-mile displacement leads to the same destination as the 3-mile displacement followed by the 5-mile displacement.

Figure 12.3: No matter which order the arrows are joined, the resulting net displacement is the same

Vectors

Many physical quantities add in the same way as displacements. Such quantities are known as *vectors*. Like displacements, vectors are often represented as arrows. A vector has *magnitude* (the arrow's length) and *direction* (which way the arrow points). Examples of vectors include:

- **Velocity** This is the speed and direction of travel.
- **Force** This is, loosely speaking, the strength and direction of a push or a pull.
- **Magnetic fields** A vector gives the direction and intensity of a magnetic field at a point.
- **Vectors in economics** Vectors are used to keep track of prices and quantities.
- **Vectors in computer animation** Computers generate animations by performing enormous numbers of vector-based calculations.
- **Population vectors** In biology, populations of different animals or age groups can be represented using vectors.

Vector Notation

In this book we write vectors as variables with arrows over them: $\vec{v}$. The notation is intended to ensure that a vector $\vec{v}$ is not mistaken for a *scalar*, which is another name for an ordinary number.

Notation for the Magnitude of a Vector

The length or magnitude of a vector $\vec{v}$ is written $\|\vec{v}\|$. This notation looks like the absolute value notation, $|x|$, used for scalars. The absolute value of a number is its size without regard to sign, so $|-10| = |+10| = 10$. Similarly, the vectors $\vec{u}$ and $\vec{v}$ in Figure 12.4 are both of length 5, even though they point in different directions. Therefore, $\|\vec{u}\| = \|\vec{v}\| = 5$ (although $\vec{u} \neq \vec{v}$).

Figure 12.4: The vectors $\vec{u}$ and $\vec{v}$ are both of magnitude 5, but they point in different directions

Addition of Vectors

As with displacements, the sum of two vectors $\vec{u}$ and $\vec{v}$ represented by arrows is found by joining the tail of $\vec{v}$ to the head of $\vec{u}$. Then $\vec{w} = \vec{u} + \vec{v}$ is represented by the arrow drawn from the tail of of $\vec{u}$ to the head of $\vec{v}$. See Figure 12.5.[1]

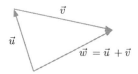

Figure 12.5: Constructing the vector sum $\vec{w} = \vec{u} + \vec{v}$

Example 2 Spacecraft such as *Voyager* and *Galileo* experience gravitational forces exerted by the sun, earth, and other planets. Vectors are used to represent the strength and direction of the gravitational forces.

Suppose a Jupiter-bound spacecraft is coasting between the orbits of Mars and Jupiter. Assume that Jupiter exerts a gravitational force of 8 units on the spacecraft, directed toward Jupiter, and that Mars exerts a force of 3 units on the spacecraft, directed toward Mars. The force $\vec{F}_M$ exerted by Mars is at an angle of $70°$ to the force $\vec{F}_J$ exerted by Jupiter, as shown in Figure 12.6. (For simplicity, we ignore the forces due to the sun and other planets.)

(a) Find $\|\vec{F}_{MJ}\|$, the magnitude of the net force on the spacecraft due to Mars and Jupiter.
(b) What is the direction of $\vec{F}_{MJ}$?
(c) Without engine power, will the spacecraft stay on course?

Figure 12.6: Forces $\vec{F}_M$ and $\vec{F}_J$ exerted by Mars and Jupiter, respectively

---

[1]If $\vec{u}$ and $\vec{v}$ are parallel, the vectors are added by the same method. However, in this case the figure is not a triangle.

Solution
(a) The net force, $\vec{F}_{\text{MJ}}$, is the sum of $\vec{F}_{\text{M}}$ and $\vec{F}_{\text{J}}$, the forces due to Mars and Jupiter, so

$$\vec{F}_{\text{MJ}} = \vec{F}_{\text{M}} + \vec{F}_{\text{J}}.$$

Figure 12.7 shows $\vec{F}_{\text{MJ}}$, obtained by joining the tail of $\vec{F}_{\text{J}}$ to the head of $\vec{F}_{\text{M}}$. The Law of Cosines tells us that $||\vec{F}_{\text{MJ}}||$, the length of the resulting vector, is given by

$$\begin{aligned}
||\vec{F}_{\text{MJ}}||^2 &= 8^2 + 3^2 - 2 \cdot 8 \cdot 3 \cos 110° \\
&= 73 - 48 \cos 110° \\
&= 89.417,
\end{aligned}$$

so $||\vec{F}_{\text{MJ}}|| = \sqrt{89.417} = 9.456$ units. Notice that 9.456 is less than the sum of the magnitudes of the individual forces $3 + 8 = 11$ units. The magnitude of the net force is less than 11 units because the forces exerted by Mars and Jupiter are not perfectly aligned.

(b) The direction of $\vec{F}_{\text{MJ}}$, denoted by θ in Figure 12.7, can be found using the Law of Sines:

$$\frac{\sin \theta}{3} = \frac{\sin 110°}{||\vec{F}_{\text{MJ}}||}$$

$$\sin \theta = 3 \left(\frac{\sin 110°}{||\vec{F}_{\text{MJ}}||} \right) = 3 \left(\frac{0.939}{9.456} \right) = 0.298,$$

so

$$\theta = \arcsin(0.298) = 17.345°.$$

(c) The gravity of Mars is pulling the spacecraft off its Jupiter-bound course by about 17.345°. The spacecraft will veer off course if it does not use its engines.

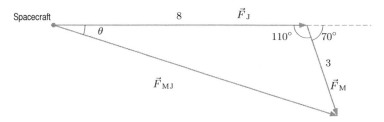

Figure 12.7: The net force, $\vec{F}_{\text{MJ}}$, on the spacecraft

Subtraction of Vectors

We have seen how vectors are added. Now we see how to subtract one vector from another. If

$$\vec{w} = \vec{u} - \vec{v},$$

then it is reasonable to assume that by adding $\vec{v}$ to both sides we obtain

$$\vec{w} + \vec{v} = \vec{u}.$$

In other words, $\vec{w}$ is the vector that when added to $\vec{v}$ gives $\vec{u}$. This is illustrated in Figure 12.8.

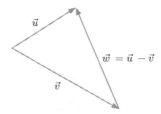

Figure 12.8: If $\vec{w} = \vec{u} - \vec{v}$, then $\vec{w}$ is
the vector that when added to $\vec{v}$ gives $\vec{u}$

Figure 12.8 suggests the following rule: To find $\vec{w} = \vec{u} - \vec{v}$, join the tails of $\vec{v}$ and $\vec{u}$, and then $\vec{w}$ is the vector drawn from the head of $\vec{v}$ to the head of $\vec{u}$.

Example 3 Suppose the spacecraft in Example 2 can fire its engine thrusters in any direction, but that the strength of the thrust is always 4 units. In what direction should the spacecraft aim its engine thrusters in order to stay on course toward Jupiter?

Solution The engine-thrust vector $\vec{F}_{engines}$ must be chosen so as to push the spacecraft back on course. The combined force on the craft due to Mars and Jupiter is given by $\vec{F}_{MJ}$. When the engines are on, the net force due to Mars, Jupiter, and the engines is given by

$$\vec{F}_{net} = \vec{F}_{MJ} + \vec{F}_{engines}.$$

We choose $\vec{F}_{engines}$ so that $\vec{F}_{net}$ points directly toward Jupiter. Solving for $\vec{F}_{engines}$ gives

$$\vec{F}_{engines} = \vec{F}_{net} - \vec{F}_{MJ}.$$

We do not know the length of $\vec{F}_{net}$, but we do know that it points toward Jupiter. From Example 2, the length of $\vec{F}_{MJ}$ is 9.456 units and the vector is directed at a 17.345° angle clockwise from $\vec{F}_{net}$. Figure 12.9 shows $\vec{F}_{engines} = \vec{F}_{net} - \vec{F}_{MJ}$. (The force $\vec{F}_{engines}$ is actually applied to the spacecraft, as shown in Figure 12.9. However, we can move a vector from one point to another when adding.)

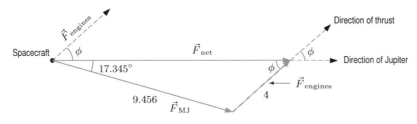

Figure 12.9: The engine-thrust vector is given by $\vec{F}_{engines} = \vec{F}_{net} - \vec{F}_{MJ}$, where $\vec{F}_{net}$ points
directly toward Jupiter and $\vec{F}_{MJ}$ is as shown in Figure 12.7

We want to find the direction of thrust, labeled ϕ in Figure 12.9. By the Law of Sines, we have

$$\frac{\sin \phi}{9.456} = \frac{\sin 17.345°}{4}$$

$$\sin \phi = 9.456 \left(\frac{\sin 17.345°}{4} \right).$$

One solution to this equation is

$$\phi = \arcsin\left(\frac{9.456}{4}\sin 17.345°\right) = 44.811°.$$

The engine thrusters should be aimed $44.811°$ counterclockwise from the direction of Jupiter.

There is another possible value for ϕ, the direction of the engine thrust in Example 3. This is because there are two solutions to the equation

$$\sin\phi = \frac{9.456}{4}\sin 17.345°.$$

The second solution, $180° - 44.811° = 135.189°$, is shown in Figure 12.10. Both values of ϕ serve to counteract the gravity of Mars, but the $44.811°$ direction helps push the craft toward Jupiter, whereas the $135.189°$ direction helps push it away from Jupiter. Thus, the first solution is probably preferable.

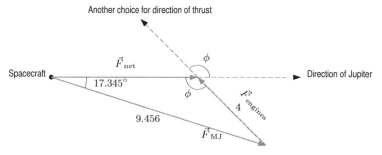

Figure 12.10: There are two possible choices for the direction of thrust. One has the effect of pushing the spacecraft toward Jupiter, the other (shown here) pushes the spacecraft away from Jupiter

Scalar Multiplication

A vector $\vec{u}$ can be added to itself. In Figure 12.11. The resulting vector, $\vec{u} + \vec{u}$, points in the same direction as $\vec{u}$ but is twice as long. The vector $\vec{u} + \vec{u} + \vec{u}$ also points in the same direction as $\vec{u}$, but is three times as long. We write

$$2\vec{u} \quad \text{for} \quad \vec{u} + \vec{u} \qquad \text{and} \qquad 3\vec{u} \quad \text{for} \quad \vec{u} + \vec{u} + \vec{u}.$$

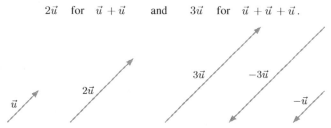

Figure 12.11: The vector $2\vec{u} = \vec{u} + \vec{u}$, points in the same direction as $\vec{u}$ but is twice as long as $\vec{u}$. Similarly, $3\vec{u} = \vec{u} + \vec{u} + \vec{u}$ points in the same direction and is 3 times as long as $\vec{u}$, and $-\vec{u}$ is in the opposite direction to $\vec{u}$

Similarly, $0.5\vec{u}$ points in the same direction as $\vec{u}$ but is only half as long. In general, if $\vec{v}$ is a vector and k a positive number (a positive scalar), then $k\vec{v}$ is a vector that is k times as long as $\vec{v}$ and pointing in the same direction as $\vec{v}$. The vector $k\vec{v}$ is called a *scalar multiple* of $\vec{v}$.

If k is a negative number, the vector $k\vec{v}$ has length $|k|$ times the length of $\vec{v}$, but points in the opposite direction to $\vec{v}$. For example, $-3\vec{u}$ is the vector that is three times as long as $\vec{u}$ but pointing in the opposite direction. See Figure 12.11.

The Zero Vector

The *zero vector*, denoted by the symbol $\vec{0}$, represents no displacement, which is the displacement that leaves you where you started. The zero vector has no direction.

The following rules summarize scalar multiplication.

- If $k > 0$, then $k\vec{v}$ points in the same direction as $\vec{v}$ and is k times as long.
- If $k < 0$, then $k\vec{v}$ points in the opposite direction as $\vec{v}$ and is $|k|$ times as long.
- If $k = 0$, then $k\vec{v} = \vec{0}$, the zero vector.

Alternate View of Subtraction

Since the vector $-\vec{v}$ points in the opposite direction to $\vec{v}$, the difference $\vec{u} - \vec{v}$ is the same as the sum $\vec{u} + (-\vec{v})$. See Figure 12.12.

Figure 12.12: Illustration of the fact that $\vec{u} - \vec{v} = \vec{u} + (-\vec{v})$

Properties of Vector Addition and Scalar Multiplication

The following properties hold true for any three vectors $\vec{u}$, $\vec{v}$, $\vec{w}$ and any two scalars a and b:

1. *Commutativity of addition:* $\vec{u} + \vec{v} = \vec{v} + \vec{u}$
2. *Associativity of addition:* $(\vec{u} + \vec{v}) + \vec{w} = \vec{u} + (\vec{v} + \vec{w})$
3. *Associativity of scalar multiplication:* $a(b\vec{v}) = (ab)\vec{v}$
4. *Distributivity of scalar multiplication:* $(a + b)\vec{v} = a\vec{v} + b\vec{v}$ and $a(\vec{u} + \vec{v}) = a\vec{u} + a\vec{v}$
5. *Identities:* $\vec{v} + \vec{0} = \vec{v}$ and $1 \cdot \vec{v} = \vec{v}$

These properties are analogous to the corresponding properties for addition and multiplication of numbers. In other words, vector addition and scalar multiplication of vectors behave as expected.

Exercises and Problems for Section 12.1

Exercises

We use scalars to describe quantities like weight because these require only a single number (for example, 50 lbs). We use vectors to describe quantities like velocity because these require more than one number (for example, 20 mph at a heading of 80°). In Exercises 1–8, should we describe the given quantity with a vector or a scalar?

1. The elevation of a national monument.
2. The temperature at a point on the earth's surface.
3. The wind velocity at a point on the earth's surface.
4. The distance from Seattle to St. Louis.
5. The population of the US.
6. The population of a city.
7. The location in space of a satellite.
8. The number of men and women living in a city.

Given the displacement vectors $\vec{v}$ and $\vec{w}$ in Figure 12.13, draw the vectors in Exercises 9–14.

Figure 12.13

9. $\vec{v} + \vec{w}$ **10.** $\vec{v} - \vec{w}$ **11.** $2\vec{v}$

12. $\vec{w} + \vec{v}/2$ **13.** $2\vec{v} + \vec{w}$ **14.** $\vec{v} - 2\vec{w}$

15. The vectors $\vec{w}$ and $\vec{u}$ are in Figure 12.14. Match the vectors $\vec{p}, \vec{q}, \vec{r}, \vec{s}, \vec{t}$ with five of the following vectors: $\vec{u} + \vec{w}, \vec{u} - \vec{w}, \vec{w} - \vec{u}, 2\vec{w} - \vec{u}, \vec{u} - 2\vec{w}, 2\vec{w}, -2\vec{w}, 2\vec{u}, -2\vec{u}, -\vec{w}, -\vec{u}$.

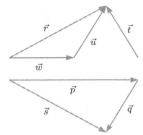

Figure 12.14

Problems

16. (a) A kite on a 50-foot string is flying at an angle of $20°$ to flat ground. What is the magnitude and the direction of the vector from the kite to the ground?

(b) A wind blows the kite upward so that its angle with the ground is $40°$. How far is the new position from the original position?

17. Oracle Road heads due north from its intersection with Route 10, which heads $20°$ west of north.

(a) If you travel 5 miles up Route 10 from the intersection, how far are you from Oracle Road?

(b) How far do you have to travel up Route 10 from the intersection to be 2 miles from Oracle Road?

18. A person leaves home and walks 2 miles due west. She then walks 3 miles southwest. How far away from home is she? In what direction must she walk to head directly home? (Your answer should be an angle in degrees and should include a sketch.)

19. The person from Problem 18 next walks 4 miles southeast. How far away from home is she? In what direction must she walk to head directly home?

20. A hockey puck starts on the edge of the rink and slides with a constant velocity $\vec{v}$, at a speed of 7 ft/sec and an angle of $35°$ with the edge. After 2 seconds, how far has the puck traveled? How far is it from the edge?

21. A helicopter is hovering at 3000 meters directly over the eastern perimeter of a secret Air Force installation. The eastern perimeter is 5000 meters straight east from the installation headquarters. The helicopter receives a transmission from headquarters that a UFO has been sighted at 7500 meters directly over the installation's western perimeter, which is 9000 meters straight west from the headquarters. How far must the helicopter travel to intercept the UFO? In what direction must it head? Be specific.

22. Suppose instead the UFO in Problem 21 is sighted directly over the installation's northern perimeter, which is 12,000 meters from headquarters. How far must the helicopter travel to intercept the UFO? In what direction must it head? Be specific.

23. A spacecraft is traveling directly toward Saturn, which exerts a gravitational force of 7 units on it. The moon Titan exerts a force of 10 units at a $40°$ angle to the right of the line joining the spacecraft to Saturn. The moon Rhea exerts a force of 5 units $80°$ to the left of this line.

(a) Find $||\vec{F}_{STR}||$, the magnitude of the sum of the forces acting on the spacecraft.

(b) Does the craft remain on course or veer to the left or to the right?

(c) If the engines have a thrust of 1 unit, is it possible to aim them in such a way as to correct the spacecraft's course?

24. A ball is thrown horizontally at 5 feet per second relative to still air. At the same time a wind blows at 3 feet per second at an angle of $45°$ to the ball's path. What is the velocity of the ball relative to the ground? (There are two answers.)

Use the definitions of addition and scalar multiplication to explain each of the properties in Problems 25–31.

25. $\vec{w} + \vec{v} = \vec{v} + \vec{w}$ **26.** $(a+b)\vec{v} = a\vec{v} + b\vec{v}$

27. $a(\vec{v} + \vec{w}) = a\vec{v} + a\vec{w}$ **28.** $\vec{v} + \vec{0} = \vec{v}$

29. $1\vec{v} = \vec{v}$ **30.** $\vec{v} + (-1)\vec{w} = \vec{v} - \vec{w}$

31. $(\vec{u} + \vec{v}) + \vec{w} = \vec{u} + (\vec{v} + \vec{w})$

12.2 THE COMPONENTS OF A VECTOR

So far, vectors have been described in terms of length and direction. There is another way to think about a vector, and that is in terms of *components*. We begin with an example illustrating the use of components; we define this term precisely later.

Example 1 A ship travels 200 miles in a direction that its compass says is due east. The captain then discovers that the compass is faulty and that the ship has actually been heading in a direction that is 17.4° to the north of due east. How far north is the ship from its intended course?

Solution In Figure 12.15, a vector $\vec{v}$ has been drawn for the ship's actual displacement. We know that $\|\vec{v}\| =$ 200 miles and the direction of $\vec{v}$ is 17.4° to the north of due east. We see that $\vec{v}$ can be considered the sum of two vectors, one pointing due east and the other pointing due north, so

$$\vec{v} = \vec{v}_{\text{north}} + \vec{v}_{\text{east}}.$$

From Figure 12.15, we have

$$\sin 17.4° = \frac{\|\vec{v}_{\text{north}}\|}{200},$$

so

$$\|\vec{v}_{\text{north}}\| = 200 \sin 17.4° = 59.808 \text{ miles.}$$

Therefore, the ship is 59.808 miles due north of its intended course.

Figure 12.15: How far north is the ship from its intended eastward course?

Unit Vectors

A *unit vector* is a vector of length 1 unit. The unit vectors in the directions of the positive x- and y-axes are called $\vec{i}$ and $\vec{j}$, respectively. See Figure 12.16. These two vectors are important because any vector in the plane can be expressed in terms of $\vec{i}$ and $\vec{j}$.

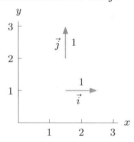

Figure 12.16: The unit vectors $\vec{i}$ and $\vec{j}$

Example 2 Let the x-axis point east and the y-axis point north. A person walks 3 miles east and then 4 miles north. Express her displacement in terms of the unit vectors $\vec{i}$ and $\vec{j}$.

Solution   The unit of distance is miles, so the unit vector $\vec{i}$ represents a displacement of 1 mile east, and the unit vector $\vec{j}$ represents a displacement of 1 mile north. The person's displacement can be written

$$\text{Displacement} = 3 \text{ miles east } + 4 \text{ miles north} = 3\vec{i} + 4\vec{j}.$$

Example 3   Let the x-axis points east and the y-axis points north. Describe the displacement $5\vec{i} - 7\vec{j}$ in words.

Solution   Since $\vec{i}$ represents a 1-mile displacement to the east, $5\vec{i}$ represents a 5-mile displacement to the east. Since $\vec{j}$ represents a 1-mile displacement to the north, $-7\vec{j}$ represents a 7-mile displacement to the south. Thus, $5\vec{i} - 7\vec{j}$ represents a 5-mile displacement to the east followed by a 7-mile displacement to the south.

Resolving a Vector in the Plane into Components

In this book, we focus chiefly on vectors that lie flat in the plane. Such vectors can always be broken (or *resolved*) into sum of two vectors,[2] one parallel to the x-axis and the other to the y-axis. These two vectors are called the *components* parallel to the axes.

For the vector $\vec{v}$ in Figure 12.17, we can write

$$\vec{v} = \vec{v}_1 + \vec{v}_2,$$

where $\vec{v}_1$ is called the *x-component* of $\vec{v}$ and $\vec{v}_2$ is the *y-component* of $\vec{v}$. What can we say about the components $\vec{v}_1$ and $\vec{v}_2$?

Figure 12.17: A vector $\vec{v}$ can be written as the sum of components, $\vec{v}_1$ and $\vec{v}_2$, parallel to the x- and y-axes

In Figure 12.17, the vector $\vec{v}$ has length $\|\vec{v}\|$ and makes an angle θ with the positive x-axis, with $0 \leq \theta < 2\pi$. Thus, we see that

$$\cos\theta = \frac{\|\vec{v}_1\|}{\|\vec{v}\|} \quad \text{and} \quad \sin\theta = \frac{\|\vec{v}_2\|}{\|\vec{v}\|}.$$

Therefore

$$\|\vec{v}_1\| = \|\vec{v}\|\cos\theta \quad \text{and} \quad \|\vec{v}_2\| = \|\vec{v}\|\sin\theta.$$

We know that $\vec{v}_1$ is parallel to the x-axis, so it is a scalar multiple of the unit vector $\vec{i}$. Similarly, $\vec{v}_2$ is a scalar multiple of $\vec{j}$. After checking that the signs of $\cos\theta$ and $\sin\theta$ give the correct directions for $\vec{v}_1$ and $\vec{v}_2$, we have

$$\vec{v}_1 = (\|\vec{v}\|\cos\theta)\,\vec{i} \quad \text{and} \quad \vec{v}_2 = (\|\vec{v}\|\sin\theta)\,\vec{j}.$$

These are the x- and y- components of $\vec{v}$. We have the following result:

In the plane, a vector $\vec{v}$ of length $\|\vec{v}\|$ that makes an angle θ with the positive x-axis can be written in terms of its components:

$$\vec{v} = (\|\vec{v}\|\cos\theta)\,\vec{i} + (\|\vec{v}\|\sin\theta)\,\vec{j}.$$

---

[2]However, one or both of the vectors may be of zero length.

Example 4 In Example 1, suppose the x-axis points east and the y-axis points north. Resolve the displacement vector $\vec{v}$ into components parallel to the axes.

Solution The vector $\vec{v}_{\text{north}}$ is the y-component of $\vec{v}$ and $\vec{v}_{\text{east}}$ is the x-component. We already know that $\|\vec{v}_{\text{north}}\| = 59.808$ miles. From Figure 12.15, we see that $\|\vec{v}_{\text{east}}\| = 200\cos 17.4° = 190.848$ miles. (This last piece of information tells us that although the ship traveled a total of 200 miles, its eastward progress amounted to only 190.848 miles.) The easterly and northerly components are

$$\vec{v}_{\text{east}} = 190.848\vec{i} \qquad \text{and} \qquad \vec{v}_{\text{north}} = 59.808\vec{j}.$$

Thus, the course taken by the ship can be written as follows:

$$\vec{v} = \vec{v}_{\text{east}} + \vec{v}_{\text{north}} = 190.848\vec{i} + 59.808\vec{j}.$$

To check the calculation, notice that

$$\|\vec{v}_{\text{east}}\|^2 + \|\vec{v}_{\text{north}}\|^2 = (190.848)^2 + (59.808)^2 \approx 40,000 = \|\vec{v}\|^2.$$

Sums and scalar multiples are easy to compute if vectors are written in terms of components. For a sum, add corresponding components; for a multiple, multiply each component by the scalar.

Example 5 Let $\vec{u} = 5\vec{i} + 7\vec{j}$, $\vec{v} = \vec{i} + \vec{j}$, and $\vec{w} = 6\vec{j} - 3\vec{i} + 2\vec{j} - 2\vec{i} - 4\vec{j} + 7\vec{i}$. Describe in words the similarities and differences between the following displacements:

$$2\vec{i} + 4\vec{j}, \quad \vec{u} - 3\vec{v}, \quad \vec{w}.$$

Solution We show that the displacements $2\vec{i} + 4\vec{j}$, $\vec{u} - 3\vec{v}$, and $\vec{w}$ are all the same. Using the properties on page 502, we have

$$\vec{u} - 3\vec{v} = (5\vec{i} + 7\vec{j}) - 3(\vec{i} + \vec{j})$$
$$= (5\vec{i} + 7\vec{j}) - (3\vec{i} + 3\vec{j})$$
$$= (5\vec{i} - 3\vec{i}) + (7\vec{j} - 3\vec{j}) = 2\vec{i} + 4\vec{j}.$$

The vector $\vec{w}$ can be simplified as

$$\vec{w} = (-3\vec{i} - 2\vec{i} + 7\vec{i}) + (6\vec{j} + 2\vec{j} - 4\vec{j}) = 2\vec{i} + 4\vec{j}.$$

Alternatively, we can see that all three displacements are the same by doing head-to-tail addition for each case, with the same starting point. Figure 12.18 shows that all three end points are the same, although the path followed is different in each case.

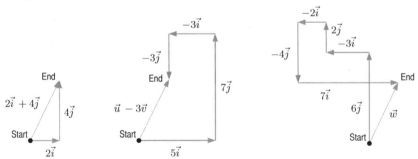

Figure 12.18: These three displacements, $2\vec{i} + 4\vec{j}$, $\vec{u} - 3\vec{v}$, $\vec{w}$, are all the same

Displacement Vectors

Vectors that indicate displacement are often designated by giving two points that specify the initial and final positions. For example, the vector $\vec{v} = \overrightarrow{PQ}$ describes a displacement or motion from point P to point Q. If we know the coordinates of P and Q, we can easily find the components of $\vec{v}$.

Example 6   If P is the point $(-3, 1)$ and Q is the point $(2, 4)$, find the components of the vector $\overrightarrow{PQ}$.

Solution   Figure 12.19 shows the vector $\overrightarrow{PQ}$ and its components $\vec{v}_1$ and $\vec{v}_2$. The length of $\vec{v}_1$ is the horizontal distance from P to Q, so

$$\|\vec{v}_1\| = 2 - (-3) = 5.$$

The length of $\vec{v}_2$ is the vertical distance from P to Q, so

$$\|\vec{v}_2\| = 4 - 1 = 3.$$

Thus, the components are $\vec{v}_1 = 5\vec{i}$ and $\vec{v}_2 = 3\vec{j}$. We write $\vec{v} = \overrightarrow{PQ} = 5\vec{i} + 3\vec{j}$.

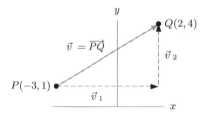

Figure 12.19: Finding components $\vec{v}_1$ and $\vec{v}_2$ from the coordinates of the points P and Q

In general, we have the following result:

> If $P = (x_1, y_1)$ and $Q = (x_2, y_2)$, then the vector $\vec{v} = \overrightarrow{PQ}$ from P to Q is given by
> $$\vec{v} = (x_2 - x_1)\vec{i} + (y_2 - y_1)\vec{j}.$$

Vectors in n Dimensions

So far we have considered 2-dimensional vectors which have two components. Vectors in space need three components and they are also very useful. In addition, there are *n-dimensional* vectors, which have n components, where n is a positive integer.

Example 7   A balloon rises vertically a distance of 2 miles, floats west a distance of 3 miles, and floats north a distance of 4 miles. The x-axis points eastward, the y-axis points northward, and the z-axis points upward. The balloon's displacement vector has three components: a vertical component, an eastward component, and a northward component. Therefore, this displacement is a 3-dimensional vector. We write this vector as

$$\text{Displacement } = -3\vec{i} + 4\vec{j} + 2\vec{k}.$$

Exercises and Problems for Section 12.2

Exercises

Resolve the vectors in Exercises 1–3 into components.

1. A vector starting at the point $Q = (4, 6)$ and ending at the point $P = (1, 2)$.

2. A vector starting at the point $P = (1, 2)$ and ending at the point $Q = (4, 6)$.

3. The vector shown in Figure 12.20, with components expressed in inches.

Figure 12.20: Scale: 1 unit on the x- and y-axes is 0.25 inches

For Exercises 4–7, perform the indicated computations.

4. $5(2\vec{i} - \vec{j}) + \vec{j}$

5. $(4\vec{i} + 2\vec{j}) - (3\vec{i} - \vec{j})$

6. $-(\vec{i} + \vec{j}) + 2(2\vec{i} - 3\vec{j})$

7. $2(0.45\vec{i} - 0.9\vec{j} - 0.01\vec{k}) - 0.5(1.2\vec{i} - 0.1\vec{k})$

8. On the graph in Figure 12.21, draw the vector $\vec{v} = 4\vec{i} + \vec{j}$ twice, once with its tail at the origin and once with its tail at the point $(3, 2)$.

Figure 12.21

Find the length of the vectors in Exercises 9–12.

9. $\vec{v} = \vec{i} - \vec{j} + 3\vec{k}$

10. $\vec{v} = \vec{i} - \vec{j} + 2\vec{k}$

11. $\vec{v} = 7.2\vec{i} - 1.5\vec{j} + 2.1\vec{k}$

12. $\vec{v} = 1.2\vec{i} - 3.6\vec{j} + 4.1\vec{k}$

Problems

13. A ship steams due north at 10 knots but experiences an ocean current that moves east to west at 5 knots.[3] Resolve into components the velocity of the ship in a coordinate system in which the x-axis points east and the y axis points north.

In Problems 14–17, use the information in Figure 12.22. Each grid square is 1 unit along each side.

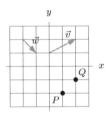

Figure 12.22

14. Write the following vectors in component form.

(a) $\vec{v}$ (b) $2\vec{w}$ (c) $\vec{v} + \vec{w}$ (d) $\vec{w} - \vec{v}$

(e) The displacement vector $\overrightarrow{PQ}$.

(f) The vector from the point P to the point $(2, 0)$.

(g) A vector perpendicular to the y-axis.

(h) A vector perpendicular to the x-axis.

15. What is the angle between the vector $\vec{w}$ and the negative y-axis?

16. What is the angle between the vectors $\vec{v}$ and $\vec{w}$?

17. What is the angle between the vector $\vec{w}$ and the displacement vector $\overrightarrow{PQ}$?

18. A car is traveling at a speed of 50 km/hr. The positive y-axis is north and the positive x-axis is east. Resolve the car's velocity vector into two components if the car is traveling in each of the following directions:

(a) East   (b) South

(c) Southeast   (d) Northwest

---

[3] 1 knot is 1 nautical mile (approximately 6080 feet) per hour.

19. Shortly after takeoff, a plane is climbing northwest through still air at an airspeed of 200 km/hr and rising at a rate of 300 m/min. Resolve into components its velocity vector in a coordinate system in which the x-axis points east, the y-axis points north, and the z-axis points up.

20. (a) Find a unit vector from the point $P = (1, 2)$ toward the point $Q = (4, 6)$.
    (b) Find a vector of length 10 pointing in the same direction.

21. Which is traveling faster, a car whose velocity vector is $21\vec{i} + 35\vec{j}$, or a car whose velocity vector is $40\vec{i}$, assuming that the units are the same for both directions?

22. A truck is traveling due north at 30 km/hr toward a crossroad. On a perpendicular road a police car is traveling west toward the intersection at 40 km/hr. Both vehicles will reach the crossroad in exactly one hour. Find the vector currently representing the displacement of the truck with respect to the police car.

23. An athlete throws a shot at a $30°$ angle to the ground at speed 50 km/hr.
    (a) What is the magnitude of the velocity vector of the shot?
    (b) Resolve the velocity vector into vertical and horizontal components.

24. Which of the following vectors are parallel?

$$\vec{u} = 2\vec{i} + 4\vec{j} - 2\vec{k}, \quad \vec{v} = \vec{i} - \vec{j} + 3\vec{k},$$
$$\vec{w} = -\vec{i} - 2\vec{j} + \vec{k}, \quad \vec{p} = \vec{i} + \vec{j} + \vec{k},$$
$$\vec{q} = 4\vec{i} - 4\vec{j} + 12\vec{k}, \quad \vec{r} = \vec{i} - \vec{j} + \vec{k}.$$

25. (a) A man swims northeast at 5 mph. Give a vector representing his velocity.
    (b) He now swims in a river at the same velocity relative to still water; the river's current flows north at 1.2 mph. What is his velocity relative to the riverbed?

26. The coastline is along the x-axis and the sea is in the region $y > 0$. A sailing boat has velocity $\vec{v} = 2.5\vec{i} + 3.1\vec{j}$ mph. What is the speed of the boat? What angle does the boat's path make with the coastline?

27. The hour hand and the minute hand of a clock are represented by the vectors $\vec{h}$ and $\vec{m}$, respectively, with $||\vec{h}|| = 2$ and $||\vec{m}|| = 3$. The origin is at the center of the clock and the positive x-axis goes through the three o'clock position.
    (a) What are the components of $\vec{h}$ and $\vec{m}$ at the following times? Illustrate with a sketch.
        (i) 12 noon   (ii) 3 pm
        (iii) 1 pm   (iv) 1:30 pm
    (b) Sketch the displacement vector from the tip of the hour hand to the tip of the minute hand at 3 pm. What are the components of this displacement vector?
    (c) Sketch the vector representing the sum $\vec{h} + \vec{m}$ at 1:30 pm. What are the components of this sum?

A cat on the ground at the point $(1, 4, 0)$ watches a squirrel at the top of a tree. The tree is one unit high with base at the point $(2, 4, 0)$. Find the displacement vectors in Problems 28–31.

28. From the origin to the cat.

29. From the bottom of the tree to the squirrel.

30. From the bottom of the tree to the cat.

31. From the cat to the squirrel.

12.3 APPLICATION OF VECTORS

Alternate Notation for the Components of a Vector

The vector $\vec{v} = 3\vec{i} + 4\vec{j}$ is sometimes written $\vec{v} = (3, 4)$. This notation can be confused with the coordinate notation used for points. For instance, $(3, 4)$ might mean the point $x = 3$, $y = 4$ or the vector $3\vec{i} + 4\vec{j}$. Nevertheless, this notation is useful for vectors in n dimensions.

Population Vectors

Vectors in n dimensions are useful for keeping track of n quantities. We add them by adding the corresponding components; scalar multiples are obtained by multiplying each component by the scalar.

Example 1 The 2005 population of the six New England states (Connecticut, Maine, Massachusetts, New Hampshire, Rhode Island, and Vermont) can be thought of as a 6-dimensional vector $\vec{P}$. The components of $\vec{P}$ are the populations of the six states. Using the alternate notation, we write

$$\vec{P} = (P_{CT}, P_{ME}, P_{MA}, P_{NH}, P_{RI}, P_{VT}),$$

where P_{CT} is the population of Connecticut, P_{ME} is the population of Maine, and so on.

The population vector $\vec{P}$ from the previous example does not have a geometrical interpretation. We cannot draw a picture of $\vec{P}$, or interpret its length and direction as we do for displacement vectors. However, the following example shows how it is used.

Example 2

The vectors $\vec{P}$ and $\vec{Q}$ give the populations of the six New England states in 1995 and 2005, respectively. According to the Census Bureau,[4] these vectors are given, in millions of people, by

$$\vec{P} = (3.28, 1.24, 6.07, 1.15, 0.99, 0.59)$$
$$\vec{Q} = (3.51, 1.32, 6.40, 1.31, 1.08, 0.62).$$

For instance, the population of Connecticut was 3.28 million in 1995 and 3.51 million in 2005.

(a) Find $\vec{R} = \vec{Q} - \vec{P}$. Explain its significance in terms of the population of New England.
(b) Let $\vec{S}$ be the estimated population of New England in the year 2015. One expert predicts that $\vec{S} = \vec{Q} + 2\vec{R}$. Find $\vec{S}$ and explain the assumption this expert is making about the New England population.
(c) Another expert makes a different prediction, claiming that $\vec{T} = 1.08\vec{Q}$ will give the population of New England in 2015. Find $\vec{T}$ and explain the assumption that this expert is making.

Solution

(a) We have

$$\vec{R} = \vec{Q} - \vec{P}$$
$$= (3.51, 1.32, 6.40, 1.31, 1.08, 0.62) - (3.28, 1.24, 6.07, 1.15, 0.99, 0.59)$$
$$= (3.51 - 3.28, 1.32 - 1.24, 6.40 - 6.07, 1.31 - 1.15, 1.08 - 0.99, 0.62 - 0.59)$$
$$= (0.23, 0.08, 0.33, 0.16, 0.09, 0.03).$$

The components of $\vec{R}$ give the change in population for each New England state. For instance, the population of Connecticut rose from 3.28 million in 1995 to 3.51 million in 2005, a change of $3.51 - 3.28 = 0.23$ million people, so $R_{CT} = 0.23$.

(b) The formula $\vec{S} = \vec{Q} + 2\vec{R}$ means that

Population in 2015 = Population in 2005 + 2 · Change between 1995 and 2005.

According to this expert, states will see their populations climb twice as much between 2005 and 2015 as they did between 1995 and 2005. Algebraically, we have

$$\vec{S} = \vec{Q} + 2\vec{R}$$
$$= (3.51, 1.32, 6.40, 1.31, 1.08, 0.62) + 2 \cdot (0.23, 0.08, 0.33, 0.16, 0.09, 0.03)$$
$$= (3.51, 1.32, 6.40, 1.31, 1.08, 0.62) + (0.46, 0.16, 0.66, 0.32, 0.18, 0.06)$$
$$= (3.97, 1.48, 7.06, 1.63, 1.26, 0.68).$$

For instance, Connecticut's population climbed by 0.23 million between 1995 and 2005. The predicted population of Connecticut in 2015 is given by

$$S_{CT} = Q_{CT} + 2 \cdot R_{CT} = 3.51 + 2 \cdot (0.23) = 3.97.$$

The 0.46 million jump in Connecticut's population between 2005 and 2015 is twice as large as the 0.23 million jump between 1995 and 2005.

---

[4]From: http://www.census.gov, accessed January 10 2006.

(c) The formula $\vec{T} = 1.08\vec{Q}$ means that each component of $\vec{T}$ is 1.08 times as large as the corresponding component of $\vec{Q}$. In other words, the population of each state is predicted to grow by 8%. We have

$$\vec{T} = 1.08\vec{Q} = 1.08 \cdot (3.51, 1.32, 6.40, 1.31, 1.08, 0.62)$$
$$= (1.08 \cdot 3.51, 1.08 \cdot 1.32, 1.08 \cdot 6.40, 1.08 \cdot 1.31, 1.08 \cdot 1.08, 1.08 \cdot 0.62)$$
$$= (3.79, 1.43, 6.91, 1.41, 1.17, 0.67).$$

For instance, the population of New Hampshire is predicted to grow from $Q_{NH} = 1.31$ million in 2005 to $T_{NH} = 1.08Q_{NH} = 1.08(1.31) = 1.41$ million in the year 2015.

Notice how vector addition and subtraction was used in parts (a) and (b) of the previous example, and scalar multiplication was used in parts (b) and (c).

Economics

The blockbuster movie *Harry Potter and the Philosopher's Stone* grossed $292 million at domestic (US) box offices, more than any other domestic release in 2001.[5] It made even more money at international box offices, where it grossed $459 million. Rounding out its wild success is the $224 million for video and DVD sales rentals as of midyear 2002, for a grand total of just under one billion dollars. The *revenue vector* $\vec{r} = (292, 459, 224)$ summarizes the domestic, international, and video/DVD gross revenues in millions of dollars.

Example 3   After *Harry Potter*, the three next most financially successful US movies in 2001 were, in order, *Shrek*, *Pearl Harbor*, and *The Mummy Returns*. If $\vec{s}$, $\vec{t}$, and $\vec{u}$ are the revenue vectors for these three movies, then

$$\vec{s} = (268, 198, 436) \qquad \vec{t} = (199, 252, 301) \qquad \vec{u} = (202, 227, 192).$$

Find $\vec{R}$, the total revenue vector for all three of these movies.

Solution   The total revenue, $\vec{R}$, is the sum of $\vec{s}$, $\vec{t}$, and $\vec{u}$:

$$\vec{R} = \vec{s} + \vec{t} + \vec{u} = (268 + 199 + 202, 198 + 252 + 227, 436 + 301 + 192) = (669, 677, 929).$$

Price and Consumption Vectors

A car dealership has several different models of cars in its inventory, with different prices for each model. A *price vector*, $\vec{P}$, gives the price of each model:

$$\vec{P} = (P_1, P_2, \ldots, P_n).$$

Here P_1 is the price of car model 1, P_2 is the price of model 2, and so on. A *consumption vector* $\vec{C}$ gives the number of each model of car purchased (or consumed) during a given month:

$$\vec{C} = (C_1, C_2, \ldots, C_n).$$

[5]Data compiled from www.variety.com and www.videobusiness.com. Video and DVD sales and rental data as of midyear 2002.

Example 4

Suppose $\vec{I}$ gives the number of cars of each model a car dealer currently has in inventory. Explain the meaning of the following in terms of the car dealership.

(a) $\vec{I} - \vec{C}$ (b) $\vec{I} - 2\vec{C}$ (c) $\vec{C} = 0.3\vec{I}$

Solution

(a) This expression represents the difference between the number of each model currently in inventory and the number of that model purchased each month. So $\vec{I} - \vec{C}$ represents the numbers of each model that remain on the lot after one month.

(b) This expression represents the number of each model the dealer has left after two months, assuming that no new cars are added to inventory and that $\vec{C}$ does not change.

(c) This equation tells us that 30% of the inventory of each model is purchased by consumers each month.

Example 5

Let $\vec{E}$ represent expenses incurred by the dealer for acquisition, insurance, and overhead, for each model. What does the vector $\vec{P} - \vec{E}$ represent?

Solution

This represents the dealer's profit for each model. For instance, a model that the dealer sells for $29,000 may cost $25,000 to acquire from the factory, insure, and maintain. The difference of $4,000 represents profit for the dealer. The vector $\vec{P} - \vec{E}$ keeps track of this profit for each model.

Physics

Newton's law of gravitation states that the magnitude of force exerted on an object of mass m by the earth is given by

$$\|\vec{F}_E\| = G\frac{mM_E}{r_E^2},$$

where M_E is the mass of the earth, r_E is the distance from the object to earth's center, and G is a constant. Similarly, the force exerted on the object by the moon has magnitude

$$\|\vec{F}_L\| = G\frac{mM_L}{r_L^2},$$

where M_L is the mass of the moon and r_L is the distance to the moon's center. The force exerted by the earth is directed toward the earth; the force exerted by the moon is exerted toward the moon.

Example 6

Figure 12.23 shows the position of a 100,000-kg spacecraft relative to the earth and moon. The vector $\vec{r}$ is the position of the moon relative to the earth, $\vec{r}_E$ is the position of the spacecraft relative to the earth, and $\vec{r}_L$ is the position of the spacecraft relative to the moon. With distances in thousands of kilometers,

$$\vec{r} = 384\vec{i} \quad \text{and} \quad \vec{r}_E = 280\vec{i} + 90\vec{j}.$$

Which force is stronger, the pull of the moon on the spacecraft or the pull of the earth? [Use $M_E = 5.98 \cdot 10^{24}$ kg, $M_L = 7.34 \cdot 10^{22}$ kg, and $G = 6.67 \cdot 10^{-23}$ if distance is in thousands of kilometers.]

Figure 12.23: Gravitational forces between the earth, the moon, and a 100,000-kg spacecraft

Solution   To use Newton's law of gravitation, we first find $||\vec{r}_E||$ and $||\vec{r}_L||$. Since $\vec{r}_E = 280\vec{i} + 90\vec{j}$,

$$||\vec{r}_E|| = \sqrt{(280)^2 + (90)^2} = \sqrt{86500} = 294.109.$$

Since $\vec{r}_L = \vec{r}_E - \vec{r}$, we have

$$\vec{r}_L = (280\vec{i} + 90\vec{j}) - 384\vec{i} - -104\vec{i} + 90\vec{j}.$$

Thus,

$$||\vec{r}_L|| = \sqrt{(-104)^2 + (90)^2} = \sqrt{18916} = 137.535.$$

Using the given values of m, M_E, M_L, and G, we calculate

$$F_E = G\frac{mM_E}{||\vec{r}_E||^2} = 461.116 \qquad \text{and} \qquad F_L = G\frac{mM_L}{||\vec{r}_L||^2} = 25.882.$$

Thus, the pull of the earth on this spacecraft is much stronger than the pull of the moon; in fact, it is over ten times as strong. The earth's pull is stronger, even though the spaceship is closer to the moon, because the earth is much more massive than the moon.

Computer Graphics: Position Vectors

Video games usually incorporate computer-generated graphics, as do the flight simulators used by commercial and military flight-training schools. Hollywood makes increasing use of computer graphics in its films. Enormous amounts of computation are involved in creating such effects and much of this computation involves vectors.

A computer screen can be thought of as an xy-grid with the origin at the lower left corner. The position of a point on the screen is specified by a vector pointing from the origin to the point. Such a vector is called a *position vector*. The tail of a position vector is always fixed at the origin.

Example 7   A video game shows two airplanes on the screen at the points $(3, 5)$ and $(7, 2)$. See Figure 12.24. Both airplanes move a distance of 3 units at an angle of $70°$ counterclockwise from the x-axis. What are the new positions of the airplanes?

Figure 12.24: Computer screen showing two airplanes moving by a displacement vector $\vec{d}$

Solution   The initial position of the first airplane is given by the position vector $\vec{p}_{\text{start}} = 3\vec{i} + 5\vec{j}$. The plane's displacement can also be thought of as a vector, $\vec{d}$. Resolving $\vec{d}$ into components gives

$$\vec{d} = (3\cos 70°)\vec{i} + (3\sin 70°)\vec{j} = 1.026\vec{i} + 2.819\vec{j}.$$

The airplane's final position, $\vec{p}_{\text{end}}$, is given by

$$\vec{p}_{\text{end}} = \vec{p}_{\text{start}} + \vec{d} = 3\vec{i} + 5\vec{j} + 1.026\vec{i} + 2.819\vec{j}$$
$$= 4.026\vec{i} + 7.819\vec{j}.$$

The second airplane's initial position is given by the position vector $\vec{q}_{\text{start}} = 7\vec{i} + 2\vec{j}$. The second plane's displacement, however, is exactly the same as the first airplane's, $\vec{d} = 1.026\vec{i} + 2.819\vec{j}$. Therefore, the final position of the second airplane, $\vec{q}_{\text{end}}$, is given by

$$\vec{q}_{\text{end}} = \vec{q}_{\text{start}} + \vec{d} = 7\vec{i} + 2\vec{j} + 1.026\vec{i} + 2.819\vec{j}$$
$$= 8.026\vec{i} + 4.819\vec{j}.$$

Example 7 illustrates the difference between position vectors and other vectors: The tail of a position vector is fixed to the origin, but the tail of the displacement vector $\vec{v}$ can be anywhere, so long as its length and orientation do not change.

Exercises and Problems for Section 12.3

Exercises

In Exercises 1–8, find the vector using $\vec{N} = (5, 6, 7, 8, 9, 10)$ and $\vec{M} = (1, 1, 2, 3, 5, 8)$.

1. $\vec{B} = 2\vec{M}$

2. $\vec{G} = \vec{N} + \vec{M}$

3. $\vec{A} = \vec{M} - \vec{N}$

4. $\vec{c} = 2\vec{N} - 7\vec{M}$

5. $\vec{K} = \dfrac{\vec{N}}{3} + \dfrac{2\vec{N}}{3}$

6. $\vec{\rho} = 1.067\vec{M} + 2.361\vec{N}$

7. $\vec{Z} = \dfrac{\vec{N}}{3} + \dfrac{\vec{M}}{2}$

8. $\vec{R} = \sqrt{3}\vec{M} + 4\sqrt{3}\vec{N}$

In Exercises 9–12, use $\vec{Q}$ from Example 2 on page 510.

9. If the population of each New England state increases by 120,000 people from 2005 to 2010, what is $\vec{S}$, the population vector for 2010?

10. If the population of each New England state increases by 2% from 2005 to 2010, what is $\vec{R}$, the population vector for 2010?

11. If the population of each New England state decreases by 43,000 people from 2005 to 2010, what is $\vec{U}$, the population vector for 2010?

12. If the population of each New England state decreases by 22% from 2005 to 2010, what is $\vec{T}$, the population vector for 2010?

Problems

13. There are five students in a class. Their scores on the midterm (out of 100) are given by the vector $\vec{v} = (73, 80, 91, 65, 84)$. Their scores on the final (out of 100) are given by $\vec{w} = (82, 79, 88, 70, 92)$. The final counts twice as much as the midterm. Find a vector giving the total scores (out of 100) of the students.

14. An airplane is heading northeast at an airspeed of 700 km/hr, but there is a wind blowing from the west at 60 km/hr. In what direction does the plane end up flying? What is its speed relative to the ground? [Hint: Resolve the velocity vectors for the airplane and the wind into components.]

15. An airplane is flying at an airspeed of 600 km/hr in a cross-wind that is blowing from the northeast at a speed of 50 km/hr. In what direction should the plane head to end up going due east?

16. Two children are throwing a ball back-and-forth straight across the back seat of a car. Suppose the ball is being thrown at 10 mph relative to the car and the car is going 25 mph down the road.

    (a) Make a sketch showing the relevant velocity vectors.

    (b) If one child does not catch the ball and it goes out an open window, what angle does the ball's horizontal motion make with the road?

17. A man walks 5 miles in a direction $30°$ north of east. He then walks a distance x miles due east. He turns around to look back at his starting point, which is at an angle of $10°$ south of west.

(a) Make a sketch. Give vectors in $\vec{i}$ and $\vec{j}$ components, for each part of the man's walk.

(b) What is x?

(c) How far is the man from his starting point?

18. A clothing store sells four different proposed children's outfits of pants, shirt, shoes, belt, and jacket. The four outfits can be represented by vectors:

$$\vec{a} = (75, 30, 120, 40, 200)$$
$$\vec{b} = (25, 20, 75, 30, 90)$$
$$\vec{c} = (145, 50, 100, 40, 300)$$
$$\vec{d} = (60, 45, 200, 35, 150)$$

(a) Which two outfits have the same belt?

(b) David's children want 3 outfits $\vec{a}$, 2 outfits $\vec{c}$ and 1 outfit $\vec{d}$.

   (i) Write their wishes as a sum of vectors.

   (ii) Write out a single vector expressing what David would pay for each of the five items.

(c) David buys 5 outfits for his children and spends $145 on shirts.

   (i) Express his purchase as a sum of the vectors $\vec{a}, \vec{b}, \vec{c}, \vec{d}$,

   (ii) Write out the vector $\vec{e}$ giving the sum.

19. Three different electric charges q_1, q_2, and q_3 exert forces on a test charge Q. The forces are, respectively, $\vec{F_1} = (3, 6)$, $\vec{F_2} = (-2, 5)$, and $\vec{F_3} = (7, -4)$. The net force, $\vec{F}_{net}$ is given by $\vec{F}_{net} = \vec{F_1} + \vec{F_2} + \vec{F_3}$.

(a) Calculate $\vec{F}_{net}$.

(b) If a fourth charge q_4 is added, what force $\vec{F_4}$ must it exert on Q so that Q feels no net force at all, that is, so that $\vec{F}_{net} = \vec{0}$?

20. Let $q = 20$ be an electric charge at the origin $(0, 0)$, and let $Q = 30$ be another charge at position $\vec{r} = (r_x, r_y)$. Then q exerts a force $\vec{F}$ on Q given by *Coulomb's Law*,

$$\|\vec{F}\| = \frac{qQ}{\|\vec{r}\|^2}.$$

The direction of $\vec{F}$ is the same as the direction of $\vec{r}$, so that Q tends to be pushed away[6] from q.

(a) Let the position of Q be $\vec{r} = (3, 5)$. Find $\|\vec{r}\|$.

(b) Using Coulomb's Law, find $\|\vec{F}\|$.

(c) Find the components of $\vec{F} = (F_x, F_y)$. [Hint: $\vec{F}$ points in the same direction as $\vec{r}$, so both vectors make the same angle with the x-axis.]

21. Figure 12.25 shows a rectangle whose four corners are the points

$$a = (2, 1), \quad b = (4, 1), \quad c = (4, 2), \quad \text{and} \quad d = (2, 2).$$

As part of a video game, this rectangle is rotated counterclockwise through an angle of $35°$ about the origin. See Figure 12.26. What are the new coordinates of the corners of the rectangle?

Figure 12.25

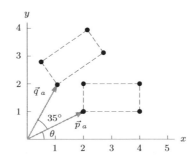

Figure 12.26: Rectangle rotated about the origin through an angle of $35°$

22. Provided that $x_1 \neq x_2$ and $y_1 \neq y_2$, the points $p_1 = (x_1, y_1)$ and $p_2 = (x_2, y_2)$ define a rectangle with p_1 in one corner and p_2 in the opposite corner. We represent this rectangle as a 4-vector $\vec{r} = (x_1, y_1, x_2, y_2)$. For instance, Figure 12.27 shows the rectangle described by $\vec{r} = (2, 2, 7, 6)$, which has $p_1 = (2, 2)$ and $p_2 = (7, 6)$.

(a) Sketch the rectangle described by $\vec{s} = (2, 4, 5, 8)$.

---

[6]This is true because q and Q have the same sign. The force would be opposite to $\vec{r}$ if Q and q had opposite signs.

(b) Let $\vec{t}$ be a rectangle and let $\vec{u} = (1, 0, 1, 0)$, $\vec{v} = (0, 1, 0, 1)$, and $\vec{w} = \vec{u} + \vec{v}$. Describe in words how the following rectangles are related to $\vec{t}$.

(i) $\vec{t} + \vec{u}$ (ii) $\vec{t} + \vec{v}$

(iii) $\vec{t} - \vec{u}$ (iv) $\vec{t} + 2\vec{u} + 3\vec{v}$

(v) $\vec{t} + \vec{w}$ (vi) $\vec{t} + k\vec{w}$, k a constant.

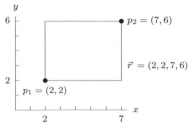

Figure 12.27

12.4   THE DOT PRODUCT

We have added and subtracted vectors and we have multiplied vectors by scalars. We now see how to multiply one vector by another vector.

To compute the product of $\vec{u}$ and $\vec{v}$, we multiply each coordinate of $\vec{u}$ by the corresponding coordinate of $\vec{v}$ and add these products. The result is called the *dot product*, written $\vec{u} \cdot \vec{v}$. Notice that the dot product of two vectors is a scalar, not a vector.

Example 1   A car dealer sells five different models of car. The number of each model sold each week is given by the consumption vector $\vec{C} = (22, 14, 8, 12, 19)$. For instance, we see that in one week the dealer sells 22 of the first model, 14 of the second, and so forth.

The price of each model is given by the vector $\vec{P} = (19, 23, 40, 47, 32)$, where the units are $1000s. Thus, the price of the first model is \$19,000, the price of the second is \$23,000, and so forth. Find the dealer's weekly revenue.

Solution   The total revenue earned by the dealer each week (in 1000s of dollars) is given by

$$\text{Revenue (in \$1000s)} = 22 \text{ cars} \cdot 19 \text{ per car} + 14 \text{ cars} \cdot 23 \text{ per car} + 8 \text{ cars} \cdot 40 \text{ per car}$$
$$+ 12 \text{ cars} \cdot 47 \text{ per car} + 19 \text{ cars} \cdot 32 \text{ per car}$$
$$= 2232.$$

The dealer brings in \$2,232,000 each week. Since the revenue is obtained by multiplying the corresponding coordinates of $\vec{C}$ and $\vec{P}$ and adding, we can write revenue as a dot product:

$$\text{Revenue} = \vec{C} \cdot \vec{P}.$$

Note the revenue is a scalar, not a vector, as the dot product always gives a number.

In general, we define the dot product of two vectors as follows:

> if $\vec{u} = (u_1, u_2, \ldots, u_n)$ and $\vec{v} = (v_1, v_2, \ldots, v_n)$ are two n-dimensional vectors, then the **dot product**, $\vec{u} \cdot \vec{v}$, is the scalar given by
>
> $$\vec{u} \cdot \vec{v} = u_1 v_1 + u_2 v_2 + \cdots + u_n v_n.$$

Example 2   The population vector $\vec{P}_{\text{NewEngland}} = (3.28, 1.24, 6.07, 1.15, 0.99, 0.59)$ gives the populations (in millions) of the six New England states (CT, ME, MA, NH, RI, VT) in 1995. The vector $\vec{r} = (7.0\%, 6.5\%, 5.4\%, 13.9\%, 9.1\%, 5.1\%)$ gives the percent change in population between 1995 and 2005 for each state. We see that

$$\text{Change in Connecticut population} = 0.07 \cdot 3.28 = 0.2296, \qquad \text{and so on.}$$

If $\Delta P_{\text{New England}}$ represents the overall change in the population of New England, then

$$\Delta P_{\text{New England}} = 0.07 \cdot 3.28 + 0.065 \cdot 1.24 + 0.054 \cdot 6.07$$
$$+ 0.139 \cdot 1.15 + 0.091 \cdot 0.99 + 0.054 \cdot 0.56$$
$$= 0.9180,$$

so the population of New England increased by 0.9180 million people ($918{,}000$) between 1995 and 2005. Notice that the total change in the New England population is given by the dot product:

$$\Delta P_{\text{New England}} = \vec{r} \cdot \vec{P}_{\text{New England}}.$$

Properties of the Dot Product

It can be shown that the following properties hold:

- $\vec{u} \cdot \vec{v} = ||\vec{u}|| \cdot ||\vec{v}|| \cos\theta$, where θ is the angle between $\vec{u}$ and $\vec{v}$
- $\vec{u} \cdot \vec{v} = \vec{v} \cdot \vec{u}$ (*Commutative Law*)
- $\vec{u} \cdot (\vec{v} + \vec{w}) = \vec{u} \cdot \vec{v} + \vec{u} \cdot \vec{w}$ (*Distributive Law*)
- $\vec{v} \cdot \vec{v} = ||\vec{v}||^2$

From the formula $\vec{u} \cdot \vec{v} = ||\vec{u}|| \cdot ||\vec{v}|| \cos\theta$, we see that if $0° < \theta < 90°$, then $\vec{u} \cdot \vec{v}$ is positive, and if $90° < \theta < 180°$, then $\vec{u} \cdot \vec{v}$ is negative. This property provides a useful way to calculate the dot product without using coordinates. We use the Law of Cosines to show why it works for 2-dimensional vectors.

The commutative law holds because multiplication of coordinates is commutative. A proof of the distributive law using coordinates is outlined in the Problem 23. For the fourth property, note that

$$\vec{v} \cdot \vec{v} = (v_1, v_2) \cdot (v_1, v_2) = v_1^2 + v_2^2.$$

By the Pythagorean theorem, $||\vec{v}||^2 = v_1{}^2 + v_2{}^2$, so $\vec{v} \cdot \vec{v} = ||v||^2$. A similar argument applies to vectors of higher dimension.

Justification of $\vec{u} \cdot \vec{v} = ||\vec{u}|| \cdot ||\vec{v}|| \cos\theta$

Figure 12.28 shows two vectors, $\vec{u}$ and $\vec{v}$, with an angle θ between them. The vectors $\vec{u}$, $\vec{v}$, and $\vec{w} = \vec{u} - \vec{v}$ form a triangle. Now, we know (from the fourth property of dot products) that $\vec{w} \cdot \vec{w} = ||\vec{w}||^2$. We can also calculate $\vec{w} \cdot \vec{w}$ using the distributive and commutative laws:

$$\vec{w} \cdot \vec{w} = (\vec{v} - \vec{u}) \cdot (\vec{v} - \vec{u})$$
$$= \vec{v} \cdot \vec{v} - \vec{u} \cdot \vec{v} - \vec{v} \cdot \vec{u} + \vec{u} \cdot \vec{u}$$
$$= ||\vec{v}||^2 + ||\vec{u}||^2 - 2\vec{u} \cdot \vec{v}.$$

Since $\vec{w} \cdot \vec{w} = ||\vec{w}||^2$, we have shown that

$$||\vec{w}||^2 = ||\vec{v}||^2 + ||\vec{u}||^2 - 2\vec{u} \cdot \vec{v}.$$

But applying the Law of Cosines to the triangle in Figure 12.28 gives

$$||\vec{w}||^2 = ||\vec{u}||^2 + ||\vec{v}||^2 - 2||\vec{u}|| \cdot ||\vec{v}|| \cos\theta.$$

Thus setting these two expressions for $||\vec{w}||^2$ equal gives

$$||\vec{u}||^2 + ||\vec{v}||^2 - 2\vec{u} \cdot \vec{v} = ||\vec{u}||^2 + ||\vec{v}||^2 - 2||\vec{u}|| \cdot ||\vec{v}|| \cos\theta,$$

which simplifies to the formula we wanted:

$$\vec{u} \cdot \vec{v} = ||\vec{u}\,|| \cdot ||\vec{v}\,|| \cos \theta.$$

Figure 12.28: Triangle used to justify $\vec{u} \cdot \vec{v} = ||\vec{u}\,|| \cdot ||\vec{v}\,|| \cos \theta$

Example 3   (a) Find $\vec{v} \cdot \vec{w}$ where $\vec{v} = 3\vec{i} + 4\vec{j}$ and $\vec{w} = 2\vec{i} + 5\vec{j}$.

(b) One person walks 3 miles east and then 4 miles north to point A. Another person walks 2 miles east and then 5 miles north to point B. Both started from the same spot, O. What is the angle of separation of these two people? (See Figure 12.29.)

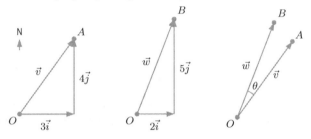

Figure 12.29: What is the angle of separation θ between the people at A and B?

Solution   (a) We have $\vec{v} \cdot \vec{w} = (3\vec{i} + 4\vec{j}) \cdot (2\vec{i} + 5\vec{j}) = 3 \cdot 2 + 4 \cdot 5 = 26$.

(b) Assuming $\vec{i}$ points east and $\vec{j}$ points north, we see that $\vec{v}$ gives the first person's position and $\vec{w}$ gives the second person's position. The angle of separation between these two people is labeled θ in Figure 12.29. We use the formula

$$\vec{v} \cdot \vec{w} = ||\vec{v}\,|| \cdot ||\vec{w}\,|| \cos \theta.$$

Since $||\vec{v}\,|| = \sqrt{3^2 + 4^2} = 5$ and $||\vec{w}\,|| = \sqrt{2^2 + 5^2} = \sqrt{29}$ and, from part (a), $\vec{v} \cdot \vec{w} = 26$, we have

$$26 = 5\sqrt{29} \cos \theta,$$
$$\cos \theta = \frac{26}{5\sqrt{29}},$$
$$\theta = \arccos \frac{26}{5\sqrt{29}} = 15.068°.$$

What Does the Dot Product Mean?

The dot product can be interpreted as a measure of the alignment of two vectors. If two vectors $\vec{u}$ and $\vec{v}$ are perpendicular, then the angle between them is $\theta = 90°$. (See Figure 12.30.) In this case, $\cos \theta = \cos 90° = 0$, so

$$\vec{u} \cdot \vec{v} = ||\vec{u}|| \cdot ||\vec{v}|| \cos 90° = 0.$$

A dot product of zero tells us that the two vectors are perpendicular.

Figure 12.30: Dot product is positive, zero, or negative depending on alignment of vectors

If the two vectors are perfectly aligned, they are parallel, so $\theta = 0°$ and $\cos \theta = \cos 0° = 1$. In this case,

$$\vec{u} \cdot \vec{v} = ||\vec{u}|| \cdot ||\vec{v}|| \cos 0° = ||\vec{u}|| \cdot ||\vec{v}||,$$

so the dot product is positive.

If θ is between $0°$ and $90°$, the vectors are partially aligned and $\cos \theta$ is between 0 and 1. In this case $\vec{u} \cdot \vec{v}$ is positive, but smaller than $||\vec{u}|| \cdot ||\vec{v}||$.

Two vectors are also perfectly aligned if they are pointing in opposite directions. In this case, $\theta = 180°$ and $\cos \theta = -1$, and we have

$$\vec{u} \cdot \vec{v} = ||\vec{u}|| \cdot ||\vec{v}|| \cos 180° = -||\vec{u}|| \cdot ||\vec{v}||,$$

so the dot product is negative.

To summarize:

- Perfect alignment results in the largest possible value for $\vec{u} \cdot \vec{v}$. It occurs if $\vec{u}$ and $\vec{v}$ are parallel, with $\theta = 0°$.
- Perpendicularity results in $\vec{u} \cdot \vec{v} = 0$. It occurs if $\vec{u}$ and $\vec{v}$ are at angle of $\theta = 90°$.
- Perfect alignment in opposite directions results in the most negative value for $\vec{u} \cdot \vec{v}$. It occurs if $\theta = 180°$.

Work

In physics, the concept of *work* is represented by the dot product. In everyday language, work means effort expended. In physics, the term has a similar, but more precise, meaning.

Suppose you load a heavy refrigerator onto a truck. The refrigerator is on casters and glides with little effort along the floor. However, to lift the refrigerator takes a lot of work. The *work* done in moving the refrigerator against the force of gravity is defined by

$$\text{Work} = \vec{F} \cdot \vec{d},$$

where $\vec{F}$ is the force exerted (assumed constant) and $\vec{d}$ is the displacement. If we measure distance in feet and force in pounds, work is measured in foot-pounds, where 1 foot-pound is the amount of work required to raise 1 pound a distance of 1 foot.

Suppose we push the refrigerator up a ramp that makes a 10° angle with the floor. If the ramp is 12 ft long and the force exerted on the refrigerator is 350 lbs vertically upward, then the displacement $\vec{d}$ has a magnitude of 12, and the angle θ between $\vec{F}$ and $\vec{d}$ is $90° - 10° = 80°$. (See Figure 12.31.) The work done by the force $\vec{F}$ is

$$\text{Work} = ||\vec{F}|| \cdot ||\vec{d}|| \cos 80° = 350 \cdot 12 \cos 80° = 729.322 \text{ ft-lbs.}$$

To push the refrigerator up the ramp, we do 729.322 ft-lbs of work.

Figure 12.31: Refrigerator being pushed up ramp; the angle between $\vec{F}$ and $\vec{r}$ is $\theta = 100°$

It is informative to consider the two extreme cases: horizontal and vertical ramps. A horizontal ramp leads to a 90° angle between $\vec{F}$ and $\vec{d}$, so

$$\text{Work} = ||\vec{F}|| \cdot ||\vec{d}|| \cos 90° = 350 \cdot 12 \cdot 0 = 0 \text{ ft-lbs.}$$

Since we push the refrigerator in a direction perpendicular to its weight, we don't have to fight the weight at all (assuming frictionless casters). For a vertical ramp, we have

$$\text{Work} = ||\vec{F}|| \cdot ||\vec{d}|| \cos 0° = 350 \cdot 12 \cdot 1 = 4200 \text{ ft-lbs.}$$

In this case, we are pushing (or hoisting) the refrigerator in a direction opposite to that of its weight, so we feel its full force.

Exercises and Problems for Section 12.4

Exercises

For Exercises 1–12, perform the following operations on the given 3-dimensional vectors.

$\vec{a} = 2\vec{j} + \vec{k}$ $\vec{b} = -3\vec{i} + 5\vec{j} + 4\vec{k}$
$\vec{c} = \vec{i} + 6\vec{j}$ $\vec{y} = 4\vec{i} - 7\vec{j}$
$\vec{z} = \vec{i} - 3\vec{j} - \vec{k}$

1. $\vec{z} \cdot \vec{a}$

2. $\vec{a} \cdot \vec{z}$

3. $\vec{c} \cdot \vec{y}$

4. $\vec{a} \cdot \vec{y}$

5. $\vec{a} \cdot \vec{b}$

6. $\vec{b} \cdot \vec{z}$

7. $\vec{c} \cdot \vec{a} + \vec{a} \cdot \vec{y}$

8. $\vec{a} \cdot (\vec{c} + \vec{y})$

9. $(\vec{a} \cdot \vec{b})\vec{a}$

10. $((\vec{c} \cdot \vec{c})\vec{a}) \cdot \vec{a}$

11. $(\vec{a} \cdot \vec{y})(\vec{c} \cdot \vec{z})$

12. $(\vec{z} \cdot \vec{c})(\vec{y} \cdot \vec{a})$

Problems

13. What is the angle between the vectors $\vec{v}$ and $\vec{w}$ in Figure 12.32?

Figure 12.32

14. The force of gravity acting on a ball is 2 lb downward. How much work is done by gravity if the ball

(a) Falls 3 feet?
(b) Moves upward 5 feet?

15. How much work is done in pushing a 350-lb refrigerator up a 12 ft ramp that makes a 30° angle with the floor?

16. Which pairs of the vectors $\sqrt{3}\,\vec{i} + \vec{j}$, $3\vec{i} + \sqrt{3}\,\vec{j}$, $\vec{i} - \sqrt{3}\,\vec{j}$ are parallel and which are perpendicular?

17. Compute the angle between the vectors $\vec{i} + \vec{j} + \vec{k}$ and $\vec{i} - \vec{j} - \vec{k}$.

18. For what values of t are $\vec{u} = t\vec{i} - \vec{j} + \vec{k}$ and $\vec{v} = t\vec{i} + t\vec{j} - 2\vec{k}$ perpendicular? Are there values of t for which $\vec{u}$ and $\vec{v}$ are parallel?

19. Suppose that $\|\vec{a}\| = 7$ and $\|\vec{b}\| = 4$, but that $\vec{a}$ and $\vec{b}$ can point in any direction. What are the maximum and minimum possible lengths for the vectors $\vec{a} + \vec{b}$ and $\vec{a} - \vec{b}$? Illustrate your answers with sketches.

20. A 100-meter dash is run on a track in the direction of the vector $\vec{v} = 2\vec{i} + 6\vec{j}$. The wind velocity $\vec{w}$ is $5\vec{i} + \vec{j}$ km/hr. The rules say that a legal wind speed measured in the direction of the dash must not exceed 5 km/hr. Will the race results be disqualified due to an illegal wind? Justify your answer.

21. Let A, B, C be the points $A = (1, 2); B = (4, 1); C = (2, 4)$. Is triangle $\triangle ABC$ a right triangle?

22. Show that the vectors $(\vec{b} \cdot \vec{c})\vec{a} - (\vec{a} \cdot \vec{c})\vec{b}$ and $\vec{c}$ are perpendicular.

23. In this problem, you will check the distributive law for 2-vectors. Show that if $\vec{u} = (u_1, u_2)$, $\vec{v} = (v_1, v_2)$, and $\vec{w} = (w_1, w_2)$, then
$$\vec{u} \cdot (\vec{v} + \vec{w}) = \vec{u} \cdot \vec{v} + \vec{u} \cdot \vec{w}.$$

24. Let $\vec{u} = u_1\vec{i} + u_2\vec{j}$ and $\vec{v} = v_1\vec{i} + v_2\vec{j}$. Using $\vec{u} \cdot \vec{v} = \|\vec{u}\| \cdot \|\vec{v}\| \cos\theta$ and the distributive law, show that $\vec{u} \cdot \vec{v} = u_1v_1 + u_2v_2$.

25. (a) Bread, eggs, and milk cost $3.00 per loaf, $2.00 per dozen, and $4.00 per gallon, respectively, at Acme Store. Use a price vector $\vec{a}$ and a consumption vector $\vec{c}$ to write a vector equation that describes what may be bought for $40.

(b) At Beta Mart, where the food is fresher, the price vector is $\vec{b} = (3.20, 1.80, 4.50)$. Explain the meaning of $(\vec{b} - \vec{a}) \cdot \vec{c}$ in practical terms. Is $\vec{b} - \vec{a}$ ever perpendicular to $\vec{c}$?

(c) Some people think Beta Mart's freshness makes each grocery item at Beta equivalent to 110% of the corresponding Acme item. What does it mean for a consumption vector to satisfy the inequality $(1/1.1)\vec{b} \cdot \vec{c} < \vec{a} \cdot \vec{c}$?

26. Recall that in 2 or 3 dimensions, if θ is the angle between $\vec{v}$ and $\vec{w}$, the dot product is given by
$$\vec{v} \cdot \vec{w} = \|\vec{v}\|\|\vec{w}\| \cos\theta.$$

We use this relationship to define the angle between two vectors in n dimensions. If $\vec{v}, \vec{w}$ are n-vectors, then the dot product, $\vec{v} \cdot \vec{w} = v_1w_1 + v_2w_2 + \cdots + v_nw_n$, is used to define the angle θ by
$$\cos\theta = \frac{\vec{v} \cdot \vec{w}}{\|\vec{v}\|\|\vec{w}\|} \qquad \text{provided } \|\vec{v}\|, \|\vec{w}\| \neq 0.$$

We now use this idea of angle to measure how close two populations are to one another genetically. Table 12.1 shows the relative frequencies of four alleles (variants of a gene) in four populations.

Table 12.1

Allele	Eskimo	Bantu	English	Korean
A_1	0.29	0.10	0.20	0.22
A_2	0.00	0.08	0.06	0.00
B	0.03	0.12	0.06	0.20
O	0.67	0.69	0.66	0.57

Let $\vec{a}_1, \vec{a}_2, \vec{a}_3, \vec{a}_4$ be the 4-vectors showing the relative frequencies of each allele in the Eskimo, Bantu, English, Korean populations, respectively. The genetic distance between two populations is defined as the angle between the corresponding vectors. Using this definition, is the English population closer genetically to the Bantus or to the Koreans? Explain.[7]

---

[7]Adapted from L. Cavalli-Sforza and A. Edwards, "Phylogenetic Analysis: Models and Estimation Procedures," *Am. J. Hum. Genet.*, Vol. 19 (1967), pp. 223-57.

27. A basketball gymnasium is 25 meters high, 80 meters wide and 200 meters long. For a half-time stunt, the cheerleaders want to run two strings, one from each of the two corners of the gym above one basket to the diagonally opposite corners of the gym floor. What is the angle made by the strings as they cross?

28. Let S be the triangle with vertices $A = (2,2,2)$, $B = (4,2,1)$, and $C = (2,3,1)$.

   (a) Find the length of the shortest side of S.

   (b) Find the cosine of the angle BAC at vertex A.

29. We can represent a rectangle as a 4-vector $\vec{r} = (x_1, y_1, x_2, y_2)$, where (x_1, y_1) and (x_2, y_2) are opposite corners. (See Problem 22 on page 516.) Assume that $x_2 > x_1$ and $y_2 > y_1$. Let $\vec{w} = (-1, 0, 1, 0)$ and $\vec{h} = (0, -1, 0, 1)$. What do the following quantities tell you about the rectangle?

   (a) $\vec{r} \cdot \vec{w}$ **(b)** $\vec{r} \cdot \vec{h}$

   (c) $2\vec{r} \cdot (\vec{w} + \vec{h})$

12.5 MATRICES

Table 12.2 shows the latest census data (in 1000s) by age group for the six New England states.[8]

Table 12.2   *Year 2000 population (1000s) by age group for the six New England states*

	CT	ME	MA	NH	RI	VT
under 15	710	244	244	249	207	119
15–24	364	145	145	142	125	67
25–34	434	147	147	165	144	73
35–44	572	214	214	210	166	98
45–54	473	194	194	185	140	94
55–64	312	118	118	115	89	57
65–74	218	95	95	75	68	44
over 74	216	83	83	60	71	35

We can treat the array of numbers in the table as a mathematical object in its own right, independent of the row and column headers. This rectangular grid of numbers is called a *matrix*,[9] usually written inside parentheses. Since the numbers in the table are populations, we use **P** to denote this matrix:

$$\mathbf{P} = \begin{pmatrix} 710 & 244 & 244 & 249 & 207 & 119 \\ 364 & 145 & 145 & 142 & 125 & 67 \\ 434 & 147 & 147 & 165 & 144 & 73 \\ 572 & 214 & 214 & 210 & 166 & 98 \\ 473 & 194 & 194 & 185 & 140 & 94 \\ 312 & 118 & 118 & 115 & 89 & 57 \\ 218 & 95 & 95 & 75 & 68 & 44 \\ 216 & 83 & 83 & 60 & 71 & 35 \end{pmatrix}.$$

The individual entries are called *entries* in the matrix; we write p_{ij} for the entry in the ith row of the jth column. Thus for example, $p_{21} = 364$ and $p_{16} = 119$.

---

[8]The US Census Bureau, www.census.gov.

[9]In general, matrices can include objects other than numbers, such as complex numbers, functions, or even operators from calculus like $\partial/\partial x$.

Addition, Subtraction, and Scalar Multiplication

Like vectors, matrices provide a convenient way of organizing information. And, as with vectors, we can manipulate matrices algebraically by adding them, subtracting them, or multiplying them by scalars.

As for vectors, to multiply a matrix by a scalar, we multiply each entry by the scalar. To add or subtract two matrices, we add or subtract the corresponding entries.[10]

Example 1 Evaluate the following matrices. What do they tell you about the population of New England?

(a) Evaluate $1.1\mathbf{P}$.

(b) Evaluate $1.1\mathbf{P} - \mathbf{P}$.

(c) Show that $1.1\mathbf{P} - \mathbf{P} = 0.1\mathbf{P}$.

Solution (a) To multiply a matrix by a scalar, we multiply each entry by the scalar. For instance, the first (upper-left) entry of $\mathbf{P}$ is 710, so the first entry of $1.1\mathbf{P}$ is $1.1(710) = 781$. This matrix tells us what the population for each age group would be for each state after a 10% increase:

$$1.1\mathbf{P} = \begin{pmatrix} 781.0 & 268.4 & 268.4 & 273.9 & 227.7 & 130.9 \\ 400.4 & 159.5 & 159.5 & 156.2 & 137.5 & 73.7 \\ 477.4 & 161.7 & 161.7 & 181.5 & 158.4 & 80.3 \\ 629.2 & 235.4 & 235.4 & 231.0 & 182.6 & 107.8 \\ 520.3 & 213.4 & 213.4 & 203.5 & 154.0 & 103.4 \\ 343.2 & 129.8 & 129.8 & 126.5 & 97.9 & 62.7 \\ 239.8 & 104.5 & 104.5 & 82.5 & 74.8 & 48.4 \\ 237.6 & 91.3 & 91.3 & 66.0 & 78.1 & 38.5 \end{pmatrix}.$$

(b) To subtract one matrix from another, we subtract the corresponding entries. For instance, the first entry of $1.1\mathbf{P}$ is 781, and the first entry of $\mathbf{P}$ is 710, and so the first entry of $1.1\mathbf{P} - \mathbf{P} = 781 - 710 = 71$. This matrix tells us how much the population in part (a) increased for each age group for each state:

$$1.1\mathbf{P} - \mathbf{P} = \begin{pmatrix} 71.0 & 24.4 & 24.4 & 24.9 & 20.7 & 11.9 \\ 36.4 & 14.5 & 14.5 & 14.2 & 12.5 & 6.7 \\ 43.4 & 14.7 & 14.7 & 16.5 & 14.4 & 7.3 \\ 57.2 & 21.4 & 21.4 & 21.0 & 16.6 & 9.8 \\ 47.3 & 19.4 & 19.4 & 18.5 & 14.0 & 9.4 \\ 31.2 & 11.8 & 11.8 & 11.5 & 8.9 & 5.7 \\ 21.8 & 9.5 & 9.5 & 7.5 & 6.8 & 4.4 \\ 21.6 & 8.3 & 8.3 & 6.0 & 7.1 & 3.5 \end{pmatrix}.$$

(c) To find each entry of $1.1\mathbf{P} - \mathbf{P}$, we multiply the original entry by 1.1 and then subtract the original entry. For instance, the first entry is $1.1(710) - 710 = 0.1(710)$. You can check for yourself that multiplying every entry of $\mathbf{P}$ by 0.1 gives the same result as obtained in part (b).

---

[10]We can add or subtract two matrices provided that they have the same number of rows and columns.

If $\mathbf{A}$ is a matrix having m rows and n columns, we say that $\mathbf{A}$ is an $m \times n$ matrix, and we let a_{ij} stand for the entry at row i, column j. If $m = 1$ or $n = 1$, the matrix has only one row or one column, and is a vector. A $1 \times n$ matrix is often called a *row* vector and a $m \times 1$ matrix is often called a *column* vector.

If $\mathbf{A}$ and $\mathbf{B}$ are $m \times n$ matrices and k is a constant:
- $\mathbf{C} = k\mathbf{A}$ is an $m \times n$ matrix such that $c_{ij} = ka_{ij}$. This is called *scalar multiplication* of a matrix.
- $\mathbf{C} = \mathbf{A} + \mathbf{B}$ is an $m \times n$ matrix such that $c_{ij} = a_{ij} + b_{ij}$. This is called *matrix addition*.
- $\mathbf{C} = \mathbf{A} - \mathbf{B}$ is an $m \times n$ matrix such that $c_{ij} = a_{ij} - b_{ij}$. This is called *matrix subtraction*.

As with vector subtraction, matrix subtraction can be defined in terms of matrix addition by rewriting $\mathbf{A} + (-1)\mathbf{B}$ as $\mathbf{A} - \mathbf{B}$.

Properties of Scalar Multiplication and Matrix Addition

The properties of scalar multiplication and matrix addition are similar to the properties for vectors.

- *Commutativity of addition*: $\mathbf{A} + \mathbf{B} = \mathbf{B} + \mathbf{A}$.
- *Associativity of addition*: $(\mathbf{A} + \mathbf{B}) + \mathbf{C} = \mathbf{A} + (\mathbf{B} + \mathbf{C})$.
- *Associativity of scalar multiplication*: $k_1(k_2\mathbf{A}) = (k_1 k_2)\mathbf{A}$.
- *Distributivity of scalar multiplication*: $(k_1 + k_2)\mathbf{A} = k_1\mathbf{A} + k_2\mathbf{A}$ and
$$k(\mathbf{A} + \mathbf{B}) = k\mathbf{A} + k\mathbf{B}.$$

Multiplication of a Matrix and a Vector

Although there are more general cases of matrix multiplication, in this text we focus on multiplying a $n \times n$ square matrix by an n-dimensional column vector. We introduce this topic by considering two dependent populations.

Matrix Multiplication of 2-Dimensional Vectors

A country begins with $x_0 = 4$ million people and another country begins with $y_0 = 2$ million people. Every year, 20% of the people in country X move to country Y, and 30% of the people in country Y move to country X. Suppose also that no one is born and no one dies. What happens to the populations of these two countries over time? After one year, x_1, the number of people (in millions) in country X, is given by

$$x_1 = x_0 - \underbrace{0.2x_0}_{20\% \text{ leave } X} + \underbrace{0.3y_0}_{30\% \text{ leave } Y}$$
$$= 0.8x_0 + 0.3y_0.$$

Likewise, y_1, the number of people (in millions) in country Y, is given by

$$y_1 = y_0 + \underbrace{0.2x_0}_{20\% \text{ leave } X} - \underbrace{0.3y_0}_{30\% \text{ leave } Y}$$
$$= 0.2x_0 + 0.7y_0.$$

Thus, we have

$$x_1 = 0.8(4) + 0.3(2) = 3.2 + 0.6 = 3.8$$
$$y_1 = 0.2(4) + 0.7(2) = 0.8 + 1.4 = 2.2.$$

The population of country X drops by 0.2 million, while the population of country Y goes up by 0.2 million. The same reasoning shows that after two years,

$$x_2 = 0.8x_1 + 0.3y_1$$
$$y_2 = 0.2x_1 + 0.7y_1,$$

so

$$x_2 = 0.8(3.8) + 0.3(2.2) = 3.04 + 0.66 = 3.7$$
$$y_2 = 0.2(3.8) + 0.7(2.2) = 0.76 + 1.54 = 2.3.$$

In general, we see that

$$x_{\text{new}} = 0.8x_{\text{old}} + 0.3y_{\text{old}}$$
$$y_{\text{new}} = 0.2x_{\text{old}} + 0.7y_{\text{old}}.$$

Thinking in terms of vectors, we can write $\vec{P}_{\text{new}} = (x_{\text{new}}, y_{\text{new}})$ and $\vec{P}_{\text{old}} = (x_{\text{old}}, y_{\text{old}})$. Then, using the dot product, we have

$$x_{\text{new}} = (0.8, 0.3) \cdot \vec{P}_{\text{old}}$$
$$y_{\text{new}} = (0.2, 0.7) \cdot \vec{P}_{\text{old}}.$$

This pair of equations tells us how the components of $\vec{P}_{\text{new}}$ are related to the components of $\vec{P}_{\text{old}}$. Notice that each component in $\vec{P}_{\text{new}}$ is a combination of both components of $\vec{P}_{\text{old}}$. Using matrices, we write the pair of equations as a single equation:

$$\vec{P}_{\text{new}} = \begin{pmatrix} x_{\text{new}} \\ y_{\text{new}} \end{pmatrix} = \underbrace{\begin{pmatrix} 0.8 & 0.3 \\ 0.2 & 0.7 \end{pmatrix} \vec{P}_{\text{old}}}_{\text{Matrix multiplication}}.$$

We place the two coefficients from the first equation, $x_{\text{new}} = 0.8x_{\text{old}} + 0.3y_{\text{old}}$, in the first row of the matrix. We place the two coefficients from the second equation, $y_{\text{new}} = 0.2x_{\text{old}} + 0.7y_{\text{old}}$, in the second row of the matrix. In general, we use the following notation:

If $\vec{P}_{\text{new}} = (x_{\text{new}}, y_{\text{new}})$ and $\vec{P}_{\text{old}} = (x_{\text{old}}, y_{\text{old}})$, then we can write the equations

$$
\begin{aligned}
x_{\text{new}} &= ax_{\text{old}} + by_{\text{old}} \\
y_{\text{new}} &= cx_{\text{old}} + dy_{\text{old}}
\end{aligned}
$$

in the compact form

$$
\vec{P}_{\text{new}} = \begin{pmatrix} a & b \\ c & d \end{pmatrix} \vec{P}_{\text{old}}.
$$

The coefficients in the first row of the matrix tell us how x_{new} is related to $\vec{P}_{\text{old}}$ and the coefficients in the second row tell us how y_{new} is related to $\vec{P}_{\text{old}}$. If we let $\mathbf{A} = \begin{pmatrix} a & b \\ c & d \end{pmatrix}$, then we can write

$$
\vec{P}_{\text{new}} = \mathbf{A}\vec{P}_{\text{old}}.
$$

Example 2 What does the following matrix equation tell you about the relationship between $\vec{P}_{\text{new}}$ and $\vec{P}_{\text{old}}$?

$$
\vec{P}_{\text{new}} = \begin{pmatrix} 0.9 & 0.4 \\ 0.1 & 0.6 \end{pmatrix} \vec{P}_{\text{old}}.
$$

Solution We have

$$
\begin{aligned}
x_{\text{new}} &= (0.9, 0.4) \cdot \vec{P}_{\text{old}} &= 0.9x_{\text{old}} + 0.4y_{\text{old}} \\
y_{\text{new}} &= (0.1, 0.6) \cdot \vec{P}_{\text{old}} &= 0.1x_{\text{old}} + 0.6y_{\text{old}}.
\end{aligned}
$$

This tells us that each year, 10% of the population of country X moves to country Y, and 40% of the population of country Y moves to country X.

Matrix Multiplication of n-Dimensional Vectors

Let $\vec{u} = (u_1, u_2, \ldots, u_n)$ be an n-dimensional vector and let $\mathbf{A}$ be an $n \times n$ square matrix with entries $a_{11}, a_{12}, \ldots, a_{nn}$. Let $\vec{v}$ be the n-dimensional vector with coordinates given by equations:

$$
\begin{aligned}
v_1 &= (a_{11}, a_{12}, \ldots, a_{1n}) \cdot (u_1, u_2, \ldots, u_n) &= a_{11}u_1 + \cdots + a_{1n}u_n \\
v_2 &= (a_{21}, a_{22}, \ldots, a_{2n}) \cdot (u_1, u_2, \ldots, u_n) &= a_{21}u_1 + \cdots + a_{2n}u_n \\
&\;\;\vdots & \vdots \\
v_n &= (a_{n1}, a_{n2}, \ldots, a_{nn}) \cdot (u_1, u_2, \ldots, u_n) &= a_{n1}u_1 + \cdots + a_{nn}u_n.
\end{aligned}
$$

Then, if

$$
\mathbf{A} = \begin{pmatrix} a_{11} & \cdots & a_{1n} \\ \vdots & & \vdots \\ a_{n1} & \cdots & a_{nn} \end{pmatrix},
$$

we see that $\vec{v}$ is the product of $\mathbf{A}$ and $\vec{u}$:

$$
\vec{v} = \mathbf{A}\vec{u}.
$$

Example 3 Let e be the number of employed people in a certain city, and u be the number of unemployed people. We define $\vec{E} = (e, u)$ as the *employment vector* of this city. Suppose that each year, 10% of employed peopled become unemployed, and 20% of unemployed people become employed. Find a matrix $\mathbf{A}$ such that $\vec{E}_{new} = \mathbf{A}\vec{E}_{old}$.

Solution We have

$$e_{new} = e_{old} - \underbrace{0.1e_{old}}_{\text{10\% become unemployed}} + \underbrace{0.2u_{old}}_{\text{20\% become employed}}$$

$$= 0.9e_{old} + 0.2u_{old}$$

$$u_{new} = u_{old} - \underbrace{0.2u_{old}}_{\text{20\% become employed}} + \underbrace{0.1e_{old}}_{\text{10\% become unemployed}}$$

$$= 0.1e_{old} + 0.8u_{old}.$$

We can rewrite this pair of equations using matrix notation:

$$\vec{E}_{new} = \mathbf{A}\vec{E}_{old} = \begin{pmatrix} 0.9 & 0.2 \\ 0.1 & 0.8 \end{pmatrix} \vec{E}_{old}.$$

Example 4 A country produces agricultural products valued at \$70 billion and industrial products valued at \$50 billion. Some of these agricultural products are used up in order to produce other products (for instance, cotton is needed to produce cloth, or soybeans are needed to feed cattle), and some of these industrial products are used up in order to produce other products (for instance, tractors are needed to harvest cotton, or ball bearings are needed to build engines). The production vector of this country is $\vec{P} = (70, 50)$.

(a) Let $\mathbf{C}$ be the consumption matrix defined in the following equation. Calculate $\vec{U}$, the amount of agricultural and industrial products used during production:

$$\vec{U} = \mathbf{C}\vec{P} = \begin{pmatrix} 0.2 & 0.1 \\ 0.3 & 0.2 \end{pmatrix} \vec{P}.$$

Find $\vec{U}$ and describe what it tells you about the country's economy.
(b) Let the surplus vector $\vec{S} = \vec{P} - \mathbf{C}\vec{P}$. Find $\vec{S}$ and describe what it tells you about the country's economy.

Solution (a) We have

$$\vec{U} = \begin{pmatrix} 0.2 & 0.1 \\ 0.3 & 0.2 \end{pmatrix} \begin{pmatrix} 70 \\ 50 \end{pmatrix},$$

so

$$U_1 = 0.2(70) + 0.1(50) = 19$$
$$U_2 = 0.3(70) + 0.2(50) = 31.$$

Thus, $\vec{U} = (19, 31)$. This tells us that \$19 billion in agricultural products are used up during production, and \$31 billion in industrial products are used up during production.

(b) We have

$$\vec{S} = \vec{P} - \mathbf{C}\vec{P}$$
$$= \vec{P} - \vec{U} \qquad \text{because } \vec{U} = \mathbf{C}\vec{P}$$
$$= (70, 50) - (19, 31), \qquad \text{from part (a)}$$

so $\vec{S} = (51, 19)$. This tells us that, after internal consumption is accounted for, $51 billion in agricultural products are available for general consumption, as are $19 billion in industrial products.

Example 5   Let $\vec{P_0} = (x_0, y_0)$ be a position vector. This vector is rotated about the origin through an angle ϕ without changing its length. What is its new position, $\vec{P_1}$? Find a matrix $\mathbf{R}$ such that $\vec{P_1} = \mathbf{R}\vec{P_0}$.

Solution   Let $r = \|\vec{P_0}\| = \|\vec{P_1}\|$. We see from Figure 12.33 that $x_0 = r\cos\theta$, $y_0 = r\sin\theta$, $x_1 = r\cos(\theta + \phi)$, and $y_1 = r\sin(\theta + \phi)$. Notice that we can rewrite the coordinates of $\vec{P_1}$ as follows:

$$x_1 = r\cos(\theta + \phi)$$
$$= r(\cos\theta\cos\phi - \sin\theta\sin\phi)$$
$$= (r\cos\theta)\cos\phi - (r\sin\theta)\sin\phi$$
$$= x_0\cos\phi - y_0\sin\phi$$
$$y_1 = r\sin(\theta + \phi)$$
$$= r(\sin\theta\cos\phi + \cos\theta\sin\phi)$$
$$= (r\sin\theta)\cos\phi + (r\cos\theta)\sin\phi$$
$$= y_0\cos\phi + x_0\sin\phi.$$

We can rewrite this pair of equations using a matrix $\mathbf{R}$:

$$\vec{P_1} = \mathbf{R}\vec{P_0} = \begin{pmatrix} \cos\phi & -\sin\phi \\ \sin\phi & \cos\phi \end{pmatrix} \vec{P_0}.$$

Notice that this equation holds for any original vector, $\vec{P_0}$, and any angle of rotation, ϕ.

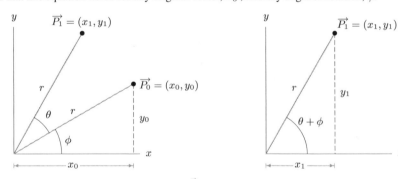

Figure 12.33: The vector $\vec{P_0}$ is rotated through an angle ϕ

402

Exercises and Problems for Section 12.5

Exercises

1. Evaluate the following expressions given that:

$$R = \begin{pmatrix} 3 & 7 \\ 2 & -1 \end{pmatrix} \quad \text{and} \quad S = \begin{pmatrix} 1 & -5 \\ 0 & 8 \end{pmatrix}.$$

  (a) $5R$ (b) $-2S$
  (c) $R+S$ (d) $S-3R$
  (e) $R+2R+2(R-S)$ (f) kS, k constant

2. Evaluate the following expressions given that:

$$A = \begin{pmatrix} 2 & 5 & 7 \\ 4 & -6 & 3 \\ 16 & -5 & 0 \end{pmatrix} \quad \text{and} \quad B = \begin{pmatrix} 8 & -6 & 0 \\ 5 & 3 & -2 \\ 3 & 7 & 12 \end{pmatrix}.$$

  (a) $2A$ (b) $-3B$ (c) $A+B$
  (d) $2A-3B$ (e) $5(A+B)$ (f) $A+(A+(A+B))$

3. Evaluate the following expressions given that:

$$U = \begin{pmatrix} 3 & 2 & 5 & 1 \\ 4 & 6 & 7 & 3 \\ 1 & 9 & 5 & 8 \\ 0 & -2 & 4 & 6 \end{pmatrix} \quad \text{and} \quad V = \begin{pmatrix} 1 & 6 & 4 & 2 \\ 3 & 5 & -1 & 7 \\ 9 & 4 & 7 & 3 \\ 2 & 8 & 4 & 5 \end{pmatrix}.$$

  (a) $4U$ (b) $-2V$
  (c) $U-V$ (d) $3U-3V$
  (e) $U+U-(U-V)$ (f) $2(2U-V)$

4. Let R and S be the matrices from Problem 1, and let $\vec{p} = (3, 1)$ and $\vec{q} = (-1, 5)$ be vectors. Evaluate the following expressions.

  (a) $R\vec{p}$ (b) $S\vec{q}$ (c) $S(\vec{q}+\vec{p})$
  (d) $(R+S)\vec{p}$ (e) $R\vec{p}\cdot S\vec{q}$ (f) $(\vec{p}\cdot\vec{q})S$

5. Let A and B be the matrices defined in Problem 2, and let $\vec{u} = (3, 2, 5)$ and $\vec{v} = (-1, 0, 3)$ be vectors. Evaluate the following expressions.

  (a) $A\vec{u}$ (b) $B\vec{v}$ (c) $A(\vec{u}+\vec{v})$
  (d) $(A+B)\vec{v}$ (e) $A\vec{u}\cdot B\vec{v}$ (f) $(\vec{u}\cdot\vec{v})A$

6. Let U and V be the matrices defined in Problem 3, and let $\vec{s} = (2, 0, -1, 7)$ and $\vec{t} = (4, 5, 1, -1)$ be vectors. Evaluate the following expressions.

  (a) $U\vec{t}$ (b) $V\vec{s}$
  (c) $U\vec{t}\cdot U\vec{s}$ (d) $U(\vec{s}-\vec{t})$
  (e) $(U+V)(\vec{s}+\vec{t})$ (f) $(\vec{s}\cdot\vec{t})(U+V)$

Problems

7. Let A and B be the matrices given by

$$A = \begin{pmatrix} 3 & 7 \\ 2 & -1 \end{pmatrix} \quad \text{and} \quad B = \begin{pmatrix} 1 & -5 & 0 \\ 0 & -1 & 1 \\ 1 & 0 & 1 \end{pmatrix}$$

and $\vec{u} = (1, 1)$ and $\vec{v} = (1, 0, 3)$ be vectors. Which of the following are defined?

  (a) $A\vec{u}$ (b) $B\vec{u}$
  (c) $A(\vec{u}+\vec{v})$ (d) $A+\vec{u}$
  (e) $(A\vec{u})/(\vec{v}\cdot\vec{v})$ (f) $(\vec{u}\cdot\vec{v})A$

8. Let

$$A = \begin{pmatrix} 1 & 2 \\ 2 & -1 \end{pmatrix} \quad \text{and} \quad \vec{u} = (5, -5).$$

  (a) Find $\vec{w}$ such that $\vec{w} = A\vec{u}$.
  (b) Find $\vec{w}$ such that $A\vec{w} = \vec{u}$.

9. A new virus emerges in a population. Each day, 10% of the susceptible population becomes infected, and 50% of the infected population recovers. Additionally, 2% of the recovered population becomes reinfected. Let $\vec{p} = (s, i, r)$ be a population vector where s is the number of susceptible (never-infected) people, i is the number of infected people, and r is the number of recovered people, all numbers in millions. Assume that initially $\vec{p_0} = (2, 0, 0)$.

  (a) Find a matrix T such that $\vec{p}_{\text{new}} = T\vec{p}_{\text{old}}$ where $\vec{p}_{\text{old}}$ is the starting population and $\vec{p}_{\text{new}}$ is the population a day later.
  (b) Find $\vec{p_1}$, $\vec{p_2}$, and $\vec{p_3}$, the populations on days 1, 2, and 3, respectively.

10. A certain species of insect has a three-year life cycle. The vector $\vec{P} = (f, s, t)$ gives the number of insects in their first, second, and third years of life, respectively. Each year, insects of all three ages lay eggs, and so the value of f_{new} depends on the values of f_{old}, s_{old}, and t_{old}. Only some first-year insects survive until their second year, and so s_{new} depends only on f_{old}; likewise, t_{new}

depends only on s_{old}.

(a) Suppose $\vec{P}_{new} = \mathbf{T}\vec{P}_{old} = \begin{pmatrix} 0.3 & 0.6 & 0.5 \\ 0.7 & 0 & 0 \\ 0 & 0.4 & 0 \end{pmatrix} \vec{P}_{old}$.

Describe in words what this tells you about the life cycle of this insect. Be specific.

(b) Let $\vec{P}_0 = (2000, 0, 0)$ be the initial population vector in year $t = 0$. Evaluate $\vec{P}_1$, $\vec{P}_2$, and $\vec{P}_3$.

11. Let $\vec{p}_{2005} = (A_{2005}, B_{2005}) = (200, 400)$ describe the populations (in 1000s) of two cities in the year 2005. Each year, 3% of the population of city A moves to the city B, and 5% of the population of the city B moves to city A.

(a) Find a matrix $\mathbf{T}$ such that $\vec{p}_{new} = \mathbf{T}\vec{p}_{old}$, where $\vec{p}_{old}$ is the starting population and $\vec{p}_{new}$ is the population 1 year later.

(b) Find $\vec{p}_{2006}$ and $\vec{p}_{2007}$, the populations in 2006 and 2007, respectively.

12. Let $\mathbf{I}_2 = \begin{pmatrix} 1 & 0 \\ 0 & 1 \end{pmatrix}$ and $\mathbf{I}_3 = \begin{pmatrix} 1 & 0 & 0 \\ 0 & 1 & 0 \\ 0 & 0 & 1 \end{pmatrix}$.

(a) Evaluate $\mathbf{I}_2\vec{u}$ for (i) $\vec{u} = (3, 2)$, (ii) $\vec{u} = (0, 7)$, and (iii) $\vec{u} = (a, b)$.

(b) Evaluate $\mathbf{I}_3\vec{v}$ for (i) $\vec{v} = (-1, 5, 7)$, (ii) $\vec{v} = (3, 8, 1)$, and (iii) $\vec{v} = (a, b, c)$.

(c) Find a matrix $\mathbf{I}_4$ such that $\mathbf{I}_4\vec{w} = \vec{w}$ where $\vec{w}$ is any 4-vector.

13. In an algebraic equation such as $y = kx$, $k \neq 0$, we can multiply through by $k^{-1} = 1/k$ in order to solve for x, giving $x = k^{-1}y$. We can do a similar thing with matrices: if $\vec{v} = \mathbf{A}\vec{u}$, it is sometimes possible to find an *inverse* of $\mathbf{A}$, written $\mathbf{A}^{-1}$, such that $\vec{u} = \mathbf{A}^{-1}\vec{v}$.

(a) Let $\mathbf{A} = \begin{pmatrix} 2 & 1 \\ 3 & 2 \end{pmatrix}$. It can be shown that $\mathbf{A}^{-1} = \begin{pmatrix} 2 & -1 \\ -3 & 2 \end{pmatrix}$. Check this fact using the vector $\vec{u} = (3, 5)$, first by multiplying $\vec{u}$ by $\mathbf{A}$ to get $\vec{v}$, and then by multiplying $\vec{v}$ by $\mathbf{A}^{-1}$ to show that we get $\vec{u}$ back.

(b) Rework part (a), this time for $\vec{u} = (-1, 7)$.

(c) Rework part (a), this time for $\vec{u} = (a, b)$.

14. In Problem 13, we introduced the notion of the inverse of a matrix $\mathbf{A}$, written $\mathbf{A}^{-1}$. If $\mathbf{A} = \begin{pmatrix} a & b \\ c & d \end{pmatrix}$, then $\mathbf{A}^{-1} = \frac{1}{D}\begin{pmatrix} d & -b \\ -c & a \end{pmatrix}$ where $D = ad - bc$. Notice that $\mathbf{A}^{-1}$ is undefined if $D = 0$.

(a) Use this formula to show that $\mathbf{A}^{-1}$ from Problem 13 is $\begin{pmatrix} 2 & -1 \\ -3 & 2 \end{pmatrix}$.

(b) Let $\mathbf{B} = \begin{pmatrix} 3 & 11 \\ 1 & 7 \end{pmatrix}$. Find $\mathbf{B}^{-1}$. Verify that if $\vec{v} = \mathbf{B}\vec{u}$ then $\vec{u} = \mathbf{B}^{-1}\vec{v}$ for $\vec{u} = (a, b)$.

(c) Show that $\mathbf{C} = \begin{pmatrix} 2 & 8 \\ 3 & 12 \end{pmatrix}$ does not have an inverse.

15. Multiplying a vector by a matrix is a much more complicated process than multiplying a vector by a scalar. However, in certain special cases, matrix and scalar multiplication can lead to the same result. If $\mathbf{A}\vec{v} = \lambda\vec{v}$ where $\mathbf{A}$ is a matrix, $\vec{v}$ a nonzero vector, and λ a scalar, then $\vec{v}$ is said to be an *eigenvector* of $\mathbf{A}$, and λ is said to be an *eigenvalue* of $\mathbf{A}$. For instance, let $\mathbf{A} = \begin{pmatrix} -2 & -1 \\ 8 & 7 \end{pmatrix}$, $\vec{v_1} = (1, -8)$, and $\lambda_1 = 6$. We have:

$$\mathbf{A}\vec{v_1} = \begin{pmatrix} -2 & -1 \\ 8 & 7 \end{pmatrix} \cdot \begin{pmatrix} 1 \\ -8 \end{pmatrix} = \begin{pmatrix} 6 \\ -48 \end{pmatrix}$$

$$\lambda_1\vec{v_1} = 6 \cdot \begin{pmatrix} 1 \\ -8 \end{pmatrix} = \begin{pmatrix} 6 \\ -48 \end{pmatrix}.$$

We see that multiplying $\vec{v_1}$ by $\lambda_1 = 6$ works out the same as multiplying $\vec{v_1}$ by $\mathbf{A}$; we say that $\vec{v_1}$ is an *eigenvector* of $\mathbf{A}$ with an *eigenvalue* of $\lambda_1 = 6$.

(a) Show that $\vec{v_2} = (1, -1)$ is an eigenvector of $\mathbf{A}$. What is the eigenvalue?

(b) Show that $\vec{v_3} = (-3, 3)$ is an eigenvector of $\mathbf{A}$. What is the eigenvalue?

(c) If $\vec{v}$ is an eigenvector of $\mathbf{A}$, explain why the vectors $\vec{v}$ and $\mathbf{A}\vec{v}$ are parallel.

16. In this problem, we will consider a new way to think about matrix multiplication of vectors. A vector such as $\vec{v} = (9, 8)$ can be written as a combination of unit vectors, like this:

$$\vec{v} = (9, 8) = 9\vec{i} + 8\vec{j} = 9\underbrace{(1, 0)}_{\vec{i}} + 8\underbrace{(0, 1)}_{\vec{j}}.$$

But we can also write $\vec{v}$ as a combination[11] of other vectors besides $\vec{i}$ and $\vec{j}$. For instance, if $\vec{c_1} = (1, 2)$, and $\vec{c_2} = (3, 1)$, notice that

$$\vec{v} = (9, 8) = 3\vec{c_1} + 2\vec{c_2} = 3\underbrace{(1, 2)}_{\vec{c_1}} + 2\underbrace{(3, 1)}_{\vec{c_2}}.$$

---

[11]This sort of combination is called a *linear combination*.

This is where matrix multiplication comes in: if we think of $\vec{c_1}$ and $\vec{c_2}$ as the columns of a matrix **C**, we see that

$$\begin{pmatrix} 9 \\ 8 \end{pmatrix} = \left(\begin{array}{c|c} 1 & 3 \\ 2 & 1 \end{array} \right) \begin{pmatrix} 3 \\ 2 \end{pmatrix}$$

$$\underbrace{}_{\vec{c_1}} \underbrace{}_{\vec{c_2}}$$

is the same as

$$\begin{pmatrix} 9 \\ 8 \end{pmatrix} = 3 \underbrace{\begin{pmatrix} 1 \\ 2 \end{pmatrix}}_{\vec{c_1}} + 2 \underbrace{\begin{pmatrix} 3 \\ 1 \end{pmatrix}}_{\vec{c_2}}.$$

In general, if $\vec{v} = \mathbf{C}\vec{u}$, then the coordinates of $\vec{u}$ tell us how to combine the columns of **C** in order to get $\vec{v}$.

(a) Let $\vec{v} = 3\vec{r_1} + 5\vec{r_2}$ where $r_1 = (3, 2)$ and $r_2 = (0, 1)$. Find $\vec{v}$, $\vec{u}$, and **R** such that $\vec{v} = \mathbf{R}\vec{u}$.

(b) Let $\vec{q} = \mathbf{S}\vec{p} = \begin{pmatrix} 3 & 4 \\ 2 & 3 \end{pmatrix} \begin{pmatrix} 3 \\ -2 \end{pmatrix}$. Show that $\vec{q}$ can be written as a combination of $\vec{s_1} = (3, 2)$ and $\vec{s_2} = (4, 3)$, the two columns of **S**.

17. Let $\vec{v} = (2, 5)$, $\vec{c_1} = (3, 2)$, and $\vec{c_2} = (5, 4)$. In this problem we will use the results of Problem 16 to write $\vec{v}$ as a combination of $\vec{c_1}$ and $\vec{c_2}$ given by $\vec{v} = a\vec{c_1} + b\vec{c_2}$.

(a) Let **C** be a matrix whose columns are given by $\vec{c_1}$ and $\vec{c_2}$, and let $\vec{u} = (a, b)$. Show that $\mathbf{C}\vec{u} = a\vec{c_1} + b\vec{c_2}$.

(b) Let $\vec{v} = \mathbf{C}\vec{u}$ where $\vec{v} = (2, 5)$. Referring to Problem 13 and Problem 14, solve for $\vec{u}$.

(c) Show that $\vec{v}$ is a combination of $\vec{c_1}$ and $\vec{c_2}$ given by $\vec{v} = a\vec{c_1} + b\vec{c_2}$.

18. Following the procedure outlined in Problem 17, write $\vec{v} = (5, 8)$ as a combination of $\vec{c_1} = (6, 1)$ and $\vec{c_2} = (7, 2)$ given by $\vec{v} = a\vec{c_1} + b\vec{c_2}$.

CHAPTER SUMMARY

- **Vectors**
  Displacement; vector notation; components.
  Length: $\|\vec{v}\| = \sqrt{v_1^2 + v_2^2 + v_3^2}$; unit vectors.
- **Addition, Subtraction, and Scalar Multiplication of Vectors**
- **Dot Product**

$$\vec{v} \cdot \vec{w} = v_1 w_1 + v_2 w_2 + v_3 w_3 = \|\vec{v}\|\|\vec{w}\| \cos\theta.$$

- **Applications**
  Economics; computer graphics; work.
- **Matrices**
  Addition; subtraction; multiplication by scalars, by vectors.

REVIEW EXERCISES AND PROBLEMS FOR CHAPTER TWELVE

Exercises

Calculate the vectors in Exercises 1–8, using $\vec{a} = (5, 1, 0)$, $\vec{b} = (2, -1, 9)$, $\vec{c} = (1, 1, 2)$.

1. $3\vec{c}$

2. $\vec{a} + \vec{b}$

3. $\vec{b} - \vec{a}$

4. $\vec{a} + 2(\vec{b} + \vec{c})$

5. $2\vec{a} - 3(\vec{b} - \vec{c})$

6. $2(\vec{b} + 4(\vec{a} + \vec{c}))$

7. $\vec{a} + \vec{b} - (\vec{a} - \vec{b})$

8. $4(\vec{c} + 2(\vec{a} - \vec{c}) - 2\vec{a})$

For Exercises 9–16, perform the indicated computations.

9. $-4(\vec{i} - 2\vec{j}) - 0.5(\vec{i} - \vec{k})$

10. $(\vec{i} + 2\vec{j}) + (-3)(2\vec{i} + \vec{j})$

11. $(3\vec{i} + \vec{j}) \cdot (5\vec{i} - 2\vec{j})$

12. $(3\vec{j} - 2\vec{k} + \vec{i}) \cdot (4\vec{k} - 2\vec{i} + 3\vec{j})$

13. $(5\vec{i} - \vec{j} - 3\vec{k}) \cdot (2\vec{i} + \vec{j} + \vec{k})$

14. $(2\vec{i} \cdot 5\vec{j})(\vec{i} + \vec{j} + \vec{k})$

15. $(2\vec{i} + 5\vec{j}) \cdot 3\vec{i}(\vec{i} + \vec{j} + \vec{k})$

16. $(\vec{i} + \vec{j} + \vec{k})(2\vec{i} + 3\vec{j} + \vec{k}) \cdot (3\vec{i} + \vec{j} + 4\vec{k})$

Resolve the vectors in Exercises 17–18 into components.

17.

18.

19. Find the length of the vectors $\vec{u}$ and $\vec{v}$ in Problem 18.

20. Find a vector of length 2 that points in the same direction as $\vec{i} - \vec{j} + 2\vec{k}$.

Problems

21. (a) Are the vectors $4\vec{i} + a\vec{j} + 6\vec{k}$ and $a\vec{i} + (a-1)\vec{j} + 3\vec{k}$ parallel for any values of the constant a?

(b) Are these vectors ever perpendicular?

22. A point P is on the rim of a moving bicycle wheel of radius 1 ft. The bicycle is moving forward at 6π ft/sec.

(a) Sketch the velocity of P relative to the wheel's axle at the 3, 6, 9, 12 o'clock positions.

(b) Sketch the velocity of the axle relative to the ground.

(c) Sketch the velocity of P relative to the ground at the positions in part (a).

(d) Does P ever stop, relative to the ground? What is the greatest speed that P moves, relative to the ground?

23. A gymnastics academy offers classes to children of different ages. Software used by the academy tracks enrollment data using vectors. Let $\vec{E} = (e_1, e_2, e_3, e_4, e_5)$ represent the number of children enrolled at each of five different experience levels, from beginner (1) to advanced (5), and let $\vec{E}_{max} = (40, 40, 30, 15, 10)$ be the maximum allowed enrollment at each level.

(a) Let $\vec{E} = (51, 47, 41, 22, 23)$ give the number of applicants at each level for the next session. After full enrollment is reached, the remaining applicants are placed on a wait list, $\vec{L}$. Find $\vec{L}$.

(b) At the start of the next session, $\vec{E} = \vec{E}_{max}$. Let $\vec{D} = (8, 4, 9, 7, 6)$ be the number of dropouts after the first week of the next session. Find $\vec{F} = \vec{E} - \vec{D}$ and $\vec{G} = \vec{L} - \vec{D}$. What do these vectors tell you about enrollment?

24. Let $\vec{E}$ be the enrollment vector for the gymnastics academy described in Problem 23, where $\vec{E}_{max} = (40, 40, 30, 15, 10)$. Also, let $\vec{T} = (30, 30, 40, 80, 120)$ be the weekly tuition (in \$).

(a) Evaluate $\vec{E}_{max} \cdot \vec{T}$. What does this tell you about the gymnastics academy?

(b) Let $\vec{R} = (5, 5, 10, 20, 30)$ describe a rate hike in weekly tuition, and let $\vec{T}_{new} = \vec{T} + \vec{R}$. Evaluate $\vec{E}_{max} \cdot \vec{R}$ and $\vec{E}_{max} \cdot \vec{T}_{new}$. What do these two quantities tell you about tuition?

In Problems 25–27, a 5-pound block sits on a plank of wood. If one end of the plank is raised, the block slides down the plank. However, friction between the block and the plank prevents it from sliding until the plank has been raised a certain height. It turns out that the *sliding force* exerted by gravity on the block is proportional to the sine of the angle made by the plank with the ground.

25. Find a formula for $F = f(\theta)$, the sliding force (in lbs) exerted on a block if the plank makes an angle of θ with

the ground. [Hint: What is sliding force if the plank is horizontal? Vertical?]

26. One end of the plank is lifted at a constant rate of 2 ft per second, while the other end rests on the ground.

(a) Find a formula for $F = h(t)$, the sliding force exerted on the block as a function of time.

(b) Suppose the block begins to slide once the sliding force equals 3 lbs. At what time will the block begin to slide?

27. The 5-lb force exerted on the block by gravity can be resolved into two components, the sliding force $\vec{F}_S$ parallel to the ramp and the normal force $\vec{F}_N$ perpendicular to the ramp. Use this information to show that your formula in Problem 25 is correct.

28. A plane is heading due east and climbing at the rate of 80 km/hr. If its airspeed is 480 km/hr and there is a wind blowing 100 km/hr to the northeast, what is the ground speed of the plane?

29. A particle moving with speed v hits a barrier at an angle of $60°$ and bounces off at an angle of $60°$ in the opposite direction with speed reduced by 20 percent, as shown in Figure 12.34. Find the velocity vector of the object after impact.

Figure 12.34

30. Figure 12.35 shows a molecule with four atoms at O, A, B and C. Show that every atom in the molecule is 2 units away from every other atom.

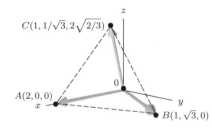

Figure 12.35

31. Two cylindrical cans of radius 2 and height 7 are shown in Figure 12.36. The cans touch down the side. Let A be the point at the top rims where they touch. Let B be the front point on the bottom rim of the left can, and C be the back point on the bottom rim of the right can. The origin is at A and the z-axis points upward; the x-axis points forward (out of the paper) and the y-axis points to the right.

   (a) Write vectors in component form for $\overrightarrow{AB}$ and $\overrightarrow{AC}$.

   (b) What is the angle between $\overrightarrow{AB}$ and $\overrightarrow{AC}$?

Figure 12.36

32. (a) Using the fact that $\vec{u} \cdot \vec{v} = \|\vec{u}\| \cdot \|\vec{v}\| \cos\theta$, show that
$$\vec{u} \cdot (-\vec{v}) = -(\vec{u} \cdot \vec{v}).$$
[Hint: What happens to the angle when you multiply $\vec{v}$ by -1?]

   (b) Using the fact that $\vec{u} \cdot \vec{v} = \|\vec{u}\| \cdot \|\vec{v}\| \cos\theta$, show that for any negative scalar λ
$$\vec{u} \cdot (\lambda\vec{v}) = \lambda(\vec{u} \cdot \vec{v})$$
$$(\lambda\vec{u}) \cdot \vec{v} = \lambda(\vec{u} \cdot \vec{v}).$$

33. A consumption vector of three goods is given by $\vec{x} = (x_1, x_2, x_3)$, where x_1, x_2 and x_3 are the quantities consumed of the three goods. Consider a budget constraint represented by the equation $\vec{p} \cdot \vec{x} = k$, where $\vec{p}$ is the price vector of the three goods and k is a constant. Show that the difference between two consumption vectors corresponding to points satisfying the same budget constraint is perpendicular to the price vector $\vec{p}$.

34. Consider the grid in Figure 12.37. Write expressions for $\overrightarrow{AB}$ and $\overrightarrow{CD}$ in terms of $\vec{i}$ and $\vec{j}$.

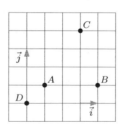

Figure 12.37

35. Consider the grid of equilateral triangles in Figure 12.38. Find expressions for $\overrightarrow{AB}$, $\overrightarrow{BC}$, $\overrightarrow{AC}$, and $\overrightarrow{AD}$ in terms of $\vec{u}$ and $\vec{v}$.

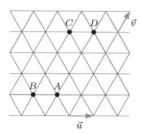

Figure 12.38

36. Consider the regular hexagon in Figure 12.39. Express the six sides and all three diameters in terms of $\vec{m}$ and $\vec{n}$.

Figure 12.39

37. Consider the grid of regular hexagons in Figure 12.40. Express $\overrightarrow{AC}$, $\overrightarrow{AB}$, $\overrightarrow{AD}$ and $\overrightarrow{BD}$ in terms of $\vec{m}$ and $\vec{n}$.

Figure 12.40

CHECK YOUR UNDERSTANDING

Are the statements in Problems 1–25 true or false? Give an explanation for your answer.

1. The vector $0.5\vec{i} + 0.5\vec{j}$ has length 1.

2. If a vector $\vec{v}$ is multiplied by a scalar, k, the resultant vector $k\vec{v}$ is longer than the original vector.

3. If $\|\vec{u}\| = 5$, then $\|-\vec{u}\| = -5$.

4. The vectors $3\vec{i} - \vec{j} + \vec{k}$ and $6\vec{i} - 2\vec{j} + 2\vec{k}$ are parallel.

5. The vectors $2\vec{i} + \vec{j}$ and $2\vec{i} - \vec{j}$ are perpendicular.

6. The two vectors $2\vec{i} + 3\vec{j}$ and $3\vec{i} + 2\vec{j}$ point in opposite directions

7. If $\vec{u} \cdot \vec{v} < 0$ then $\vec{u}$ and $\vec{v}$ form an acute angle (between $0°$ and $90°$).

8. If $\vec{u}$ and $\vec{v}$ are vectors, then their dot product is also a vector.

9. For any two vectors $\vec{u}$ and $\vec{v}$ we have $\vec{u} + \vec{v} = \vec{v} + \vec{u}$.

10. For any two vectors $\vec{u}$ and $\vec{v}$ we have $\|\vec{u} + \vec{v}\| = \|\vec{u}\| + \|\vec{v}\|$.

11. For any two vectors $\vec{u}$ and $\vec{v}$ we have $\vec{u} \cdot \vec{v} = \vec{v} \cdot \vec{u}$.

12. If the dot product of two nonzero vectors is zero, then the vectors are perpendicular.

13. The distance between the points $P = (2, 3)$ and $Q = (3, 4)$ is the vector $\vec{i} + \vec{j}$.

14. The vector starting at the point $P = (1, 2)$ and ending at the point $Q = (-3, 7)$ can be represented by $-2\vec{i} + 9\vec{j}$.

15. To add any two vectors, we add their corresponding components.

16. If $\vec{v}$ is any vector, $\vec{v} \cdot \vec{v}$ is the length of $\vec{v}$.

17. The two vectors $2\vec{i} + 3\vec{j}$ and $3\vec{i} + 2\vec{j}$ have the same length.

18. If A is a $m \times n$ matrix, the matrix A has m rows and n columns.

19. If $\mathbf{A} = \begin{pmatrix} 1 & 2 & 3 \\ 4 & 5 & 6 \\ 7 & 8 & 9 \end{pmatrix}$ then $a_{23} = 8$.

20. The matrix $\mathbf{A} = \begin{pmatrix} 1 & 2 & 3 \\ 4 & 5 & 6 \end{pmatrix}$ is a 3×2 matrix.

21. If A is a 5×5 matrix, then a_{35} refers to the element of A that is in the third row and fifth column.

22. To rotate a vector $\vec{v}$ through an angle ϕ, multiply $\vec{v}$ by the matrix $R = \begin{pmatrix} -\cos\phi & \sin\phi \\ \sin\phi & \cos\phi \end{pmatrix}$.

23. If A, B are 2×2 matrices, then $AB = BA$.

24. You cannot add a 2×2 matrix $\mathbf{A}$ and a 3×3 matrix $\mathbf{B}$.

25. If $A = \begin{pmatrix} 2 & 3 \\ -1 & 5 \end{pmatrix}$ and $\vec{v} = \begin{pmatrix} 10 \\ 5 \end{pmatrix}$, then $A\vec{v} = \begin{pmatrix} 35 \\ 15 \end{pmatrix}$.

Finite Mathematics: An Applied Approach, Eleventh Edition

Michael Sullivan

12.6 Multiplication of Matrices

PREPARING FOR THIS SECTION *Before getting started, review the following:*
• Properties of Real Numbers (Appendix A, Section A.1, pp. A-8 to A-12)

 NOW WORK THE 'ARE YOU PREPARED?' PROBLEMS ON PAGE 131

OBJECTIVES **1** Find the product of two matrices (p. 122)
2 Work with properties of matrix multiplication (p. 126)
3 Solve applied problems involving matrices (p. 129)

While addition and subtraction of matrices and the product of a scalar and a matrix are fairly straightforward, defining the *product* of two matrices requires a bit more detail.

We explain first what we mean by the product of a row matrix (a matrix with one row) with a column matrix (a matrix with one column).

Let's look at a simple example. In a given month suppose 23 units of material and 7 units of labor were required to manufacture 4-door sedans. We can represent this by the column matrix

$$\begin{bmatrix} 23 \\ 7 \end{bmatrix}$$

Also, suppose the cost per unit of material is $450 and the cost per unit of labor is $600. We represent these costs by the row matrix

$$[450 \quad 600]$$

The total cost of producing the sedans is calculated as follows:

$$\text{Total cost} = (\text{Cost per unit of material}) \times (\text{Units of material})$$
$$+ (\text{Cost per unit of labor}) \times (\text{Units of labor})$$
$$= \$450 \times 23 + \$600 \times 7 = \$14,550$$

In terms of the matrix representations,

$$\text{Total cost} = [450 \quad 600]\begin{bmatrix} 23 \\ 7 \end{bmatrix} = 450 \times 23 + 600 \times 7 = 14,550$$

This leads to the following definition for multiplying a row matrix times a column matrix:

Definition

If $R = [r_1 r_2 \ldots r_n]$ is a row matrix of dimension $1 \times n$ and $C = \begin{bmatrix} c_1 \\ c_2 \\ \vdots \\ c_n \end{bmatrix}$ is a column

matrix of dimension $n \times 1$, then by the **product of R and C** we mean the number

$$RC = r_1 c_1 + r_2 c_2 + r_3 c_3 + \cdots + r_n c_n$$

EXAMPLE 1   **Finding the Product of a 1 × 3 Row Matrix and a 3 × 1 Column Matrix**

If $\qquad R = [1 \quad 5 \quad 3] \quad$ and $\quad C = \begin{bmatrix} 2 \\ -1 \\ 4 \end{bmatrix}$

then the product of R and C is

$$RC = [1 \quad 5 \quad 3]\begin{bmatrix} 2 \\ -1 \\ 4 \end{bmatrix} = 1\cdot 2 + 5\cdot(-1) + 3\cdot 4 = 9$$

Notice that for the product of a row matrix R and a column matrix C to be defined, if R is a $1 \times n$ row matrix, then C must be of dimension $n \times 1$.

EXAMPLE 2   **Finding the Product of a 1 × 4 Row Matrix and a 4 × 1 Column Matrix**

Let $\qquad R = [1 \quad 0 \quad 1 \quad 5] \quad$ and $\quad C = \begin{bmatrix} 0 \\ -11 \\ 0 \\ 8 \end{bmatrix}$

Then the product of R and C is

$$RC = [1 \quad 0 \quad 1 \quad 5]\begin{bmatrix} 0 \\ -11 \\ 0 \\ 8 \end{bmatrix} = 1\cdot 0 + 0\cdot(-11) + 1\cdot 0 + 5\cdot 8 = 40$$

NOW WORK PROBLEM 7.

Given two matrices A and B, the rows of A can be thought of as row matrices, while the columns of B can be thought of as column matrices. This observation will be used in the following definition.

Definition   **Multiplication of Matrices**

Let A denote an $m \times r$ matrix, and let B denote an $r \times n$ matrix. The **product** AB is defined as the $m \times n$ matrix whose entry in row i, column j is the product of the ith row of A and the jth column of B.

1 Find the Product of Two Matrices

EXAMPLE 3   **Finding the Product of Two Matrices**

Find the product AB if

$$A = \begin{bmatrix} 2 & 4 & -1 \\ 5 & 8 & 0 \end{bmatrix} \quad \text{and} \quad B = \begin{bmatrix} 2 & 5 & 1 & 4 \\ 4 & 8 & 0 & 6 \\ -3 & 1 & -2 & -1 \end{bmatrix}$$

SOLUTION First, we note that A is 2×3 and B is 3×4, so the product AB is defined and will be a 2×4 matrix.

Suppose that we want the entry in row 2, column 3 of AB. To find it, we find the product of the row vector from row 2 of A and the column vector from column 3 of B.

$$\text{Row 2 of } A \quad \begin{bmatrix} 5 & 8 & 0 \end{bmatrix} \overset{\displaystyle \text{Column 3 of } B}{\begin{bmatrix} 1 \\ 0 \\ -2 \end{bmatrix}} = 5 \cdot 1 + 8 \cdot 0 + 0(-2) = 5$$

So far we have

$$AB = \begin{bmatrix} \rule{1cm}{0.4pt} & \rule{1cm}{0.4pt} & \overset{\text{Column 3}}{\rule{1cm}{0.4pt}} & \rule{1cm}{0.4pt} \\ \rule{1cm}{0.4pt} & \rule{1cm}{0.4pt} & 5 & \rule{1cm}{0.4pt} \end{bmatrix} \quad \text{Row 2}$$

Now, to find the entry in row 1, column 4 of AB, we find the product of row 1 of A and column 4 of B.

$$\text{Row 1 of } A \quad \begin{bmatrix} 2 & 4 & -1 \end{bmatrix} \overset{\displaystyle \text{Column 4 of } B}{\begin{bmatrix} 4 \\ 6 \\ -1 \end{bmatrix}} = 2 \cdot 4 + 4 \cdot 6 + (-1)(-1) = 33$$

Continuing in this fashion, we find AB.

$$AB = \begin{bmatrix} 2 & 4 & -1 \\ 5 & 8 & 0 \end{bmatrix} \begin{bmatrix} 2 & 5 & 1 & 4 \\ 4 & 8 & 0 & 6 \\ -3 & 1 & -2 & -1 \end{bmatrix}$$

$$= \begin{bmatrix} \begin{matrix} \text{Row 1 of } A \\ \text{times} \\ \text{column 1 of } B \end{matrix} & \begin{matrix} \text{Row 1 of } A \\ \text{times} \\ \text{column 2 of } B \end{matrix} & \begin{matrix} \text{Row 1 of } A \\ \text{times} \\ \text{column 3 of } B \end{matrix} & \begin{matrix} \text{Row 1 of } A \\ \text{times} \\ \text{column 4 of } B \end{matrix} \\ \begin{matrix} \text{Row 2 of } A \\ \text{times} \\ \text{column 1 of } B \end{matrix} & \begin{matrix} \text{Row 2 of } A \\ \text{times} \\ \text{column 2 of } B \end{matrix} & \begin{matrix} \text{Row 2 of } A \\ \text{times} \\ \text{column 3 of } B \end{matrix} & \begin{matrix} \text{Row 2 of } A \\ \text{times} \\ \text{column 4 of } B \end{matrix} \end{bmatrix}$$

$$= \begin{bmatrix} 2 \cdot 2 + 4 \cdot 4 + (-1)(-3) & 2 \cdot 5 + 4 \cdot 8 + (-1)1 & 2 \cdot 1 + 4 \cdot 0 + (-1)(-2) & 33 \text{ (from earlier)} \\ 5 \cdot 2 + 8 \cdot 4 + 0(-3) & 5 \cdot 5 + 8 \cdot 8 + 0 \cdot 1 & 5 \text{ (from earlier)} & 5 \cdot 4 + 8 \cdot 6 + 0(-1) \end{bmatrix}$$

$$= \begin{bmatrix} 23 & 41 & 4 & 33 \\ 42 & 89 & 5 & 68 \end{bmatrix}$$

NOW WORK PROBLEM 33. ∎

USING TECHNOLOGY

EXAMPLE 4   Finding the Product of Two Matrices Using a Graphing Utility

Rework Example 3 using a graphing utility.

SOLUTION   Enter the matrices A and B into a graphing utility. Figure 3 shows the product AB.

FIGURE 3

NOW WORK PROBLEM 33 USING A GRAPHING UTILITY.

EXAMPLE 5   Manufacturing Cost

One month's production at Motors, Inc., may be given in matrix form as

$$A = \begin{bmatrix} \overset{\text{Sedan}}{23} & \overset{\text{Convertible}}{16} & \overset{\text{SUV}}{10} \\ 7 & 9 & 11 \end{bmatrix} \begin{matrix} \text{Units of material} \\ \text{Units of labor} \end{matrix}$$

Suppose that in this month's production, the cost for each unit of material is $450 and the cost for each unit of labor is $600. What is the total cost to manufacture the sedans, the convertibles, and the SUVs?

SOLUTION   For sedans, the cost is 23 units of material at $450 each, plus 7 units of labor at $600 each, for a total cost of

$$23 \cdot \$450 + 7 \cdot \$600 = 10{,}350 + 4200 = \$14{,}550$$

Similarly, for convertibles, the total cost is

$$16 \cdot \$450 + 9 \cdot \$600 = 7200 + 5400 = \$12{,}600$$

Finally, for SUVs, the total cost is

$$10 \cdot \$450 + 11 \cdot \$600 = 4500 + 6600 = \$11{,}100$$

If we represent the cost of units of material and units of labor by the 1×2 matrix

$$U = [\overset{\substack{\text{Unit cost of} \\ \text{material}}}{450} \quad \overset{\substack{\text{Unit cost of} \\ \text{labor}}}{600}]$$

then the total cost is the product UA.

$$UA = [450 \quad 600] \begin{bmatrix} 23 & 16 & 10 \\ 7 & 9 & 11 \end{bmatrix}$$

$$= [450 \cdot 23 + 600 \cdot 7 \quad 450 \cdot 16 + 600 \cdot 9 \quad 450 \cdot 10 + 600 \cdot 11]$$

$$= [14{,}550 \quad 12{,}600 \quad 11{,}100]$$

We conclude that the total cost to manufacture the sedans is $14,550, to manufacture the convertibles is $12,600, and to manufacture the SUVs is $11,100.

NOW WORK PROBLEM 65.

USING TECHNOLOGY

EXAMPLE 6   **Using Excel**

Spreadsheets, such as Excel, can also be used to multiply matrices. Such utilities are especially useful when the dimensions of the matrices are large. Use Excel to do Example 5.

SOLUTION

STEP 1   Enter the matrices for A and U into an Excel spreadsheet as follows:

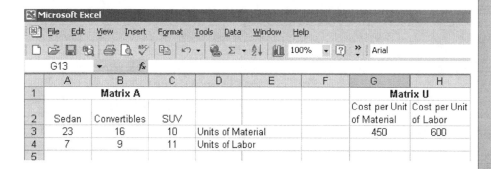

STEP 2   Highlight the cells that are to contain the product matrix. Since U is a 1×2 matrix and A is a 2×3 matrix, the product must be a 1×3 matrix.

STEP 3   Type: =MMULT(*highlight U, highlight A*)

STEP 4   Press Ctrl-Shift-Enter at the same time.

Microsoft Excel

File Edit View Insert Format Tools Data Window Help

D9   {=MMULT(G3:H3,A3:C4)}

	A	B	C	D	E	F	G	H
1		**Matrix A**						**Matrix U**
2	Sedan	Convertible	SUV				Cost per Unit of Material	Cost per Unit of Labor
3	23	16	10	Units of Material			450	600
4	7	9	11	Units of Labor				
5								
6								
7					**U*A**			
8				Total Cost for Sedans	Total Cost for Convertibles	Total Cost for SUVs		
9				14550	12600	11100		
10								

NOW WORK PROBLEM 65 USING EXCEL.

2   Work with Properties of Matrix Multiplication

If A is a matrix of dimension $m \times r$ (which has r columns) and B is a matrix of dimension $p \times n$ (which has p rows) and if $r \neq p$, the product AB is not defined.

Multiplication of matrices is possible only if the number of columns of the matrix on the left equals the number of rows of the matrix on the right.
If A is of dimension $m \times r$ and B is of dimension $r \times n$, then the product AB is of dimension $m \times n$.

FIGURE 4

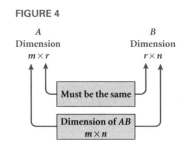

A
Dimension
$m \times r$

B
Dimension
$r \times n$

Must be the same

Dimension of AB
$m \times n$

Figure 4 illustrates the result stated above.
For example, if A is a matrix of dimension 2×3, and B is a matrix of dimension 3×4, the product AB is defined, but the product BA is not defined.

EXAMPLE 7 | **Multiplying Two Matrices**

If

$$A = \begin{bmatrix} 2 & 1 & 3 \\ 1 & -1 & 0 \end{bmatrix} \quad \text{and} \quad B = \begin{bmatrix} 1 & 0 \\ 2 & 1 \\ 3 & 2 \end{bmatrix}$$

find: (a) AB (b) BA

SOLUTION **(a)** $AB = \begin{bmatrix} 2 & 1 & 3 \\ 1 & -1 & 0 \end{bmatrix} \begin{bmatrix} 1 & 0 \\ 2 & 1 \\ 3 & 2 \end{bmatrix} = \begin{bmatrix} 13 & 7 \\ -1 & -1 \end{bmatrix}$

$\quad\quad\quad\quad 2 \times 3 \quad\quad 3 \times 2 \quad\quad 2 \times 2$

(b) $BA = \begin{bmatrix} 1 & 0 \\ 2 & 1 \\ 3 & 2 \end{bmatrix} \begin{bmatrix} 2 & 1 & 3 \\ 1 & -1 & 0 \end{bmatrix} = \begin{bmatrix} 2 & 1 & 3 \\ 5 & 1 & 6 \\ 8 & 1 & 9 \end{bmatrix}$

$\quad\quad\quad\quad 3 \times 2 \quad\quad 2 \times 3 \quad\quad 3 \times 3$ ■

Notice in Example 7 that AB is 2×2 and BA is 3×3. It is possible for both AB and BA to be defined yet be unequal. In fact, even if A and B are both $n \times n$ matrices, so that AB and BA are each defined and each are $n \times n$ matrices, AB and BA will usually be unequal.

EXAMPLE 8 | **Multiplying Two Square Matrices**

If

$$A = \begin{bmatrix} 2 & 1 \\ 0 & 4 \end{bmatrix} \quad \text{and} \quad B = \begin{bmatrix} -3 & 1 \\ 1 & 2 \end{bmatrix}$$

find: **(a)** AB **(b)** BA

SOLUTION **(a)** $AB = \begin{bmatrix} 2 & 1 \\ 0 & 4 \end{bmatrix} \begin{bmatrix} -3 & 1 \\ 1 & 2 \end{bmatrix} = \begin{bmatrix} -5 & 4 \\ 4 & 8 \end{bmatrix}$

(b) $BA = \begin{bmatrix} -3 & 1 \\ 1 & 2 \end{bmatrix} \begin{bmatrix} 2 & 1 \\ 0 & 4 \end{bmatrix} = \begin{bmatrix} -6 & 1 \\ 2 & 9 \end{bmatrix}$ ■

The preceding examples demonstrate that an important property of real numbers, the commutative property of multiplication, is not shared by matrices.

Theorem   Matrix multiplication is not commutative. That is, in general,

> **AB is not always equal to BA**

Matrix multiplication is associative.

Associative Property of Matrix Multiplication

Let A be a matrix of dimension $m \times r$, let B be a matrix of dimension $r \times p$, and let C be a matrix of dimension $p \times n$, so that $A(BC)$ and $(AB)C$ are defined. Then matrix multiplication is **associative.** That is,

> **$A(BC) = (AB)C$**

The resulting matrix ABC is of dimension $m \times n$.

NOW WORK PROBLEM 47.

Distributive Property

Let A be a matrix of dimension $m \times r$. Let B and C be matrices of dimension $r \times n$ so that $A(B+C)$ and $AB+AC$ are defined. Then the **distributive property** states that

$$A(B + C) = AB + AC$$

The resulting matrix $AB + AC$ is of dimension $m \times n$.

The Identity Matrix

For an $n \times n$ square matrix, the entries located in row i, column i, $1 \le i \le n$, are called the **diagonal entries.** An $n \times n$ square matrix whose diagonal entries are 1s, while all other entries are 0s, is called the **identity matrix** I_n. For example,

$$I_2 = \begin{bmatrix} 1 & 0 \\ 0 & 1 \end{bmatrix} \qquad I_3 = \begin{bmatrix} 1 & 0 & 0 \\ 0 & 1 & 0 \\ 0 & 0 & 1 \end{bmatrix}$$

and so on.

EXAMPLE 9 **Finding the Product of a Matrix and the Identity Matrix I_2**

For $\qquad A = \begin{bmatrix} 3 & 2 \\ -4 & 5 \end{bmatrix} \quad$ find

(a) AI_2 (b) I_2A

SOLUTION

(a) $AI_2 = \begin{bmatrix} 3 & 2 \\ -4 & 5 \end{bmatrix}\begin{bmatrix} 1 & 0 \\ 0 & 1 \end{bmatrix} = \begin{bmatrix} 3 & 2 \\ -4 & 5 \end{bmatrix} = A$

(b) $I_2A = \begin{bmatrix} 1 & 0 \\ 0 & 1 \end{bmatrix}\begin{bmatrix} 3 & 2 \\ -4 & 5 \end{bmatrix} = \begin{bmatrix} 3 & 2 \\ -4 & 5 \end{bmatrix} = A$

Example 9 demonstrates a more general result.

Theorem If A is a square matrix of dimension $n \times n$, then $AI_n = I_nA = A$.

For square matrices the identity matrix plays the role that the number 1 plays for multiplication in the set of real numbers.

When a matrix A is not square, care must be taken when forming the products AI and IA. For example, if

$$A = \begin{bmatrix} 1 & 2 \\ 3 & 2 \\ 1 & 1 \end{bmatrix}$$

then A is of dimension 3×2 and

$$AI_2 = A \begin{bmatrix} 1 & 0 \\ 0 & 1 \end{bmatrix} = \begin{bmatrix} 1 & 2 \\ 3 & 2 \\ 1 & 1 \end{bmatrix} \begin{bmatrix} 1 & 0 \\ 0 & 1 \end{bmatrix} = \begin{bmatrix} 1 & 2 \\ 3 & 2 \\ 1 & 1 \end{bmatrix} = A$$

Although the product I_2A is not defined, we can calculate the product I_3A as follows:

$$I_3A = \begin{bmatrix} 1 & 0 & 0 \\ 0 & 1 & 0 \\ 0 & 0 & 1 \end{bmatrix} \begin{bmatrix} 1 & 2 \\ 3 & 2 \\ 1 & 1 \end{bmatrix} = \begin{bmatrix} 1 & 2 \\ 3 & 2 \\ 1 & 1 \end{bmatrix} = A$$

The above observations can be generalized as follows:

> ## Identity Property
>
> If A is a matrix of dimension $m \times n$ and if I_n denotes the identity matrix of dimension $n \times n$, and I_m denotes the identity matrix of dimension $m \times m$, then
>
> $$I_mA = A \quad \text{and} \quad AI_n = A$$

3   Solve Applied Problems Involving Matrices

EXAMPLE 10   Applying Matrix Multiplication

The price per share for Wal-Mart (WMT), Target (TGT), and Costco (Cost) common stock at the close of trading on November 1 of the years 2007, 2008, and 2009 are shown in matrix A. Over these years, Kathleen and Shannon have each kept constant numbers of shares of the three stocks in their portfolios as shown in matrix B.

$$A = \begin{array}{c} \\ 2007 \\ 2008 \\ 2009 \end{array} \begin{array}{ccc} \text{WMT} & \text{TGT} & \text{COST} \\ \begin{bmatrix} 42.16 & 56.58 & 63.17 \\ 54.54 & 39.24 & 56.03 \\ 50.03 & 49.17 & 57.75 \end{bmatrix} \end{array} \qquad B = \begin{array}{c} \\ \text{WMT} \\ \text{TGT} \\ \text{COST} \end{array} \begin{array}{cc} \text{Kathleen} & \text{Shannon} \\ \begin{bmatrix} 150 & 125 \\ 100 & 75 \\ 50 & 100 \end{bmatrix} \end{array}$$

Compute AB and interpret the result.

Source: Yahoo Finance

SOLUTION   Notice that matrix A is 3×3 and matrix B is 3×2, so the matrix AB is defined and will be a 3×2 matrix. Also notice that the columns of matrix A are named WMT, TGT, and COST, the same names given the rows of matrix B. This means the rows of the product matrix AB will be named the same as the rows of A and the columns of AB will be named the same as the columns of B. Now,

$$AB = \begin{bmatrix} 42.16 & 56.58 & 63.17 \\ 54.54 & 39.24 & 56.03 \\ 50.03 & 49.17 & 57.75 \end{bmatrix} \begin{bmatrix} 150 & 125 \\ 100 & 75 \\ 50 & 100 \end{bmatrix}$$

$$= \begin{bmatrix} 42.16 \cdot 150 + 56.58 \cdot 100 + 63.17 \cdot 50 & 42.16 \cdot 125 + 56.58 \cdot 75 + 63.17 \cdot 100 \\ 54.54 \cdot 150 + 39.24 \cdot 100 + 56.03 \cdot 50 & 54.54 \cdot 125 + 39.24 \cdot 75 + 56.03 \cdot 100 \\ 50.03 \cdot 150 + 49.17 \cdot 100 + 57.75 \cdot 50 & 50.03 \cdot 125 + 49.17 \cdot 75 + 57.75 \cdot 100 \end{bmatrix}$$

$$= \begin{array}{c} 2007 \\ 2008 \\ 2009 \end{array} \begin{matrix} \text{Kathleen} & \text{Shannon} \\ \begin{bmatrix} \$15,140,50 & \$15,830.50 \\ \$14,906,50 & \$15,363.50 \\ \$15,309,00 & \$15,716.50 \end{bmatrix} \end{matrix}$$

The entries in the product matrix indicate the total value of the stocks in the portfolios on November 1 of each year. The value of Kathleen's portfolio was \$15,140.50 in 2007, \$14,906.50 in 2008, and \$15,309.00 in 2009. The value of Shannon's portfolio was \$15,830.50 in 2007, \$15,363.50 in 2008, and \$15,716.50 in 2009. ∎

EXAMPLE 11   Applying Matrix Multiplication

Margareta and Emilio are taking classes at both Joliet Junior College and Chicago State University. The number of credit hours taken and the cost per credit hour are as follows:

	JJC	CSU
Margareta	12	3
Emilio	9	6

	Cost per Credit Hour
JJC	\$73
CSU	\$189

(a) Write a matrix A for the credit hours taken by each student and a matrix B for the cost per credit hour.

(b) Compute AB.

(c) Interpret the results.

Sources: www.jjc.edu, www.csu.edu, for the 2006–2007 academic year

SOLUTION   **(a)** If we name the rows as Margareta and Emilio and the columns as JJC and CSU, then we can write the matrix A as the 2×2 matrix

$$A = \begin{matrix} \\ \text{Margareta} \\ \text{Emilio} \end{matrix} \begin{matrix} \text{JJC} \quad \text{CSU} \\ \begin{bmatrix} 12 & 3 \\ 9 & 6 \end{bmatrix} \end{matrix}$$

For the matrix B, if we name the rows as JJC and CSU and the column as Cost per Credit Hour, then we can write the matrix B as the 2×1 matrix

$$B = \begin{matrix} \\ \text{JJC} \\ \text{CSU} \end{matrix} \begin{matrix} \text{Cost per Credit Hour} \\ \begin{bmatrix} 73 \\ 189 \end{bmatrix} \end{matrix}$$

(b) Since A is 2×2 and B is 2×1, the product AB is defined and will be a 2×1 matrix. Then

$$AB = \begin{bmatrix} 12 & 3 \\ 9 & 6 \end{bmatrix} \begin{bmatrix} 73 \\ 189 \end{bmatrix} = \begin{bmatrix} 1443 \\ 1791 \end{bmatrix}$$

(c) Because the columns of A are named the same as the rows of B, JJC and CSU, the product AB will give us the cost for each student to attend classes. That is, it costs Margareta $1443 to take her 15 credit hours (12 at JJC and 3 at CSU) and it costs Emilio $1791 to take his 15 credit hours (9 at JJC and 6 at CSU). ■

EXERCISE 12.6 Answers Begin on Page AN–15.

'Are You Prepared?' Problems Answers are given at the end of these exercises. If you get a wrong answer, read the pages listed in red.

1. *True or False* For real numbers, multiplication is commutative. (pp. A–8 to A–12)

2. The Associative Property for Multiplication of real numbers states that _____. (pp. A–8 to A–12)

Concepts and Vocabulary

3. If A is of dimension 3×5 and B is of dimension 5×7, the dimension of the matrix AB is _____.

4. *True or False*
$$\begin{bmatrix} 1 & 3 \\ -2 & 5 \end{bmatrix} \begin{bmatrix} 0 & 1 \\ -1 & 2 \end{bmatrix} = \begin{bmatrix} -3 & 7 \\ -5 & 8 \end{bmatrix}$$

5. *True or False* There are examples of matrices for which $AB \neq BA$.

6. *True or False* Two matrices can always be multiplied as long as they are each of the same dimension.

Skill Building

In Problems 7–22, find each product.

 7. $\begin{bmatrix} 1 & 3 \end{bmatrix} \begin{bmatrix} 2 \\ 4 \end{bmatrix}$

8. $\begin{bmatrix} -1 & 4 \end{bmatrix} \begin{bmatrix} 5 \\ 2 \end{bmatrix}$

9. $\begin{bmatrix} 1 & -2 & 3 \end{bmatrix} \begin{bmatrix} 0 \\ 1 \\ 2 \end{bmatrix}$

10. $\begin{bmatrix} -1 & 1 & 0 \end{bmatrix} \begin{bmatrix} 1 \\ -1 \\ 1 \end{bmatrix}$

11. $\begin{bmatrix} 1 & 4 \end{bmatrix} \begin{bmatrix} 2 & 0 \\ 4 & -2 \end{bmatrix}$

12. $\begin{bmatrix} 2 & 0 \\ 4 & -2 \end{bmatrix} \begin{bmatrix} 2 \\ 4 \end{bmatrix}$

13. $\begin{bmatrix} 2 & 0 \\ 4 & -2 \end{bmatrix} \begin{bmatrix} 2 & 1 \\ 3 & -2 \end{bmatrix}$

14. $\begin{bmatrix} 1 & 4 \\ -1 & 2 \end{bmatrix} \begin{bmatrix} 3 & 0 \\ -2 & 2 \end{bmatrix}$

15. $\begin{bmatrix} 1 & -2 & 3 \end{bmatrix} \begin{bmatrix} 0 & 1 \\ 1 & 2 \\ 2 & 3 \end{bmatrix}$

16. $\begin{bmatrix} 1 & -2 & 3 \\ 4 & 0 & 6 \end{bmatrix} \begin{bmatrix} 0 \\ 1 \\ 2 \end{bmatrix}$

17. $\begin{bmatrix} 1 & -2 & 3 \\ 4 & 0 & 6 \end{bmatrix} \begin{bmatrix} 0 & -2 \\ 1 & 0 \\ 2 & -4 \end{bmatrix}$

18. $\begin{bmatrix} 1 & -2 & 3 \\ 4 & 0 & 6 \end{bmatrix} \begin{bmatrix} -1 & 2 & 1 \\ 1 & 3 & 0 \\ 0 & 4 & -2 \end{bmatrix}$

19. $\begin{bmatrix} 2 & 0 \\ 4 & -2 \\ 6 & -1 \end{bmatrix} \begin{bmatrix} 2 & 1 \\ 3 & -2 \end{bmatrix}$

20. $\begin{bmatrix} 1 & 4 \\ -1 & 2 \end{bmatrix} \begin{bmatrix} 2 & 0 & 6 \\ -1 & 4 & 1 \end{bmatrix}$

21. $\begin{bmatrix} 1 & -1 & 6 \\ 2 & 0 & -1 \\ 3 & 1 & 2 \end{bmatrix} \begin{bmatrix} 3 & 2 \\ 0 & 1 \\ 1 & 0 \end{bmatrix}$

22. $\begin{bmatrix} 2 & 0 & 1 \\ -1 & 1 & 1 \end{bmatrix} \begin{bmatrix} 1 & 0 & 0 \\ 2 & 1 & 2 \\ 3 & 2 & 4 \end{bmatrix}$

In Problems 23–32, let A be of dimension 3×4, B be of dimension 3×3, C be of dimension 2×3, and D be of dimension 3×2. Determine which of the following expressions are defined and, for those that are, give the dimension.

23. BA **24.** CD **25.** AB **26.** DC **27.** $(BA)C$

28. $A(CD)$ **29.** $BA + A$ **30.** $CD + BA$ **31.** $CB - A$ **32.** $DC + B$

In Problems 33–48, use the matrices given below.
For Problems 33–46, perform the indicated operation(s); for Problems 47 and 48, verify the indicated property.

$$A = \begin{bmatrix} 1 & 2 \\ 0 & 4 \end{bmatrix} \quad B = \begin{bmatrix} 1 & 2 & 3 \\ -1 & 4 & -2 \end{bmatrix} \quad C = \begin{bmatrix} 3 & 1 \\ 4 & -1 \\ 0 & 2 \end{bmatrix} \quad D = \begin{bmatrix} 1 & 0 & 4 \\ 0 & 1 & 2 \\ 0 & -1 & 1 \end{bmatrix} \quad E = \begin{bmatrix} 3 & -1 \\ 4 & 2 \end{bmatrix}$$

33. AB **34.** DC **35.** BC **36.** AA **37.** $(D + I_3)C$

38. $DC + C$ **39.** EI_2 **40.** I_3D **41.** $(2E)B$ **42.** $E(2B)$

43. $-5E + A$ **44.** $3A + 2E$ **45.** $3CB + 4D$ **46.** $2EA - 3BC$

 47. Verify the associative property of matrix multiplication by finding $D(CB)$ and $(DC)B$.

48. Verify the distributive property by finding $(A + E)B$ and $AB + EB$.

49. For
$$A = \begin{bmatrix} 1 & -1 \\ 2 & 0 \end{bmatrix} \quad \text{and} \quad B = \begin{bmatrix} 3 & 2 \\ -2 & 4 \end{bmatrix}$$
find AB and BA. Notice that $AB \neq BA$.

50. For
$$A = \begin{bmatrix} 1 & 4 \\ -4 & 1 \end{bmatrix} \quad \text{and} \quad B = \begin{bmatrix} 8 & -3 \\ 3 & 8 \end{bmatrix}$$
find AB and BA. Notice that $AB = BA$.

In Problems 51–58, use a graphing utility or EXCEL and the matrices given below to perform the indicated operations.

$$A = \begin{bmatrix} -1 & -1 & 3 & 0 \\ 2 & 6 & 2 & 2 \\ -4 & 2 & 3 & 2 \\ 7 & 0 & 5 & -1 \end{bmatrix} \quad B = \begin{bmatrix} -1 & 2 & 4 & 5 \\ 2 & 0 & 5 & 3 \\ 0.5 & 6 & -7 & 11 \\ 5 & -1 & 2 & 7 \end{bmatrix} \quad C = \begin{bmatrix} 13 & -8 & 7 & 0 \\ 0 & 5 & 0 & -2 \\ 5 & 0 & 7 & 0 \\ 7 & 7 & 7 & 7 \end{bmatrix}$$

51. AB **52.** BA **53.** $(AB)C$ **54.** $A(BC)$

55. $B(A + C)$ **56.** $(A + C)B$ **57.** $A(2B - 3C)$ **58.** $(A + B)(A - B)$

Applications and Extensions

59. Stock Purchases The price per share at the close of trading on July 7, 2009, for stock in Chevron, ConocoPhillips, and Exxon Mobil was

Chevron Corporation—$62.70
ConocoPhillips—$39.99
Exxon Mobil Corporation—$66.56

Let
$$A = [62.70 \quad 39.99 \quad 66.56]$$

Let B be the following 3×3 matrix showing the number of shares of stock purchased at the close of trading on July 7 by Kevin, Timmy, and Nolan.

$$
\begin{array}{c}
\\
\text{Chevron} \\
B = \text{ConocoPhillips} \\
\text{Exxon Mobil}
\end{array}
\begin{array}{ccc}
\text{Kevin} & \text{Timmy} & \text{Nolan} \\
\begin{bmatrix} 100 & 415 & 175 \\ 250 & 90 & 200 \\ 325 & 225 & 130 \end{bmatrix}
\end{array}
$$

(a) What does the matrix A represent? What is the dimension of A?

(b) Find the matrix product AB and give an interpretation of the entries in this product.

(c) Let C be the 3×1 matrix having a 1 as each entry. Find the matrix product BC and give an interpretation of the entries in this product.

60. Gasoline Prices Average gasoline prices in Los Angeles on January 4, 2010, were:

Regular—$3.035 per gallon
Midgrade—$3.144 per gallon
Premium—$3.243 per gallon

Suppose a company made gasoline purchases (in gallons) at the prices gives above for vehicles based at three different retail stores as shown in the matrix C below.

$$
\begin{array}{c}
\\
\text{Store Alpha} \\
C = \text{Store Beta} \\
\text{Store Gamma}
\end{array}
\begin{array}{ccc}
\text{Reg.} & \text{Mid.} & \text{Prem.} \\
\begin{bmatrix} 900 & 350 & 225 \\ 750 & 500 & 150 \\ 1050 & 730 & 75 \end{bmatrix}
\end{array}
$$

(a) Let $A = [3.035 \quad 3.144 \quad 3.243]$ and $B = \begin{bmatrix} 3.035 \\ 3.144 \\ 3.243 \end{bmatrix}$. What are the dimensions of A and B? Interpret A and B.

(b) Which matrix product AC or CB will give the gasoline costs for each store?

(c) Perform the appropriate matrix multiplication to find the gasoline costs for each store.

Source: U.S. Energy Administration

61. Cost of College John and Marsha take classes in Fall 2010 at both Joliet Junior College (JJC) and Chicago State University (CSU). John takes 12 credit hours at JJC and 4 credit hours at CSU, while Marsha takes 8 credit hours at each school. The cost per credit hour at JJC is $103 and at CSU is $249.

(a) Write a matrix A that gives the credit hours each student is taking at each school and a matrix B that gives the cost per credit hour at each school. Be sure to name the rows and columns and be sure that the columns of A are named the same as the rows of B.

(b) What is the dimension of A?

(c) What is the dimension of B?

(d) Find the product AB.

(e) What is the dimension of AB? What are the names of its rows and columns?

(f) Interpret the entries in AB.

Source: Each school's website.

62. Cost of College Sean, Kevin, and Bill take classes in Fall 2010 at both Joliet Junior College (JJC) and Chicago State University (CSU). Sean takes 8 credit hours at JJC and 4 credit hours at CSU; Kevin takes 10 credit hours at JJC and 6 at CSU, and Bill takes 6 credit hours at JJC and 4 at CSU. The cost per credit hour at JJC is $103 and at CSU is $249.

(a) Write a matrix A that gives the credit hours each student is taking at each school and a matrix B that gives the cost per credit at each school. Be sure to name the rows and columns and be sure that the columns of A are named the same as the rows of B.

(b) What is the dimension of A?

(c) What is the dimension of B?

(d) Find the product AB.

(e) What is the dimension of AB? What are the names of its rows and columns?

(f) Interpret the entries in AB.

(g) Does BA have any meaning? Explain.

63. Portfolio Values The price per share for General Electric (GE), Toyota Motors (TM), and Johnson & Johnson (JNJ) common stock in October 2008, April 2009, and October 2009 are shown in the table below. Over this period of time, Bill and Dan owned shares in these companies, as shown in the table.

	Price per Share				Shares Owned		
	GE	TM	JNJ		GE	TM	JNJ
Oct 2008	22	73	64	Bill	50	30	20
Apr 2009	11	78	53	Dan	40	60	30
Oct 2009	17	79	61				

(a) Write a matrix A that gives the price per share of the three stocks on the three dates and a matrix B that gives the shares owned by Bill and Dan. Be sure to name the rows and columns and be sure that the columns of A are named the same as the rows of B.

(b) What is the dimension of A?

(c) What is the dimension of B?

(d) Find the product AB.

(e) What is the dimension of AB? What are the names of its rows and columns?

(f) Interpret the entries in AB.

64. Portfolio Values The price per share for Boeing (BA), Verizon (VZ), and Exxon Mobil (XOM) common stock in October 2008, April 2009, and October 2009 are shown in the table below. Over this period of time, Colleen, Mary, and Kathleen have owned shares in these companies, as shown in the table.

	Price per Share				Shares Owned		
	BA	VZ	XOM		BA	VZ	XOM
Oct 2008	50.5	29	75	Colleen	20	40	30
Apr 2009	40.5	31	68	Mary	30	30	20
Oct 2009	50	29	73	Kathleen	40	20	60

(a) Write a matrix A that gives the price per share of the three stocks on the three dates and a matrix B that gives the shares owned by Colleen, Mary, and Kathleen. Be sure to name the rows and columns and be sure that the columns of A are named the same as the rows of B.

(b) What is the dimension of A?

(c) What is the dimension of B?

(d) Find the product AB.

(e) What is the dimension of AB? What are the names of its rows and columns?

(f) Interpret the entries in AB.

65. Department Store Purchases Lee went to a department store and purchased 6 pairs of pants, 8 shirts, and 2 jackets. Chan purchased 2 pairs of pants, 5 shirts, and 3 jackets. If pants are $25 each, shirts are $18 each, and jackets are $39 each, use matrix multiplication to find the amounts spent by Lee and Chan.

66. Factory Production Suppose a factory is asked to produce three types of products, which we will call P_1, P_2, P_3. Suppose the following purchase order was received: $P_1 = 7, P_2 = 12, P_3 = 5$. Represent this purchase order by a row vector and call it P:

$$P = [7 \quad 12 \quad 5]$$

To produce each of the products, raw material of four kinds is needed. Call the raw material $M_1, M_2, M_3,$ and M_4. The matrix Q below gives the amount of material needed for each product:

$$\begin{array}{cccc} & M_1 & M_2 & M_3 & M_4 \end{array}$$
$$Q = \begin{array}{c} P_1 \\ P_2 \\ P_3 \end{array}\begin{bmatrix} 2 & 3 & 1 & 12 \\ 7 & 9 & 5 & 20 \\ 8 & 12 & 6 & 15 \end{bmatrix}$$

Suppose the cost for each of the materials $M_1, M_2, M_3,$ and M_4 is $10, $12, $15, and $20, respectively. The cost vector C is

$$C = \begin{bmatrix} 10 \\ 12 \\ 15 \\ 20 \end{bmatrix}$$

Compute each of the following and interpret each one:

(a) PQ (b) QC (c) PQC

67. For what numbers x will the following be true?

$$[x \quad 4 \quad 1] \begin{bmatrix} 2 & 1 & 0 \\ 1 & 0 & 2 \\ 0 & 2 & 4 \end{bmatrix} \begin{bmatrix} x \\ -7 \\ \dfrac{5}{4} \end{bmatrix} = 0$$

68. Let

$$A = \begin{bmatrix} 1 & 2 & 5 \\ 2 & 4 & 10 \\ -1 & -2 & -5 \end{bmatrix}$$

Show that $A \cdot A = A^2 = \mathbf{0}$. This shows the rule in the real number system that if $a^2 = 0$, then $a = 0$ does not hold for matrices.

69. What must be true about a, b, c, and d if we demand that $AB = BA$ for the following matrices?

$$A = \begin{bmatrix} a & b \\ c & d \end{bmatrix} \qquad B = \begin{bmatrix} 1 & 1 \\ -1 & 1 \end{bmatrix}$$

Assume that

$$\begin{bmatrix} a & b \\ c & d \end{bmatrix} \neq \begin{bmatrix} 1 & 0 \\ 0 & 1 \end{bmatrix}$$

70. Let

$$A = \begin{bmatrix} a & b \\ b & a \end{bmatrix}$$

Find a and b such that $A^2 + A = \mathbf{0}$, where $A^2 = A \cdot A$.

71. For the matrix

$$A = \begin{bmatrix} a & 1 - a \\ 1 + a & -a \end{bmatrix}$$

show that $A^2 = A \cdot A = I_2$.

72. Find the row vector $[x_1 \quad x_2]$ for which

$$[x_1 \quad x_2] \begin{bmatrix} \dfrac{1}{2} & \dfrac{1}{2} \\ \dfrac{1}{4} & \dfrac{3}{4} \end{bmatrix} = [x_1 \quad x_2]$$

under the condition that $x_1 + x_2 = 1$. Here, the row vector $[x_1 \quad x_2]$ is called a **fixed vector** of the matrix

$$\begin{bmatrix} \dfrac{1}{2} & \dfrac{1}{2} \\ \dfrac{1}{4} & \dfrac{3}{4} \end{bmatrix}$$

73. Show that, for all values $a, b, c,$ and d, the matrices

$$A = \begin{bmatrix} a & b \\ -b & a \end{bmatrix} \quad \text{and} \quad B = \begin{bmatrix} c & d \\ -d & c \end{bmatrix}$$

are commutative; that is, $AB = BA$.

Problems 74–81 require the following definition:

Powers of Matrices *For a square matrix A it is possible to find $A \cdot A = A^2$. We can also compute*

$$A^n = \underbrace{A \cdot A \cdot \cdots \cdot A}_{n \text{ factors}}$$

In Problems 74–77, find A^2, A^3, and A^4.

74. $A = \begin{bmatrix} 1 & 0 \\ 3 & 2 \end{bmatrix}$

75. $A = \begin{bmatrix} 3 & 1 \\ -2 & -1 \end{bmatrix}$

76. $A = \begin{bmatrix} 1 & 0 \\ 0 & 1 \end{bmatrix}$

77. $A = \begin{bmatrix} \dfrac{1}{2} & \dfrac{1}{2} \\ \dfrac{1}{4} & \dfrac{3}{4} \end{bmatrix}$

78. Can you guess what A^n looks like for the matrix given in Problem 76?

79. Can you guess what A^n looks like for the matrix given in Problem 77?

In Problems 80 and 81 use a graphing utility to compute B^2, B^{10}, and B^{15}.

80. $B = \begin{bmatrix} 0.4 & 0 & 0.3 & 0 & 0.3 \\ 0 & 0.6 & 0 & 0 & 0.4 \\ 0.1 & 0 & 0.7 & 0 & 0.2 \\ 0.1 & 0.2 & 0.3 & 0.4 & 0 \\ 0.1 & 0.5 & 0.4 & 0 & 0 \end{bmatrix}$

81. $B = \begin{bmatrix} 0.74 & 0.02 & 0.24 & 0 \\ 0.3 & 0.2 & 0.2 & 0.3 \\ 0.5 & 0.1 & 0.2 & 0.2 \\ 0 & 0.1 & 0.2 & 0.7 \end{bmatrix}$

Discussion and Writing

82. Make up two matrices A and B for which $AB = BA$.

83. Make up two square matrices A and B for which AB and BA are both defined, but $AB \neq BA$.

84. Make up two matrices A and B for which AB is defined but BA is not.

'Are You Prepared?' Answers

1. True   **2.** $a(bc) = (ab)c$

12.7 The Inverse of a Matrix

PREPARING FOR THIS SECTION *Before getting started, review the following:*

• Properties of Real Numbers (Appendix A, Section A.1, pp. A-8 to A-12)

  NOW WORK THE 'ARE YOU PREPARED?' **PROBLEMS ON PAGE 148**

OBJECTIVES   **1** Find the inverse of a matrix (p. 136)

   2 Use the inverse of a matrix to solve a system of n linear equations containing n variables (p. 141)

   3 Solve applied problems involving matrices (p. 143)

   4 Application: Use matrices in cryptography (p. 145)

The *inverse* of a matrix, when it exists, plays the role in matrix algebra that the reciprocal of a number plays in the set of real numbers. For example, the product of 2 and its reciprocal, $\dfrac{1}{2}$, equals 1, the multiplicative identity. The product of a matrix and its inverse equals the identity matrix.

Definition ▶ **Inverse of a Matrix**

Let A be a matrix of dimension $n \times n$. A matrix B of dimension $n \times n$ is called the **inverse** of A if $AB = BA = I_n$. We denote the inverse of a matrix A, if it exists, by A^{-1}.

EXAMPLE 1   **Verifying That One Matrix Is the Inverse of Another Matrix**

Show that $\begin{bmatrix} \dfrac{1}{2} & -\dfrac{1}{2} \\ 0 & 1 \end{bmatrix}$ is the inverse of $\begin{bmatrix} 2 & 1 \\ 0 & 1 \end{bmatrix}$.

SOLUTION   Since

$$\begin{bmatrix} 2 & 1 \\ 0 & 1 \end{bmatrix} \begin{bmatrix} \dfrac{1}{2} & -\dfrac{1}{2} \\ 0 & 1 \end{bmatrix} = \begin{bmatrix} 1 & 0 \\ 0 & 1 \end{bmatrix}$$

and

$$\begin{bmatrix} \dfrac{1}{2} & -\dfrac{1}{2} \\ 0 & 1 \end{bmatrix} \begin{bmatrix} 2 & 1 \\ 0 & 1 \end{bmatrix} = \begin{bmatrix} 1 & 0 \\ 0 & 1 \end{bmatrix}$$

the required condition is met.   ∎

  NOW WORK PROBLEM 5.

The definition of an inverse matrix requires that the matrix is square. What about nonsquare matrices? Can they have inverses? The answer is "No." By definition, whenever a matrix has an inverse, it will commute with its inverse under multiplication. So if the nonsquare matrix A had the alleged inverse B, then AB would have to be equal to BA. But the fact that A is not square causes AB and BA to have different dimensions and prevents them from being equal. So such a B could not exist.

A nonsquare matrix has no inverse.

1   Find the Inverse of a Matrix

EXAMPLE 2   Finding the Inverse of a Matrix

Find the inverse of the matrix

$$A = \begin{bmatrix} 4 & 2 \\ 3 & 1 \end{bmatrix}$$

SOLUTION   Assuming A has an inverse, denote it by

$$X = \begin{bmatrix} x_1 & x_2 \\ x_3 & x_4 \end{bmatrix}$$

Then the product of A and X is the identity matrix of dimension 2×2. That is,

$$AX = I_2$$

$$\begin{bmatrix} 4 & 2 \\ 3 & 1 \end{bmatrix}\begin{bmatrix} x_1 & x_2 \\ x_3 & x_4 \end{bmatrix} = \begin{bmatrix} 1 & 0 \\ 0 & 1 \end{bmatrix}$$

Performing the multiplication on the left yields

$$\begin{bmatrix} 4x_1 + 2x_3 & 4x_2 + 2x_4 \\ 3x_1 + x_3 & 3x_2 + x_4 \end{bmatrix} = \begin{bmatrix} 1 & 0 \\ 0 & 1 \end{bmatrix}$$

This matrix equation can be written as the following system of four equations containing four variables:

$$\begin{cases} 4x_1 + 2x_3 = 1 & \quad 4x_2 + 2x_4 = 0 \\ 3x_1 + x_3 = 0 & \quad 3x_2 + x_4 = 1 \end{cases}$$

We find the solution to be

$$x_1 = -\frac{1}{2} \qquad x_2 = 1 \qquad x_3 = \frac{3}{2} \qquad x_4 = -2$$

The inverse of A is

$$A^{-1} = \begin{bmatrix} -\dfrac{1}{2} & 1 \\ \dfrac{3}{2} & -2 \end{bmatrix}$$

Let's look at this example more closely. The system of four equations containing four variables can be written as two systems:

$$(a) \begin{cases} 4x_1 + 2x_3 = 1 \\ 3x_1 + x_3 = 0 \end{cases} \qquad (b) \begin{cases} 4x_2 + 2x_4 = 0 \\ 3x_2 + x_4 = 1 \end{cases}$$

Their augmented matrices are

$$(a) \begin{bmatrix} 4 & 2 & | & 1 \\ 3 & 1 & | & 0 \end{bmatrix} \qquad (b) \begin{bmatrix} 4 & 2 & | & 0 \\ 3 & 1 & | & 1 \end{bmatrix}$$

Since the matrix A appears in both (a) and (b), any row operation performed on (a) and (b) can be performed on the single augmented matrix that combines the two right-hand columns. Denote this matrix by $A|I_2$ and write

$$[A|I_2] = \begin{bmatrix} 4 & 2 & | & 1 & 0 \\ 3 & 1 & | & 0 & 1 \end{bmatrix}$$

Now perform the row operations on $[A|I_2]$ needed to obtain the reduced row echelon form of A. The result is

$$\begin{bmatrix} 1 & 0 & | & -\dfrac{1}{2} & 1 \\ 0 & 1 & | & \dfrac{3}{2} & -2 \end{bmatrix}$$

The 2×2 matrix on the right-hand side of the vertical bar is A^{-1}.

Steps for Finding the Inverse of a Matrix of Dimension $n \times n$

STEP 1 Form the matrix $[A|I_n]$.

STEP 2 Using row operations, write $[A|I_n]$ in reduced row echelon form.

STEP 3 If the resulting matrix is of the form $[I_n|B]$, that is, if the identity matrix appears on the left side of the bar, then B is the inverse of A. Otherwise, A has no inverse.

EXAMPLE 3   **Finding the Inverse of a Matrix**

Find the inverse of

$$A = \begin{bmatrix} 1 & 1 & 2 \\ 2 & 1 & 0 \\ 1 & 2 & 2 \end{bmatrix}$$

SOLUTION

STEP 1   Since A is of dimension 3×3, use the identity matrix I_3. The matrix $[A|I_3]$ is

$$\begin{bmatrix} 1 & 1 & 2 & | & 1 & 0 & 0 \\ 2 & 1 & 0 & | & 0 & 1 & 0 \\ 1 & 2 & 2 & | & 0 & 0 & 1 \end{bmatrix}$$

STEP 2   Proceed to obtain the reduced row echelon form of this matrix:

Use $\begin{array}{l} R_2 = -2r_1 + r_2 \\ R_3 = -1r_1 + r_3 \end{array}$ to obtain $\begin{bmatrix} 1 & 1 & 2 & | & 1 & 0 & 0 \\ 0 & -1 & -4 & | & -2 & 1 & 0 \\ 0 & 1 & 0 & | & -1 & 0 & 1 \end{bmatrix}$

Use $R_2 = -1r_2$ to obtain $\begin{bmatrix} 1 & 1 & 2 & | & 1 & 0 & 0 \\ 0 & 1 & 4 & | & 2 & -1 & 0 \\ 0 & 1 & 0 & | & -1 & 0 & 1 \end{bmatrix}$

Use $\begin{array}{l} R_1 = -1r_2 + r_1 \\ R_3 = -1r_2 + r_3 \end{array}$ to obtain $\begin{bmatrix} 1 & 0 & -2 & | & -1 & 1 & 0 \\ 0 & 1 & 4 & | & 2 & -1 & 0 \\ 0 & 0 & -4 & | & -3 & 1 & 1 \end{bmatrix}$

Use $R_3 = -\dfrac{1}{4}r_3$ to obtain $\begin{bmatrix} 1 & 0 & -2 & | & -1 & 1 & 0 \\ 0 & 1 & 4 & | & 2 & -1 & 0 \\ 0 & 0 & 1 & | & \dfrac{3}{4} & -\dfrac{1}{4} & -\dfrac{1}{4} \end{bmatrix}$

Use $\begin{array}{l} R_1 = 2r_3 + r_1 \\ R_2 = -4r_3 + r_2 \end{array}$ to obtain $\begin{bmatrix} 1 & 0 & 0 & | & \dfrac{1}{2} & \dfrac{1}{2} & -\dfrac{1}{2} \\ 0 & 1 & 0 & | & -1 & 0 & 1 \\ 0 & 0 & 1 & | & \dfrac{3}{4} & -\dfrac{1}{4} & -\dfrac{1}{4} \end{bmatrix}$

The matrix $[A|I_3]$ is in reduced row echelon form.

STEP 3   Since the identity matrix I_3 appears on the left side, the matrix appearing on the right is the inverse. That is,

$$A^{-1} = \begin{bmatrix} \dfrac{1}{2} & \dfrac{1}{2} & -\dfrac{1}{2} \\ -1 & 0 & 1 \\ \dfrac{3}{4} & -\dfrac{1}{4} & -\dfrac{1}{4} \end{bmatrix}$$

You should verify that $AA^{-1} = A^{-1}A = I_3$.

NOW WORK PROBLEM 19.

USING TECHNOLOGY

EXAMPLE 4   Finding the Inverse of a Matrix Using a Graphing Utility

Rework Example 3 using a graphing utility.

SOLUTION   Enter the matrix A into a graphing utility and use the $\boxed{x^{-1}}$ key to obtain $[A]^{-1}$. Figure 5 shows A^{-1}.

FIGURE 5

 NOW WORK PROBLEM 51 USING A GRAPHING UTILITY.

EXAMPLE 5   Finding the Inverse of a Matrix Using Excel

Rework Example 3 using EXCEL.

SOLUTION

STEP 1   Enter the matrix A.

STEP 2   Highlight the cells that will contain A^{-1}; A^{-1} is a 3×3 matrix.

STEP 3   Type: **= MINVERSE** (*highlight matrix A*). The Excel screen should look like the one below.

STEP 4   Press **Ctrl-Shift-Enter** all at the same time. The inverse will be displayed in the highlighted cells, as in the screen below.

✔ **CHECK:** Multiply $A*A^{-1}$ using the steps below. This product should be the identity matrix.

1. Highlight the cells that are to contain the product matrix.
2. Type: = **MMULT** (*highlight A, highlight* A^{-1})
3. Press **Ctrl-Shift-Enter** at the same time.

Notice that $a_{13} = 1.11\text{E-}16$ is in scientific notation. In decimal notation it is 0.000000000000000111, very close to zero. So, $A*A^{-1} = \begin{bmatrix} 1 & 0 & 0 \\ 0 & 1 & 0 \\ 0 & 0 & 1 \end{bmatrix}$, as required.   ■

 NOW WORK PROBLEM 51 USING EXCEL.

EXAMPLE 6   **Showing That a Matrix Has No Inverse**

Show that the matrix given below has no inverse.

$$\begin{bmatrix} 3 & 2 \\ 6 & 4 \end{bmatrix}$$

SOLUTION   Set up the matrix

$$\left[\begin{array}{cc|cc} 3 & 2 & 1 & 0 \\ 6 & 4 & 0 & 1 \end{array}\right]$$

Use $R_1 = \dfrac{1}{3}r_1$ to obtain $\left[\begin{array}{cc|cc} 1 & \dfrac{2}{3} & \dfrac{1}{3} & 0 \\ 6 & 4 & 0 & 1 \end{array}\right]$

Use $R_2 = -6r_1 + r_2$ to obtain $\left[\begin{array}{cc|cc} 1 & \dfrac{2}{3} & \dfrac{1}{3} & 0 \\ 0 & 0 & -2 & 1 \end{array}\right]$

The 0s in row 2 tell us we cannot get the identity matrix. This, in turn, tells us the original matrix has no inverse.   ■

COMMENT If a matrix has no inverse, a graphing utility will display an Error message. See Figure 6 for the result of doing Example 6.

FIGURE 6

 NOW WORK PROBLEM 25.

2 Use the Inverse of a Matrix to Solve a System of n Linear Equations Containing n Variables

The inverse of a matrix can be used to solve a system of n linear equations containing n variables. We begin with a system of three linear equations containing three variables:

$$\begin{cases} x + y + 2z = 1 \\ 2x + y \quad\;\; = 2 \\ x + 2y + 2z = 3 \end{cases} \tag{1}$$

Let

$$A = \begin{bmatrix} 1 & 1 & 2 \\ 2 & 1 & 0 \\ 1 & 2 & 2 \end{bmatrix} \qquad X = \begin{bmatrix} x \\ y \\ z \end{bmatrix} \qquad B = \begin{bmatrix} 1 \\ 2 \\ 3 \end{bmatrix}$$

Then, since

$$AX = \begin{bmatrix} 1 & 1 & 2 \\ 2 & 1 & 0 \\ 1 & 2 & 2 \end{bmatrix}\begin{bmatrix} x \\ y \\ z \end{bmatrix} = \begin{bmatrix} x + y + 2z \\ 2x + y \\ x + 2y + 2z \end{bmatrix}$$

the system of equations (1) can be written compactly as the matrix equation

$$AX = B$$

In general, any system of n linear equations containing n variables $x_1, x_2, \ldots, x_n$, can be written in the form

$$AX = B$$

where A is the $n \times n$ matrix of the coefficients of the variables, B is an $n \times 1$ column matrix whose entries are the numbers appearing to the right of each equal sign in the system, and X is an $n \times 1$ column matrix containing the n variables.

To find X, start with the matrix equation $AX = B$ and use properties of matrices. Assume that the $n \times n$ matrix A has an inverse A^{-1}.

$$AX = B \qquad \text{A has an inverse A^{-1}.}$$
$$A^{-1}(AX) = A^{-1}B \qquad \text{Multiply both sides by A^{-1}.}$$
$$(A^{-1}A)X = A^{-1}B \qquad \text{Apply the Associative Property on the left side.}$$
$$I_nX = A^{-1}B \qquad \text{Apply the Inverse Property: $A^{-1}A = I_n$.}$$
$$X = A^{-1}B \qquad \text{Apply the Identity Property: $I_nX = X$.}$$

This leads to the following result:

Theorem   A system of n linear equations containing n variables

$$AX = B$$

for which A is a square matrix and A^{-1} exists, always has a unique solution that is given by

$$X = A^{-1}B$$

EXAMPLE 7   **Solving a System of Equations Using Inverses**

Solve the system of equations:

$$\begin{cases} x + y + 2z = 1 \\ 2x + y \quad\quad = 2 \\ x + 2y + 2z = 3 \end{cases}$$

SOLUTION   Here

$$A = \begin{bmatrix} 1 & 1 & 2 \\ 2 & 1 & 0 \\ 1 & 2 & 2 \end{bmatrix} \quad X = \begin{bmatrix} x \\ y \\ z \end{bmatrix} \quad B = \begin{bmatrix} 1 \\ 2 \\ 3 \end{bmatrix}$$

From Example 5 we know the inverse of A is

$$A^{-1} = \begin{bmatrix} \dfrac{1}{2} & \dfrac{1}{2} & -\dfrac{1}{2} \\ -1 & 0 & 1 \\ \dfrac{3}{4} & -\dfrac{1}{4} & -\dfrac{1}{4} \end{bmatrix}$$

Based on the result just stated, the solution X of the system is

$$X = A^{-1}B$$

$$\begin{bmatrix} x \\ y \\ z \end{bmatrix} = \begin{bmatrix} \dfrac{1}{2} & \dfrac{1}{2} & -\dfrac{1}{2} \\ -1 & 0 & 1 \\ \dfrac{3}{4} & -\dfrac{1}{4} & -\dfrac{1}{4} \end{bmatrix} \begin{bmatrix} 1 \\ 2 \\ 3 \end{bmatrix} = \begin{bmatrix} 0 \\ 2 \\ -\dfrac{1}{2} \end{bmatrix}$$

The solution is $x = 0, y = 2, z = -\dfrac{1}{2}$.   ■

 NOW WORK PROBLEMS 39 AND 45.

The method used to solve the system in Example 7 requires that A have an inverse. If, for a system of equations $AX = B$, the matrix A has no inverse, then the system must be analyzed using the methods discussed in Sections 2.2 and 2.3.

The method used in Example 7 for solving a system of equations is particularly useful for applications in which the constants appearing to the right of the equal sign change while the coefficients of the variables on the left side do not. See Problems 39–50 for an illustration. See also the discussion of Leontief models in Section 13.4.

USING TECHNOLOGY

EXAMPLE 8   **Solving a System of Equations Using EXCEL**

Rework Example 7 using EXCEL.

SOLUTION   From Example 5, we know the inverse of A is $A^{-1} = \begin{bmatrix} 0.5 & 0.5 & -0.5 \\ -1 & 0 & 1 \\ 0.75 & -0.25 & -0.25 \end{bmatrix}$.

To find the solution to the system of equations, multiply $A^{-1} * B$, where $B = \begin{bmatrix} 1 \\ 2 \\ 3 \end{bmatrix}$.

STEP 1   Highlight the cells that are to contain the product matrix. This will be a 3×1 matrix.

STEP 2   Type: $= $ **MMULT** (*highlight* A^{-1}, *highlight* B)

STEP 3   Press **Ctrl-Shift-Enter** at the same time, to get $A^{-1}B$.

So, $x = 0$, $y = 2$, and $z = -0.5$.

 NOW WORK PROBLEMS 39 AND 45 USING EXCEL.

3   **Solve Applied Problems Involving Matrices**

EXAMPLE 9   **Mutual Fund Investing**

The average annual return (over the 5-year period prior to January 12, 2010) of three mutual funds offered by Franklin Templeton is shown in the table:

Mutual Fund	Average Annual Return
High Income	13.82
Conservative Target	5.36
Mutual Shares	4.05

Source: Franklin Templeton

Suppose you have $6000 to invest in these three funds. You will invest $200 more in the High Income fund than you will in the Conservative Target fund.

(a) Assuming the accounts will earn the annual rates shown, how much should you invest for a year in each fund if you want your average return to be 7%?

(b) How much should you invest in each fund if you want your average return to be 8%?

(c) How much if you want 9%?

(d) Comment on the results found in (a), (b), and (c).

SOLUTION   Begin by naming the variables, Since parts (a), (b), (c) are repetitive, let i be the annual rate of return (in decimal form) we want. Let x represent the amount invested in the High Income fund, y represent the amount invested in the Conservative Target fund, and z represent the amount invested in the Mutual Shares fund. The amount earned on the investment of $6000 for one year is $6000i$. We have the following system of equations:

$$\begin{cases} x + y + z = 6000 & \text{Total invested is \$6000.} \\ x - y = 200 & \text{\$200 more in High Income than in Conservative Target} \\ 0.1382x + 0.0536y + 0.0978z = 6000i & \text{Total rate of return equals } 6000i. \end{cases}$$

If

$$A = \begin{bmatrix} 1 & 1 & 1 \\ 1 & -1 & 0 \\ 0.1382 & 0.0536 & 0.0978 \end{bmatrix} \qquad X = \begin{bmatrix} x \\ y \\ z \end{bmatrix} \qquad B = \begin{bmatrix} 6000 \\ 200 \\ 6000i \end{bmatrix}$$

the system of equations is given by

$$AX = B$$

The solution of the system is

$$X = A^{-1}B$$

Proceed to find A^{-1} using a graphing utility or EXCEL:

$$A^{-1} = \begin{bmatrix} -0.365 & 0.12 & 9.025 \\ -0.365 & -0.88 & 9.025 \\ 1.73 & 0.76 & -18.05 \end{bmatrix}$$

Then

$$X = A^{-1}B = \begin{bmatrix} -0.365 & 0.12 & 9.025 \\ -0.365 & -0.88 & 9.025 \\ 1.73 & 0.76 & -18.05 \end{bmatrix} \begin{bmatrix} 6000 \\ 200 \\ 6000i \end{bmatrix}$$

(a) If the average annual rate of return is to be $i = 0.07$, then

$$B = \begin{bmatrix} 6000 \\ 200 \\ 6000(0.07) \end{bmatrix} = \begin{bmatrix} 6000 \\ 200 \\ 420 \end{bmatrix}$$

and

$$\begin{bmatrix} x \\ y \\ z \end{bmatrix} = \begin{bmatrix} -0.365 & 0.12 & 9.025 \\ -0.365 & -0.88 & 9.025 \\ 1.73 & 0.76 & -18.05 \end{bmatrix} \begin{bmatrix} 6000 \\ 200 \\ 420 \end{bmatrix} \approx \begin{bmatrix} 1624.50 \\ 1424.50 \\ 2951.00 \end{bmatrix}$$

(b) If the average annual rate of return is to be $i = 0.08$, then

$$B = \begin{bmatrix} 6000 \\ 200 \\ 480 \end{bmatrix} \quad \text{and} \quad \begin{bmatrix} x \\ y \\ z \end{bmatrix} = \begin{bmatrix} -0.365 & 0.12 & 9.025 \\ -0.365 & -0.88 & 9.025 \\ 1.73 & 0.76 & -18.05 \end{bmatrix} \begin{bmatrix} 6000 \\ 200 \\ 480 \end{bmatrix} \approx \begin{bmatrix} 2166.00 \\ 1966.00 \\ 1868.00 \end{bmatrix}$$

(c) If the average annual rate of return is to be $i = 0.09$, then

$$B = \begin{bmatrix} 6000 \\ 200 \\ 540 \end{bmatrix} \quad \text{and} \quad \begin{bmatrix} x \\ y \\ z \end{bmatrix} = \begin{bmatrix} -0.365 & 0.12 & 9.025 \\ -0.365 & -0.88 & 9.025 \\ 1.73 & 0.76 & -18.05 \end{bmatrix} \begin{bmatrix} 6000 \\ 200 \\ 540 \end{bmatrix} \approx \begin{bmatrix} 2707.50 \\ 2507.50 \\ 785.00 \end{bmatrix}$$

The amount to invest in each fund to achieve the three rates of return is summarized in the following table.

	Expected Rate of Return		
	7%	8%	9%
High Income	1624.50	2166.00	2707.50
Conservative Target	1424.50	1966.00	2507.50
Mutual Shares	2951.00	1868.00	785.00

(d) Notice that to achieve higher rates of return, you need to invest less and less in the Mutual Shares fund and more in the other two funds. Setting your expected rate of return at 7% allow for a more level diversifiaction among the three funds. ■

 NOW WORK PROBLEM 63.

4 Application: Use Matrices in Cryptography

Cryptography is the art of writing or deciphering secret codes. We begin by giving examples of elementary codes.

EXAMPLE 10   **Encoding a Message**

A message can be encoded by associating each letter of the alphabet with some other letter of the alphabet according to a prescribed pattern. For example, we might have

A	B	C	D	E	F	G	H	I	J	K	L	M	N	O	P	Q	R	S	T	U	V	W	X	Y	Z
↓	↓	↓	↓	↓	↓	↓	↓	↓	↓	↓	↓	↓	↓	↓	↓	↓	↓	↓	↓	↓	↓	↓	↓	↓	↓
C	D	E	F	G	H	I	J	K	L	M	N	O	P	Q	R	S	T	U	V	W	X	Y	Z	A	B

With the above code the word MESSAGE would become OGUUCIG. ■

EXAMPLE 11   **Encoding a Message**

Another code may associate numbers with the letters of the alphabet. For example, we might have

A	B	C	D	E	F	G	H	I	J	K	L	M	N	O	P	Q	R	S	T	U	V	W	X	Y	Z
↓	↓	↓	↓	↓	↓	↓	↓	↓	↓	↓	↓	↓	↓	↓	↓	↓	↓	↓	↓	↓	↓	↓	↓	↓	↓
26	25	24	23	22	21	20	19	18	17	16	15	14	13	12	11	10	9	8	7	6	5	4	3	2	1

In this code the word PEACE looks like 11 22 26 24 22. ■

Both of the above codes have one important feature in common. The association of letters with the coding symbols is made using a one-to-one correspondence so that no possible ambiguities can arise.

Suppose we want to encode the following message:

TOP SECURITY CLEARANCE

If we decide to divide the message into pairs of letters, the message becomes

TO PS EC UR IT YC LE AR AN CE

(If there is a letter left over, arbitrarily assign Z to the last position.) Using the correspondence of letters to numbers given in Example 12, and writing each pair of letters as a column vector, we obtain

$$\begin{bmatrix} T \\ O \end{bmatrix} = \begin{bmatrix} 7 \\ 12 \end{bmatrix} \quad \begin{bmatrix} P \\ S \end{bmatrix} = \begin{bmatrix} 11 \\ 8 \end{bmatrix} \quad \begin{bmatrix} E \\ C \end{bmatrix} = \begin{bmatrix} 22 \\ 24 \end{bmatrix} \quad \begin{bmatrix} U \\ R \end{bmatrix} = \begin{bmatrix} 6 \\ 9 \end{bmatrix} \quad \begin{bmatrix} I \\ T \end{bmatrix} = \begin{bmatrix} 18 \\ 7 \end{bmatrix}$$

$$\begin{bmatrix} Y \\ C \end{bmatrix} = \begin{bmatrix} 2 \\ 24 \end{bmatrix} \quad \begin{bmatrix} L \\ E \end{bmatrix} = \begin{bmatrix} 15 \\ 22 \end{bmatrix} \quad \begin{bmatrix} A \\ R \end{bmatrix} = \begin{bmatrix} 26 \\ 9 \end{bmatrix} \quad \begin{bmatrix} A \\ N \end{bmatrix} = \begin{bmatrix} 26 \\ 13 \end{bmatrix} \quad \begin{bmatrix} C \\ E \end{bmatrix} = \begin{bmatrix} 24 \\ 22 \end{bmatrix}$$

Next, arbitrarily choose a 2×2 matrix A, which has an inverse A^{-1} (we'll see why later). Let's choose

$$A = \begin{bmatrix} 2 & 3 \\ 1 & 2 \end{bmatrix}$$

The inverse A^{-1} of A is

$$A^{-1} = \begin{bmatrix} 2 & -3 \\ -1 & 2 \end{bmatrix}$$

Now transform the column vectors representing the message by multiplying each of them on the left by matrix A:

$$A\begin{bmatrix} T \\ O \end{bmatrix} = \begin{bmatrix} 2 & 3 \\ 1 & 2 \end{bmatrix}\begin{bmatrix} 7 \\ 12 \end{bmatrix} = \begin{bmatrix} 50 \\ 31 \end{bmatrix}$$

$$A\begin{bmatrix} P \\ S \end{bmatrix} = \begin{bmatrix} 2 & 3 \\ 1 & 2 \end{bmatrix}\begin{bmatrix} 11 \\ 8 \end{bmatrix} = \begin{bmatrix} 46 \\ 27 \end{bmatrix}$$

$$A\begin{bmatrix} E \\ C \end{bmatrix} = \begin{bmatrix} 2 & 3 \\ 1 & 2 \end{bmatrix}\begin{bmatrix} 22 \\ 24 \end{bmatrix} = \begin{bmatrix} 116 \\ 70 \end{bmatrix}$$

$$A\begin{bmatrix} U \\ R \end{bmatrix} = \begin{bmatrix} 2 & 3 \\ 1 & 2 \end{bmatrix}\begin{bmatrix} 6 \\ 9 \end{bmatrix} = \begin{bmatrix} 39 \\ 24 \end{bmatrix}$$

$$A\begin{bmatrix} I \\ T \end{bmatrix} = \begin{bmatrix} 2 & 3 \\ 1 & 2 \end{bmatrix}\begin{bmatrix} 18 \\ 7 \end{bmatrix} = \begin{bmatrix} 57 \\ 32 \end{bmatrix}$$

$$A\begin{bmatrix} Y \\ C \end{bmatrix} = \begin{bmatrix} 2 & 3 \\ 1 & 2 \end{bmatrix}\begin{bmatrix} 2 \\ 24 \end{bmatrix} = \begin{bmatrix} 76 \\ 50 \end{bmatrix}$$

$$A\begin{bmatrix} L \\ E \end{bmatrix} = \begin{bmatrix} 2 & 3 \\ 1 & 2 \end{bmatrix}\begin{bmatrix} 15 \\ 22 \end{bmatrix} = \begin{bmatrix} 96 \\ 59 \end{bmatrix}$$

$$A\begin{bmatrix} A \\ R \end{bmatrix} = \begin{bmatrix} 2 & 3 \\ 1 & 2 \end{bmatrix}\begin{bmatrix} 26 \\ 9 \end{bmatrix} = \begin{bmatrix} 79 \\ 44 \end{bmatrix}$$

$$A\begin{bmatrix} A \\ N \end{bmatrix} = \begin{bmatrix} 2 & 3 \\ 1 & 2 \end{bmatrix}\begin{bmatrix} 26 \\ 13 \end{bmatrix} = \begin{bmatrix} 91 \\ 52 \end{bmatrix}$$

$$A\begin{bmatrix} C \\ E \end{bmatrix} = \begin{bmatrix} 2 & 3 \\ 1 & 2 \end{bmatrix}\begin{bmatrix} 24 \\ 22 \end{bmatrix} = \begin{bmatrix} 114 \\ 68 \end{bmatrix}$$

The coded message is

50 31 46 27 116 70 39 24 57 32 76 50 96 59 79 44 91 52 114 68

To decode or unscramble the above message, pair the numbers in 2×1 column vectors. Then on the left multiply each column vector by A^{-1}. For example, the first two column vectors then become

$$A^{-1}\begin{bmatrix} 50 \\ 31 \end{bmatrix} = \begin{bmatrix} 2 & -3 \\ -1 & 2 \end{bmatrix}\begin{bmatrix} 50 \\ 31 \end{bmatrix} = \begin{bmatrix} 7 \\ 12 \end{bmatrix} = \begin{bmatrix} T \\ O \end{bmatrix}$$

$$A^{-1}\begin{bmatrix} 46 \\ 17 \end{bmatrix} = \begin{bmatrix} 2 & -3 \\ -1 & 2 \end{bmatrix}\begin{bmatrix} 46 \\ 27 \end{bmatrix} = \begin{bmatrix} 11 \\ 8 \end{bmatrix} = \begin{bmatrix} P \\ S \end{bmatrix} \text{ etc.}$$

Continuing in this way, the original message is obtained.

 NOW WORK PROBLEM 67.

EXAMPLE 12 Encoding a Message

The message to be encoded is

SEPTEMBER IS OKAY

The encoded message is to be formed using triplets of numbers and the 3×3 matrix

$$A = \begin{bmatrix} 1 & 0 & 0 \\ 3 & 1 & 5 \\ -2 & 0 & 1 \end{bmatrix} \text{ whose inverse is } A^{-1} = \begin{bmatrix} 1 & 0 & 0 \\ -13 & 1 & -5 \\ 2 & 0 & 1 \end{bmatrix}.$$

Use the following association of letters to numbers:

A B C D E F G H I J K L M N O P Q R S T U V W X Y Z
↓ ↓
1 2 3 4 5 6 7 8 9 10 11 12 13 14 15 16 17 18 19 20 21 22 23 24 25 26

SOLUTION Divide the message into triplets of letters as follows:

SEP TEM BER ISO KAY

Now multiply the matrix A times each column vector of the message.
[*Note:* If additional letters had been required to complete a triplet, we would have used *Z* or *YZ*.]

437

$$A\begin{bmatrix} S \\ E \\ P \end{bmatrix} = \begin{bmatrix} 1 & 0 & 0 \\ 3 & 1 & 5 \\ -2 & 0 & 1 \end{bmatrix}\begin{bmatrix} 19 \\ 5 \\ 16 \end{bmatrix} = \begin{bmatrix} 19 \\ 142 \\ -22 \end{bmatrix}$$

$$A\begin{bmatrix} T \\ E \\ M \end{bmatrix} = \begin{bmatrix} 1 & 0 & 0 \\ 3 & 1 & 5 \\ -2 & 0 & 1 \end{bmatrix}\begin{bmatrix} 20 \\ 5 \\ 13 \end{bmatrix} = \begin{bmatrix} 20 \\ 130 \\ -27 \end{bmatrix}$$

$$A\begin{bmatrix} B \\ E \\ R \end{bmatrix} = \begin{bmatrix} 1 & 0 & 0 \\ 3 & 1 & 5 \\ -2 & 0 & 1 \end{bmatrix}\begin{bmatrix} 2 \\ 5 \\ 18 \end{bmatrix} = \begin{bmatrix} 2 \\ 101 \\ 14 \end{bmatrix}$$

$$A\begin{bmatrix} I \\ S \\ O \end{bmatrix} = \begin{bmatrix} 1 & 0 & 0 \\ 3 & 1 & 5 \\ -2 & 0 & 1 \end{bmatrix}\begin{bmatrix} 9 \\ 19 \\ 15 \end{bmatrix} = \begin{bmatrix} 9 \\ 121 \\ -3 \end{bmatrix}$$

$$A\begin{bmatrix} K \\ A \\ Y \end{bmatrix} = \begin{bmatrix} 1 & 0 & 0 \\ 3 & 1 & 5 \\ -2 & 0 & 1 \end{bmatrix}\begin{bmatrix} 11 \\ 1 \\ 25 \end{bmatrix} = \begin{bmatrix} 11 \\ 159 \\ 3 \end{bmatrix}$$

The coded message is

19   142 -22 20   130 -27 2   101   14   9   121 -3 11   159   3   ■

To decode the message in Example 12, form 3×1 column vectors of the numbers in the coded message and multiply on the left by A^{-1}.

The above are elementary examples of encoding and decoding. Modern-day cryptography uses sophisticated computer-implemented codes that depend on higher-level mathematics.

EXERCISE 12.7   Answers Begin on Page AN–16.

'Are You Prepared?' Problems   Answers are given at the end of these exercises. If you get a wrong answer, read the pages listed in red.

1. *True or False* For every nonzero number a, there is a nonzero number b so that $ab = 1$. (pp. A–8 to A–12)

2. The number 1 is called the _____ _____. (pp. A–8 to A–12)

Concepts and Vocabulary

3. If A and B are matrices of dimension $n \times n$ and if $AB = BA = I_n$, the identity matrix, then B is called the _____ of A.

4. *True or False* Every square matrix has an inverse.

Skill Building

In Problems 5–10, show that the given matrices are inverses of each other.

5. $\begin{bmatrix} 1 & 2 \\ 2 & 3 \end{bmatrix}\begin{bmatrix} -3 & 2 \\ 2 & -1 \end{bmatrix}$

6. $\begin{bmatrix} 1 & 5 \\ 2 & 0 \end{bmatrix}\begin{bmatrix} 0 & \frac{1}{2} \\ \frac{1}{5} & -\frac{1}{10} \end{bmatrix}$

7. $\begin{bmatrix} -1 & -2 \\ 3 & 4 \end{bmatrix}\begin{bmatrix} 2 & 1 \\ -\frac{3}{2} & -\frac{1}{2} \end{bmatrix}$

8. $\begin{bmatrix} 1 & 3 \\ 2 & -1 \end{bmatrix}\begin{bmatrix} \frac{1}{7} & \frac{3}{7} \\ \frac{2}{7} & -\frac{1}{7} \end{bmatrix}$

9. $\begin{bmatrix} 1 & 2 & 3 \\ 2 & 3 & 4 \\ 1 & 2 & 1 \end{bmatrix}\begin{bmatrix} -\frac{5}{2} & 2 & -\frac{1}{2} \\ 1 & -1 & 1 \\ \frac{1}{2} & 0 & -\frac{1}{2} \end{bmatrix}$

10. $\begin{bmatrix} 1 & 3 & 3 \\ 1 & 4 & 3 \\ 1 & 3 & 4 \end{bmatrix}\begin{bmatrix} 7 & -3 & -3 \\ -1 & 1 & 0 \\ -1 & 0 & 1 \end{bmatrix}$

In Problems 11–24, find the inverse of each matrix using the reduced row echelon technique.

11. $\begin{bmatrix} 3 & 7 \\ 2 & 5 \end{bmatrix}$

12. $\begin{bmatrix} 4 & 1 \\ 3 & 1 \end{bmatrix}$

13. $\begin{bmatrix} 1 & -1 \\ 3 & -4 \end{bmatrix}$

14. $\begin{bmatrix} 5 & 3 \\ 3 & 2 \end{bmatrix}$

15. $\begin{bmatrix} 2 & 1 \\ 4 & 3 \end{bmatrix}$

16. $\begin{bmatrix} 2 & 3 \\ 2 & -2 \end{bmatrix}$

17. $\begin{bmatrix} 0 & 0 & 1 \\ 0 & 1 & 0 \\ 1 & 0 & 0 \end{bmatrix}$

18. $\begin{bmatrix} -1 & 1 & 0 \\ 1 & 0 & 2 \\ 3 & 1 & 0 \end{bmatrix}$

19. $\begin{bmatrix} 1 & 1 & -1 \\ 3 & -1 & 0 \\ 2 & -3 & 4 \end{bmatrix}$

20. $\begin{bmatrix} 1 & 1 & 1 \\ 2 & 1 & 1 \\ 1 & 1 & 2 \end{bmatrix}$

21. $\begin{bmatrix} 1 & 1 & -1 \\ 2 & 1 & 1 \\ 1 & 0 & 1 \end{bmatrix}$

22. $\begin{bmatrix} 2 & 3 & -1 \\ 1 & 1 & 1 \\ 0 & 2 & -1 \end{bmatrix}$

23. $\begin{bmatrix} 1 & 1 & 0 & 0 \\ 0 & 1 & -1 & 1 \\ 1 & -1 & 1 & 1 \\ 0 & 1 & 0 & -1 \end{bmatrix}$

24. $\begin{bmatrix} 1 & 2 & -3 & -2 \\ 0 & 1 & 4 & -2 \\ 3 & -1 & 4 & 0 \\ 2 & 1 & 0 & 3 \end{bmatrix}$

In Problems 25–30, show that each matrix has no inverse.

25. $\begin{bmatrix} 4 & 6 \\ 2 & 3 \end{bmatrix}$

26. $\begin{bmatrix} -1 & 2 \\ 3 & -6 \end{bmatrix}$

27. $\begin{bmatrix} -8 & 4 \\ -4 & 2 \end{bmatrix}$

28. $\begin{bmatrix} 2 & 10 \\ 1 & 5 \end{bmatrix}$

29. $\begin{bmatrix} 1 & 1 & 1 \\ 3 & -4 & 2 \\ 0 & 0 & 0 \end{bmatrix}$

30. $\begin{bmatrix} -1 & 2 & 3 \\ 5 & 2 & 0 \\ 2 & -4 & -6 \end{bmatrix}$

In Problems 31–34, find the inverse, if it exists, of each matrix.

31. $\begin{bmatrix} 1 & 1 \\ 1 & 2 \end{bmatrix}$

32. $\begin{bmatrix} 2 & 1 \\ 1 & 1 \end{bmatrix}$

33. $\begin{bmatrix} 3 & 2 \\ 6 & 4 \end{bmatrix}$

34. $\begin{bmatrix} 4 & 2 \\ 2 & 1 \end{bmatrix}$

35. For the matrices

$$A = \begin{bmatrix} 1 & 2 \\ 2 & -1 \end{bmatrix} \quad \text{and} \quad B = \begin{bmatrix} 1 & 3 \\ 2 & 1 \end{bmatrix}$$

find $A^{-1} - B^{-1}$.

36. For the matrices

$$A = \begin{bmatrix} 1 & -4 \\ 2 & -3 \end{bmatrix} \quad \text{and} \quad B = \begin{bmatrix} 2 & -2 \\ 3 & 2 \end{bmatrix}$$

find $A^{-1} - B^{-1}$.

37. Write the matrix product $A^{-1}B$ used to find the solution to the system $AX = B$.

$$\begin{cases} x + 3y + 2z = 2 \\ 2x + 7y + 3z = 1 \\ x \quad\quad + 6z = 3 \end{cases}$$

38. Write the matrix product $A^{-1}B$ used to find the solution to the system $AX = B$.

$$\begin{cases} x + 2y + 2z = 3 \\ 2x + 5y + 7z = 2 \\ 2x + y - 4z = 4 \end{cases}$$

In Problems 39–50, solve each system of equations by the method of Example 7. For Problems 39–44, use the inverse found in Problem 11. For Problems 45–50, use the inverse found in Problem 19.

39. $\begin{cases} 3x + 7y = 10 \\ 2x + 5y = 2 \end{cases}$

40. $\begin{cases} 3x + 7y = -4 \\ 2x + 5y = -3 \end{cases}$

41. $\begin{cases} 3x + 7y = 13 \\ 2x + 5y = 9 \end{cases}$

42. $\begin{cases} 3x + 7y = 0 \\ 2x + 5y = 14 \end{cases}$

43. $\begin{cases} 3x + 7y = 12 \\ 2x + 5y = -4 \end{cases}$

44. $\begin{cases} 3x + 7y = -2 \\ 2x + 5y = 10 \end{cases}$

45. $\begin{cases} x + y - z = 3 \\ 3x - y = -4 \\ 2x - 3y + 4z = 6 \end{cases}$

46. $\begin{cases} x + y - z = 6 \\ 3x - y = 8 \\ 2x - 3y + 4z = -3 \end{cases}$

47. $\begin{cases} x + y - z = 12 \\ 3x - y = -4 \\ 2x - 3y + 4z = 16 \end{cases}$

48. $\begin{cases} x + y - z = -8 \\ 3x - y = 12 \\ 2x - 3y + 4z = -2 \end{cases}$

49. $\begin{cases} x + y - z = 0 \\ 3x - y = -8 \\ 2x - 3y + 4z = -6 \end{cases}$

50. $\begin{cases} x + y - z = 21 \\ 3x - y = 12 \\ 2x - 3y + 4z = 14 \end{cases}$

In Problems 51–56, use a graphing utility or EXCEL to find the inverse, if it exists, of each matrix.

51. $\begin{bmatrix} 25 & 61 & -12 \\ 18 & -2 & 4 \\ 8 & 35 & 21 \end{bmatrix}$

52. $\begin{bmatrix} 18 & -3 & 4 \\ 6 & -20 & 14 \\ 10 & 25 & -15 \end{bmatrix}$

53. $\begin{bmatrix} 44 & 21 & 18 & 6 \\ -2 & 10 & 15 & 5 \\ 21 & 12 & -12 & 4 \\ -8 & -16 & 4 & 9 \end{bmatrix}$

54. $\begin{bmatrix} 16 & 22 & -3 & 5 \\ 21 & -17 & 4 & 8 \\ 2 & 8 & 27 & 20 \\ 5 & 15 & -3 & -10 \end{bmatrix}$

55. $A = \begin{bmatrix} 3 & 0 & 2 & -1 & 3 \\ -2 & 1 & 2 & 3 & 0 \\ 2 & 2 & 1 & 1 & -1 \\ 1 & 2 & 0 & 2 & -3 \\ 4 & 0 & -1 & 1 & -1 \end{bmatrix}$

56. $A = \begin{bmatrix} 0 & 0 & 2 & -1 & 3 \\ -2 & 0 & 2 & 3 & 0 \\ 2 & 2 & 0 & 0 & -1 \\ 1 & 2 & 0 & 2 & -3 \\ 4 & 4 & 0 & 0 & -2 \end{bmatrix}$

In Problems 57–60, use the idea behind Example 7 and either a graphing utility or EXCEL to solve each system of equations.

57. $\begin{cases} 25x + 61y - 12z = 10 \\ 18x - 12y + 7z = -9 \\ 3x + 4y - z = 12 \end{cases}$

58. $\begin{cases} 25x + 61y - 12z = 5 \\ 18x - 12y + 7z = -3 \\ 3x + 4y - z = 12 \end{cases}$

59. $\begin{cases} 25x + 61y - 12z = 21 \\ 18x - 12y + 7z = 7 \\ 3x + 4y - z = -2 \end{cases}$

60. $\begin{cases} 25x + 61y - 12z = 25 \\ 18x - 12y + 7z = 10 \\ 3x + 4y - z = -4 \end{cases}$

Applications and Extensions

61. **Investing** The average annual return (over the 5-year period prior to December 31, 2009) of two mutual funds is shown in the table:

Mutual Fund	Average Annual Return
Mid Cap Growth Fund	4.57%
Bond Fund	6.39%

Source: Vanguard

You have $3000 to invest in these two funds. Assuming the accounts will continue to earn the annual rates shown, how much should you invest for a year in each fund if you want your average return to be

(a) 5%?   (b) 5.5%?   (c) 6%?

62. **Theater Seating** The University of Wisconsin–Milwaukee's Main Stage at the Peck School of the Arts can seat 500 people. For an upcoming production of *Our Town*, the price of admission for students is $10 per ticket and admission for the general public is $15 per ticket. If the theater sells out, how many of each type of ticket must be sold if the total box office receipts are to be

(a) $6000?   (b) $6500?   (c) $7000?

Source: www4.uwm.edu/psoa

63. **Investing** The average annual return (over the 5-year period prior to December 31, 2009) of three mutual funds is shown in the table:

Mutual Fund	Average Annual Return
Small Cap Growth Fund	2.56%
Large Cap Value Fund	4.79%
International Fund	8.73%

Source: Vanguard.

Suppose you have $8000 to invest in these three funds. You will invest $1000 more in the Small Cap Growth fund than you will in the Large Cap Value fund. Assuming the accounts will continue to earn the annual rates shown, how much should you invest for a year in each fund if you want your average return to be

(a) 4%?   (b) 4.5%?   (c) 5%?

64. **Annual Bonuses** A small company has three executives, a president, a chief financial officer (CFO), and a vice president, each of whom it rewards with annual bonuses. The bonus each executive receives is calculated as a percentage of the profits that remain after the bonuses of all three executives have been deducted from the profits. The president receives 5%, the CFO receives 4%, and the vice president receives 2.5%. What will be the bonus amount for each executive if the profits are

(a) $200,000?

(b) $250,000?

(c) $300,000?

65. **Annual Bonuses Revisited** Refer to Problem 64. Because business has been good, the company's board of directors decided to increase the bonuses for the three executives as follows: The president receives 8%, the CFO receives 5%, and the vice president receives 4%. What will be the bonus amount for each executive if the profits are

(a) $300,000?

(b) $500,000?

(c) $750,000?

In Problems 66–71, use the correspondence

A	B	C	D	E	F	G	H	I	J	K	L	M	N	O	P	Q	R	S	T	U	V	W	X	Y	Z
↓	↓	↓	↓	↓	↓	↓	↓	↓	↓	↓	↓	↓	↓	↓	↓	↓	↓	↓	↓	↓	↓	↓	↓	↓	↓
1	2	3	4	5	6	7	8	9	10	11	12	13	14	15	16	17	18	19	20	21	22	23	24	25	26

66. The matrix

$$A = \begin{bmatrix} 2 & 3 \\ 1 & 2 \end{bmatrix}$$

was used to code the following messages:
(a) 64 36 75 47 75 47 49 29 60 36 60 37 53 33 71 39 35 18
(b) 76 49 64 41 95 55 43 24 69 42 59 32 77 45 27 15 37 21 128 77
Use the inverse to decode each message.

67. Use the inverse of matrix

$$A = \begin{bmatrix} 1 & 0 & 0 \\ 3 & 1 & 5 \\ -2 & 0 & 1 \end{bmatrix}$$

to decode the message
   4 152 17 15 106 −22 1 50 3 1 52 7 19 195 −12

68. The matrix A used to encode a message has as its inverse the matrix

$$A^{-1} = \begin{bmatrix} 2 & -3 \\ -1 & 2 \end{bmatrix}$$

Decode the message
70 39 62 41 113 69 93 57 51 28 29 15 54 33 14 9 62 40 67 43 116 71

69. Use the matrix

$$A = \begin{bmatrix} 1 & 0 & 0 \\ 3 & 1 & 5 \\ -2 & 0 & 1 \end{bmatrix}$$

to encode the message: I HAVE TICKETS TO THE FINAL FOUR.

70. Use the matrix $A = \begin{bmatrix} 2 & 3 \\ 1 & 2 \end{bmatrix}$ to encode each of the following messages:
(a) I AM GOING TO DISNEY
(b) WE SURF THE NET
(c) LETS GO CLUBBING

71. Use the matrix

$$A = \begin{bmatrix} 1 & 0 & 0 \\ 3 & 1 & 5 \\ -2 & 0 & 1 \end{bmatrix}$$

to encode the messages given in Problem 70.

72. Pin Codes A four-digit pin code is required for a bank's ATM card. For security reasons, the bank does not store a card's pin code with the bank account. An encrypted code is stored with the account instead. The code is placed within a 2×2 matrix C. For example, the pin code 1234 forms the code matrix $C = \begin{bmatrix} 1 & 2 \\ 3 & 4 \end{bmatrix}$. The code matrix C is then multiplied by a key matrix K to obtain the encrypted matrix E. That is, $E = C \cdot K$. To determine an original pin code, the bank uses $C = E \cdot K^{-1}$.

(a) If the bank uses the key matrix $K = \begin{bmatrix} 1 & 1 \\ 1 & 0 \end{bmatrix}$, known as the *Fibonacci Q-matrix*, encrypt the pin code 7, 3, 4, 1.
(b) Determine the pin code if the encrypted code is 2, 0, 13, 4.
Source: goldenmuseum.com

73. Student IDs A university assigns a unique 12-digit identification number to each of its students upon admission. For security, the university encrypts the ID by placing the digits into a 4×3 matrix D and multiplying by a key matrix K obtaining the encrypted matrix E. That is, $E = D \cdot K$. To determine an original ID, the university uses $D = E \cdot K^{-1}$.

(a) If the university uses the key matrix $K = \begin{bmatrix} 0 & 0 & 1 \\ 1 & 1 & 1 \\ 0 & 1 & 0 \end{bmatrix}$, known as the *Tribonacci matrix*, encrypt the following student ID number: 8, 3, 0, 1, 9, 6, 8, 7, 0, 2, 4, 9.
(b) Determine the original ID number if the encrypted ID is 6, 14, 10, 2, 6, 2, 6, 7, 15, 9, 14, 17.
Source: http://webpages.charter.net/jtlien/padovan.powers

74. Show that the inverse of $A = \begin{bmatrix} a & b \\ c & d \end{bmatrix}$ is given by the formula

$$A^{-1} = \begin{bmatrix} \dfrac{d}{\Delta} & \dfrac{-b}{\Delta} \\ \dfrac{-c}{\Delta} & \dfrac{a}{\Delta} \end{bmatrix} \text{ where } \Delta = ad - bc \neq 0.$$

The number Δ is called the **determinant** of A.

In Problems 75–78, use the result of Problem 74 to find the inverse of each matrix.

75. $\begin{bmatrix} 1 & 2 \\ 2 & 3 \end{bmatrix}$ **76.** $\begin{bmatrix} 1 & 5 \\ 2 & 0 \end{bmatrix}$ **77.** $\begin{bmatrix} -1 & -2 \\ 3 & 4 \end{bmatrix}$ **78.** $\begin{bmatrix} 1 & 2 \\ 8 & 15 \end{bmatrix}$

Discussion and Writing

79. Refer to Example 9. Discuss the risk/reward of trying to achieve an 11% rate of return.

'Are You Prepared?' Answers

1. True   **2.** Multiplicative identity

Exercise 12.6

3. 3×7 **4.** True **5.** True **6.** False **7.** $[14]$ **9.** $[4]$ **11.** $[18 \quad -8]$ **13.** $\begin{bmatrix} 4 & 2 \\ 2 & 8 \end{bmatrix}$ **15.** $[4 \quad 6]$ **17.** $\begin{bmatrix} 4 & -14 \\ 12 & -32 \end{bmatrix}$ **19.** $\begin{bmatrix} 4 & 2 \\ 2 & 8 \\ 9 & 8 \end{bmatrix}$

21. $\begin{bmatrix} 9 & 1 \\ 5 & 4 \\ 11 & 7 \end{bmatrix}$ **23.** BA is defined and is a 3×4 matrix. **25.** AB is not defined. **27.** $(BA)C$ is not defined. **29.** $BA + A$ is defined and is a

3×4 matrix. **31.** $CB - A$ is not defined. **33.** $\begin{bmatrix} -1 & 10 & -1 \\ -4 & 16 & -8 \end{bmatrix}$ **35.** $\begin{bmatrix} 11 & 5 \\ 13 & -9 \end{bmatrix}$ **37.** $\begin{bmatrix} 6 & 10 \\ 8 & 2 \\ -4 & 5 \end{bmatrix}$ **39.** $\begin{bmatrix} 3 & -1 \\ 4 & 2 \end{bmatrix}$ **41.** $\begin{bmatrix} 8 & 4 & 22 \\ 4 & 32 & 16 \end{bmatrix}$

43. $\begin{bmatrix} -14 & 7 \\ -20 & -6 \end{bmatrix}$ **45.** $\begin{bmatrix} 10 & 30 & 37 \\ 15 & 16 & 50 \\ -6 & 20 & -8 \end{bmatrix}$ **47.** $D(CB) = \begin{bmatrix} -6 & 42 & -9 \\ 1 & 20 & 6 \\ -7 & 4 & -18 \end{bmatrix} = (DC)B$ **49.** $AB = \begin{bmatrix} 5 & -2 \\ 6 & 4 \end{bmatrix} \neq \begin{bmatrix} 7 & -3 \\ 6 & 2 \end{bmatrix} = BA$

51. $\begin{bmatrix} 0.5 & 16 & -30 & 25 \\ 21 & 14 & 28 & 64 \\ 19.5 & 8 & -23 & 33 \\ -9.5 & 45 & -9 & 83 \end{bmatrix}$ **53.** $\begin{bmatrix} 31.5 & 251 & -31.5 & 143 \\ 861 & 350 & 791 & 420 \\ 369.5 & 115 & 206.5 & 215 \\ 412.5 & 882 & 451.5 & 491 \end{bmatrix}$ **55.** $\begin{bmatrix} 66 & 74 & 94 & 38 \\ 71 & 13 & 106 & 28 \\ 165 & 124.5 & 79 & 52 \\ 158 & -3 & 152 & 46 \end{bmatrix}$ **57.** $\begin{bmatrix} -5 & 23 & -102 & 44 \\ -108 & -56 & -70 & 122 \\ 108 & -152 & -67 & 36 \\ -346 & 279 & -249 & 187 \end{bmatrix}$

59. (a) Matrix A represents the price at the close of the trading on July 7, 2009, of a share of Chevron Corporation, Conoco Phillips, and Exxon Mobil Corporation, respectively. A is 1×3. (b) $AB = [37,899.50 \quad 44,595.60 \quad 27,623.30]$; matrix AB represents the amount each of the three persons spent on

the three stocks on July 7, 2009, at their closing price. (c) $BC = \begin{bmatrix} 690 \\ 540 \\ 680 \end{bmatrix}$; matrix BC represents the total number shares of Chevron Corporation, Conoco

Phillips, and Exxon Mobil Corporation, respectively, purchased by the three persons at the close of trading on July 7, 2009.

61. (a)

	Credit Hours				Cost per
	JJC	CSU			Credit
$A =$ John	12	4	$B =$	JJC	103
Marsha	8	8		CSU	249

(b) A is 2×2 (c) B is 2×1 (d) $AB = \begin{bmatrix} 2232 \\ 2816 \end{bmatrix}$

(e) AB is 2×1. The rows are John and Marsha; the column is cost of tuition. (f) The entries in AB are the total amounts (in dollars) that each student spends on tuition.

63. (a)

	GE	TM	JNJ			Bill	Dan
Oct. 2008	22	73	64		GE	50	40
$A =$ April 2009	11	78	53	$B =$ TM	30	60
Oct. 2009	17	79	61		JNJ	20	30

(b) A is 3×3 (c) B is 3×2 (d) $AB = \begin{bmatrix} 4570 & 7180 \\ 3950 & 6710 \\ 4440 & 7250 \end{bmatrix}$

(e) AB is 3×2; The rows are the dates and the columns are Bill and Dan. (f) The entries are the total value of the three stocks Dan and Bill

own in October 2008, April 2009, and October 2009. **65.** Lee spent \$372 and Chan spent \$257. **67.** $x = 1$ or $x = \dfrac{1}{2}$ **69.** $a = d$ and $b = -c$

71. $A^2 = \begin{bmatrix} a & 1-a \\ 1+a & -a \end{bmatrix} \cdot \begin{bmatrix} a & 1-a \\ 1+a & -a \end{bmatrix} = \begin{bmatrix} 1 & 0 \\ 0 & 1 \end{bmatrix}$ **73.** $AB = \begin{bmatrix} ac - bd & ad + bc \\ -bc - ad & -bd + ac \end{bmatrix} = \begin{bmatrix} ca - db & cb + da \\ -da - cb & -db + ca \end{bmatrix} = BA$

75. $A^2 = \begin{bmatrix} 7 & 2 \\ -4 & -1 \end{bmatrix} A^3 = \begin{bmatrix} 17 & 5 \\ -10 & -3 \end{bmatrix} A^4 = \begin{bmatrix} 41 & 12 \\ -24 & -7 \end{bmatrix}$ **77.** $A^2 = \begin{bmatrix} \dfrac{3}{8} & \dfrac{5}{8} \\ \dfrac{5}{16} & \dfrac{11}{16} \end{bmatrix} A^3 = \begin{bmatrix} \dfrac{11}{32} & \dfrac{21}{32} \\ \dfrac{21}{64} & \dfrac{43}{64} \end{bmatrix} A^4 = \begin{bmatrix} \dfrac{43}{128} & \dfrac{85}{128} \\ \dfrac{85}{256} & \dfrac{171}{256} \end{bmatrix}$

79. Answers will vary, but as n gets larger A^n becomes approximately equal to $\begin{bmatrix} \dfrac{1}{3} & \dfrac{2}{3} \\ \dfrac{1}{3} & \dfrac{2}{3} \end{bmatrix}$.

81.

```
[B]²
[[.674 .043 .23…        …043 .230 .054]
 [.382 .096 .21…        …096 .212 .310]
 [.500 .070 .22…        …070 .220 .210]
 [.130 .110 .20…        …110 .200 .560]]
```

```
[B]^10
[[.514 .065 .22…        …065 .221 .201]
 [.491 .068 .22…        …068 .220 .222]
 [.500 .067 .22…        …067 .220 .213]
 [.470 .070 .21…        …070 .218 .241]]
```

```
[B]^15
[[.503 .066 .22…        …066 .220 .211]
 [.498 .067 .22…        …067 .220 .215]
 [.500 .067 .22…        …067 .220 .213]
 [.494 .067 .22…        …067 .220 .219]]
```

Exercise 12.7

3. inverse **4.** False **5.** $\begin{bmatrix} 1 & 2 \\ 2 & 3 \end{bmatrix}\begin{bmatrix} -3 & 2 \\ 2 & -1 \end{bmatrix} = \begin{bmatrix} 1 & 0 \\ 0 & 1 \end{bmatrix}$ **7.** $\begin{bmatrix} -1 & -2 \\ 3 & 4 \end{bmatrix}\begin{bmatrix} 2 & 1 \\ -\frac{3}{2} & -\frac{1}{2} \end{bmatrix} = \begin{bmatrix} 1 & 0 \\ 0 & 1 \end{bmatrix}$ **9.** $\begin{bmatrix} 1 & 2 & 3 \\ 2 & 3 & 4 \\ 1 & 2 & 1 \end{bmatrix}\begin{bmatrix} -\frac{5}{2} & 2 & -\frac{1}{2} \\ 1 & -1 & 1 \\ \frac{1}{2} & 0 & -\frac{1}{2} \end{bmatrix} = \begin{bmatrix} 1 & 0 & 0 \\ 0 & 1 & 0 \\ 0 & 0 & 1 \end{bmatrix}$

11. $\begin{bmatrix} 5 & -7 \\ -2 & 3 \end{bmatrix}$ **13.** $\begin{bmatrix} 4 & -1 \\ 3 & -1 \end{bmatrix}$ **15.** $\begin{bmatrix} 3 & -1 \\ \frac{3}{2} & -\frac{1}{2} \\ -2 & 1 \end{bmatrix}$ **17.** $\begin{bmatrix} 0 & 0 & 1 \\ 0 & 1 & 0 \\ 1 & 0 & 0 \end{bmatrix}$ **19.** $\begin{bmatrix} \frac{4}{9} & \frac{1}{9} & \frac{1}{9} \\ \frac{4}{3} & -\frac{2}{3} & \frac{1}{3} \\ \frac{7}{9} & -\frac{5}{9} & \frac{4}{9} \end{bmatrix}$ **21.** $\begin{bmatrix} 1 & -1 & 2 \\ -1 & 2 & -3 \\ -1 & 1 & -1 \end{bmatrix}$ **23.** $\begin{bmatrix} 2 & -1 & -1 & -2 \\ -1 & 1 & 1 & 2 \\ -2 & 1 & 2 & 3 \\ -1 & 1 & 1 & 1 \end{bmatrix}$

25. $\begin{bmatrix} 4 & 6 & | & 1 & 0 \\ 2 & 3 & | & 0 & 1 \end{bmatrix} \Rightarrow \begin{bmatrix} 1 & \frac{3}{2} & | & \frac{1}{4} & 0 \\ 0 & 0 & | & -\frac{1}{2} & 1 \end{bmatrix}$ **27.** $\begin{bmatrix} -8 & 4 & | & 1 & 0 \\ -4 & 2 & | & 0 & 1 \end{bmatrix} \Rightarrow \begin{bmatrix} 1 & -\frac{1}{2} & | & -\frac{1}{8} & 0 \\ 0 & 0 & | & -\frac{1}{2} & 1 \end{bmatrix}$ **29.** $\begin{bmatrix} 1 & 1 & 1 & | & 1 & 0 & 0 \\ 3 & -4 & 2 & | & 0 & 1 & 0 \\ 0 & 0 & 0 & | & 0 & 0 & 1 \end{bmatrix}$ **31.** $\begin{bmatrix} 2 & -1 \\ -1 & 1 \end{bmatrix}$

33. Inverse does not exist. **35.** $A^{-1} = \begin{bmatrix} \frac{1}{5} & \frac{2}{5} \\ \frac{2}{5} & -\frac{1}{5} \end{bmatrix}$; $B^{-1} = \begin{bmatrix} -\frac{1}{5} & \frac{3}{5} \\ \frac{2}{5} & -\frac{1}{5} \end{bmatrix}$; $A^{-1} - B^{-1} = \begin{bmatrix} \frac{2}{5} & -\frac{1}{5} \\ 0 & 0 \end{bmatrix}$ **37.** $\begin{bmatrix} 42 & -18 & -5 \\ -9 & 4 & 1 \\ -7 & 3 & 1 \end{bmatrix}\begin{bmatrix} 2 \\ 1 \\ 3 \end{bmatrix} = \begin{bmatrix} 51 \\ -11 \\ -8 \end{bmatrix}$

39. $x = 36, y = -14$ or $(36, -14)$ **41.** $x = 2, y = 1$ or $(2, 1)$ **43.** $x = 88, y = -36$ or $(88, -36)$

45. $x = \frac{14}{9}, y = \frac{26}{3}, z = \frac{65}{9}$ or $\left(\frac{14}{9}, \frac{26}{3}, \frac{65}{9}\right)$ **47.** $x = \frac{20}{3}, y = 24, z = \frac{56}{3}$ or $\left(\frac{20}{3}, 24, \frac{56}{3}\right)$ **49.** $x = -\frac{14}{9}, y = \frac{10}{3}, z = \frac{16}{9}$ or $\left(-\frac{14}{9}, \frac{10}{3}, \frac{16}{9}\right)$

51. $\begin{bmatrix} 0.00545 & 0.0509 & -0.0066 \\ 0.01036 & -0.0186 & 0.0095 \\ -0.0193 & 0.0116 & 0.0344 \end{bmatrix}$ **53.** $\begin{bmatrix} 0.0249 & -0.0360 & -0.0057 & 0.0059 \\ -0.0171 & 0.0521 & 0.0292 & -0.0305 \\ 0.0206 & 0.0081 & -0.0421 & 0.0005 \\ -0.0175 & 0.0570 & 0.0657 & 0.0619 \end{bmatrix}$

55. $\begin{bmatrix} \frac{1}{4} & -\frac{1}{16} & -\frac{9}{32} & \frac{5}{16} & \frac{3}{32} \\ \frac{3}{2} & \frac{1}{8} & \frac{49}{16} & -\frac{21}{8} & \frac{5}{16} \\ \frac{7}{4} & -\frac{3}{16} & -\frac{91}{32} & \frac{47}{16} & -\frac{23}{32} \\ -\frac{1}{2} & \frac{3}{8} & \frac{11}{16} & -\frac{7}{8} & \frac{7}{16} \\ -\frac{5}{4} & \frac{5}{16} & \frac{77}{32} & -\frac{41}{16} & \frac{17}{32} \end{bmatrix}$

57. $x = 4.567, y = -6.444, z = -24.075$ **59.** $x = -1.187, y = 2.457, z = 8.265$ **61. (a)** Invest $2291.21 in the mid cap fund and $708.79 in the bond fund for a 5% rate of return. **(b)** Invest $1467.03 in the mid cap fund and $1532.97 in the bond fund for an $5\frac{1}{2}$% rate of return. **(c)** Invest $642.86 in the mid cap fund and $2357.14 in the bond fund for a 6% rate of return. **63. (a)** Invest $4132.54 in the small cap growth fund, $3132.54 in the large cap value fund, and $734.92 in the international fund for a 4% rate of return. **(b)** Invest $3736.89 in the small cap growth fund, $2736.89 in the large cap value fund, and $1526.22 in the international fund for a 4.5% rate of return. **(c)** Invest $3341.25 in the small cap growth fund, $2341.25 in the large cap value fund, and $2317.50 in the international fund for a 5% rate of return.

65. (a) When profit is $300,000, the president's bonus is $20,512.82, the CFO's bonus is $12,820.51, and the vice president's bonus is $10,256.41.
(b) When profit is $500,000, the president's bonus is $34,188.03 the CFO's bonus is $21,367.52, and the vice president's bonus is $17,094.01.
(c) When profit is $750,000, the president's bonus is $51,282.05, the CFO's bonus is $32,051.28, and the vice president's bonus is $25,641.03. **67.** Do you have a dish? **69.** 9 40 −17 22 171 −24 9 85 −7 5 130 9 20 175 −20 8 59 −10 9 46 −17 12 117 −9 21 211 −16 **71.** (a) 9 93 −5 7 81 −5 14 149 −8 15 94 −21 19 96 −33 25 230 −24 (b) 23 169 −27 21 111 −36 20 93 − 35 14 147 −8 (c) 12 141 −4 19 139 −23 3 126 15 2 53 5 14 179 −2

73. (a) The encrypted ID is $E = \begin{bmatrix} 3 & 3 & 11 \\ 9 & 15 & 10 \\ 7 & 7 & 15 \\ 4 & 13 & 6 \end{bmatrix}$
or written out: 3 3 11 9 15 10 7 7 15 4 13 6.

(b) The original ID is $D = \begin{bmatrix} 4 & 6 & 8 \\ 0 & 2 & 4 \\ 9 & 6 & 1 \\ 8 & 9 & 5 \end{bmatrix}$
or written out: 4 6 8 0 2 4 9 6 1 8 9 5.

75. $\begin{bmatrix} -3 & 2 \\ 2 & -1 \end{bmatrix}$ **77.** $\begin{bmatrix} 2 & 1 \\ -\dfrac{3}{2} & -\dfrac{1}{2} \end{bmatrix}$

Technical Mathematics, Sixth Edition

Paul A. Calter
Michael A. Calter, Ph.D.

12–8 Second-Order Determinants

Every square matrix has a special quantity associated with it, called its *determinant*. The determinant is important because we will soon see that it gives us another way to solve a set of equations.

We indicate or denote the determinant of a square matrix either by writing **det** before the matrix, or by a symbol consisting of the elements of the matrix enclosed between vertical bars. Thus

$$\det\begin{pmatrix} 1 & 2 \\ 3 & 4 \end{pmatrix} = \begin{vmatrix} 1 & 2 \\ 3 & 4 \end{vmatrix}$$

The words *element, row, column, principal* and *secondary diagonal* for a determinant have the same meaning as for a square matrix.

◆◆◆ **Example 15:** In the determinant

$$\begin{vmatrix} 2 & 5 \\ 6 & 1 \end{vmatrix}$$

each of the numbers 2, 5, 6, and 1 is called an *element*. There are two *rows*, the first row containing the elements 2 and 5, and the second row having the elements 6 and 1. There are also two *columns*, the first with elements 2 and 6, and the second with elements 5 and 1. The elements along the principal diagonal are 2 and 1, and along the secondary diagonal they are 5 and 6. ◆◆◆

Value of a Determinant

We find the *value* of a second order determinant by applying the following rule:

> *The value of a second-order determinant is equal to the product of the elements on the principal diagonal, minus the product of the elements on the secondary diagonal.*

or

Second-Order Determinant	$\begin{vmatrix} a_1 & b_1 \\ a_2 & b_2 \end{vmatrix} = a_1b_2 - a_2b_1$	54

◆◆◆ **Example 16:** The value of the determinant of Example 15 is

$$\begin{vmatrix} 2 & 5 \\ 6 & 1 \end{vmatrix} = 2(1) - 6(5) = -28$$
◆◆◆

It is common practice to use the word *determinant* to refer to the *symbol*, $\begin{vmatrix} a_1 & b_1 \\ a_2 & b_2 \end{vmatrix}$ but also to the *rule* for its evaluation, as well as to the *value* $(a_1b_2 - a_2b_1)$.

Here we will usually refer to the symbol as the determinant, and to $(a_1b_2 - a_2b_1)$ as the value of the determinant.

◆◆◆ **Example 17:** Here are a few more second-order determinants. See if you get the same resultss.

(a) $\begin{vmatrix} 2 & -1 \\ 3 & 5 \end{vmatrix} = 2(5) - 3(-1) = 13$

(b) $\begin{vmatrix} 4 & a \\ x & 3b \end{vmatrix} = 4(3b) - x(a) = 12b - ax$

(c) $\begin{vmatrix} 0 & 3 \\ 5 & 2 \end{vmatrix} = 0(2) - 5(3) = -15$

◆◆◆

Common Error	Students sometimes *add* the numbers on a diagonal instead of *multiplying*. Be careful not to do that.
	Don't just ignore a zero element. It causes the product along its diagonal to be zero.

Determinants by Calculator

In the preceding section we showed how to enter a matrix into a calculator. Now we will find the determinant of a square matrix.

◆◆◆ **Example 18:** Find the determinant of the following matrix by TI-83/84 calculator.

$$\begin{vmatrix} 4 & -2 \\ -3 & 5 \end{vmatrix}$$

Solution: We first enter the matrix as was described in Example 10. Then we perform the steps shown in the following three screens.

TI-83/84 screens for Example 18.
(1) Enter the MATRIX menu and choose MATH.

(2) Select **det,** which stands for determinant.

(3) Return to the MATRIX menu and select the matrix for which we want the determinant. We select [A] and press ENTER .

◆◆◆

The TI-89 can evaluate determinants, even when the elements contain letter values.

◆◆◆ **Example 19:** Evaluate the following determinant using the TI-89 calculator.

$$\begin{vmatrix} x & 3 \\ 2y & w \end{vmatrix}$$

Solution: We enter the matrix as was shown in Example 11, and name it **q.** To display the matrix, type ALPHA **q** on the entry line of the HOME screen. To obtain the determinant we enter **det** from the MATH Matrix menu, followed by the name of the matrix, as shown.

◆◆◆

TI-89 screen for Example 19.

Solving a System of Two Linear Equations by Determinants

■ Exploration:

Try this. We saw in the preceding chapter that the solution to the set of equations

$$a_1x + b_1y + c_1 = 0$$
$$a_2x + b_2y + c_2 = 0 \qquad (1)$$

is

$$x = \frac{b_2c_1 - b_1c_2}{a_1b_2 - a_2b_1} \qquad (2)$$

$$y = \frac{a_1c_2 - a_2c_1}{a_1b_2 - a_2b_1} \qquad (3)$$

and in this section that the value of a second-order determinant is

$$\begin{vmatrix} a_1 & b_1 \\ a_2 & b_2 \end{vmatrix} = a_1b_2 - a_2b_1 \qquad (4)$$

Now compare Eqs. 2, 3, and 4. What similarities do you see? Could you replace any parts of Eqs. 2 and 3 by Eq. 4? ■

You have probably noticed that the denominators in both Eqs. 2 and 3 are identical to the determinant in Eq. 4. This denominator is called the *determinant of the coefficients,* or sometimes the *determinant of the system.* It is usually given the Greek capital letter delta (Δ). If this determinant equals zero, the set of equations has no unique solution.

Thus we can rewrite the solution for x as

$$x = \frac{b_2c_1 - b_1c_2}{\begin{vmatrix} a_1 & b_1 \\ a_2 & b_2 \end{vmatrix}}$$

Now look at the numerator of Eq. 2, which is $b_2c_1 - b_1c_2$. If this expression were the value of some determinant, it is clear that the elements on the principal diagonal must be b_2 and c_1 and that the elements on the secondary diagonal must be b_1 and c_2. One such determinant is

$$\begin{vmatrix} c_1 & b_1 \\ c_2 & b_2 \end{vmatrix} = b_2c_1 - b_1c_2$$

Our solution for x can then be expressed as the quotient of two determinants

$$x = \frac{\begin{vmatrix} c_1 & b_1 \\ c_2 & b_2 \end{vmatrix}}{\begin{vmatrix} a_1 & b_1 \\ a_2 & b_2 \end{vmatrix}}$$

An expression for y can be developed in a similar way. Thus the solution to the system of Eqs. 1, in terms of determinants, is given by the following rule:

Named after the Swiss mathematician Gabriel Cramer (1704–52), Cramer's rule, as we will see, can be expanded for systems with any number of linear equations.

| Cramer's Rule | $x = \dfrac{\begin{vmatrix} c_1 & b_1 \\ c_2 & b_2 \end{vmatrix}}{\begin{vmatrix} a_1 & b_1 \\ a_2 & b_2 \end{vmatrix}}$ and $y = \dfrac{\begin{vmatrix} a_1 & c_1 \\ a_2 & c_2 \end{vmatrix}}{\begin{vmatrix} a_1 & b_1 \\ a_2 & b_2 \end{vmatrix}}$ | 59 |

In the array made from the coeffiecients in the set of Eqs. 1

$$\begin{pmatrix} a_1 & b_1 & c_1 \\ a_2 & b_2 & c_2 \end{pmatrix}$$

We will refer to the values

$$\begin{vmatrix} a_1 \\ a_2 \end{vmatrix} \text{ as the column of } x \text{ coefficients,}$$

$$\begin{vmatrix} b_1 \\ b_2 \end{vmatrix} \text{ as the column of } y \text{ coefficients, and}$$

$$\begin{vmatrix} c_1 \\ c_2 \end{vmatrix} \text{ as the column of constants.}$$

Cramer's rule, in words, is then

Cramer's Rule	The solution for each variable is a fraction; its denominator is the determinant of the coefficients Δ; its numerator is also Δ but with its column of coefficients for the variable we seek replaced by the column of constants.

Of course, the denominator Δ cannot be zero, or we get division by zero, indicating that the set of equations has no unique solution.

◆◆◆ **Example 20:** Solve by determinants:

$$2x - 3y = 1$$
$$x + 4y = -5$$

Solution: The array of the coefficient is

$$\begin{pmatrix} 2 & -3 & 1 \\ 1 & 4 & -5 \end{pmatrix}$$

We first evaluate the determinant Δ, because if it is zero there is no unique solution, and we need not proceed further.

$$\Delta = \begin{vmatrix} 2 & -3 \\ 1 & 4 \end{vmatrix} = 2(4) - 1(-3) = 8 + 3 = 11$$

Solving for x, we have

$$x = \frac{\begin{vmatrix} 1 & -3 \\ -5 & 4 \end{vmatrix}}{\Delta} = \frac{1(4) - (-5)(-3)}{11} = \frac{4 - 15}{11} = -1$$

(column of constants)

It is easiest to find y by substituting back into one of the preceding equations, but we will use determinants instead to show how it is done.

Solving for y yields

column of constants

$$y = \frac{\begin{vmatrix} 2 & 1 \\ 1 & -5 \end{vmatrix}}{\Delta} = \frac{2(-5) - 1(1)}{11} = \frac{-10 - 1}{11} = -1$$

Check: The screen shows a graphical check. The equations are graphed, after being rewritten in explicit form, and show an intersection at $(-1, -1)$. We could, of course, check our answers by substituting back into the original equations.

◆◆◆

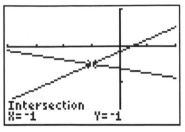

Graphical check for Example 20.

Common Error	Don't forget to first arrange the given equations into the form $a_1x + b_1y = c_1$ $a_2x + b_2y = c_2$ before writing the determinants.

Calculator Solution Using Determinants

We can have our calculators evaluate the determinants and perform the divisions in one operation, as in the following example.

◆◆◆ **Example 21:** Solve the equations in the preceding example by calculator.

Solution: We first name and enter each of the three arrays as was shown earlier. Let us choose

TI-83/84 screen for Example 21.

[A] as the determinant of the coefficients

[B] as the determinant used to find x

[C] as the determinant used to find y

We then find x by dividing the determinant of [B] by the determinant of [A], and find y by dividing the determinant of [C] by the determinant of [A], as shown in the calculator screen.

◆◆◆

Literal Equations

The procedure is no different when our equation contains literal quantities. We will not, of course, get a numerical answer, but one that contains the letter quantities.

◆◆◆ **Example 22:** Solve for x and y by determinants:

$$2ax - by + 3a = 0$$
$$4y = 5x - a$$

Solution: We first rearrange our equations.

$$2ax - by = -3a$$
$$5x - 4y = a$$

The determinant of the coefficients is

$$\Delta = \begin{vmatrix} 2a & -b \\ 5 & -4 \end{vmatrix} = 2a(-4) - 5(-b) = 5b - 8a$$

So

$$x = \frac{\begin{vmatrix} -3a & -b \\ a & -4 \end{vmatrix}}{\Delta} = \frac{(-3a)(-4) - a(-b)}{5b - 8a}$$

$$= \frac{12a + ab}{5b - 8a}$$

and

$$y = \frac{\begin{vmatrix} 2a & -3a \\ 5 & a \end{vmatrix}}{\Delta} = \frac{2a(a) - 5(-3a)}{5b - 8a}$$

$$= \frac{2a^2 + 15a}{5b - 8a} \qquad \qquad \text{◆◆◆}$$

12–9 Higher-Order Determinants

To solve a system of more than two equations by determinants, we must be able to write and evaluate determinants of orders greater than 2. We show how to do that here, first by calculator and then by the use of *minors*. The calculator method is, of course, the fastest and easiest but can only be used with equations that have numerical coefficients. The method of minors will work for literal equations as well as numerical.

Evaluating a Higher-Order Determinant by Calculator

The procedure for evaluating a higher-order determinant by calculator is no different from that for a second-order determinant.

♦♦♦ **Example 23:** Evaluate the determinant

$$\begin{vmatrix} 2 & 1 & 0 \\ 3 & -2 & 1 \\ 5 & 1 & 0 \end{vmatrix}$$

Solution: The calculator screens are as shown.   ♦♦♦

Development by Minors

The following method may be used to evaluate determinants of any size. It is more difficult than using a calculator but can be used for determinants that contain letters.

The *minor of an element in a determinant* is a determinant of next lower order, obtained by deleting the row and the column in which that element lies.

♦♦♦ **Example 24:** We find the minor of element c in the determinant

$$\begin{vmatrix} a & b & c \\ d & e & f \\ g & h & i \end{vmatrix}$$

by striking out the first row and the third column.

$$\begin{vmatrix} a & b & c \\ d & e & f \\ g & h & i \end{vmatrix} \quad \text{or} \quad \begin{vmatrix} d & e \\ g & h \end{vmatrix}$$ ♦♦♦

The *sign factor* for an element depends upon the position of the element in the determinant. To find the sign factor, add the row number and the column number of the element. If the sum is even, the sign factor is $+1$; if the sum is odd, the sign factor is -1.

♦♦♦ **Example 25:**

(a) For the determinant in Example 24, element c is in the first row and the third column. The sum of the row and column numbers

$$1 + 3 = 4$$

is even, so the sign factor for the element c is $+1$.

(b) The sign factor for the element b in Example 24 is -1.   ♦♦♦

The sign factor for the element in the upper left-hand corner of the determinant is $+1$, and the signs alternate according to the pattern

$$\begin{vmatrix} + & - & + & - & + & - & \cdot \\ - & + & - & + & - & \cdot & \cdot \\ + & - & + & - & \cdot & \cdot & \cdot \\ - & + & - & \cdot & \cdot & \cdot & \cdot \\ + & - & \cdot & \cdot & \cdot & \cdot & \cdot \\ - & \cdot & \cdot & \cdot & \cdot & \cdot & \cdot \\ \cdot & \cdot & \cdot & \cdot & \cdot & \cdot & \cdot \end{vmatrix}$$

so that the sign factor may be found simply by *counting off* from the upper-left corner.

A minor with the sign factor attached is called a *signed minor*. Thus

TI-83/84 screens for Example 23.

(1) In the MATRIX EDIT screen we enter the matrix dimensions and the nine elements.

(2) We then choose **det** from the MATRIX MATH menu and select matrix [A]. Press ENTER to get the value, 3, of the determinant.

TI-89 screen for Example 23. Here we have named the given determinant k.

	The signed minor of element b in the determinant	
Signed Minor	$\begin{vmatrix} a & b & c \\ d & e & f \\ g & h & i \end{vmatrix}$ is $-\begin{vmatrix} d & f \\ g & i \end{vmatrix}$	**56**

◆◆◆ **Example 26:** The element in the second row and the first column in the following determinant is 3.

$$\begin{vmatrix} -2 & 5 & 1 \\ 3 & -2 & 4 \\ 1 & -4 & 2 \end{vmatrix}$$

The sign factor of that element is -1 so the signed minor of that element is

$$-\begin{vmatrix} 5 & 1 \\ -4 & 2 \end{vmatrix} \qquad ◆◆◆$$

We now define the *value of a determinant* as follows:

	To find the value of a determinant,	
Value of a Determinant	1. Choose any row or any column to develop by minors. 2. Write the product of every element in that row or column and its signed minor. 3. Add these products to get the value of the determinant.	**57**

◆◆◆ **Example 27:** Evaluate by minors:

$$\begin{vmatrix} 3 & 2 & 4 \\ 1 & 6 & -2 \\ -1 & 5 & -3 \end{vmatrix}$$

Solution: We first choose a row or a column for development. The work of expansion is greatly reduced if that row or column contains zeros. Our given determinant has no zeros, so let us choose column 1, which at least contains some 1's.

Elements of column 1

$$\begin{vmatrix} 3 & 2 & 4 \\ 1 & 6 & -2 \\ -1 & 5 & -3 \end{vmatrix} = 3(1)\begin{vmatrix} 6 & -2 \\ 5 & -3 \end{vmatrix} + 1(-1)\begin{vmatrix} 2 & 4 \\ 5 & -3 \end{vmatrix} + (-1)(1)\begin{vmatrix} 2 & 4 \\ 6 & -2 \end{vmatrix}$$

Sign factor of each element

Minor of each element

$$= 3[(6)(-3) - (-2)(5)] - 1[(2)(-3) - (4)(5)] - 1[(2)(-2) - 4(6)]$$
$$= -24 + 26 + 28$$
$$= 30$$

Thus, 30 is the value of the given determinant. We would have gotten the same result if we had chosen any other row or column for development. ◆◆◆

◆◆◆ **Example 28:** Evaluate by minors:

$$\begin{vmatrix} a_1 & b_1 & c_1 \\ a_2 & b_2 & c_2 \\ a_3 & b_3 & c_3 \end{vmatrix}$$

Solution: We can choose any row or column for development and would get the same result for each. Let us choose the first row for development. We get

$$a_1 \begin{vmatrix} b_2 & c_2 \\ b_3 & c_3 \end{vmatrix} - b_1 \begin{vmatrix} a_2 & c_2 \\ a_3 & c_3 \end{vmatrix} + c_1 \begin{vmatrix} a_2 & b_2 \\ a_3 & b_3 \end{vmatrix}$$

$$= a_1(b_2c_3 - b_3c_2) - b_1(a_2c_3 - a_3c_2) + c_1(a_2b_3 - a_3b_2)$$
$$= a_1b_2c_3 - a_1b_3c_2 - a_2b_1c_3 + a_3b_1c_2 + a_2b_3c_1 - a_3b_2c_1$$
$$= a_1b_2c_3 + a_3b_1c_2 + a_2b_3c_1 - a_3b_2c_1 - a_1b_3c_2 - a_2b_1c_3 \qquad ◆◆◆$$

The value of the determinant is thus given by the following formula:

Third-Order Determinant	$\begin{vmatrix} a_1 & b_1 & c_1 \\ a_2 & b_2 & c_2 \\ a_3 & b_3 & c_3 \end{vmatrix} = \begin{matrix} a_1b_2c_3 + a_3b_1c_2 + a_2b_3c_1 \\ - a_3b_2c_1 - a_1b_3c_2 - a_2b_1c_3 \end{matrix}$	55

Solving a System of Equations by Determinants

If we were to *algebraically* solve the system of equations

$$a_1x + b_1y + c_1z = k_1$$
$$a_2x + b_2y + c_2z = k_2$$
$$a_3x + b_3y + c_3z = k_3$$

we would get the following solution:

Three Equations in Three Unknowns	$x = \dfrac{b_2c_3k_1 + b_1c_2k_3 + b_3c_1k_2 - b_2c_1k_3 - b_3c_2k_1 - b_1c_3k_2}{a_1b_2c_3 + a_3b_1c_2 + a_2b_3c_1 - a_3b_2c_1 - a_1b_3c_2 - a_2b_1c_3}$ $y = \dfrac{a_1c_3k_2 + a_3c_2k_1 + a_2c_1k_3 - a_3c_1k_2 - a_1c_2k_3 - a_2c_3k_1}{a_1b_2c_3 + a_3b_1c_2 + a_2b_3c_1 - a_3b_2c_1 - a_1b_3c_2 - a_2b_1c_3}$ $z = \dfrac{a_1b_2k_3 + a_3b_1k_2 + a_2b_3k_1 - a_3b_2k_1 - a_1b_3k_2 - a_2b_1k_3}{a_1b_2c_3 + a_3b_1c_2 + a_2b_3c_1 - a_3b_2c_1 - a_1b_3c_2 - a_2b_1c_3}$	53

Notice that the three denominators are identical and are equal to the value of the determinant formed from the coefficients of the unknowns (Eq. 55). As before, we call it the *determinant of the coefficients,* Δ.

Furthermore, we can obtain the numerator of each from the determinant of the coefficients by replacing the coefficients of the variable in question with the constants k_1, k_2, and k_3, as we did with a set of two equations. The solution to our set of equations

$$a_1x + b_1y + c_1z = k_1$$
$$a_2x + b_2y + c_2z = k_2$$
$$a_3x + b_3y + c_3z = k_3$$

is then given by

| Cramer's Rule | $x = \dfrac{\begin{vmatrix} k_1 & b_1 & c_1 \\ k_2 & b_2 & c_2 \\ k_3 & b_3 & c_3 \end{vmatrix}}{\Delta}$ $y = \dfrac{\begin{vmatrix} a_1 & k_1 & c_1 \\ a_2 & k_2 & c_2 \\ a_3 & k_3 & c_3 \end{vmatrix}}{\Delta}$ $z = \dfrac{\begin{vmatrix} a_1 & b_1 & k_1 \\ a_2 & b_2 & k_2 \\ a_3 & b_3 & k_3 \end{vmatrix}}{\Delta}$ where $\Delta = \begin{vmatrix} a_1 & b_1 & c_1 \\ a_2 & b_2 & c_2 \\ a_3 & b_3 & c_3 \end{vmatrix} \neq 0$ | 60 |

Although we do not prove it, Cramer's rule works for higher-order systems as well. We restate it now in words.

| Cramer's Rule | The solution for any variable is a fraction whose denominator is the determinant of the coefficients and whose numerator is the same determinant, except that the column of coefficients for the variable for which we are solving is replaced by the column of constants. | 58 |

◆◆◆ **Example 29:** Solve by determinants:

$$x + 2y + 3z = 14$$
$$2x + y + 2z = 10$$
$$3x + 4y - 3z = 2$$

Solution: We first write the determinant of the coefficients

$$\Delta = \begin{vmatrix} 1 & 2 & 3 \\ 2 & 1 & 2 \\ 3 & 4 & -3 \end{vmatrix}$$

We now make a new determinant by replacing the coefficients of x,

$\begin{vmatrix} 1 \\ 2 \\ 3 \end{vmatrix}$, by the column of constants $\begin{vmatrix} 14 \\ 10 \\ 2 \end{vmatrix}$, getting $\begin{vmatrix} 14 & 2 & 3 \\ 10 & 1 & 2 \\ 2 & 4 & -3 \end{vmatrix}$

Next we replace the coefficients of y with the column of constants and get

$$\begin{vmatrix} 1 & 14 & 3 \\ 2 & 10 & 2 \\ 3 & 2 & -3 \end{vmatrix}$$

We can evaluate these three determinants by minors or by calculator, as shown here. We enter the three matrices as shown earlier. Here [A] is the determinant of the coefficients, [B] is the determinant used for finding x, and [C] is the determinant used for finding y, screens (1) – (3).

Next we use **det** from the |MATRIX| MATH menu to evaluate each determinant, screen (4), and then calculate x and y.

$$x = \frac{[B]}{[A]} = \frac{28}{28} = 1$$

$$y = \frac{[C]}{[A]} = \frac{56}{28} = 2$$

We can get z also by determinants or, more easily, by substituting back. Substituting $x = 1$ and $y = 2$ into the first equation, we obtain

$$1 + 2(2) + 3z = 14$$
$$3z = 9$$
$$z = 3$$

The solution is thus $(1, 2, 3)$.　　　　　　　　　　◆◆◆

Often, some terms will have zero coefficients or decimal coefficients. Further, the terms may be out of order, as in the following example. We will show a solution by minors, but a calculator could be used as well.

◆◆◆ **Example 30:** Solve for x, y, and z:

$$23.7y + 72.4x = 82.4 - 11.3x$$
$$25.5x - 28.4z + 19.3 = 48.2y$$
$$13.4 + 66.3z = 39.2x - 10.5$$

Solution: We rewrite each equation in the form $ax + by + cz = k$, combining like terms as we go and putting in the missing terms with zero coefficients. We do this *before* writing the determinant.

$$83.7x + 23.7y + \quad 0z = 82.4 \qquad (1)$$
$$25.5x - 48.2y - 28.4z = -19.3$$
$$-39.2x + \quad 0y + 66.3z = -23.9 \qquad (2)$$

The determinant of the system is then

$$\Delta = \begin{vmatrix} 83.7 & 23.7 & 0 \\ 25.5 & -48.2 & -28.4 \\ -39.2 & 0 & 66.3 \end{vmatrix}$$

Let us develop the first row by minors.

$$\Delta = 83.7 \begin{vmatrix} -48.2 & -28.4 \\ 0 & 66.3 \end{vmatrix} - 23.7 \begin{vmatrix} 25.5 & -28.4 \\ -39.2 & 66.3 \end{vmatrix} + 0$$

$$= 83.7(-48.2)(66.3) - 23.7[25.5(66.3) - (-28.4)(-39.2)]$$

$$= -281,000 \text{ (to three significant digits)}$$

Now solving for x gives us

$$x = \frac{\begin{vmatrix} 82.4 & 23.7 & 0 \\ -19.3 & -48.2 & -28.4 \\ -23.9 & 0 & 66.3 \end{vmatrix}}{\Delta}$$

(1)

(2)

(3)

(4)

TI-83/84 screens for Example 29.

Let us develop the first row of the determinant in the numerator by minors. We get

$$82.4 \begin{vmatrix} -48.2 & -28.4 \\ 0 & 66.3 \end{vmatrix} - 23.7 \begin{vmatrix} -19.3 & -28.4 \\ -23.9 & 66.3 \end{vmatrix} + 0$$

$$= 82.4(-48.2)(66.3) - 23.7[(-19.3)(66.3) - (-28.4)(-23.9)]$$

$$= -217,000$$

Dividing by Δ yields

$$x = \frac{-217,000}{-281,000} = 0.772$$

For this system, it is easiest to solve for y and z by substituting back. From Eq.1, we get

$$23.7y = 82.4 - 83.7(0.772) = 17.8$$

$$y = 0.751$$

and from Eq. 2

$$66.3z = -23.9 + 39.2(0.772) = 6.36$$

$$z = 0.0959$$

The solution is then $x = 0.772$, $y = 0.751$, and $z = 0.0959$. ◆◆◆

Systems of More than Three Equations

We can evaluate a determinant of any order by repeated use of the method of minors. Thus any row or column of a fifth-order determinant can be developed, thereby reducing the determinant to five fourth-order determinants. Each of these can then be developed into four third-order determinants, and so on, until only second-order determinants remain.

Obviously this is a lot of work, which can be made easier by first simplifying the determinant by various means. Instead, we will use the calculator to evaluate large determinants, or use the unit matrix method shown earlier.

◆◆◆ CHAPTER 12 REVIEW PROBLEMS ◆◆◆◆◆◆◆◆◆◆◆◆◆◆◆◆◆◆◆◆◆◆◆◆◆◆◆◆◆

Evaluate.

1. $\begin{vmatrix} 6 & \frac{1}{2} & -2 \\ 3 & \frac{1}{4} & 4 \\ 2 & -\frac{1}{2} & 3 \end{vmatrix}$

2. $\begin{vmatrix} 2 & 7 & -2 & 8 \\ 4 & 1 & 1 & -3 \\ 0 & 3 & -1 & 4 \\ 6 & 4 & 2 & -8 \end{vmatrix}$

3. $\begin{vmatrix} 0 & n & m \\ -n & 0 & l \\ -m & -l & 0 \end{vmatrix}$

4. $\begin{vmatrix} 8 & 2 & 0 & 1 & 4 \\ 0 & 1 & 4 & 2 & 7 \\ 2 & 6 & 3 & 8 & 0 \\ 1 & 4 & 2 & 6 & 5 \\ 4 & 6 & 8 & 3 & 5 \end{vmatrix}$

5. $\begin{vmatrix} 25 & 23 & 19 \\ 14 & 11 & 9 \\ 21 & 17 & 14 \end{vmatrix}$

6. $\begin{vmatrix} x + y & x - y \\ x - y & x + y \end{vmatrix}$

7. $\begin{vmatrix} 9 & 13 & 17 \\ 11 & 15 & 19 \\ 17 & 21 & 25 \end{vmatrix}$

8. $\begin{vmatrix} 5 & -3 & -2 & 0 \\ 4 & 1 & -6 & 2 \\ -1 & 4 & 3 & -5 \\ 0 & 6 & -4 & 2 \end{vmatrix}$

9. $\begin{vmatrix} 1 & 2 & 3 \\ 3 & 1 & 2 \\ 2 & 3 & 1 \end{vmatrix}$

10. $\begin{vmatrix} 2 & -3 & 1 \\ -2 & 4 & 5 \\ 3 & -1 & -4 \end{vmatrix}$

11. $\begin{vmatrix} 1 & 2 & 2 & 4 \\ 1 & 4 & 4 & 1 \\ 1 & 1 & 2 & 2 \\ 4 & 8 & 11 & 13 \end{vmatrix}$

12. $\begin{vmatrix} a - b & -2a \\ 2b & a - b \end{vmatrix}$

13. $\begin{vmatrix} 3 & 1 & 5 & 2 \\ 4 & 10 & 14 & 6 \\ 8 & 9 & 1 & 4 \\ 6 & 15 & 21 & 9 \end{vmatrix}$

14. $\begin{vmatrix} 7 & 8 & 9 \\ 28 & 35 & 40 \\ 21 & 26 & 30 \end{vmatrix}$

15. $\begin{vmatrix} 1 & 5 & 2 \\ 4 & 7 & 3 \\ 9 & 8 & 6 \end{vmatrix}$

16. $\begin{vmatrix} 3 & -6 \\ -5 & 4 \end{vmatrix}$

17. $\begin{vmatrix} 6 & 4 & 7 \\ 9 & 0 & 8 \\ 5 & 3 & 2 \end{vmatrix}$

18. $\begin{vmatrix} 3 & 2 & 1 & 3 \\ 4 & 2 & 2 & 4 \\ 2 & 3 & 1 & 6 \\ 10 & 4 & 5 & 8 \end{vmatrix}$

Solve by any method.

19. $\begin{aligned} x + y + z + w &= -4 \\ x + 2y + 3z + 4w &= 0 \\ x + 3y + 6z + 10w &= 9 \\ x + 4y + 10z + 20w &= 24 \end{aligned}$

20. $\begin{aligned} x + 2y + 3z &= 4 \\ 3x + 5y + z &= 18 \\ 4x + y + 2z &= 12 \end{aligned}$

21. $\begin{aligned} 4x + 3y &= 27 \\ 2x - 5y &= -19 \end{aligned}$

22. $\begin{aligned} 8x - 3y - 7z &= 85 \\ x + 6y - 4z &= -12 \\ 2x - 5y + z &= 33 \end{aligned}$

23. $\begin{aligned} x + 2y &= 10 \\ 2x - 3y &= -1 \end{aligned}$

24. $\begin{aligned} x + y + z + u &= 1 \\ 2x + 3y - 4z + 5u &= -31 \\ 3x - 4y + 5z + 6u &= -22 \\ 4x + 5y - 6z - u &= -13 \end{aligned}$

25. $2x - 3y = 7$
    $5x + 2y = 27$

26. $6x + y = 60$
    $3x + 2y = 39$

27. $2x + 5y = 29$
    $2x - 5y = -21$

28. $4x + 3y = 7$
    $2x - 3y = -1$

29. $4x - 5y = 3$
    $3x + 5y = 11$

30. $x + 5y = 41$
    $3x - 2y = 21$

31. $x + 2y = 7$
    $x + y = 5$

32. $8x - 3y = 22$
    $4x + 5y = 18$

33. $3x + 4y = 25$
    $4x + 3y = 21$

34. $37.7x = 59.2 + 24.6y$
    $28.3x - 39.8y - 62.5 = 0$

35. $5.03a = 8.16 + 5.11b$
    $3.63b + 7.26a = 28.8$

36. $541x + 216y + 412z = 866$
    $211x + 483y - 793z = 315$
    $215x + 495y + 378z = 253$

37. $72.3x + 54.2y + 83.3z = 52.5$
    $52.2x - 26.6y + 83.7z = 75.2$
    $33.4x + 61.6y + 30.2z = 58.5$

38. A link in a certain mechanism starts at a speed v_0 and travels 27.5 inches in 8.25 s, at constant acceleration a. Its motion is described by

$$s = v_0 t + \tfrac{1}{2}at^2$$

or

$$27.5 = 8.25v_0 + \tfrac{1}{2}a(8.25)^2$$

In another trial, the link is found to travel 34.6 inches in 11.2 s, with the same initial speed and acceleration. Find v_0 and a.

39. *Writing:* We have had a number of methods for solving a system of equations, both in this chapter and the preceding one. List them, give a one-line description of each, and briefly state the advantages and disadvantages of each.

40. *On our Web site:* Our treatment of matrices here has just scratched the surface. A much fuller treatment is available at our companion Web site at www.wiley.com/college/calter

There you will learn how to

Transpose a matrix
Add and subtract matrices
Multiply a scalar and a matrix
Multiply a vector and a matrix
Multiply two matrices
Multiply a row vector and a matrix
Find the inverse of a matrix
Solve a system of equations by matrix inversion

D

Note: The graphs in this appendix are so tiny that it is difficult to convey highly accurate information with them. Please look at these graphs for general trends only. For larger graphs, please see the SSM and ISM.

Answers to Selected Problems

CHAPTER 12

Exercise 1

1. A, B, D, E, F, I, J, K   **3.** C, H   **5.** I   **7.** B, I   **9.** F   **11.** 6   **13.** 4×3 **15.** 2×4

Exercise 2

1. $(3, 5)$ **3.** $(-3, 3)$ **5.** $(1, 2)$ **7.** $(3, 2)$ **9.** $(15, 6)$ **11.** $(3, 4)$ **13.** $(2, 3)$ **15.** $(1.63, 0.0971)$
17. $m = 2, n = 3$ **19.** $w = 6, z = 1$ **21.** $(-0.462, 2.31)$ **23.** $(5, 6, 7)$ **25.** $(15, 20, 25)$ **27.** $(1, 2, 3)$
29. $(3, 4, 5)$ **31.** $(6, 8, 10)$ **33.** $(-2.30, 4.80, 3.09)$ **35.** $(3, 6, 9)$ **37.** $x = 2, y = 3, z = 4, w = 5$
39. $x = -4, y = -3, z = 2, w = 5$ **41.** $x = a - c, y = b + c, z = 0, w = a - b$
43. $x = 4, y = 5, z = 6, w = 7, u = 8$ **45.** $v = 3, w = 2, x = 4, y = 5, z = 6$ **47.** $t = 53.2$ min; $d = 200$ mi
49. $1.54, -0.377, -1.15$ **51.** $-1.01, 1.69, 2.01, 1.20$ **53.** $1597, 774, 453, 121$

Exercise 3

1. -14 **3.** 15 **5.** -27 **7.** 17.3 **9.** $-2/5$ **11.** $ad - bc$ **13.** $\left(-\dfrac{3}{4}, 3\right)$
15. $(-3, 3)$ **17.** $(1, 2)$ **19.** $(3, 2)$ **21.** $(87/7, 108/7)$ **23.** $(15, 12)$ **25.** $(15, 6)$ **27.** $(3, 4)$
29. $(2, 3)$ **31.** $(-3, 5)$ **33.** $m = 4, n = 3$ **35.** $m = 2, n = 3$ **37.** $w = 6, z = 1$
39. $v = 1.05, w = 2.58$ **41.** $\left(\dfrac{dp - bq}{ad - bc}, \dfrac{aq - cp}{ad - bc}\right)$ **43.** $x = \dfrac{12 - bd}{8 - bc}, y = \dfrac{2d - 3c}{8 - bc}$

Exercise 4

1. 11 **3.** 45 **5.** 48 **7.** -28 **9.** 2 **11.** 18 **13.** -66 **15.** $(5, 6, 7)$ **17.** $(15, 20, 25)$
19. $(1, 2, 3)$ **21.** $(3, 4, 5)$ **23.** $(6, 8, 10)$ **25.** $(-2.30, 4.80, 3.09)$ **27.** $(3, 6, 9)$
29. $x = 2, y = 3, z = 4, w = 5$ **31.** $x = -4, y = -3, z = 2, w = 5$ **33.** $x = a - c, y = b + c, z = 0, w = a - b$
35. $x = 4, y = 5, z = 6, w = 7, u = 8$ **37.** $v = 3, w = 2, x = 4, y = 5, z = 6$
39. $x = -0.927, y = 2.28, z = 1.38, u = -0.385, v = 2.48$

Review Problems

1. 20 **3.** 0 **5.** -3 **7.** 0 **9.** 18 **11.** 15 **13.** 0 **15.** -29 **17.** 133
19. $x = -4, y = -3, z = 2, w = 1$ **21.** $(3, 5)$ **23.** $(4, 3)$ **25.** $(5, 1)$ **27.** $(2, 5)$ **29.** $(2, 1)$
31. $(3, 2)$ **33.** $(9/7, 37/7)$ **35.** $(3.19, 1.55)$ **37.** $(-15.1, 3.52, 11.4)$

Functions Modeling Change:
A Preparation for Calculus

Fourth Edition

Chapter Thirteen

SEQUENCES AND SERIES

Contents

13.1 SEQUENCES

Elections for president of the United States have been held every four years since 1792, that is, in 1792, 1796, 1800, 1804, and so on up to the year 2004. Any ordered list of numbers, such as

$$1792, 1796, 1800, 1804, \ldots, 2004$$

is called a *sequence*, and the individual numbers are the *terms* of the sequence. A sequence can be a finite list, such as the sequence of past presidential election years, or it can be an infinite list, such as the sequence of positive integers

$$1, 2, 3, 4, \ldots.$$

Example 1 (a) $0, 1, 4, 9, 16, 25, \ldots$ is the sequence of squares of integers.
(b) $2, 4, 8, 16, 32, \ldots$ is the sequence of positive integer powers of 2.
(c) $3, 1, 4, 1, 5, 9, \ldots$ is the sequence of digits in the decimal expansion of π.
(d) $3.9, 5.3, 7.2, 9.6, 12.9, 17.1, 23.1, 38.6, 50.2$ is the sequence of U.S. population figures, in millions, for the first 10 census reports (1790 to 1880).
(e) $3.5, 4.2, 5.1, 5.9, 6.7, 8.1, 9.4, 10.6, 10.1, 7.1, 3.8, 2.1, 1.4, 1.1$ is the sequence of pager subscribers in Japan, in millions, from the years 1989 to 2002.

Notation for Sequences

We denote the terms of a sequence by

$$a_1, a_2, a_3, \ldots, a_n, \ldots$$

so that a_1 is the first term, a_2 is the second term, and so on. We use a_n to denote the nth or *general term* of the sequence. If there is a pattern in the sequence, we may be able to find a formula for a_n.

Example 2 Find the first three terms and the 98th term of the sequence.

(a) $a_n = 1 + \sqrt{n}$ 　　　　　　　　　　(b) $b_n = (-1)^n \dfrac{n}{n+1}$

Solution (a) $a_1 = 1 + \sqrt{1}, a_2 = 1 + \sqrt{2} \approx 2.414, a_3 = 1 + \sqrt{3} \approx 2.732$, and $a_{98} = 1 + \sqrt{98} \approx 10.899$.
(b) $b_1 = (-1)^1 \dfrac{1}{1+1} = -\dfrac{1}{2}, b_2 = (-1)^2 \dfrac{2}{2+1} = \dfrac{2}{3}, b_3 = (-1)^3 \dfrac{3}{3+1} = -\dfrac{3}{4}$, and $b_{98} =$
$(-1)^{98} \dfrac{98}{98+1} = \dfrac{98}{99}$. This sequence is called *alternating* because the terms alternate in sign.

A sequence can be thought of as a function whose domain is a set of integers. Each term of the sequence is an output value for the function, so $a_n = f(n)$.

Example 3 List the first 5 terms of the sequence $a_n = f(n)$, where $f(x) = 500 - 10x$.

Solution Evaluate $f(x)$ for $x = 1, 2, 3, 4, 5$:

$$a_1 = f(1) = 500 - 10 \cdot 1 = 490 \quad \text{and} \quad a_2 = f(2) = 500 - 10 \cdot 2 = 480.$$

Similarly, $a_3 = 470, a_4 = 460$, and $a_5 = 450$.

Arithmetic Sequences

You buy a used car that has already been driven 15,000 miles and drive it 8000 miles per year. The odometer registers 23,000 miles 1 year after your purchase, 31,000 miles after 2 years, and so on. The yearly odometer readings form a sequence a_n whose terms are

$$15{,}000, \quad 23{,}000, \quad 31{,}000, \quad 39{,}000, \quad \ldots.$$

Each term of the sequence is obtained from the previous term by adding 8000; that is, the difference between successive terms is 8000. A sequence in which the difference between pairs of successive terms is a fixed quantity is called an *arithmetic sequence*.

Example 4 Which of the following sequences are arithmetic?

(a) $9, 5, 1, -3, -7$ (b) $3, 6, 12, 24, 48$
(c) $2, 2 + p, 2 + 2p, 2 + 3p$ (d) $10, 5, 0, 5, 10$

Solution

(a) Each term is obtained from the previous term by subtracting 4. This sequence is arithmetic.
(b) This sequence is not arithmetic: each terms is twice the previous term. The differences are 3, 6, 12, 24.
(c) This sequence is arithmetic: p is added to each term to obtain the next term.
(d) This is not arithmetic. The difference between the second and first terms is -5, but the difference between the fifth and fourth terms is 5.

We can write a formula for the general term of an arithmetic sequence. Look at the sequence $2, 6, 10, 14, 18, \ldots$ in which the terms increase by 4, and observe that

$$a_1 = 2$$
$$a_2 = 6 = 2 + 1 \cdot 4$$
$$a_3 = 10 = 2 + 2 \cdot 4$$
$$a_4 = 14 = 2 + 3 \cdot 4.$$

When we get to the nth term, we have added $(n-1)$ copies of 4, so that $a_n = 2 + (n-1)4$. In general:

For $n \geq 1$, the nth term of an arithmetic sequence is

$$a_n = a_1 + (n-1)d,$$

where a_1 is the first term, and d is the difference between consecutive terms.

Example 5 (a) Write a formula for the general term of the odometer sequence of the car that is driven 8000 miles per year and had gone 15,000 miles when it was bought.
(b) What is the car's mileage seven years after its purchase?

Solution

(a) The odometer reads 15,000 miles initially, so $a_1 = 15{,}000$. Each year the odometer reading increases by 8000, so $d = 8000$. Thus, $a_n = 15{,}000 + (n-1)8000$.
(b) Seven years from the date of purchase is the start of the 8th year, so $n = 8$. The mileage is

$$a_8 = 15{,}000 + (8-1) \cdot 8000 = 71{,}000.$$

Arithmetic Sequences and Linear Functions

You may have noticed that the arithmetic sequence for the car's odometer reading looks like a linear function. The formula for the nth term, $a_n = 15{,}000 + (n-1)8000$, can be simplified to $a_n = 7000 + 8000n$, a linear function with slope $m = 8000$ and initial value $b = 7000$. However, for a sequence we consider only positive integer inputs, whereas a linear function is defined for all values of n. We can think of an arithmetic sequence as a linear function whose domain has been restricted to the positive integers.

Geometric Sequences

You are offered a job at a salary of \$40,000 for the first year with a 5% pay raise every year. Under this plan, your annual salaries form a sequence with terms

$$a_1 = 40{,}000$$
$$a_2 = 40{,}000(1.05) = 42{,}000$$
$$a_3 = 42{,}000(1.05) = 40{,}000(1.05)^2 = 44{,}100$$
$$a_4 = 44{,}100(1.05) = 40{,}000(1.05)^3 = 46{,}305,$$

and so on, where each term is obtained from the previous one by multiplying by 1.05. A sequence in which each term is a constant multiple of the preceding term is called a *geometric sequence*. In a geometric sequence, the ratio of successive terms is constant.

Example 6 Which of the following sequences are geometric?

(a) $5, 25, 125, 625, \ldots$ (b) $-8, 4, -2, 1, -\frac{1}{2}, \ldots$ (c) $12, 6, 4, 3, \ldots$

Solution (a) This sequence is geometric. Each term is 5 times the previous term. Note that the ratio of any term to its predecessor is 5.

(b) This sequence is geometric. The ratio of any term to the previous term is $-\frac{1}{2}$.

(c) This sequence is not geometric. The ratios of successive terms are not constant: $\dfrac{a_2}{a_1} = \dfrac{6}{12} = \dfrac{1}{2}$, but $\dfrac{a_3}{a_2} = \dfrac{4}{6} = \dfrac{2}{3}$.

As for arithmetic sequences, there is a formula for the general term of a geometric sequence. Consider the sequence $8, 2, \frac{1}{2}, \frac{1}{8}, \ldots$ in which each term is $\frac{1}{4}$ times the previous term. We have

$$a_1 = 8$$
$$a_2 = 2 = 8\left(\frac{1}{4}\right)$$
$$a_3 = \frac{1}{2} = 8\left(\frac{1}{4}\right)^2$$
$$a_4 = \frac{1}{8} = 8\left(\frac{1}{4}\right)^3.$$

When we get to the nth term, we have multiplied 8 by $(n-1)$ factors of $\frac{1}{4}$, so that $a_n = 8\left(\frac{1}{4}\right)^{n-1}$. In general,

For $n \geq 1$, the nth term of a geometric sequence is

$$a_n = a_1 r^{n-1},$$

where a_1 is the first term, and r is the ratio of consecutive terms.

Example 7   (a) Write a formula for the general term of the salary sequence that starts at \$40,000 and increases by 5% each year.
(b) What is your salary after 10 years on the job?

Solution   (a) Your starting salary is \$40,000, so $a_1 = 40{,}000$. Each year your salary increases by 5%, so $r = 1.05$. Thus, $a_n = 40{,}000(1.05)^{n-1}$.
(b) After 10 years on the job, you are at the start of your 11th year, so $n = 11$. Your salary is

$$a_{11} = 40{,}000(1.05)^{11-1} \approx 65{,}156 \text{ dollars.}$$

Geometric Sequences and Exponential Functions

The formula for the salary sequence, $a_n = 40{,}000(1.05)^{n-1}$, looks like a formula for an exponential function, $f(t) = a \cdot b^t$. A geometric sequence is an exponential function whose domain is restricted to the positive integers. For many applications, this restricted domain is more realistic than an interval of real numbers. For example, salaries are usually increased once a year, rather than continuously.

Exercises and Problems for Section 13.1

Exercises

Are the sequences in Exercises 1–4 arithmetic?

1. $2, 7, 11, 14, \ldots$

2. $2, -5, -12, -19, \ldots$

3. $2, 7, 12, 17, \ldots$

4. $2, -5, -11, -16, \ldots$

Are the sequences in Exercises 5–7 arithmetic? For those that are, give a formula for the nth term.

5. $6, 9, 12, 15, \ldots$

6. $1, -1, 2, -2, \ldots$

7. $-1, -1.1, -1.2, -1.3, \ldots$

Are the sequences in Exercises 8–11 geometric?

8. $2, 6, 18, 54, \ldots$

9. $2, 4, 8, 12, \ldots$

10. $2, -1, \frac{1}{2}, -\frac{1}{4}, \frac{1}{8}, \ldots$

11. $2, 0.2, 0.02, 0.002, \ldots$

Are the sequences in Exercises 12–17 geometric? For those that are, give a formula for the nth term.

12. $4, 12, 36, 108, \ldots$

13. $4, 1, \frac{1}{4}, \frac{1}{8}, \ldots$

14. $2, -4, 8, -16, \ldots$

15. $4, 2, 1, \frac{1}{2}, \frac{1}{4}, \ldots$

16. $4, 0.4, 0.04, 0.004, \ldots$

17. $1, \dfrac{1}{1.2}, \dfrac{1}{(1.2)^2}, \dfrac{1}{(1.2)^3}, \ldots$

Problems

In Problems 18–23, write out the first four terms of each sequence and state if it is geometric.

18. $a_n = 2^n$

19. $a_n = \frac{2n+1}{n+2}$

20. $a_n = \left(-\frac{1}{3}\right)^n$

21. $a_n = \cos(n\pi)$

22. $a_n = n^2 - n$

23. $a_n = \frac{1}{\sqrt{n}}$

24. An arithmetic sequence has first term of 10 and difference of 5; what is the tenth term?

25. An arithmetic sequence has first term of 5 and difference of 10. After how many terms will the sequence exceed 1000?

In Problems 26–29, find the 5th, 50th, n^{th} term of the arithmetic sequences.

26. $3, 5, 7, \ldots$

27. $6, 7.2, \ldots$

28. $a_1 = 2.1, a_3 = 4.7$

29. $a_3 = 5.7, a_6 = 9$

In Problems 30–33, find the 6th and n^{th} of the geometric sequences.

30. $1, 2, 4, \ldots$

31. $7, 5.25, \ldots$

32. $a_1 = 3, a_3 = 48$

33. $a_2 = 6, a_4 = 54$

34. During 2004, about 81 million barrels of oil a day were consumed worldwide.[1] Over the previous decade, consumption had been rising at 1.2% a year; assume that it continues to increase at this rate.

(a) Write the first four terms of the sequence a_n giving daily oil consumption n years after 2003; give a formula for the general term a_n.

(b) In what year is consumption expected to exceed 100 million barrels a day?

35. In 2004, US natural gas consumption was 646.7 billion cubic meters. Asian consumption was 367.7 billion cubic meters.[2] During the previous decade, US consumption increased by 0.6% a year, while Asian consumption grew by 7.9% a year. Assume these rates continue into the future.

(a) Give the first four terms of the sequence, a_n, giving US consumption of natural gas n years after 2003.

(b) Give the first four terms of a similar sequence b_n showing Asian gas consumption.

(c) According to this model, when will Asian yearly gas consumption exceed US consumption?

36. The population[3] of Nevada grew from 2.2 million in 2002 to 2.4 million in 2005. Assuming a constant percent growth rate:

(a) Find a formula for a_n, the population in millions n years after 2005.

(b) When is the population predicted to reach 10 million?

37. Florida's population[4] was 17.960 million in 2005 and 17.613 million in 2004. Assuming the population continues to increase at the same percentage rate:

(a) Find the first three terms of the sequence a_n giving the population, in millions, n years after 2005.

(b) Write a formula for a_n.

(c) What is the doubling time of the population?

The graphs in Problems 38–41 represent either an arithmetic or a geometric sequence; decide which. For an arithmetic sequence, say if the common difference, d, is positive or negative. For a geometric sequence, say if the common ratio, r, is greater or smaller than 1.

38.

39.

40.

41.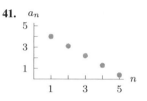

A sequence a_n can be defined by a *recurrence relation*, which gives a_n in terms of the previous term, a_{n-1}, and the first term a_1. In Problems 42–45, find the first four terms of the sequence and a formula for the general term.

42. $a_n = 2a_{n-1}; a_1 = 3$

43. $a_n = a_{n-1} + 5; a_1 = 2$

44. $a_n = -a_{n-1}; a_1 = 1$

45. $a_n = 2a_{n-1} + 1; a_1 = 3$

46. A geometric sequence has first term of 10 and ratio of -0.2. After how many terms will the sequence have absolute value less than 10^{-7}?

47. The sequence defined by

$$p_{n+1} = 2p_n - \frac{p_n^2}{200}, \quad p_0 = 150,$$

is called a discrete logistic equation. Such a sequence is often used to model a population p_n, where the initial population is p_0.

(a) Compute the first 6 terms of the sequence. What do you conclude?

(b) Show that if $0 < p_0 < 200$, then p_n increases but never exceeds 200.

---

[1] www.bp.com/downloads, Statistical Review of World Energy 2005, accessed January 15, 2006.
[2] www.bp.com/downloads, Statistical Review of World Energy 2005, accessed January 15, 2006.
[3] health2k.state.nv.us and www.city-data.com, accessed December 26, 2005.
[4] www.floridacharts.com, accessed December 26, 2005.

48. The Fibonacci sequence starts with $1, 1, 2, 3, 5, \ldots$, and each term is the sum of the previous two terms.

   (a) Write the next three terms in the sequence.

   (b) Write an expression for a_n in terms of a_{n-1} and a_{n-2}.

   (c) Suppose r_n is the ratio a_n/a_{n-1} and r_{n-1} is the ratio a_{n-1}/a_{n-2}. Using your answer to part (b), find a formula for r_n in terms of r_{n-1} and without any of the as.

   (d) The terms r_n form another sequence. Suppose r_n tends to a fixed value, r as n increases without bound; that is, $r_n \to r$ as $n \to \infty$. Use your answer to part (c) to find an equation for r. Solve this equation. The number that you find is called the *golden ratio*.

49. Some people believe they can make money from a chain letter (they are usually disappointed). A chain letter works roughly like this: A letter arrives with a list of four names attached and instructions to mail a copy to four more friends and to send \$1 to the top name on the list. When you mail the four letters, you remove the top name (to whom the money was sent) and add your own name to the bottom of the list.

   (a) If no one breaks the chain, how much money do you receive?

   (b) Let d_n be the number of dollars you receive if there are n names on the list instead of 4, but you still mailed to four friends. Find a formula for d_n.

50. For a positive integer n, let a_n be the fraction of the US population with income less than or equal to \$$n$ thousand dollars.

   (a) Which is larger, a_{40} or a_{50}? Why?

   (b) What does the quantity $a_{50} - a_{40}$ represent in terms of US population?

   (c) Is there any value of n with $a_n = 0$? Explain.

   (d) What happens to the value of a_n as n increases?

13.2 DEFINING FUNCTIONS USING SUMS: ARITHMETIC SERIES

Domestic Deaths from AIDS n years after 1980

Table 13.1 shows the number of US AIDS deaths[5] that occurred each year since 1980, where a_n is the number of deaths in year n, and $n = 1$ corresponds to 1981. For each year, we can calculate the total number of death from AIDS since 1980. For example, in 1985

$$\text{Total number of AIDS deaths (1981-1985)} = 159 + 463 + 1508 + 3505 + 6972 = 12{,}607.$$

We write S_n to denote the sum of the first n terms of a sequence. In this example, 1985 corresponds to $n = 5$, so we have $S_5 = 12{,}607$.

Table 13.1   *US deaths from AIDS each year from 1981 to 2003*

n	a_n	n	a_n	n	a_n	n	a_n	n	a_n
1	159	6	12,110	11	36,616	16	38,025	21	18,524
2	463	7	16,412	12	41,094	17	21,999	22	17,557
3	1508	8	21,119	13	45,598	18	18,397	23	18,017
4	3505	9	27,791	14	50,418	19	17,172		
5	6972	10	31,538	15	51,117	20	15,245		

Example 1   Find and interpret S_8 for the AIDS sequence.

[5] www.cdc.gov/hiv/stats/hasr1301/table28.htm, from the HIV/AIDS Surveillance Report, 2001, Vol 13, No. 1, p. 34, US Department of Health and Human Services, Centers for Disease Control and Prevention, Atlanta, and www.cdc.gove/hiv/PUBS/Facts/At-A-Glance.htm, accessed January 14, 2006.

Solution   Since S_8 is the sum of the first 8 terms of the sequence, we have.

$$S_8 = \underbrace{a_1 + a_2 + a_3 + a_4 + a_5}_{S_5 = 12{,}607} + a_6 + a_7 + a_8$$
$$= 12{,}607 + 12{,}110 + 16{,}412 + 21{,}119$$
$$= 62{,}248.$$

Here, S_8 is the number of deaths from AIDS from 1980 to 1988.

The sum of the terms of a sequence is called a *series*. We write S_n for the sum of the first n terms of the sequence, called the nth *partial sum*. We see that S_n is a function of n, the number of terms in the partial sum. In this section we see how to evaluate functions defined by sums.

Arithmetic Series

Landscape timbers are large beams of wood used to landscape gardens. To make the terrace in Figure 13.1, one timber is set into the slope, followed by a stack of two, then a stack of three, then a stack of four. The stacks are separated by earth.

The total number of timbers in 4 stacks is S_4, the sum of the number of timbers in each stack:

$$\text{Total number of timbers} = S_4 = 1 + 2 + 3 + 4 = 10.$$

For a larger terrace using 5 stacks of timbers, the total number is given by

$$S_5 = 1 + 2 + 3 + 4 + 5 = 15.$$

For an even larger terrace using 6 stacks, the total number is given by

$$S_6 = 1 + 2 + 3 + 4 + 5 + 6 = 21.$$

For a terrace made from n stacks of landscape timbers, S_n, the total number of timbers needed is a function of n, so

$$S_n = f(n) = 1 + 2 + \cdots + n.$$

The symbol $\cdots$ means that all the integers from 1 to n are included in the sum.

Notice that each stack of landscape timbers contains one more timber than the previous one. Thus, the number of timbers in each stack,

$$1, 2, 3, 4, 5, \ldots$$

is an arithmetic sequence, so S_n is the sum of the terms of an arithmetic sequence. Such a sum is called an *arithmetic series*.

Figure 13.1: A slope terraced for planting using landscape timbers

The Sum of an Arithmetic Series

We now find a formula for the sum of an arithmetic series.[6] A famous story concerning this series[6] is told about the great mathematician Carl Friedrich Gauss (1777–1855), who as a young boy was asked by his teacher to add the numbers from 1 to 100. He did so almost immediately:

$$S_{100} = 1 + 2 + 3 + \cdots + 100 = 5050.$$

Of course, no one really knows how Gauss accomplished this, but he probably did not perform the calculation directly, by adding 100 terms. He might have noticed that the terms in the sum can be regrouped into pairs, as follows:

$$S_{100} = 1 + 2 + \cdots + 99 + 100 = \underbrace{(1 + 100) + (2 + 99) + \cdots + (50 + 51)}_{50 \text{ pairs}}$$

$$= \underbrace{101 + 101 + \cdots + 101}_{50 \text{ terms}} \qquad \text{Each pair adds to 101}$$

$$= 50 \cdot 101 = 5050.$$

The approach of pairing numbers works for the sum from 1 to n, no matter how large n is. Provided n is an even number, we can write

$$S_n = 1 + 2 + \cdots + (n - 1) + n = \underbrace{(1 + n) + (2 + (n - 1)) + (3 + (n - 2)) + \cdots}_{\frac{1}{2}n \text{ pairs}}$$

$$= \underbrace{(1 + n) + (1 + n) + \cdots}_{\frac{1}{2}n \text{ pairs}} \qquad \text{Each pair adds to } 1 + n$$

so we have the formula:

$$S_n = 1 + 2 + \cdots + n = \frac{1}{2}n(n + 1).$$

Example 2   Check this formula for S_n with $n = 100$.

Solution   Using the formula, we get the same answer, 5050, as before:

$$S_{100} = 1 + 2 + \cdots + 100 = \frac{1}{2} \cdot 100(100 + 1) = 50 \cdot 101 = 5050.$$

A similar derivation shows that this formula for S_n also holds for odd values of n.

To find a formula for the sum of a general arithmetic series, we first assume that n is even and write

$$S_n = a_1 + a_2 + \cdots + a_n$$

$$= \underbrace{(a_1 + a_n) + (a_2 + a_{n-1}) + (a_3 + a_{n-2}) + \cdots}_{\frac{1}{2}n \text{ pairs}}.$$

---

[6] As told by E.T. Bell, *The Men of Mathematics*, p. 221 (New York: Simon and Schuster, 1937), the series involved was arithmetic, but more complicated than this one.

We pair the first term with the last term, the second term with the next to last term, and so on, just as Gauss may have done. Each pair of terms adds up to the same value, just as each of Gauss's pairs added to 101. Using the formula for the terms of an arithmetic sequence, $a_n = a_1 + (n-1)d$, the first pair, $a_1 + a_n$, can be written as

$$a_1 + a_n = a_1 + \underbrace{a_1 + (n-1)d}_{a_n} = 2a_1 + (n-1)d,$$

and the second pair, $a_2 + a_{n-1}$, can be written as

$$a_2 + a_{n-1} = \underbrace{a_1 + d}_{a_2} + \underbrace{a_1 + (n-2)d}_{a_{n-1}} = 2a_1 + (n-1)d.$$

Both the first two pairs have the same sum: $2a_1 + (n-1)d$. The remaining pairs also all have the same sum, so

$$S_n = \underbrace{(a_1 + a_n) + (a_2 + a_{n-1}) + (a_3 + a_{n-2}) + \cdots}_{\frac{1}{2}n \text{ pairs}} = \frac{1}{2}n\left(2a_1 + (n-1)d\right).$$

The same formula gives the sum of the series when n is odd. See Problem 45 on page 548.

The **sum**, S_n, of the first n terms of the **arithmetic series** with $a_n = a_1 + (n-1)d$ is

$$S_n = \frac{1}{2}n(a_1 + a_n) = \frac{1}{2}n(2a_1 + (n-1)d).$$

Example 3 Calculate the sum $1 + 2 + \cdots + 100$ using the formula for S_n.

Solution Here, $a_1 = 1$, $n = 100$, and $d = 1$. We get the same answer as before:

$$S_{100} = \frac{1}{2}n\left(2a_1 + (n-1)d\right) = \frac{1}{2} \cdot 100\left(2 \cdot 1 + (100-1) \cdot 1\right) = 50 \cdot 101 = 5050.$$

Summation Notation

The symbol Σ is used to indicate addition. This symbol, pronounced *sigma*, is the Greek capital letter for S, which stands for sum. Using this notation, we write

$$\sum_{i=1}^{n} a_i \quad \text{to stand for the sum } a_1 + a_2 + \cdots + a_n.$$

The Σ tells us we are adding some numbers. The a_i tells us that the numbers we are adding are called a_1, a_2, and so on. The sum begins with a_1 and ends with a_n because the subscript i starts at

$i = 1$ (at the bottom of the Σ sign) and ends at $i = n$ (at the top of the Σ sign):

This tells us that the sum
ends at a_n
↓

$$\sum_{i=1}^{n} a_i \longleftarrow \text{This tells us that the numbers we are adding are called } a_1, a_2, a_3, \ldots$$

↑
This tells us that the sum
starts at a_1

Example 4 Write $S_n = f(n)$, the total number of landscape timbers in n stacks, using sigma notation, and give a formula for S_n.

Solution Since $S_n = f(n) = 1 + 2 + \cdots + n$, we have $a_i = i$. We start at $i = 1$ and end at $i = n$. Thus, $S_n = \sum_{i=1}^{n} i$. The formula for the sum of an arithmetic series with $a_1 = d = 1$ gives

$$S_n = f(n) = \sum_{i=1}^{n} i = \frac{1}{2}n(n+1).$$

Example 5 Use sigma notation to write the sum of the first 20 positive odd numbers. Evaluate this sum.

Solution The odd numbers form an arithmetic sequence: 1, 3, 5, 7, ... with $a_1 = 1$ and $d = 2$. The ith odd number is

$$a_i = 1 + (i-1)2 = 2i - 1.$$

(As a check: $a_1 = 1 + (1-1)2 = 1$ and $a_2 = 1 + (2-1)2 = 3$.) Thus, we have

$$\text{Sum of the first 20 odd numbers} = \sum_{i=1}^{20} a_i = \sum_{i=1}^{20} (2i - 1).$$

We evaluate the sum using $n = 20$, $a_1 = 1$, and $d = 2$:

$$\text{Sum} = \frac{1}{2}n\left(2a_1 + (n-1)d\right) = \frac{1}{2} \cdot 20\left(2 \cdot 1 + (20-1) \cdot 2\right) = 400.$$

Example 6 If air resistance is neglected, a falling object travels 16 ft during the first second, 48 ft during the next, 80 ft during the next, and so on. These distances form the arithmetic sequence 16, 48, 80, ... In this sequence, $a_1 = 16$ and $d = 32$.

(a) Find a formula for the nth term in the sequence of distances. Calculate the fifth and tenth terms.
(b) Calculate S_1, S_2, and S_3, the total distance an object falls in 1, 2, and 3 seconds, respectively.
(c) Give a formula for S_n, the distance fallen in n seconds.

Solution   (a) The nth term is $a_n = a_1 + (n-1)d = 16 + 32(n-1) = 32n - 16$. Thus, the fifth term is $a_5 = 32(5) - 16 = 144$. The value of $a_{10} = 32(10) - 16 = 304$.

         (b) Since $a_1 = 16$ and $d = 32$,

$$S_1 = a_1 = 16 \text{ feet}$$
$$S_2 = a_1 + a_2 = a_1 + (a_1 + d) = 16 + 48 = 64 \text{ feet}$$
$$S_3 = a_1 + a_2 + a_3 = 16 + 48 + 80 = 144 \text{ feet}.$$

         (c) The formula for S_n is $S_n = \dfrac{1}{2}n\left(2a_1 + (n-1)d\right)$. We can check our answer to part (b) using this formula:

$$S_1 = \frac{1}{2}\cdot 1(2\cdot 16 + 0\cdot 32) = 16, \quad S_2 = \frac{1}{2}\cdot 2(2\cdot 16 + 1\cdot 32) = 64, \quad S_3 = \frac{1}{2}\cdot 3(2\cdot 16 + 2\cdot 32) = 144.$$

Example 7   An object falls from 1000 feet starting at time $t = 0$ seconds. What is its height, h, in feet above the ground at $t = 1, 2, 3$ seconds? Show these values on a graph of height against time.

Solution   At time $t = 0$, the height $h = 1000$ feet. At time $t = 1$, the object has fallen $S_1 = 16$ feet, so

$$h = 1000 - 16 = 984 \text{ feet}.$$

At time $t = 2$, the object has fallen a total distance of $S_2 = 64$ feet, so

$$h = 1000 - 64 = 936 \text{ feet}.$$

At time $t = 3$, the object has fallen a total distance of $S_3 = 144$ feet, so

$$h = 1000 - 144 = 856 \text{ feet}.$$

These heights are marked on the graph in Figure 13.2.

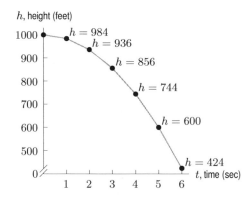

Figure 13.2: Height of a falling object

Exercises and Problems for Section 13.2

Exercises

Are the series in Exercises 1–4 arithmetic?

1. $2 + 4 + 8 + 16 + \cdots$

2. $10 + 8 + 6 + 4 + 2 + \cdots$

3. $1 + 2 + 4 + 5 + 7 + 8 + \cdots$

4. $-\dfrac{1}{3} + \dfrac{2}{3} + \dfrac{5}{3} + \dfrac{8}{3} + \cdots$

Expand the sums in Exercises 5–10. (Do not evaluate.)

5. $\displaystyle\sum_{i=-1}^{5} i^2$

6. $\displaystyle\sum_{i=10}^{20} (i+1)^2$

7. $\displaystyle\sum_{k=0}^{5} 2k + 1$

8. $\displaystyle\sum_{j=1}^{6} 3(j-3)$

9. $\displaystyle\sum_{j=2}^{10} (-1)^j$

10. $\displaystyle\sum_{n=1}^{7} (-1)^{n-1} 2^n$

In Exercises 11–14, write the sum using sigma notation.

11. $3 + 6 + 9 + 12 + 15 + 18 + 21$

12. $10 + 13 + 16 + 19 + 22$

13. $1/2 + 1 + 3/2 + 2 + 5/2 + 3 + 7/2 + 4$

14. $30 + 25 + 20 + 15 + 10 + 5$

15. (a) Use sigma notation to write the sum $2 + 4 + 6 + \cdots + 20$ of the first 10 even numbers.
  (b) Without a calculator, find the sum in part (a).

In Exercises 16–20, complete the tables with the terms of the arithmetic series $a_1, a_2, \ldots, a_n$, and the sequence of partial sums, $S_1, S_2, \ldots, S_n$. State the values of a_1 and d where $a_n = a_1 + (n-1)d$.

16.

n	1	2	3	4	5	6	7	8
a_n	2	7	12	17				
S_n	2	9	21	38				

17.

n	1	2	3	4	5	6	7	8
a_n	3	7	11					
S_n	3	10						

18.

n	1	2	3	4	5	6	7	8
a_n	7			16				
S_n								

19.

n	1	2	3	4	5	6	7	8
a_n	2							
S_n	2	13	33	62				

20.

n	1	2	3	4	5	6	7	8
a_n								
S_n						201	273	356

21. Find the sum of the first 1000 integers: $1 + 2 + 3 + \cdots + 1000$.

Without using a calculator, find the sum of the series in Problems 22–29.

22. $\displaystyle\sum_{i=1}^{50} 3i$

23. $\displaystyle\sum_{i=1}^{30} (5i + 10)$

24. $\displaystyle\sum_{n=0}^{15} \left(2 + \frac{1}{2}n\right)$

25. $\displaystyle\sum_{n=0}^{10} (8 - 4n)$

26. $\sqrt{2} + 2\sqrt{2} + 3\sqrt{2} + \cdots + 25\sqrt{2}$

27. $-101 - 91 - 81 - 71 - 61 - \cdots - 11 - 1$

28. $26.5 + 24.5 + 22.5 + \cdots + 2.5 + 0.5$

29. $-3.01 - 3.02 - 3.03 - \cdots - 3.35$

Problems

30. Jenny decides to raise money for her local charity by encouraging people to lay quarters on the floor of a classroom in the shape of an equilateral triangle. She puts one quarter in the first row, two in the second, three in the third, and so on. Her target is to raise $400. How many rows does she need?

31. Find the thirtieth positive multiple of 5 and the sum of the first thirty positive multiples of 5.

32. For the AIDS data in Table 13.1 on page 541,

    (a) Find and interpret in terms of AIDS

        (i) The partial sums S_5, S_6, S_7, S_8.

        (ii) $S_6 - S_5, S_7 - S_6, S_8 - S_7$.

    (b) Use your answer to part (a) (ii) to explain the value of $S_{n+1} - S_n$ for any positive integer n.

33. Table 13.2 shows US Census figures, in millions. Interpret these figures as partial sums, S_n of a sequence, a_n, where n is the number of decades since 1940, so $S_1 = 150.7$, $S_2 = 179.3$, $S_3 = 203.3$, and so on.

    (a) Find and interpret in terms of population

        (i) S_4, S_5, S_6

        (ii) a_2, a_5, a_6

        (iii) $a_6/10$

    (b) For any positive integer n, what are the meanings of S_n, a_n, and $a_n/10$ in terms of population?

Table 13.2

Year	1950	1960	1970	1980	1990	2000
Population	150.7	179.3	203.3	226.6	248.7	281.4

Simplify the expressions in Problems 34–37.

34. $\displaystyle\sum_{i=1}^{5} i^2 - \sum_{j=0}^{4} (j+1)^2$ **35.** $\displaystyle\sum_{i=4}^{20} i - \sum_{j=4}^{20} (-2j)$

36. $\displaystyle\sum_{i=1}^{20} 1$ **37.** $\displaystyle\sum_{i=1}^{15} i^3 - \sum_{j=3}^{15} j^3$

Problems 38–41 refer to the falling object of Example 6 on page 545.

38. Calculate the distance, S_7, the object falls in 7 seconds.

39. **(a)** Find the total distance that the object falls in 4, 5, 6 seconds.

    (b) The object falls from 1000 feet at time $t = 0$. Calculate its height at $t = 4$, $t = 5$, $t = 6$ seconds. Explain how you can check your answer using Figure 13.2.

40. Find a formula for $f(n)$, the distance fallen by the object in n seconds.

41. If the object falls from 1000 feet, how long does it take to hit the ground?

42. A boy is dividing M&Ms between himself and his sister. He gives one to his sister and takes one for himself. He gives another to his sister and takes two for himself. He

gives a third one to his sister and takes three for himself, and so on.

    (a) On the nth round, how many M&Ms does the boy give his sister? How many does he take himself?

    (b) After n rounds, how many M&Ms does his sister have? How many does the boy have?

43. An auditorium has 30 seats in the first row, 34 seats in the second row, 38 seats in the third row, and so on. If there are twenty rows in the auditorium, how many seats are there in the last row? How many seats are there in the auditorium?

44. **(a)** Show that $n^3 - (n-1)^3 = 3n^2 - 3n + 1$.

    (b) Write $n^3 = n^3 - (n-1)^3 + (n-1)^3 - (n-2)^3 + (n-2)^3 - \ldots - 2^3 + 2^3 - 1^3 + 1^3 - 0^3$ and then show

$$n^3 = \sum_{j=1}^{j=n} (3j^2 - 3j + 1).$$

    (c) Use the result $\sum_{j=1}^{j=n} j = \frac{1}{2}n(n+1)$ to show that

$$\sum_{j=1}^{j=n} j^2 = \frac{n}{6}(n+1)(2n+1).$$

45. In the text we showed how to calculate the sum of an arithmetic series with an even number of terms. Consider the arithmetic series

$$5 + 12 + 19 + 26 + 33 + 40 + 47 + 54 + 61.$$

Here, there are $n = 9$ terms, and the difference between each term is $d = 7$. Adding these terms directly, we find that their sum is 297. In this problem we find the sum of this arithmetic sequence in two different ways. We then use our results to obtain a general formula for the sum of an arithmetic series with an odd number of terms.

    (a) The sum of the first and last terms is $5 + 61 = 66$, the sum of the second and next-to-last terms is $12 + 54 = 66$, and so on. Find the sum of this arithmetic series by pairing off terms in this way. Notice that since the number of terms is odd, one of them will be unpaired.

    (b) This arithmetic series can be thought of as a series of eight terms $(5 + \cdots + 54)$ plus an additional term (61). Use the formula we found for the sum of an arithmetic series containing an even number of terms to find the sum of the given arithmetic series.

    (c) Find a formula for the sum of an arithmetic series with n terms where n is odd. Let a_1 be the first term in the series, and let d be the difference between consecutive terms. Show that the two approaches used in parts (a) and (b) give the same result, and show that your formula is the same as the formula given for even values of n.

13.3 FINITE GEOMETRIC SERIES

In the previous section, we studied *arithmetic series*. An arithmetic series is the sum of terms in a sequence in which each term is obtained by adding a constant to the preceding term. In this section, we study another type of sum, a *geometric series*. In a geometric series, each term is a constant multiple of the preceding term.

Bank Balance

A person deposits \$2000 every year in an IRA that pays 6% interest per year, compounded annually. After the first deposit (but before any interest has been earned), the balance in the account in dollars is

$$B_1 = 2000.$$

After 1 year has passed, the first deposit has earned interest, so the balance becomes $2000(1.06)$ dollars. Then the second deposit is made and the balance becomes

$$B_2 = \underbrace{2^{\text{nd}} \text{ deposit}}_{2000} + \underbrace{1^{\text{st}} \text{ deposit with interest}}_{2000(1.06)}$$
$$= 2000 + 2000(1.06) \text{ dollars.}$$

After 2 years have passed, the third deposit is made, and the balance is

$$B_3 = \underbrace{3^{\text{rd}} \text{ deposit}}_{2000} + \underbrace{2^{\text{nd}} \text{ dep. with 1 year interest}}_{2000(1.06)} + \underbrace{1^{\text{st}} \text{ deposit with 2 years interest}}_{2000(1.06)^2}$$
$$= 2000 + 2000(1.06) + 2000(1.06)^2.$$

Let B_n be the balance in dollars after n deposits. Then we see that

After 4 deposits $\quad B_4 = 2000 + 2000(1.06) + 2000(1.06)^2 + 2000(1.06)^3$

After 5 deposits $\quad B_5 = 2000 + 2000(1.06) + 2000(1.06)^2 + 2000(1.06)^3 + 2000(1.06)^4$

$$\vdots$$

After n deposits $\quad B_n = 2000 + 2000(1.06) + 2000(1.06)^2 + \cdots + 2000(1.06)^{n-1}.$

Example 1 How much money is in this IRA in 5 years, right after a deposit is made? In 25 years, right after a deposit is made?

Solution After 5 years, we have made 6 deposits. A calculator gives

$$B_6 = 2000 + 2000(1.06) + 2000(1.06)^2 + \cdots + 2000(1.06)^5$$
$$= \$13{,}950.64.$$

In 25 years, we have made 26 deposits. Even using a calculator, it would be tedious to evaluate B_{26} by adding 26 terms. Fortunately, there is a shortcut. Start with the formula for B_{26}:

$$B_{26} = 2000 + 2000(1.06) + 2000(1.06)^2 + \cdots + 2000(1.06)^{25}.$$

Multiply both sides of this equation by 1.06 and add 2000, giving

$$1.06B_{26} + 2000 = 1.06\left(2000 + 2000(1.06) + 2000(1.06)^2 + \cdots + 2000(1.06)^{25}\right) + 2000.$$

We simplify the right-hand side to get

$$1.06B_{26} + 2000 = 2000(1.06) + 2000(1.06)^2 + \cdots + 2000(1.06)^{25} + 2000(1.06)^{26} + 2000.$$

Notice that the right-hand side of this equation and the formula for B_{26} have almost every term in common. We can rewrite this equation as

$$1.06B_{26} + 2000 = \underbrace{2000 + 2000(1.06) + 2000(1.06)^2 + \cdots + 2000(1.06)^{25}}_{B_{26}} + 2000(1.06)^{26}$$

$$= B_{26} + 2000(1.06)^{26}.$$

Solving for B_{26} gives

$$1.06B_{26} - B_{26} = 2000(1.06)^{26} - 2000$$
$$0.06B_{26} = 2000(1.06)^{26} - 2000$$
$$B_{26} = \frac{2000(1.06)^{26} - 2000}{0.06}.$$

Using a calculator to evaluate this expression for B_{26}, we find that $B_{26} = 118{,}312.77$ dollars.

Geometric Series

The formula for the IRA balance,

$$B_{26} = 2000 + 2000(1.06) + 2000(1.06)^2 + \cdots + 2000(1.06)^{25},$$

is an example of a *geometric series*. This is a finite geometric series, because there are a finite number of terms (in this case, 26). In general, a geometric series is the sum of the terms of a geometric sequence—that is, in which each term is a constant multiple of the preceding term.

A **finite geometric series** is a sum of the form

$$S_n = a + ar + ar^2 + \cdots + ar^{n-1} = \sum_{i=0}^{n-1} ar^i.$$

Notice that S_n is defined to contain exactly n terms. Since the first term is $a = ar^0$, we stop at ar^{n-1}. For instance, the series

$$50 + 50(1.06) + 50(1.06)^2 + \cdots + 50(1.06)^{25}$$

contains 26 terms, so $n = 26$. For this series, $r = 1.06$ and $a = 50$.

The Sum of a Geometric Series

The shortcut from Example 1 can be used to find the sum of a general geometric series. Let S_n be the sum of a geometric series of n terms, so that

$$S_n = a + ar + ar^2 + \cdots + ar^{n-1}.$$

Multiply both sides of this equation by r and add a, giving

$$rS_n + a = r\left(a + ar + ar^2 + \cdots + ar^{n-1}\right) + a$$
$$= \left(ar + ar^2 + ar^3 + \cdots + ar^{n-1} + ar^n\right) + a.$$

The right-hand side can be rewritten as

$$rS_n + a = \underbrace{a + ar + ar^2 + \cdots + ar^{n-1}}_{S_n} + ar^n$$
$$= S_n + ar^n.$$

Solving the equation $rS_n + a = S_n + ar^n$ for S_n gives

$$rS_n - S_n = ar^n - a$$
$$S_n(r - 1) = ar^n - a \qquad \text{factoring out } S_n$$
$$S_n = \frac{ar^n - a}{r - 1}$$
$$= \frac{a(r^n - 1)}{r - 1}.$$

By multiplying the numerator and denominator by -1, this formula can be rewritten as follows:

The sum of a finite **geometric series of n terms** is given by

$$S_n = a + ar + ar^2 + \cdots + ar^{n-1} = \frac{a(1 - r^n)}{1 - r}, \quad \text{for } r \neq 1.$$

This formula is called a *closed form* of the sum.

Example 2 Use the formula for the sum of a geometric series to solve Example 1.

Solution We need to find B_6 and B_{26} where

$$B_n = 2000 + 2000(1.06) + 2000(1.06)^2 + \cdots + 2000(1.06)^{n-1}.$$

Using the formula for S_n with $a = 2000$ and $r = 1.06$, we get the same answers as before:

$$B_6 = \frac{2000(1 - (1.06)^6)}{1 - 1.06} = 13{,}950.64,$$
$$B_{26} = \frac{2000(1 - (1.06)^{26})}{1 - 1.06} = 118{,}312.77.$$

Drug Levels in The Body

Geometric series arise naturally in many different contexts. The following example illustrates a geometric series with decreasing terms.

Example 3 A patient is given a 20-mg injection of a therapeutic drug. Each day, the patient's body metabolizes 50% of the drug present, so that after 1 day only one-half of the original amount remains, after 2 days only one-fourth remains, and so on. The patient is given a 20-mg injection of the drug every day at the same time. Write a geometric series that gives the drug level in this patient's body right after the nth injection.

Solution Immediately after the 1st injection, the drug level in the body is given by

$$Q_1 = 20.$$

One day later, the original 20 mg has fallen to $20 \cdot \frac{1}{2} = 10$ mg and the second 20-mg injection is given. Right after the second injection, the drug level is given by

$$Q_2 = \underbrace{2^{\text{nd}} \text{ injection}}_{20} + \underbrace{\text{Residue of } 1^{\text{st}} \text{ injection}}_{\frac{1}{2} \cdot 20}$$

$$= 20 + 20 \left(\frac{1}{2}\right).$$

Two days later, the original 20 mg has fallen to $(20 \cdot \frac{1}{2}) \cdot \frac{1}{2} = 20(\frac{1}{2})^2 = 5$ mg, the second 20 mg injection has fallen to $20 \cdot \frac{1}{2} = 10$ mg, and the third 20 mg injection is given. Right after the third injection, the drug level is given by

$$Q_3 = \underbrace{3^{\text{rd}} \text{ injection}}_{20} + \underbrace{\text{Residue of } 2^{\text{nd}} \text{ injection}}_{20 \cdot \frac{1}{2}} + \underbrace{\text{Residue of } 1^{\text{st}} \text{ injection}}_{20 \cdot \frac{1}{2} \cdot \frac{1}{2}}$$

$$= 20 + 20 \left(\frac{1}{2}\right) + 20 \left(\frac{1}{2}\right)^2.$$

Continuing, we see that

$$\text{After } 4^{\text{th}} \text{ injection} \quad Q_4 = 20 + 20 \left(\frac{1}{2}\right) + 20 \left(\frac{1}{2}\right)^2 + 20 \left(\frac{1}{2}\right)^3$$

$$\text{After } 5^{\text{th}} \text{ injection} \quad Q_5 = 20 + 20 \left(\frac{1}{2}\right) + 20 \left(\frac{1}{2}\right)^2 + \cdots + 20 \left(\frac{1}{2}\right)^4$$

$$\vdots$$

$$\text{After } n^{\text{th}} \text{ injection} \quad Q_n = 20 + 20 \left(\frac{1}{2}\right) + 20 \left(\frac{1}{2}\right)^2 + \cdots + 20 \left(\frac{1}{2}\right)^{n-1}.$$

This is another example of a geometric series. Here, $a = 20$ and $r = 1/2$ in the geometric series formula

$$Q_n = a + ar + ar^2 + \cdots + ar^{n-1}.$$

To calculate the drug level for a specific value of n, we use the formula for the sum of a geometric series.

Example 4 What quantity of the drug remains in the patient's body after the 10th injection?

Solution After the 10th injection, the drug level in the patient's body is given by

$$Q_{10} = 20 + 20 \left(\frac{1}{2}\right) + 20 \left(\frac{1}{2}\right)^2 + \cdots + 20 \left(\frac{1}{2}\right)^9.$$

Using the formula for S_n with $n = 10$, $a = 20$, and $r = 1/2$, we get

$$Q_{10} = \frac{20(1 - (\frac{1}{2})^{10})}{1 - \frac{1}{2}} = 39.961 \text{ mg}.$$

Exercises and Problems for Section 13.3

Exercises

How many terms are there in the series in Exercises 1–2? Find the sum.

1. $\displaystyle\sum_{j=5}^{18} 3 \cdot 2^j$

2. $\displaystyle\sum_{k=2}^{20} (-1)^k 5(0.9)^k$

Find the sum of the series in Exercises 3–7.

3. $3 + \dfrac{3}{2} + \dfrac{3}{4} + \dfrac{3}{8} + \cdots + \dfrac{3}{2^{10}}$

4. $5 + 15 + 45 + 135 + \cdots + 5(3^{12})$

5. $1/125 + 1/25 + 1/5 + \cdots + 625$

6. $\displaystyle\sum_{n=1}^{10} 4(2^n)$

7. $\displaystyle\sum_{k=0}^{7} 2\left(\frac{3}{4}\right)^k$

In Exercises 8–11, decide which of the following are geometric series. For those which are, give the first term and the ratio between successive terms. For those which are not, explain why not.

8. $2 + 1 + \dfrac{1}{2} + \dfrac{1}{4} + \dfrac{1}{8} + \cdots + \dfrac{1}{128}$

9. $1 - \dfrac{1}{2} + \dfrac{1}{4} - \dfrac{1}{8} + \dfrac{1}{16} + \cdots + \dfrac{1}{256}$

10. $1 + \dfrac{1}{2} + \dfrac{1}{3} + \dfrac{1}{4} + \dfrac{1}{5} + \cdots + \dfrac{1}{100}$

11. $5 - 10 + 20 - 40 + 80 - \cdots - 2560$

Write each of the sums in Exercises 12–15 in sigma notation.

12. $1 + 4 + 16 + 64 + 256$

13. $3 - 9 + 27 - 81 + 243 - 729$

14. $2 + 10 + 50 + 250 + 1250 + 6250 + 31250$

15. $32 - 16 + 8 - 4 + 2 - 1$

Evaluate the sums in Exercises 16–19.

16. $\displaystyle\sum_{n=0}^{n=4} (0.1)^n$

17. $\displaystyle\sum_{n=0}^{n=5} \frac{3}{2^n}$

18. $\displaystyle\sum_{j=0}^{j=n-1} e^{jx}$

19. $\displaystyle\sum_{n=0}^{n=N} (-1)^n$

Problems

20. Write $ar^3 + ar^5 + ar^7 + ar^9 + ar^{11}$ in $\sum$ notation.

21. Worldwide consumption of oil was about 81 billion barrels in 2004.[7] Assume that consumption continues to increase at 1.2% per year, the rate for the previous decade.

    (a) Write a sum representing the total oil consumption for 25 years, starting with 2004.

    (b) Evaluate this sum.

22. Figure 13.3 shows the quantity of the drug atenolol in the blood as a function of time, with the first dose at time $t = 0$. Atenolol is taken in 50-mg doses once a day to lower blood pressure.

    (a) If the half-life of atenolol in the blood is 6.3 hours, what percentage of the atenolol present at the start of a 24-hour period is still there at the end?

---

[7] www.bp.com/downloads, Statistical Review of World Energy 2005, accessed January 15, 2006.

(b) Find expressions for the quantities Q_0, Q_1, Q_2, Q_3, ..., and Q_n shown in Figure 13.3. Write the expression for Q_n in closed-form.

(c) Find expressions for the quantities $P_1, P_2, P_3, \ldots$, and P_n shown in Figure 13.3. Write the expression for P_n in closed-form.

Figure 13.3

23. Annual deposits of $3000 are made into a bank account earning 5% interest per year. What is the balance in the account right after the 15th deposit if interest is calculated

(a) Annually   **(b)** Continuously

24. A deposit of $1000 is made once a year, starting today, into a bank account earning 3% interest per year, compounded annually. If 20 deposits are made, what is the balance in the account on the day of the last deposit?

25. What effect does doubling each of the following quantities (leaving other quantities the same) have on the answer to Problem 24? Is the answer doubled, more than doubled, or less than doubled?

(a) The deposit
(b) The interest rate
(c) The number of deposits made

26. To save for a new car, you put $500 a month into an account earning interest at 3% per year, compounded continuously.

(a) How much money do you have 2 years after the first deposit, right before you make a deposit?
(b) When does the balance first go over $10,000?

27. A bank account in which interest is earned at 4% per year, compounded annually, starts with a balance of $50,000. Payments of $1000 are made out of the account once a year for ten years, starting today. Interest is earned right before each payment is made.

(a) What is the balance in the account right after the tenth payment is made?
(b) Assume that the tenth payment exhausts the account. What is the largest yearly payment that can be made from this account?

13.4 INFINITE GEOMETRIC SERIES

In this section, we look at geometric series with an infinite number of terms and see under what circumstances they have a finite sum.

Long-term Drug Level in the Body

Suppose the patient from Example 3 on page 552 receives injections over a long period of time. What happens to the drug level in the patient's body? To find out, we calculate the drug level after 10, 15, 20, and 25 injections:

$$Q_{10} = \frac{20(1 - (\frac{1}{2})^{10})}{1 - \frac{1}{2}} = 39.960938 \text{ mg},$$

$$Q_{15} = \frac{20(1 - (\frac{1}{2})^{15})}{1 - \frac{1}{2}} = 39.998779 \text{ mg},$$

$$Q_{20} = \frac{20(1 - (\frac{1}{2})^{20})}{1 - \frac{1}{2}} = 39.999962 \text{ mg},$$

$$Q_{25} = \frac{20(1 - (\frac{1}{2})^{25})}{1 - \frac{1}{2}} = 39.999999 \text{ mg}.$$

The drug level appears to approach 40 mg. To see why this happens, notice that if there is exactly 40 mg of drug in the body, then half of this amount is metabolized in one day, leaving 20 mg. The next 20 mg injection replaces what was lost, and the level returns to 40 mg. We say that the *equilibrium* drug level is 40 mg.

Initially the patient has less than 40 mg of the drug in the body. Then the amount metabolized in one day is less than 20 mg. Thus, after the next 20 mg injection, the drug level is higher than it was before. For instance, if there are currently 30 mg, then after one day, half of this has been metabolized, leaving 15 mg. At the next injection the level rises to 35 mg, or 5 mg higher than where it started. Eventually, the quantity levels off to 40 mg.

Another way to think about the patient's drug level over time is to consider an *infinite geometric series*. After n injections, the drug level is given by the sum of the finite geometric series

$$Q_n = 20 + 20\left(\frac{1}{2}\right) + 20\left(\frac{1}{2}\right)^2 + \cdots + 20\left(\frac{1}{2}\right)^{n-1} = \frac{20(1 - (\frac{1}{2})^n)}{1 - \frac{1}{2}}.$$

What happens to the value of this sum as the number of terms approaches infinity? It does not seem possible to add up an infinite number of terms. However, we can look at the *partial sums*, Q_n, to see what happens for large values of n. For large values of n, we see that $(1/2)^n$ is very small, so that

$$Q_n = \frac{20\left(1 - \text{Small number}\right)}{1 - \frac{1}{2}} = \frac{20\left(1 - \text{Small number}\right)}{1/2}.$$

We write $\rightarrow$ to mean "tends toward." Thus, as $n \rightarrow \infty$, we know that $(1/2)^n \rightarrow 0$, so

$$Q_n \rightarrow \frac{20(1 - 0)}{1/2} = \frac{20}{1/2} = 40 \text{ mg.}$$

The Sum of an Infinite Geometric Series

Consider the geometric series $S_n = a + ar + ar^2 + \cdots + ar^{n-1}$. In general, if $|r| < 1$, then $r^n \rightarrow 0$ as $n \rightarrow \infty$, so

$$S_n = \frac{a(1 - r^n)}{1 - r} \rightarrow \frac{a(1 - 0)}{1 - r} = \frac{a}{1 - r} \text{ as } n \rightarrow \infty.$$

Thus, if $|r| < 1$, the partial sums S_n approach a finite value, S, as $n \rightarrow \infty$. In this case, we say that the series *converges* to S.

For $|r| < 1$, the **sum of the infinite geometric series** is given by

$$S = a + ar + ar^2 + \cdots + ar^n + \cdots = \sum_{i=0}^{\infty} ar^i = \frac{a}{1 - r}.$$

On the other hand, if $|r| > 1$, then we say that the series does not converge. The terms in the series get larger and larger as $n \rightarrow \infty$, so adding infinitely many of them does not give a finite sum.

What happens when $r = \pm 1$? For $|r| \geq 1$, the value of S_n does not approach a fixed number as $n \rightarrow \infty$, so we say that the infinite series does not converge. (To see why, consider what happens to 1^n and $(-1)^n$ as n increases.)

Example 1   Find the sum of the geometric series $\sum_{i=0}^{17} 7(-z)^i$ and $\sum_{i=0}^{\infty} (-z)^i$ provided $|z| < 1$.

Solution   We have

$$\sum_{i=0}^{17} 7(-z)^i = 7(-z)^0 + 7(-z)^1 + 7(-z)^2 + \cdots + 7(-z)^{17}.$$

Since $(-z)^0 = 1$, this is a geometric series with $a = 7$ and $r = -z$. There are 18 terms, so

$$\sum_{i=0}^{17} 7(-z)^i = \frac{7(1 - (-z)^{18})}{1 - (-z)} = \frac{7(1 - z^{18})}{1 + z}.$$

As for $\sum_{i=0}^{\infty} (-z)^i$, this is an infinite geometric series. Since $|z| < 1$, we have

$$\sum_{i=0}^{\infty} (-z)^i = \frac{1}{1 - (-z)} = \frac{1}{1 + z}.$$

Present Value of a Series of Payments

When baseball player Alex Rodriguez was signed by the Texas Rangers, before being traded to the New York Yankees, he was given a signing bonus for $10 million: $2 million a year for five years. Of course, since much of the money was to be paid in the future, the team's owners did not have to have all $10 million available on the day of the signing. How much money would the owners have to deposit in a bank account on the day of the signing in order to cover all the future payments? Assuming the account was earning interest, the owners would have to deposit less than $10 million. This smaller amount is called the *present value* of $10 million. We calculate the present value of Rodriguez's bonus on the day he signed.

Definition of Present Value

Let's consider a simplified version of this problem, with only one future payment: How much money would we need to deposit in a bank account today in order to have $2 million in one year? At an annual interest rate of 5%, compounded annually, the deposit would grow by a factor of 1.05. Thus,

$$\text{Deposit} \cdot 1.05 = \$2 \text{ million},$$
$$\text{Deposit} = \frac{\$2,000,000}{1.05} = \$1,904,761.91.$$

We need to deposit $1,904,761.91. This is the *present value* of the $2 million. Similarly, if we need $2 million in 2 years, the amount we need to deposit is given by

$$\text{Deposit} \cdot (1.05)^2 = \$2 \text{ million},$$
$$\text{Deposit} = \frac{\$2,000,000}{(1.05)^2} = \$1,814,058.96.$$

The $1,814,058.96 is the present value of $2 million payable two years from today. In general,

> The **present value**, $\$P$, of a future payment, $\$B$, is the amount that would have to be deposited (at some interest rate, r) in a bank account today to have exactly $\$B$ in the account at the relevant time in the future.

If r is the yearly interest rate (compounded annually) and if n is the number of years, then

$$B = P\left(1 + r\right)^n, \quad \text{or equivalently,} \quad P = \frac{B}{\left(1 + r\right)^n}.$$

Calculating the Present Value of Rodriguez's Bonus

The present value of Rodriguez's bonus represents what it was worth on the day it was signed. Suppose that he receives his money in 5 payments of \$2 million each, the first payment to be made on the day the contract was signed. We calculate the present values of all 5 payments assuming that interest is compounded annually at a rate of 5% per year. Since the first payment is made the day the contract is signed, we have, in millions of dollars,

$$\text{Present value of first payment} = 2.$$

Since the second payment is made a year in the future, in millions of dollars we have:

$$\text{Present value of second payment} = \frac{2}{(1.05)^1} = \frac{2}{1.05}.$$

The third payment is made two years in the future, so in millions of dollars:

$$\text{Present value of third payment} = \frac{2}{(1.05)^2},$$

and so on. Similarly, in millions of dollars:

$$\text{Present value of fifth payment} = \frac{2}{(1.05)^4}.$$

Thus, in millions of dollars,

$$\text{Total present value} = 2 + \frac{2}{1.05} + \frac{2}{(1.05)^2} + \cdots + \frac{2}{(1.05)^4}.$$

Rewriting this expression, we see that it is a finite geometric series with $a = 2$ and $r = 1/1.05$:

$$\text{Total present value} = 2 + 2\left(\frac{1}{1.05}\right) + 2\left(\frac{1}{1.05}\right)^2 + \cdots + 2\left(\frac{1}{1.05}\right)^4.$$

The formula for the sum of a finite geometric series gives

$$\text{Total present value of contract in millions of dollars} = \frac{2\left(1 - \left(\frac{1}{1.05}\right)^5\right)}{1 - \frac{1}{1.05}} \approx 9.09.$$

Thus, the total present value of the bonus is about \$9.09 million dollars.

Example 2   Suppose Alex Rodriguez's bonus with the Rangers guaranteed him and his heirs an annual payment of \$2 million *forever*. How much would the owners need to deposit in an account today in order to provide these payments?

Solution   At 5%, the total present value of an infinite series of payments is given by the infinite series

$$\text{Total present value} = 2 + \frac{2}{1.05} + \frac{2}{(1.05)^2} + \cdots$$

$$= 2 + 2\left(\frac{1}{1.05}\right) + 2\left(\frac{1}{1.05}\right)^2 + \cdots.$$

The sum of this infinite geometric series can be found using the formula:

$$\text{Total present value} = \frac{2}{1 - \frac{1}{1.05}} = 42 \text{ million dollars.}$$

To see that this answer is reasonable, suppose that $42 million is deposited in an account today, and that a $2 million payment is immediately made to Alex Rodriguez. Over the course of a year, the remaining $40 million earns 5% interest, which works out to $2 million, so the next year the account again has $42 million. Thus, it would have cost the Texas Rangers only about $33 million more (than the $9.09 million) to pay Rodriguez and his heirs $2 million a year forever.

Example 3 Using summation notation, write the present value of Alex Rodriguez's bonus, first for the 5-payment case and then for the infinite sequence of payments.

Solution For the 5 payments, we have

$$\text{Total present value} = 2 + \frac{2}{1.05} + \frac{2}{(1.05)^2} + \frac{2}{(1.05)^3} + \frac{2}{(1.05)^4} = \sum_{i=0}^{4} 2\left(\frac{1}{1.05}\right)^i.$$

For the infinite sequence of payments, the series goes to ∞ instead of stopping at 4, so we have

$$\text{Total present value} = 2 + \frac{2}{1.05} + \frac{2}{(1.05)^2} + \cdots = \sum_{i=0}^{\infty} 2\left(\frac{1}{1.05}\right)^i.$$

Exercises and Problems for Section 13.4

Exercises

In Exercises 1–7, decide which of the following are geometric series. For those that are, give the first term and the ratio between successive terms. For those that are not, explain why not.

1. $1 - x + x^2 - x^3 + x^4 - \cdots$

2. $y^2 + y^3 + y^4 + y^5 + \cdots$

3. $1 + x + 2x^2 + 3x^3 + 4x^4 + \cdots$

4. $3 + 3z + 6z^2 + 9z^3 + 12z^4 + \cdots$

5. $e^x + e^{2x} + e^{3x} + e^{4x} + \cdots$

6. $1 - e^{-3x} + e^{-6x} - e^{-9x} + \cdots$

7. $1 + \sqrt{2} + 2 + 2\sqrt{2} + \cdots$

8. Find the sum of the series in Problem 2.

9. Find the sum of the series in Problem 1.

Find the sum of the series in Exercises 10–17.

10. $-2 + 1 - \frac{1}{2} + \frac{1}{4} - \frac{1}{8} + \frac{1}{16} - \cdots$

11. $11 - 11(0.1) + 11(0.1)^2 - \cdots$

12. $\sum_{i=2}^{\infty} (0.1)^i$

13. $\sum_{i=4}^{\infty} \left(\frac{1}{3}\right)^i$

14. $\sum_{i=0}^{\infty} \frac{3^i + 5}{4^i}$

15. $\sum_{i=0}^{\infty} \frac{3^i}{2^{2i}}$

16. $\sum_{j=1}^{\infty} 7((0.1)^j + (0.2)^{j+2})$

17. $\sum_{i=1}^{\infty} x^{2i}, \quad |x| < 1$

Problems

18. A repeating decimal can always be expressed as a fraction. This problem shows how writing a repeating decimal as a geometric series enables you to find the fraction. Consider the decimal $0.232323\ldots$.

(a) Use the fact that $0.232323\ldots = 0.23 + 0.0023 + 0.000023 + \cdots$ to write $0.232323\ldots$ as a geometric series.

(b) Use the formula for the sum of a geometric series to show that $0.232323\ldots = 23/99$.

In Problems 19–23, use the method of Problem 18 to write each of the decimals as fractions.

19. $0.235235235\ldots$

20. $6.19191919\ldots$

21. $0.12222222\ldots$

22. $0.4788888\ldots$

23. $0.7638383838\ldots$

24. You have an ear infection and are told to take a 250-mg tablet of ampicillin (a common antibiotic) four times a day (every six hours). It is known that at the end of six hours, about 4% of the drug is still in the body. What quantity of the drug is in the body right after the third tablet? The fortieth? Assuming you continue taking tablets, what happens to the drug level in the long run?

25. In Problem 24 we found the quantity Q_n, the amount (in mg) of ampicillin left in the body right after the nth tablet is taken.

    (a) Make a similar calculation for P_n, the quantity of ampicillin (in mg) in the body right *before* the nth tablet is taken.

    (b) Find a simplified formula for P_n.

    (c) What happens to P_n in the long run? Is this the same as what happens to Q_n? Explain in practical terms why your answer makes sense.

26. Draw a graph like that in Figure 13.3 for 250 mg of ampicillin taken every 6 hours, starting at time $t = 0$. Put on the graph the values of $Q_1, Q_2, Q_3, \ldots$ calculated in Problem 24 and the values of $P_1, P_2, P_3, \ldots$ calculated in Problem 25.

27. Basketball player Patrick Ewing received a contract from the New York Knicks in which he was offered $3 million a year for ten years. Determine the present value of the contract on the date of the first payment if the interest rate is 7% per year, compounded continuously.

Problems 28–30 are about *bonds*, which are issued by a government to raise money. An individual who buys a $1000 bond gives the government $1000 and in return receives a fixed sum of money, called the *coupon*, every six months or every year for the life of the bond. At the time of the last coupon, the individual also gets the $1000, or *principal*, back.

28. What is the present value of a $1000 bond that pays $50 a year for 10 years, starting one year from now? Assume interest rate is 6% per year, compounded annually.

29. What is the present value of a $1000 bond that pays $50 a year for 10 years, starting one year from now? Assume the interest rate is 4% per year, compounded annually.

30. **(a)** What is the present value of a $1000 bond that pays $50 a year for 10 years, starting one year from now? Assume the interest rate is 5% per year, compounded annually.

    (b) Since $50 is 5% of $1000, this bond is often called a 5% bond. What does your answer to part (a) tell you about the relationship between the principal and the present value of this bond when the interest rate is 5%?

    (c) If the interest rate is more than 5% per year, compounded annually, which one is larger: the principal or the value of the bond? Why do you think the bond is then described as *trading at discount*?

    (d) If the interest rate is less than 5% per year, compounded annually, why is the bond described as *trading at a premium*?

CHAPTER SUMMARY

- **Sequences**
  Arithmetic: $a_n = a_1 + (n-1)d$.
  Geometric: $a_n = a_1 r^{n-1}$
- **Sigma Notation**
  $\sum_{i=i}^{n} a_i$
- **Arithmetic Series**
  Partial sum:
  $$S_n = a_1 + a_2 + \cdots + a_n = \frac{1}{2}n(2a_1 + (n-1)d).$$

- **Geometric Series**
  Finite:
  $$S_n = a + ar + ar^2 + \cdots + ar^{n-1} = \frac{a(1-r^n)}{1-r}, \quad r \neq 1.$$
  Infinite:
  $$S = a + ar + ar^2 + \cdots = \frac{a}{1-r},$$
  converges for $|r| < 1$, does not converge for $|r| > 1$.
- **Applications**
  Bank balance; drug levels.
  Present value: $P = \dfrac{B}{(1+r)^n}$ or $P = \dfrac{B}{e^{kt}}$.

REVIEW EXERCISES AND PROBLEMS FOR CHAPTER THIRTEEN

Exercises

1. Find the sum of the first eighteen terms of the series: $8 + 11 + 14 + \cdots$. What is the eighteenth term?

2. Write the following using sigma notation: $100 + 90 + 80 + 70 + \cdots + 0$.

3. (a) Write the sum $\sum_{n=1}^{5}(4n - 3)$ in expanded form.

   (b) Compute the sum.

In Exercises 4–6, decide which of the following are geometric series. For those that are, give the first term and the ratio between successive terms. For those that are not, explain why not.

4. $1 + 2z + (2z)^2 + (2z)^3 + \cdots$

5. $1 + \frac{x}{2} + \frac{x^2}{3} + \frac{x^3}{4} + \cdots$

6. $1 - y^2 + y^4 - y^6 + \cdots$

7. Find the sum of the series in Problem 4.

8. Find the sum of the series in Problem 6.

9. Find the sum of the first nine terms of the series: $7 + 14 + 21 + \cdots$.

Problems

10. Figure 13.4 shows the first four members in a sequence of square-shaped grids. In each successive grid, new dots are shown in black ($\bullet$). For instance, the second grid has 3 more dots than the first grid, the third has 5 more dots than the second, and the fourth has 7 more dots than the third.

   (a) Write down the sequence of the total number of dots in each grid (black and white). Using the fact that each grid is a square, find a formula in terms of n for the number of dots in the nth grid.

   (b) Write down the sequence of the number of black dots in each grid. Find a formula in terms of n for the number of black dots in the nth grid.

   (c) State the relationship between the two sequences in parts (a) and (b). Use the formulas you found in parts (a) and (b) to confirm this relationship.

Figure 13.4

11. The numbers in the sequence 1, 4, 9, 16, ... from Problem 10 are known as *square numbers* because they describe the number of dots in successive square grids. Analogously, the numbers in the sequence 1, 3, 6, 10, ... are known as *triangular numbers* because they describe the number of dots in successive triangular patterns, as shown in Figure 13.5: Find a formula for the nth triangular number.

Figure 13.5

12. In a workshop, it costs $300 to make one piece of furniture. The second piece costs a bit less, $280. The third costs even less, $263, and the fourth costs only $249. The cost for each additional piece of furniture is called the *marginal cost* of production. Table 13.3 gives the marginal cost, c, and the change in marginal cost, Δc, in terms of the number of pierces of furniture, n. As the quantity produced increases, the marginal cost generally decreases and then increases again.

Table 13.3

n	1		2		3		4
c (\$)	300		280		263		249
Δc (\$)		-20		-17		-14	

   (a) Assume that the arithmetic sequence -20, -17, -14, ..., continues. Complete the table for $n = 5$, 6, ..., 12.

(b) Find a formula for c_n, the marginal cost for producing the nth piece of furniture. Use the fact that c_n is found by adding the terms in an arithmetic sequence. Using your formula, find the cost for producing the 12th piece and the 50th piece of furniture.

(c) A piece of furniture can be sold at a profit if it costs less than \$400 to make. How many pieces of furniture should the workshop make each day? Discuss.

13. A store clerk has 108 cans to stack. He can fit 24 cans on the bottom row and can stack the cans 8 rows high. Use arithmetic series to determine how he can stack the cans so that each row contains fewer cans than the row beneath it and that the number of cans in each row decreases at a constant rate.

14. A university with an enrollment of 8000 students in 2007 is projected to grow by 2% in each of the next three years and by 3.5% in each of the following seven years. Find the sequence of the university's student enrollment for the next 10 years.

15. Each person in a group of 30 shakes hands with each other person exactly once. How many total handshakes take place?

16. A bank account with a \$75,000 initial deposit is used to make annual payments of \$1000, starting one year after the initial \$75,000 deposit. Interest is earned at 2% a year, compounded annually, and paid into the account right before the payment is made.

(a) What is the balance in the account right after the 24th payment?

(b) Answer the same question for yearly payments of \$3000.

17. One way of valuing a company is to calculate the present value of all its future earnings. A farm expects to sell \$1000 worth of Christmas trees once a year forever, with the first sale in the immediate future. What is the present value of this Christmas tree business? Assume that the interest rate is 4% per year, compounded continuously.

18. You inherit \$100,000 and put the money in a bank account earning 3% per year, compounded annually. You withdraw \$2000 from the account each year, right after the interest is earned. Your first \$2000 is withdrawn before any interest is earned.

(a) Compare the balance in the account right after the first withdrawal and right after the second withdrawal. Which do you expect to be higher?

(b) Calculate the balance in the account right after the 20th withdrawal is made.

(c) What is the largest yearly withdrawal you can take from this account without the balance decreasing over time?

19. After breaking his leg, a patient retrains his muscles by going for walks. The first day, he manages to walk 300 yards. Each day after that he walks 50 yards farther than the day before.

(a) Write a sequence that represents the distances walked each day during the first week.

(b) How far is he walking after two weeks?

(c) How long until he is walking at least one mile?

20. Before email made it easy to contact many people quickly, groups used telephone trees to pass news to their members. In one group, each person is in charge of calling 4 people. One person starts the tree by calling 4 people. At the second stage, each of these 4 people call another 4 people. In the third stage, each of the people in stage two calls 4 people, and so on.

(a) How many people have the news by the end of the 5th stage?

(b) Write a formula for the total number of members in a tree of 10 stages.

(c) How many stages are required to cover a group with 5000 members?

21. A ball is dropped from a height of 10 feet and bounces. Each bounce is $3/4$ of the height of the bounce before. Thus after the ball hits the floor for the first time, the ball rises to a height of $10(3/4) = 7.5$ feet, and after it hits the floor for the second time, it rises to a height of $7.5(3/4) = 10(3/4)^2 = 5.625$ feet.

(a) Find an expression for the height to which the ball rises after it hits the floor for the nth time.

(b) Find an expression for the total vertical distance the ball has traveled when it hits the floor for the first, second, third, and fourth times.

(c) Find an expression for the total vertical distance the ball has traveled when it hits the floor for the nth time. Express your answer in closed form.

22. You might think that the ball in Problem 21 keeps bouncing forever since it takes infinitely many bounces. This is not true! It can be shown that a ball dropped from a height of h feet reaches the ground in $\frac{1}{4}\sqrt{h}$ seconds. It is also true that it takes a bouncing ball the same amount of time to rise h feet. Use these facts to show that the ball in Problem 21 stops bouncing after

$$\frac{1}{4}\sqrt{10} + \frac{1}{2}\sqrt{10}\sqrt{\frac{3}{4}}\left(\frac{1}{1-\sqrt{3/4}}\right)$$

seconds, or approximately 11 seconds.

23. This problem illustrates how banks create credit and can thereby lend out more money than has been deposited.

Suppose that initially $100 is deposited in a bank. Experience has shown bankers that on average only 8% of the money deposited is withdrawn by the owner at any time. Consequently, bankers feel free to lend out 92% of their deposits. Thus $92 of the original $100 is loaned out to other customers (to start a business, for example). This $92 will become someone else's income and, sooner or later, will be redeposited in the bank. Then 92% of $92, or $92(0.92) = $84.64, is loaned out again and eventually redeposited. Of the $84.64, the bank again loans out 92%, and so on.

(a) Find the total amount of money deposited in the bank.

(b) The total amount of money deposited divided by the original deposit is called the *credit multiplier*. Calculate the credit multiplier for this example and explain

what this number tells us.

24. Take a rectangle whose sides have length 1 and 2, divide it into two equal pieces, and shade one of them. Now, divide the unshaded half into two equal pieces and shade one of them. Take the unshaded area and divide it into two equal pieces and shade one of them. Continue doing this.

(a) Draw a picture that illustrates this process.

(b) Find a series that describes the shaded area after n divisions.

(c) If you continue this process indefinitely, what would the total shaded area be? Make two arguments, one using your picture, another using the series you found in part (b).

CHECK YOUR UNDERSTANDING

Are the statements in Problems 1–34 true or false? Give an explanation for your answer.

1. If $a_n = n^2 + 1$, then $a_1 = 2$.

2. The first term of a sequence must be a positive integer.

3. The sequence $1, 1, 1, 1, \ldots$ is both arithmetic and geometric.

4. The sequence $a, 2a, 3a, 4a$ is arithmetic.

5. The sequence $a, a + 1, a + 2, a + 3$ is arithmetic.

6. If the difference between successive terms of an arithmetic sequence is d, then $a_n = a_1 + dn - d$.

7. The sequence $3x^2, 3x^4, 3x^6, \ldots$ is geometric.

8. The sequence $2, 4, 2, 4, 2, 4, \ldots$ is alternating.

9. For all series $S_1 = a_1$.

10. The accumulation of college credit is an example of a finite series.

11. The sum formula for a finite series with n terms is $S_n = \frac{1}{2}n(n + 1)$.

12. There are four terms in $\sum_{i=0}^{4} a_i$.

13. $\sum_{i=1}^{n} 3 = 3n$.

14. The sum of a finite arithmetic series is the average of the first and last terms, times the number of terms.

15. If C_n denotes your college credits earned by the end of year n, then C_4 is your credits earned during your fourth year of college.

16. If C_n denotes your college credits earned by the end of year n, then $C_3 - C_2$ is your credits earned in year 2.

17. For any series S_n, we must have $S_3 \leq S_4$.

18. If $a_n = (-1)^{n+1}$ then the sequence is alternating.

19. The sum formula for a finite geometric series, $S_n = \dfrac{a(1 - r^n)}{1 - r}$, can be simplified by dividing by $(1 - r)$ to get $S_n = a(1 - r^{n-1})$.

20. With the same interest rate, a bank balance after 5 years of $2000 annual payments is the same as the balance after by 10 years of $1000 annual payments.

21. $1 - \frac{1}{2} + \frac{1}{4} - \frac{1}{8} + \frac{1}{16} - \frac{1}{32}$ is a geometric series.

22. $2000(1.06)^3 + 2000(1.06)^4 + \cdots + 2000(1.06)^{10}$ is a geometric series.

23. $5000 + 2000(1.06) + 2000(1.06)^2 \cdots + 2000(1.06)^{10}$ is a geometric series.

24. $5000 + 2000(1.06) + 2000(1.06)^2 \cdots + 2000(1.06)^{10} = 3000 + \dfrac{2000(1 - 1.06^{11})}{-0.06}$.

25. Payments of $2000 are made yearly into an account earning 5% interest compounded annually. If the interest rate is doubled, the balance at the end of 20 years is doubled.

26. The present value of a sequence of payments is the amount that you would need to invest at this moment in order to exactly make the future payments.

27. If the present value of a sequence of payments is 1 million dollars, then the present value of a sequence of payments which are doubled in size, would be 2 million.

28. The series $\sum_{i=0}^{\infty} \dfrac{1}{i^2}$ is geometric.

29. For $Q_n = \sum\limits_{i=1}^{n}(-1)^i$, we see $Q_2 = 0$, $Q_4 = 0$, $Q_6 = 0$, etc. Thus, the series converges to a sum of

$$Q = \sum_{i=1}^{\infty}(-1)^i = 0.$$

30. A patient takes 100 mg of a drug each day; 5% of the amount of the drug in the body decays each day. Then, the long-run level of the drug in the body is 2000 mg.

31. If $S = a + ar + ar^2 + \cdots$ and $|a| < 1$ then the infinite series converges.

32. It is possible to add an infinite number of positive terms and get a finite sum.

33. The sum of an infinite arithmetic series with difference $d = 0.01$ converges.

34. All infinite geometric series converge.

Chapter Fourteen

PARAMETRIC EQUATIONS AND CONIC SECTIONS

Contents

14.1 PARAMETRIC EQUATIONS

The Mars Pathfinder

On July 4, 1997, the Mars Pathfinder bounced down onto the surface of the red planet, its impact cushioned by airbags. The next day, the Sojourner—a small, six-wheeled robot—rolled out of the spacecraft and began a rambling exploration of the surrounding terrain. Figure 14.1 shows a photograph of the Sojourner and a diagram of the path it took before radio contact was lost.

In Figure 14.1, Sojourner's path is labeled according to the elapsed number of Martian days or *sols* (short for solar periods). The robot's progress was slow because instructions for every movement had to be calculated by NASA engineers and sent from Earth.

 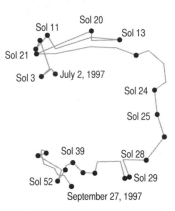

Figure 14.1: The Pathfinder Sojourner robot and the path it followed on the surface of the planet Mars. Image from NASA/Jet Propulsion Laboratory. Diagram adapted from *The New York Times*, July 21, 1998

The Path of the Sojourner Robot

How can Sojourner's path be represented? How can we tell a robot where it should go, how fast, and when? The path in Figure 14.1 is not the graph of a function in the ordinary sense—for instance, it crosses over itself in several different places. However, positions on the path can be determined by knowing t, the elapsed time. In this section, we describe a path by giving the x- and y-coordinates of points on the path as functions of a *parameter* such as t.

Programming a Robot Using Coordinates

One way to program a robot's motion is to send it coordinates to tell it where to go. Imagine that a robot like the Sojourner is moving around the xy-plane.[1] If we choose the origin $(0,0)$ to be the spot where the robot's spacecraft lands, we can direct its motion by giving it (x, y) coordinates of the points to which it should move.

We select the positive y-axis so that it points north (that is, toward the northern pole of Mars) and the positive x-axis so that it points east. Our units of measurement are meters, so that, the coordinates $(2, 4)$ indicate a point that is 2 meters to the east and 4 meters to the north of the landing site. We program the robot to move to the following points:

$$(0,0) \quad \rightarrow \quad (1,1) \quad \rightarrow \quad (2,2) \quad \rightarrow \quad (2,3) \quad \rightarrow \quad (2,4).$$

---

[1]The surface of Mars is not as flat as the xy-plane, but this is a useful first approximation.

These points have been plotted in Figure 14.2.

Figure 14.2: The robot is programmed to move along this path

Programming the Robot Using a Parameter

In order to represent the robot's path using a parameter, we need two functions: one for the robot's x-coordinate, $x = f(t)$, and one for its y-coordinate, $y = g(t)$. The function for x describes the robot's east-west motion, and the function for y describes its north-south motion. Together, they are called *parametric equations* for the robot's path.

Example 1   If t is time in minutes, describe the path followed by a robot given by

$$x = 2t, \qquad y = t \qquad \text{for} \quad 0 \le t \le 5.$$

Solution   At time $t = 0$, the robot's position is given by

$$x = 2 \cdot 0 = 0, \qquad y = 0, \qquad \text{so it starts at the point } (0,0).$$

One minute later, at $t = 1$, its position is given by

$$x = 2 \cdot 1 = 2, \qquad y = 1, \qquad \text{so it has moved to the point } (2,1).$$

At time $t = 2$, its position is given by

$$x = 2 \cdot 2 = 4, \qquad y = 2, \qquad \text{so it has moved to the point } (4,2).$$

The path followed by the robot is given by

$$(0,0) \quad \rightarrow \quad (2,1) \quad \rightarrow \quad (4,2) \quad \rightarrow \quad (6,3) \quad \rightarrow \quad (8,4) \quad \rightarrow \quad (10,5).$$

At time $t = 5$, the robot stops at the point $(10,5)$ because we have restricted the values of t to the interval $0 \le t \le 5$. In Figure 14.3 we see the path followed by the robot; it is a straight line.

In the previous example, we can use substitution to rewrite the formula for x in terms of y. Since $x = 2t$ and $t = y$, we have $x = 2y$. Thus, the path followed by the robot has the equation

$$y = \frac{1}{2}x.$$

Since the parameter t can be easily eliminated from our equations, you may wonder why we use it. One reason is that it is useful to know when the robot gets to each point. The values of x and y tell us where the robot is, while the parameter t tells us when it gets there. In addition, for some pairs of parametric equations, the parameter t cannot be so easily eliminated.

So far, we have assumed that a robot moves in a straight line between two points. We now imagine that a robot can be continuously redirected along a curved path.

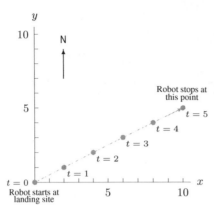

Figure 14.3: Path followed by the robot if $x = 2t, y = t$ for $0 \le t \le 5$

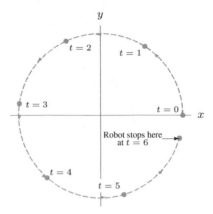

Figure 14.4: Path followed by the robot if $x = \cos t, y = \sin t$ for $0 \le t \le 6$

Example 2 A robot begins at the point $(1, 0)$ and follows the path given by the equations

$$x = \cos t, \qquad y = \sin t \qquad \text{where } t \text{ is in minutes,} \quad 0 \le t \le 6.$$

(a) Describe the path followed by the robot.

(b) What happens when you try to eliminate the parameter t from these equations?

Solution (a) At time $t = 0$, the robot's position is given by

$$x = \cos 0 = 1, \qquad y = \sin 0 = 0$$

so it starts at the point $(1, 0)$, as required. At time $t = 1$, its position is given by

$$x = \cos 1 = 0.54, \qquad y = \sin 1 = 0.84.$$

Thus, the robot has moved west and north. At time $t = 2$, its position is given by

$$x = \cos 2 = -0.42, \qquad y = \sin 2 = 0.91.$$

Now it is farther west and slightly farther north. Continuing, we see that the path followed by the robot is given by

$$(1, 0) \to (0.54, 0.84) \quad \to \quad (-0.42, 0.91) \quad \to \quad (-0.99, 0.14)$$
$$\to (-0.65, -0.76) \quad \to \quad (0.28, -0.96) \quad \to \quad (0.96, -0.28).$$

In Figure 14.4 we see the path followed by the robot; it is circular with a radius of one meter. At the end of 6 minutes the robot has not quite returned to its starting point at $(1, 0)$.

(b) One way to eliminate t from this pair of equations is to use the Pythagorean identity,

$$\cos^2 t + \sin^2 t = 1.$$

Since $x = \cos t$ and $y = \sin t$, we can substitute x and y into this equation:

$$(\underbrace{\cos t}_{x})^2 + (\underbrace{\sin t}_{y})^2 = 1,$$

giving

$$x^2 + y^2 = 1.$$

This is the equation of a circle of radius 1 centered at $(0, 0)$. Attempting to solve for y in terms of x, we have

$$x^2 + y^2 = 1$$
$$y^2 = 1 - x^2$$
$$y = +\sqrt{1 - x^2} \quad \text{or} \quad y = -\sqrt{1 - x^2}.$$

Thus, we obtain two different equations for y in terms of x. The first, $y = +\sqrt{1 - x^2}$, returns positive values for y (as well as 0), while the second returns negative values for y (as well as 0). The first equation gives the top half of the circle, while the second gives the bottom half.

In the previous example, y is not a function of x, because for all x-values (except 1 and -1) there are two possible y values. This confirms what we already knew, because the graph in Figure 14.4 fails the vertical-line test.

Different Motions Along the Same Path

It is possible to parameterize the same curve in more than one way, as the following example illustrates.

Example 3 Describe the motion of the robot that follows the path given by

$$x = \cos \frac{1}{2}t, \qquad y = \sin \frac{1}{2}t \qquad \text{for} \quad 0 \le t \le 6.$$

Solution At time $t = 0$, the robot's position is given by

$$x = \cos\left(\frac{1}{2} \cdot 0\right) = 1, \qquad y = \sin\left(\frac{1}{2} \cdot 0\right) = 0$$

so it starts at the point $(1, 0)$, as before. After one minute, that is, at time $t = 1$, its position (rounded to thousandths) is given by

$$x = \cos\left(\frac{1}{2} \cdot 1\right) = 0.878, \qquad y = \sin\left(\frac{1}{2} \cdot 1\right) = 0.479.$$

At time $t = 2$ its position is given by

$$x = \cos\left(\frac{1}{2} \cdot 2\right) = 0.540, \qquad y = \sin\left(\frac{1}{2} \cdot 2\right) = 0.841.$$

Continuing, we see that the path followed by the robot is given by

$$(1, 0) \rightarrow (0.878, 0.479) \quad \rightarrow \quad (0.540, 0.841) \quad \rightarrow \quad (0.071, 0.997)$$
$$\rightarrow (-0.416, 0.909) \quad \rightarrow \quad (-0.801, 0.598) \quad \rightarrow \quad (-0.990, 0.141).$$

Figure 14.5 shows the path; it is again circular with a radius of one meter. However, at the end of six minutes the robot has not even made it half way around the circle. Because we have multiplied the parameter t by a factor of $1/2$, the robot moves at half its original rate.

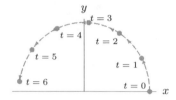

Figure 14.5: Path followed by the robot if $x = \cos\frac{1}{2}t, y = \sin\frac{1}{2}t$ for $0 \le t \le 6$

Example 4 Describe the motion of the robot that follows the path given by:

(a) $x = \cos(-t), y = \sin(-t)$ for $0 \le t \le 6$ (b) $x = \cos t, y = \sin t$ for $0 \le t \le 10$

Solution (a) Figure 14.6 shows the robot's path. The robot travels around the circle in the clockwise direction, opposite to that in Examples 2 and 3.

(b) See Figure 14.7. The robot travels around the circle more than once but less than twice, coming to a stop roughly southwest of the landing site.

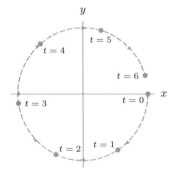

Figure 14.6: Path given by
$x = \cos(-t), y = \sin(-t)$ for
$0 \le t \le 6$

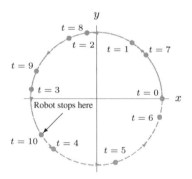

Figure 14.7: Path given by $x = \cos t$,
$y = \sin t$ for $0 \le t \le 10$

Other Parametric Curves

Parametric equations can be used to describe extremely complicated motions. For instance, suppose the robot follows the rambling path described by the parametric equations

$$x = 20\cos t + 4\cos(4\sqrt{5}t) \qquad y = 20\sin t + 4\sin(4\sqrt{8}t).$$

See Figure 14.8. The path is roughly circular, and the robot moves in a more or less counterclockwise direction. The dashed circle in Figure 14.8 is given by the parametric equations

$$x = 20\cos t, \qquad y = 20\sin t \qquad \text{for } 0 \le t \le 2\pi.$$

The other terms, $4\cos(4\sqrt{5}t)$ and $4\sin(4\sqrt{8}t)$, are responsible for the robot's deviations from the circle.

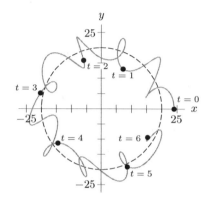

Figure 14.8: Rambling path, parametrically defined

The Archimedean Spiral

In polar coordinates, the Archimedean spiral is the graph of the equation introduced on page 352:

$$r = \theta.$$

Since the relationship between polar coordinates and Cartesian coordinates is

$$x = r\cos\theta \qquad \text{and} \qquad y = r\sin\theta,$$

we can write the Archimedean spiral $r = \theta$ as

$$x = \theta\cos\theta \qquad \text{and} \qquad y = \theta\sin\theta.$$

Replacing θ (an angle) by t (a time), we obtain the parametric equations for the spiral in Figure 14.9:

$$x = t\cos t \qquad y = t\sin t.$$

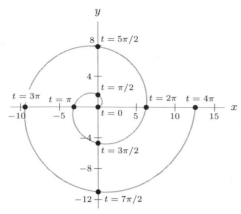

Figure 14.9: Archimedean spiral given by
$x = t \cos t, y = t \sin t, 0 \leq t \leq 4\pi$

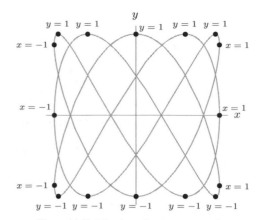

Figure 14.10: Lissajous figure: $x = \cos 3t$,
$y = \sin 5t, 0 \leq t \leq 2\pi$

Lissajous Figures

The beautiful curve in Figure 14.10 is called a *Lissajous figure*. Its equations are

$$x = \cos 3t, \qquad y = \sin 5t \qquad \text{for } 0 \leq t \leq 2\pi.$$

To explain the shape of this Lissajous figure, notice that $y = \sin 5t$ completes five full oscillations on the interval $0 \leq t \leq 2\pi$. Thus, since the amplitude of $y = \sin 5t$ is 1, the value of y reaches a maximum of 1 at five different values of t. Similarly, the value of y is -1 at another five different values of t. Figure 14.10 shows the curve climbs to a high point of $y = 1$ five times and falls to a low of $y = -1$ five times.

Meanwhile, since $x = \cos 3t$, the value of x oscillates between 1 and -1 a total of 3 times on the interval $0 \leq t \leq 2\pi$. Figure 14.10 shows that the curve moves to its right boundary, $x = 1$, three times and to its left boundary, $x = -1$, three times.

Foxes and Rabbits

In a wildlife park, foxes prey on rabbits. Suppose F is the number of foxes, R is the number of rabbits, t is the number of months since January 1, and that

$$R = 1000 - 500 \sin\left(\frac{\pi}{6}t\right) \qquad \text{and} \qquad F = 150 + 50 \cos\left(\frac{\pi}{6}t\right).$$

These equations are a parameterization of the curve in Figure 14.11. Since this curve fails the vertical-line test, F is not a function of R.

We can use the curve to analyze the relationship between the rabbit population and the fox population. In January, there are 1000 rabbits but they are dying off; in April only 500 rabbits remain. By July the population has rebounded to 1000 rabbits, and by October it has soared to 1500 rabbits. Then the rabbit population begins to fall again; the following April there are once more only 500 rabbits.

The fox population also rises and falls, though not at the same time of year as the rabbits. In January, the fox population numbers 200. By April, it has fallen to 150 foxes. The fox population continues to fall, perhaps because there are so few rabbits to eat at that time. By July, only 100 foxes remain. The fox population then begins to increase again. By October, when the rabbit population is largest, the fox population is growing rapidly, so that by January it has returned to its maximum size of 200 foxes. By this point, though, the rabbit population is already dropping, perhaps because there are so many hungry foxes around. Then the cycle repeats.

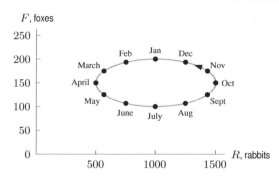

Figure 14.11: The relationship between F, the number of foxes, and R, the number of rabbits

Using Graphs to Parameterize a Curve

Example 5   Figure 14.12 shows the graphs of two functions, $f(t)$ and $g(t)$. Describe the motion of the particle whose coordinates at time t are given by $x = f(t), y = g(t)$.

Figure 14.12: Graphs of $x = f(t)$ and $y = g(t)$ used to trace out the path in Figure 14.13

Figure 14.13: Square parameterized by $x = f(t), y = g(t)$ from Figure 14.12

Solution   As t increases from 0 to 1, the x-coordinate increases from 0 to 1, while the y-coordinate stays fixed at 0. The particle moves along the x-axis from $(0, 0)$ to $(1, 0)$. As t increases from 1 to 2, the x-coordinate stays fixed at $x = 1$, while the y-coordinate increases from 0 to 1. Thus, the particle moves along the vertical line from $(1, 0)$ to $(1, 1)$. Between times $t = 2$ and $t = 3$, it moves horizontally backward to $(0, 1)$, and between times $t = 3$ and $t = 4$ it moves down the y-axis to $(0, 0)$. Thus, it traces out the square in Figure 14.13.

Exercises and Problems for Section 14.1

Exercises

Find the parametric equations for the lines given in Exercises 1–4.

1. The straight line between $(1, 3)$ and $(3, 4)$.

2. The straight line between $(1, 3)$ and $(-3, 5)$.

3. The straight line from $(0, 0)$ to $(1, 1)$ and then to $(2, 0)$.

4. The quarter circle from $(3, 0)$ to $(0, 3)$.

Determine whether the parameterizations in Exercises 5–8 are valid.

5. The straight line between $(0, 3)$ and $(3, 4)$: $x = 3t$, $y = 3 + t, 0 \leq t \leq 1$.

6. The straight line between $(-3, 5)$ and $(1, 1)$: $x = 1 - 4t$, $y = 1 + 4t, 0 \leq t \leq 1$.

7. The half circle of radius 2 in the half plane $x > 0$: $x = -2 \cos t, y = 2 \sin t, -\frac{\pi}{2} \leq t \leq \frac{\pi}{2}$.

8. A circle of radius 2 centered at $(3, 4)$: $x = 3 + 2 \cos t$, $y = 4 - 2 \sin t, -\pi \leq t \leq \pi$.

Graph the parametric equations in Exercises 9–20. Assume that the parameter is restricted to values for which the functions are defined. Indicate the direction of the curve. Eliminate the parameter, t, to obtain an equation for y as a function of x. Check your sketches by graphing y as a function of x.

9. $x = 5 - 2t$, $y = 1 + 4t$

10. $x = t + 1$, $y = 3t - 2$

11. $x = \sqrt{t}$, $y = 2t + 1$

12. $x = \sqrt{t}$, $y = t^2 + 4$

13. $x = t - 3$, $y = t^2 + 2t + 1$

14. $x = e^t$, $y = e^{2t}$

15. $x = e^{2t}$, $y = e^{3t}$

16. $x = \ln t$, $y = t^2$

17. $x = t^3$, $y = 2 \ln t$

18. $x = 2 \cos t$, $y = 2 \sin t$

19. $x = 2 \cos t$, $y = 3 \sin t$

20. $x = 3 + \sin t$, $y = 2 + \cos t$

For Exercises 21–24, describe the motion of a particle whose position at time t is given by $x = f(t)$, $y = g(t)$.

21.

22.

23.

24.

Problems

Problems 25–28 give parameterizations of the unit circle or a part of it. In each case, describe in words how the circle is traced out, including when and where the particle is moving clockwise and when and where it is moving counterclockwise.

25. $x = \cos t$, $y = -\sin t$

26. $x = \sin t$, $y = \cos t$

27. $x = \cos(t^2)$, $y = \sin(t^2)$

28. $x = \cos(\ln t)$, $y = \sin(\ln t)$

29. Describe the similarities and differences among the motions in the plane given by the following three pairs of parametric equations:
  (a) $x = t$, $y = t^2$ (b) $x = t^2$, $y = t^4$
  (c) $x = t^3$, $y = t^6$.

30. As t varies, the following parametric equations trace out a line in the plane

$$x = 2 + 3t, \quad y = 4 + 7t.$$

  (a) What part of the line is obtained by restricting t to nonnegative numbers?

  (b) What part of the line is obtained if t is restricted to $-1 \le t \le 0$?

  (c) How should t be restricted to give the part of the line to the left of the y-axis?

31. Write two different parameterizations for each of the curves in the xy-plane.

  (a) A parabola whose equation is $y = x^2$.
  (b) The parabola from part (a) shifted to the left 2 units and up 1 unit.

Graph the Lissajous figures in Problems 32–35 using a calculator or computer.

32. $x = \cos 2t$, $y = \sin 5t$

33. $x = \cos 3t$, $y = \sin 7t$

34. $x = \cos 2t$, $y = \sin 4t$

35. $x = \cos 2t$, $y = \sin \sqrt{3}t$

36. Suppose $a, b, c, d, m, n, p, q > 0$. Match each of the following pairs of parametric equations with one of the lines l_1, l_2, l_3, l_4 in Figure 14.14.

I. $\begin{cases} x = a + ct, \\ y = -b + dt. \end{cases}$ II. $\begin{cases} x = m + pt, \\ y = n - qt. \end{cases}$

Figure 14.14

37. A bug is crawling around the Cartesian plane. Let $x = f(t)$ be the function denoting the x-coordinate of the bug's position as a function of time, t, and let $y = g(t)$ be the y-coordinate of the bug's position.

    (a) Let $f(t) = t$ and $g(t) = t$. What path does the bug follow?

    (b) Now let $f(t) = \cos t$ and $g(t) = \sin t$. What path does the bug follow? What is its starting point? (That is, where is the bug when $t = 0$?) When does the bug get back to its starting point?

    (c) Now let $f(t) = \cos t$ and $g(t) = 2\sin t$. What path does the bug follow? What is its starting point? When does the bug get back to its starting point?

Write a parameterization for the lines in the xy-plane in Problems 38–39.

38. A vertical line through the point $(-2, -3)$.

39. The line through the points $(2, -1)$ and $(1, 3)$.

40. Motion along a straight line is given by a single equation, say, $x = t^3 - t$ where x is distance along the line. It is difficult to see the motion from a plot; it just traces out the x-line, as in Figure 14.15. To visualize the motion,

we introduce a y-coordinate and let it slowly increase, giving Figure 14.16. Try the following on a calculator or computer. Let $y = t$. Now plot the parametric equations $x = t^3 - t$, $y = t$ for, say, $-3 \le t \le 3$. What does the plot in Figure 14.16 tell you about the particle's motion?

Figure 14.15

Figure 14.16

For Problems 41–42, plot the motion along the x-line by introducing a y-coordinate, as in Problem 40. What does the plot tell you about the particle's motion?

41. $x = \cos t$, $\quad -10 \le t \le 10$

42. $x = t^4 - 2t^2 + 3t - 7$, $\quad -3 \le t \le 2$

43. A ball is thrown vertically into the air at time $t = 0$. Its height $d(t)$, in feet, above the ground at time t, in seconds, is given by:

$$d(t) = -16t^2 + 48t + 6.$$

    (a) Write a parameterization for the curve.

    (b) Sketch a graph of the curve.

    (c) What is the height of the ball at $t = 0$? Explain how this makes sense.

    (d) Does the ball ever reach this height again? If so when? Why?

    (e) When does the ball reach its maximum height? What is the maximum height?

14.2 IMPLICITLY DEFINED CURVES AND CIRCLES

In the previous section, we saw that the parametrically defined curve $x = \cos t$, $y = \sin t$ is the circle of radius 1 centered at the origin. Eliminating the parameter t gives the equation

$$x^2 + y^2 = 1.$$

The circle is described by the *implicit function* $x^2 + y^2 = 1$. To be explicit is to state a fact outright; to be implicit is to make a statement in a roundabout way. If a curve has an equation of the form $y = f(x)$, then we say that y is an *explicit* function of x. However, the equation $x^2 + y^2 = 1$ does not explicitly state that y depends on x. Instead, this dependence is implied by the equation. If we try to solve for y in terms of x, we do not obtain a function. Rather, we obtain *two* functions, one for the top half of the unit circle and one for the bottom half:

$$y = \sqrt{1 - x^2} \quad \text{and} \quad y = -\sqrt{1 - x^2}.$$

Example 1   Graph the equation $y^2 = x^2$. Can you find an explicit formula for y in terms of x?

Solution   The equation $y^2 = x^2$ is implicit because it does not tell us what y equals; instead, it tells us what y^2 equals. Suppose $x = 2$. What values can y equal? Since

$$y^2 = 2^2 = 4, \quad \text{we have} \quad y = 2 \text{ or } -2,$$

because for either of these y-values $y^2 = 4$. What if x is negative? If $x = -3$, we have

$$y^2 = (-3)^2 = 9, \quad \text{then} \quad y = 3 \text{ or } -3,$$

because these are the solutions to $y^2 = 9$.

For almost all x-values, there are two y-values, one given by $y = x$ and one by $y = -x$. The only exception is at $x = 0$, because the only solution to the equation $y^2 = 0$ is $y = 0$. Thus, the graph of $y^2 = x^2$ has two parts, given by

$$y = x \quad \text{and} \quad -x.$$

When both parts of the graph of $y^2 = x^2$ are plotted together, the resulting graph looks like an X. (See Figure 14.17.)

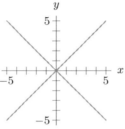

Figure 14.17: Graph of $y^2 = x^2$

Conic Sections

The curves known as *conic sections* include two we are already familiar with, circles and parabolas. They also include *ellipses* and *hyperbolas*. An ellipse is a "squashed" circle; an example is given by Figure 14.11 on page 573. An example of a hyperbola is the graph of the function $y = 1/x$.

Conic sections are so called because, as was demonstrated by the Greeks, they can be constructed by slicing, or sectioning, a cone. Conic sections arise naturally in physics, since the path of a body orbiting the sun is a conic section. We will study them in terms of parametric and implicit equations. As we have already studied parabolas, we now focus on circles, ellipses and hyperbolas.

Circles

Example 2   Graph the parametric equations

$$x = 5 + 2\cos t \quad \text{and} \quad y = 3 + 2\sin t.$$

Solution   We see that x varies between 3 and 7 with a midline of 5 while y varies between 1 and 5 with a midline of 3. Figure 14.18 gives a graph of this function. It appears to be a circle of radius 2 centered at the point $(5, 3)$.

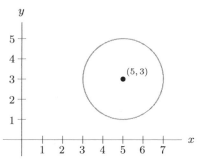

Figure 14.18: The circle defined by
$x = 5 + 2\cos t$, $y = 3 + 2\sin t$,
$0 \leq t \leq 2\pi$

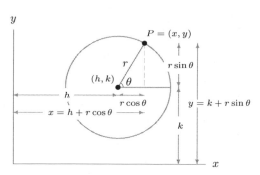

Figure 14.19: A circle of radius r centered at the point (h, k)

Compare Figure 14.18 with Figure 14.19, which shows a circle of radius r centered at the point (h, k). The coordinates of a point $P = (x, y)$, corresponding to an angle θ, are given by

$$x = h + r\cos\theta \quad \text{and} \quad y = k + r\sin\theta.$$

The equations in Example 2 are of this form, with t instead of θ and with $h = 5$, $k = 3$, and $r = 2$. This curve is a circle because the point P is always a fixed distance, 2, from the point $(5, 3)$.

For $r > 0$, the parametric equations of a **circle** of radius r centered at the point (h, k) are:

$$x = h + r\cos t \quad y = k + r\sin t \quad 0 \leq t \leq 2\pi.$$

Eliminating the Parameter t in the Equations for a Circle

To eliminate the parameter t from the parametric equations for a circle, we rewrite the equations as

$$x - h = r\cos t \quad \text{so} \quad (x - h)^2 = r^2\cos^2 t$$

and

$$y - k = r\sin t \quad \text{so} \quad (y - k)^2 = r^2\sin^2 t.$$

Adding these two equations and applying the Pythagorean identity, $\cos^2 t + \sin^2 t = 1$, gives

$$\begin{aligned}
(x - h)^2 + (y - k)^2 &= r^2\cos^2 t + r^2\sin^2 t \\
&= r^2(\cos^2 t + \sin^2 t) \\
&= r^2.
\end{aligned}$$

An implicit equation for the **circle** of radius r centered at the point (h, k) is:

$$(x - h)^2 + (y - k)^2 = r^2.$$

This is called the **standard form** of the equation of a circle.

For the unit circle, we have $h = 0$, $k = 0$, and $r = 1$. This gives

$$x^2 + y^2 = 1.$$

Example 3   Write the circle in Example 2 in standard form.

Solution   We have $h = 5$, $k = 3$, and $r = 2$. This gives

$$(x - 5)^2 + (y - 3)^2 = 2^2 = 4.$$

If we expand the equation for the circle in Example 3, we get a quadratic equation in two variables:

$$x^2 - 10x + 25 + y^2 - 6y + 9 = 4,$$

or

$$x^2 + y^2 - 10x - 6y + 30 = 0.$$

Note that the coefficients of x^2 and y^2 (in this case, 1) are equal. Such equations often describe circles; we put them into standard form, $(x - h)^2 + (y - k)^2 = r^2$, by completing the square.

Example 4   Describe in words the curve defined by the equation

$$x^2 + 10x + 20 = 4y - y^2.$$

Solution   Rearranging terms gives

$$x^2 + 10x + y^2 - 4y = -20.$$

We complete the square for the terms involving x and (separately) for the terms involving y:

$$\underbrace{(x^2 + 10x + 25)}_{(x+5)^2} + \underbrace{(y^2 - 4y + 4)}_{(y-2)^2} \underbrace{-25 - 4}_{\substack{\text{Compensating} \\ \text{terms}}} = -20$$

$$(x + 5)^2 + (y - 2)^2 - 29 = -20$$
$$(x + 5)^2 + (y - 2)^2 = 9.$$

This equation is a circle of radius $r = 3$ with center $(h, k) = (-5, 2)$.

Exercises and Problems for Section 14.2

Exercises

Decide whether the curves given in Exercises 1–5 are implicit or explicit.

1. $y = 2x - 1$, $0 \leq x \leq 2$.
2. $x = 3 + 2\cos t$, $y = 4 - 2\sin t$, $-\pi \leq t \leq \pi$.
3. $\frac{x^2}{a^2} + \frac{y^2}{b^2} = 1$
4. $x^2 + 2x - y + 1 = 0$
5. $x - y^2 + 2y + 1 = 0$

What are the center and radius of the circles in Exercises 6–9?

6. $4x^2 + 4y^2 - 9 = 0$
7. $10 - 3(x^2 + y^2) = 0$
8. $(x + 1)^2 + 2(y + 3)^2 = 32 - (x + 1)^2$
9. $\frac{4 - (x - 4)^2}{(y - 4)^2} - 1 = 0$

In Exercises 10–17, parameterize the circles.

10. Radius 3, centered at the origin, traversed clockwise starting at $(0, 3)$.

11. Radius 4, centered at the origin, traversed clockwise starting at $(4, 0)$.

12. Radius 7, centered at the origin, traversed counterclockwise starting at $(-7, 0)$.

13. Radius 5, centered at the origin, traversed counterclockwise starting at $(0, -5)$.

14. Radius 4, centered at $(3, 1)$, traversed clockwise starting at $(3, 5)$.

15. Radius 5, centered at $(3, 4)$, traversed counterclockwise starting at $(8, 4)$.

16. Radius 3, centered at $(-1, -2)$, traversed counterclockwise starting at $(-4, -2)$.

17. Radius $\sqrt{5}$, centered at $(-2, 1)$, traversed counterclockwise starting at $(-2, 1 + \sqrt{5})$.

Problems

Are the center and radius given in Exercises 18–20 true or false?

18. $(x - 2)^2 + (y + 2)^2 = 2$, center $(2, -2)$, radius 2

19. $x^2 + 2x + y^2 - 2y = 2$, center $(-1, 1)$, radius 2

20. $(x - 2)^2 + y^2 = 4$, center $(2, 0)$, radius 2

21. Identify the center and radius for each of the following circles.

  (a) $(x - 2)^2 + (y + 4)^2 = 20$
  (b) $2x^2 + 2y^2 + 4x - 8y = 12$

What curves do the parametric equations in Problems 22–25 trace out? Find an implicit or explicit equation for each curve.

22. $x = 2 + \cos t, \; y = 2 - \sin t$

23. $x = 2 + \cos t, \; y = \cos^2 t$

24. $x = 2 + \cos t, \; y = 2 - \cos t$

25. $x = 4 \sin^2 t, \; y = 3 + \sin t$

26. An ant, starting at the origin, moves at 2 units/sec along the x-axis to the point $(1, 0)$. The ant then moves counterclockwise along the unit circle to $(0, 1)$ at a speed of $3\pi/2$ units/sec, then straight down to the origin at a speed of 2 units/sec along the y-axis.

  (a) Express the ant's coordinates as a function of time, t, in secs.
  (b) Express the reverse path as a function of time.

State whether the equations in Problems 27–30 represent a curve parametrically, implicitly, or explicitly. Give the two other types of representations for the same curve.

27. $xy = 1 \quad$ for $x > 0$

28. $x = e^t, \quad y = e^{2t} \quad$ for all t

29. $y = \sqrt{4 - x^2}$

30. $x^2 - 2x + y^2 = 0 \quad$ for $y < 0$

31. In Figure 14.20 a wheel of radius 1 meter rests on the x-axis with its center on the y-axis. There is a spot on the rim at the point $(1, 1)$. At time $t = 0$ the wheel starts rolling on the x-axis in the direction shown at a rate of 1

radian per second. Find parametric equations describing the motion of

(a) The center of the wheel.
(b) The motion of the spot on the rim. Plot its path.

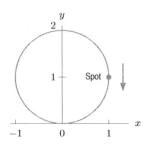

Figure 14.20

32. What can you say about the values of a, b and k if the equations

$$x = a + k \cos t, \quad y = b + k \sin t, \qquad 0 \le t \le 2\pi,$$

trace out each of the circles in Figure 14.21?

(a) C_1 **(b)** C_2 **(c)** C_3

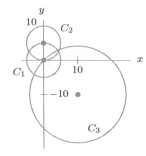

Figure 14.21

14.3 ELLIPSES

In this section we consider the graph of an ellipse, which is a "squashed" circle.

> The parametric equations of an **ellipse** centered at (h, k) are:
>
> $$x = h + a\cos t \qquad y = k + b\sin t \qquad 0 \leq t \leq 2\pi.$$
>
> We usually take $a > 0$ and $b > 0$.

In the special case where $a = b$, these equations give a circle of radius $r = a$. Thus, a circle is a special kind of ellipse. The parametric equations of an ellipse are transformations of the parametric equations of the unit circle, $x = \cos t$, $y = \sin t$. These transformations have the effect of shifting and stretching the unit circle into an ellipse.

Example 1 Graph the ellipse given by

$$x = 7 + 5\cos t, \qquad y = 4 + 2\sin t, \qquad 0 \leq t \leq 2\pi.$$

Solution See Figure 14.22. The center of the ellipse is $(h, k) = (7, 4)$. The value $a = 5$ determines the horizontal "radius" of the ellipse, while $b = 2$ determines the vertical "radius". The value of x varies from a maximum of 12 to a minimum of 2 about the vertical midline $x = 7$. Similarly, the value of y varies from a maximum of 6 to a minimum of 2 about the horizontal midline $y = 4$. The ellipse is symmetric about the midlines $x = 7$ and $y = 4$.

In general, the horizontal axis of an ellipse has length $2a$, and the vertical axis has length $2b$. This is similar to a circle, which has diameter $2r$. The difference here is that the diameter of a circle is the same in every direction, whereas the "diameter" of an ellipse depends on the direction.

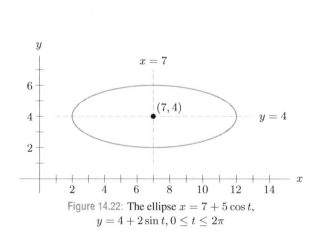

Figure 14.22: The ellipse $x = 7 + 5\cos t$, $y = 4 + 2\sin t, 0 \leq t \leq 2\pi$

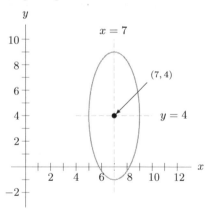

Figure 14.23: $x = 7 + 2\cos t$, $y = 4 + 5\sin t, 0 \leq t \leq 2\pi$

The longer axis of an ellipse is called the *major* axis and the shorter axis is called the *minor* axis. Either the horizontal or the vertical axis can be the longer axis.

Example 2   Graph the ellipse given by

$$x = 7 + 2\cos t, \qquad y = 4 + 5\sin t, \qquad 0 \le t \le 2\pi.$$

How is this ellipse similar to the one in Example 1? How is it different?

Solution   This ellipse has the same center $(h, k) = (7, 4)$ as the ellipse in Example 1. However, as we see in Figure 14.23, the vertical axis of this ellipse is the longer one and the horizontal axis is the shorter one. This is the opposite of the situation in Example 1.

Eliminating the Parameter t in the Equations for an Ellipse

As with circles, we can eliminate t from the parametric equations for an ellipse. We first rewrite the equation for x as follows:

$$x = h + a\cos t$$
$$x - h = a\cos t$$
$$\frac{x - h}{a} = \cos t.$$

Similarly, we rewrite the equation for y as

$$\frac{y - k}{b} = \sin t.$$

Using the Pythagorean Identity gives

$$\left(\frac{x - h}{a}\right)^2 + \left(\frac{y - k}{b}\right)^2 = \cos^2 t + \sin^2 t = 1.$$

The implicit equation for an **ellipse** centered at (h, k) and with horizontal axis $2a$ and vertical axis $2b$ is:

$$\frac{(x - h)^2}{a^2} + \frac{(y - k)^2}{b^2} = 1.$$

Exercises and Problems for Section 14.3

Exercises

For the ellipses in Exercises 1–4, find

(a) The coordinates of the center and the "diameter" in the x- and y-directions.

(b) An implicit equation for the ellipse.

1.

2.

3.

4.

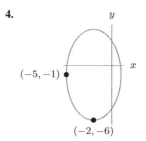

5. Parameterize the ellipse in Exercise 1 counterclockwise, starting at $(-2, 0)$.

6. Parameterize the ellipse in Exercise 2 counterclockwise, starting at $(12, 0)$.

7. Parameterize the ellipse in Exercise 3 clockwise, starting at $(9, 0)$.

8. Parameterize the ellipse in Exercise 4 clockwise, starting at $(-5, -1)$.

9. Compare the ellipse in Example 2 on page 581 with the ellipse given by

$$x = 7 + 2\cos(-s), \quad y = 4 + 5\sin(-s), \quad 0 \le s \le 2\pi.$$

10. Compare the ellipse in Example 2 on page 581 with the ellipse given by

$$x = 7 + 2\cos(2t), \quad y = 4 + 5\sin(2t), \quad 0 \le t \le 2\pi.$$

Problems

11. For each of the following ellipses, find the center and lengths of the major and minor axes, and graph it.

    (a) $\dfrac{(x+1)^2}{4} + \dfrac{(y-3)^2}{6} = 1$

    (b) $2x^2 + 3y^2 - 6x + 6y = 12$

By completing the square, rewrite the equations in Problems 12–17 in the form

$$\frac{(x-h)^2}{a^2} + \frac{(y-k)^2}{b^2} = 1.$$

What is the center of the ellipse? The values of a and b?

12. $\dfrac{x^2 + 4x}{9} + \dfrac{y^2 + 10y}{25} = -\dfrac{4}{9}$

13. $\dfrac{x^2 - 2x}{4} + y^2 + 4y + \dfrac{13}{4} = 0$

14. $4x^2 - 4x + y^2 + 2y = 2$

15. $4x^2 + 16x + y^2 + 2y + 13 = 0$

16. $9x^2 - 54x + 4y^2 - 16y + 61 = 0$

17. $9x^2 + 9x + 4y^2 - 4y = \dfrac{131}{4}$

For positive a, b, the equation of an ellipse can be written in the form

$$\frac{(x-h)^2}{a^2} + \frac{(y-k)^2}{b^2} = 1.$$

In Problems 18–19, rank h, k, a, b, and the number 0 in ascending order (i.e. increasing order). Assume the x- and y-scales are equal.

18.

19.

20. Show, by completing the square, that the equation $Ax^2 - Bx + y^2 = r_0^2$ represents an ellipse, where A, B, and r_0 are constants and $A > 0$. (See Problem 21.)

21. Consider the following equation in polar coordinates, where r_0 is a positive constant and where $0 \le \epsilon < 1$ is a constant:

$$r = \frac{r_0}{1 - \epsilon \cos \theta}, \quad 0 \le \theta < 2\pi.$$

    (a) Show, by converting to Cartesian coordinates, that this equation describes an ellipse. You may use the results of Problem 20.

    (b) What are the minimum and maximum values of r? At what values of θ do they occur?

    (c) Graph the ellipse for $r_0 = 6$ and $\epsilon = 0.5$, labeling the points from part (b) as well as the y-intercepts, that is, the points at $\theta = \pi/2$ and $\theta = 3\pi/2$. What is its center?

    (d) Find a formula in terms of r_0 and ϵ for the length of the horizontal axis of the ellipse.

    (e) The constant ϵ is known as the *eccentricity* of the ellipse. Describe in words the appearance of an ellipse of eccentricity $\epsilon = 0$. What happens to the appearance of the ellipse as the eccentricity gets closer and closer to $\epsilon = 1$?

22. If you look at a circular disk, such as a quarter, head on, you see a circle. But if you tilt the disk away from your line of sight, as shown in Figure 14.24, the disk appears elliptical. The length of the apparent ellipse's horizontal axis does not change, but the length of the vertical axis decreases.

    (a) Find a formula for ℓ, the length of the ellipse's vertical axis, in terms of θ, the angle of tilt with respect to the line of sight.

(b) What does your formula say about the appearance of the coin after being tilted through an angle of $\theta = 0°$? $\theta = 90°$? $\theta = 180°$? Does this make sense?

(c) Find a formula for the ellipse formed by tilting a disk of radius r through an angle of θ. Assume that the disk is centered at the origin and that the disk is being tilted around the x-axis, so that the length of its horizontal axis does not change.

(d) The equation $x^2/16 + y^2/7 = 1$ describes an ellipse. If we think of this ellipse as a tilted disk, then what is the disk's radius, and through what angle θ has it been tilted?

Front view   Side view   Front view   Side view

r θ

Before tilting   After tilting

Figure 14.24: At left, front and side views of a circular disc of radius r. At right, the same disk as it appears after being tilted through an angle θ relative to the line of sight.

23. A fuel-efficient way to travel from earth to Mars is to follow a semi-elliptical orbit known as a *Hohmann transfer orbit*.[2] The spacecraft leaves the earth at the point on the ellipse closest to the sun, and arrives at Mars at the point on the ellipse farthest from the sun, as shown in

Figure 14.25. Let r_e be the radius of earth's orbit and r_m the radius of Mars' orbit, and let $2a$ and $2b$ be the respective lengths of the horizontal and vertical axes of the ellipse.

(a) Orienting the ellipse as shown in the figure, with the sun at the origin, find a formula for this orbit in terms of r_e, r_m, and b.

(b) It can be shown that $b^2 = 2ar_e - r_e^2$. Given this and your answer to part (a), find a formula for b in terms of r_m and r_e.

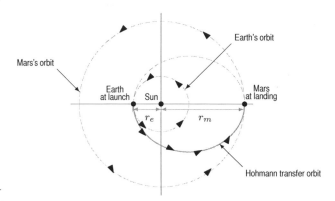

Earth's orbit

Mars's orbit

Earth at launch   Sun   Mars at landing

r_e r_m

Hohmann transfer orbit

Figure 14.25

14.4 HYPERBOLAS

We now use another form of the Pythagorean identity to parameterize a curve. With $\tan t = \sin t / \cos t$ and $\sec t = 1 / \cos t$, on page 370 we showed that

$$\sec^2 t - \tan^2 t = 1.$$

We use this identity to investigate the curve described by the parametric equations

$$x = \sec t \qquad \text{and} \qquad y = \tan t.$$

By eliminating the parameter t, we get

$$x^2 - y^2 = 1.$$

This implicit equation looks similar to the equation for a unit circle $x^2 + y^2 = 1$. However, the curve it describes is very different. Solving for y, we find that

$$y^2 = x^2 - 1.$$

---

[2] *Scientific American*, March, 2000. Note that in an actual Hohmann transfer, the spacecraft would begin in low earth orbit, not from the earth's surface. Timing is critical in order for the two planets to be correctly aligned. Calculations show that at launch, Mars must lead earth by about 45 degrees, which happens only once every 26 months. Note also that the orbits of earth and Mars are actually themselves elliptical, though here we treat them as circular.

For large values of x, the values of y^2 and x^2 are very nearly equal. For instance, when $x = 100$, we see that $x^2 = 10{,}000$ and $y^2 = x^2 - 1 = 9999$. Thus, for large values of x,

$$y^2 \approx x^2,$$

$$y \approx \pm x.$$

The graph of $y = \pm x$ is in Figure 14.17 on page 576; it looks like an X.

What happens for smaller values of x? Writing the equation as $y^2 = x^2 - 1$, shows us that x^2 cannot be less than 1; otherwise y^2 would be negative. See Table 14.1 and Figure 14.26.

Table 14.1   *Points on the graph of the hyperbola $x^2 - y^2 = 1$*

x	y	Points	x	y	Points
-3	± 2.83	$(-3, 2.83)$ and $(-3, -2.83)$	3	± 2.83	$(3, 2.83)$ and $(3, -2.83)$
-2	± 1.73	$(-2, 1.73)$ and $(-2, -1.73)$	2	± 1.73	$(2, 1.73)$ and $(2, -1.73)$
-1	± 0	$(-1, 0)$ and $(-1, -0)$	1	± 0	$(1, 0)$ and $(1, -0)$
0	Undefined	None			

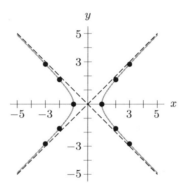

Figure 14.26: A graph of $x^2 - y^2 = 1$. The X-shaped graph of $y^2 = x^2$ has been dashed in

This graph is an example of a *hyperbola*. By analogy to the unit circle, it is called the *unit hyperbola*. It has two branches, one to the right of the y-axis and one to the left. As x grows large in magnitude, toward either $+\infty$ or $-\infty$, the graph approaches the asymptotes, $y^2 = x^2$. To see how the two branches of a similar hyperbola are traced as t increases from 0 to 2π, see Exercise 2.

A General Formula for Hyperbolas

We can shift and stretch the unit hyperbola using the equations $x = h + a \sec t$ and $y = k + b \tan t$. This has the effect of centering the hyperbola at the point (h, k).

> The parametric equations for a **hyperbola** centered at (h, k) and opening to the left and right are
> $$x = h + a \sec t \qquad y = k + b \tan t \qquad 0 \le t \le 2\pi.$$
> We usually take $a > 0$ and $b > 0$.

We eliminate the parameter, t, from the parametric equations to obtain the implicit equation

$$\frac{(x-h)^2}{a^2} - \frac{(y-k)^2}{b^2} = 1.$$

Notice that this equation is similar to the general equation for an ellipse.

Example 1   Graph the equation $\dfrac{(x-4)^2}{9} - \dfrac{(y-7)^2}{25} = 1.$

Solution   Since $h = 4$ and $k = 7$, we have shifted the unit hyperbola 4 units to the right and 7 units up. We have $a^2 = 9$ and $b^2 = 25$, so $a = 3$ and $b = 5$. Thus, we have stretched the unit hyperbola horizontally by a factor of 3 and vertically by a factor of 5.

To make it easier to draw hyperbolas, we imagine a "unit square" centered at the origin. This unit square helps us locate the vertices and asymptotes of the hyperbola $x^2 - y^2 = 1$. See Figure 14.27. Stretching and shifting the hyperbola causes this square to be transformed into a rectangle centered at the point $(h, k) = (4, 7)$ with width $2a = 6$ and height $2b = 10$. See Figure 14.28. The rectangle enables us to draw the X-shaped asymptotes as diagonal lines through the corners. The vertices of the transformed hyperbola are located at the midpoints of the vertical sides of the rectangle.

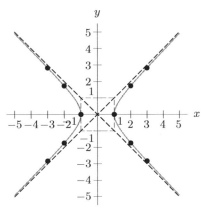

Figure 14.27: The hyperbola $x^2 - y^2 = 1$, with the unit square dashed in

Figure 14.28: A graph of $\frac{(x-4)^2}{9} - \frac{(y-7)^2}{25} = 1$. A rectangle of width $2a = 6$ height $2b = 10$ has been dashed in, centered at the point $(h, k) = (4, 7)$

Note that the ellipse $\frac{(x-4)^2}{9} + \frac{(y-7)^2}{25} = 1$ would exactly fit inside the rectangle in Figure 14.28. In this sense, a hyperbola is an ellipse turned "inside-out."

Example 2   Graph the equation $\dfrac{(y-7)^2}{25} - \dfrac{(x-4)^2}{9} = 1.$

Solution   This equation is similar to that in Example 1, except that the terms have opposite signs. The graph in Figure 14.29 is similar to the one in Figure 14.28 except that it opens up and down instead of right and left.

Figure 14.29: A graph of $\frac{(y-7)^2}{25} - \frac{(x-4)^2}{9} = 1$. This graph is similar to the one in Figure 14.28 except that here the hyperbola opens up and down instead of right and left

In summary:

The implicit equation for a **hyperbola**,

$$\frac{(x-h)^2}{a^2} - \frac{(y-k)^2}{b^2} = 1,$$

describes a hyperbola that opens left and right. Its asymptotes are diagonal lines through the corners of a rectangle of width $2a$ and height $2b$ centered at the point (h, k). The graph with equation

$$\frac{(y-k)^2}{b^2} - \frac{(x-h)^2}{a^2} = 1$$

has a similar shape, except that it opens up and down.

Exercises and Problems for Section 14.4

Exercises

For the hyperbolas in Exercises 1–4, find

(a) The coordinates of the vertices of the hyperbola and the coordinates of its center.

(b) The equations of the asymptotes.

(c) An implicit equation for the hyperbola.

1.

2.

3.

4.

5. Parameterize the hyperbola in Exercise 1. What t values give the upper half?

6. Parameterize the hyperbola in Exercise 2. What t values give the right half?

7. Parameterize the hyperbola in Exercise 3. What t values give the left half?

8. Parameterize the hyperbola in Exercise 4. What t values give the lower half?

Problems

By completing the square, rewrite the equations in Problems 9–14 in the form

$$\frac{(x-h)^2}{a^2} - \frac{(y-k)^2}{b^2} = 1 \text{ or } \frac{(y-k)^2}{b^2} - \frac{(x-h)^2}{a^2} = 1.$$

What is the center, and does the hyperbola open left-right or up-down? What are the values of a and b?

9. $\dfrac{x^2 - 2x}{4} - y^2 + 4y = \dfrac{19}{4}$

10. $\dfrac{y^2 + 2y}{4} - \dfrac{x^2 - 4x}{9} = \dfrac{43}{36}$

11. $x^2 + 2x - 4y^2 - 24y = 39$

12. $9x^2 - 36x - 4y^2 + 8y = 4$

13. $4x^2 - 8x = 36y^2 - 36y - 31$

14. $9y^2 + 6y = 89 + 8x^2 + 24x$

For positive a, b, the equation of a hyperbola can be written in one of the two forms

I. $\dfrac{(x-h)^2}{a^2} - \dfrac{(y-k)^2}{b^2} = 1.$

II. $\dfrac{(y-k)^2}{b^2} - \dfrac{(x-h)^2}{a^2} = 1.$

In Problems 15–16, which form applies? Rank h, k, a, b, and the number 0 in ascending order (i.e. increasing order). Assume the x- and y-scales are equal.

15.

16.

17. For each of the following hyperbolas, find the center, vertices, and asymptotes, and graph it.

(a) $\dfrac{(x+5)^2}{6} - \dfrac{(y-2)^2}{4} = 1$

(b) $x^2 - y^2 + 2x = 4y + 17$

18. By scattering positively charged alpha particles off of atoms in gold foil, Ernest Lord Rutherford demonstrated that atoms contain a nucleus of concentrated charge. The scattered alpha particles followed hyperbolic trajectories, as shown in Figure 14.30, and Rutherford was able to measure the angle θ. However, the value of θ alone was not enough for Rutherford to determine whether the nuclear charge is negative or positive. A negatively charged nucleus would exert an attractive force on the alpha particles, and the positively charged nucleus would exert a repulsive force, but in either case, the trajectory would be a hyperbola specified by the angle θ. Note that in Figure 14.30, the incoming particle would pass through the origin if it were not scattered by the nucleus at $(d, 0)$.

(a) The hyperbola is $x^2/a^2 - y^2/b^2 = 1$. Find a formula for b in terms of a and θ.

(b) It turns out that the charge in the nucleus is positive, and that the alpha particles undergo a repulsive force. What must be true about the parameter a?

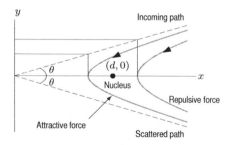

Figure 14.30

14.5 GEOMETRIC PROPERTIES OF CONIC SECTIONS

Having defined functions numerically, graphically, and algebraically, in this section we define the conic sections using geometry. The geometric properties of the conic sections lead to many applications in astronomy and engineering.

Using Geometry in Mathematical Models: Orbits

For centuries, natural philosophers tried to explain the motion of the planets. Over time, accounts based on the gods for whom the planets are named gave way to increasingly mathematical accounts. The seventeenth-century German astronomer Johannes Kepler believed nature could be explained mathematically, although today his approach would be considered mystical. He believed the planets orbited the sun within a geometrical framework of spheres nested within a cube, a pyramid, and other polyhedra.[3] After twenty years of attempting to fit a circle to the orbit of Mars, Kepler realized its orbit is not a circle, but an ellipse.

Other scientists have used geometry to build mathematical models. For instance, just as Kepler abandoned the perfect circle for the more complicated ellipse, Einstein abandoned perfectly flat Euclidean geometry in favor of the more complicated Riemannian geometry in his development of general relativity.

Orbits Are Conic Sections

Although Kepler discovered that an orbit can take the shape of an ellipse, it was Newton's laws of motion and gravity that provided the explanation. Newton showed that the orbit of any object that cannot escape the gravitational pull of another object is an ellipse.[4] Planets in the solar system follow an elliptical orbit around the sun, satellites orbiting the earth follow an elliptical orbit around the earth, and many comets follow elliptical orbits through the solar system. The most famous of these is Halley's comet, which passes within sight of earth once approximately every 76 years.[5] See Figure 14.31.

In contrast, when a body is not held in an elliptical orbit by another object, its trajectory is hyperbolic.[6] Comets that follow hyperbolic orbits through the solar system have paths that are deflected as they pass the sun, but they do not return. See Figure 14.32.

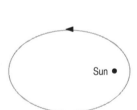

Figure 14.31: Halley's comet
follows an elliptical orbit
around the sun, like the one
shown here

Figure 14.32: Some comets follow a
hyperbolic trajectory, deflected by the
sun but never to return

---

[3] See http://en.wikipedia.org/wiki/Johannes_Kepler for more information. Page last accessed February 8, 2006.
[4] Unless, of course, the two objects collide.
[5] Halley's comet passed within sight of earth in 1986, and is predicted to return in 2061.
[6] In principle an orbit can be parabolic but in real systems such orbits are essentially impossible.

Slicing a Cone

The ancient Greeks studied the curves formed when a plane cuts a cone. These curves are called *conic sections*, where *section* is another word for a cut (as in dissection).

Although conic sections get their name from slicing cones, the Greek mathematician and astronomer Apollonius of Perga gave alternative definitions of the conics using distances in the plane. His work on conics is considered one of the wonders of mathematics, and he wrote it without benefit of either Cartesian coordinates or algebra.

Geometric Definitions of Conics

In a perfectly circular orbit, the sun would be at the circle's center. We have seen two ways of defining a circle. On page 577, a circle of radius r centered at point (h, k) is defined parametrically by the equations

$$x = h + r \cos t \qquad y = k + r \sin t \qquad 0 \leq t \leq 2\pi.$$

On page 577, the same circle is defined by the equation

$$(x - h)^2 + (y - k)^2 = r^2.$$

Circles: A Geometric Definition

These definitions of a circle are algebraic: they specify a set of points whose x- and y-coordinates satisfy certain equations. We can also give a geometric definition using the distance between points, not functions like squares, sines, and cosines. The geometric definition of the circle follows:

A *circle* of radius r is the set of points in the plane a distance r from a given point.

Notice that unless we restrict our points to the plane, our definition gives a sphere of radius r.

Ellipses: A Geometric Definition

In an elliptical orbit, like that of Halley's comet, the sun is not located at the center, but at a point called a *focus*. Any ellipse (other than a circle) has two foci. These points are used to give the geometric definition:

An *ellipse* is the set of points in the plane for which the sum of the distances to the foci is constant. [7]
- Each of the two points is called a *focus* or *focal point* of the ellipse.
- The two focal points lie on the major axis, and are equally spaced about the minor axis. The constant sum of distances is the length of the major axis.

No matter which point we pick on the ellipse, the sum of the distances from that point to the two focal points is the same. See Figures 14.33 and 14.34.

---

[7] If the constant equals the distance between the two points, we get a degenerate ellipse.

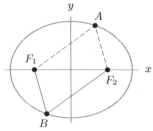

Figure 14.33: Sum of the distances
from any point on the ellipse,
such as A or B, to the foci, F_1
and F_2, is constant

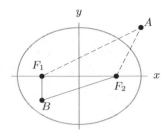

Figure 14.34: Sum of distances
from points A and B, which do
not lie on ellipse, to the foci, F_1
and F_2, is not constant

Example 1   Pluto's distance from the the sun ranges from 29.7 astronomical units (AU) at its closest point to
49.3 AU at its farthest. Center Pluto's elliptical orbit at the origin with the major axis on the x-axis.

(a) What is the length of the major axis?

(b) What are the coordinates of the two focal points?

(c) What is the length of the minor axis?

(d) Give an equation for this ellipse in rectangular coordinates.

(e) Give parametric equations for this ellipse.

Solution   (a) In Figure 14.35, Pluto is closest to the sun at $(a, 0)$; Pluto is farthest from the sun at $(-a, 0)$.
We see that

$$\text{Length of major axis} = 29.7 + 49.3 = 79 \text{ AU.}$$

(b) The two focal points are at $(c, 0)$ and $(-c, 0)$ in Figure 14.35. Half the length of the major axis
is 39.5, so $a = 39.5$. Since a is 29.7 units from the closest focus, $c = 39.5 - 29.7 = 9.8$. The
coordinates of the two focal points are $(9.8, 0)$ and $(-9.8, 0)$.

(c) When Pluto is at the point $(a, 0)$, the sum of its distances to the focal points is 79. Since the value
of this sum is the same at every point on the ellipse, at the point $(0, b)$, the sum of the distances
to the focal points is also 79. By symmetry, the distance from $(0, b)$ to the focus $(9.8, 0)$ is
$79/2 = 39.5$. Using the Pythagorean Theorem, we have:

$$(9.8)^2 + b^2 = (39.5)^2$$
$$b^2 = (39.5)^2 - (9.8)^2$$
$$b = 38.3.$$

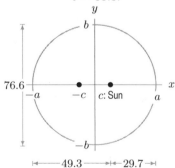

Figure 14.35: Pluto's orbit around the sun
appears circular, but is actually an ellipse

522

We see that
$$\text{Length of minor axis} = 2 \cdot 38.3 = 76.6 \text{ astronomical units.}$$

(d) In Section 14.3, we saw that the equation in rectangular coordinates for an ellipse centered at the origin is
$$\frac{x^2}{a^2} + \frac{y^2}{b^2} = 1.$$
For Pluto's orbit, we have $a = 39.5$ and $b = 38.3$, so the equation is
$$\frac{x^2}{(39.5)^2} + \frac{y^2}{(38.3)^2} = 1.$$

(e) Parametric equations for this ellipse are:
$$x = 39.5 \cos t$$
$$y = 38.3 \sin t.$$

In part (e) of Example 1, we give parametric equations for the orbit of Pluto. It would be natural to assume t stands for time. However, Kepler discovered that a planet travels fastest in its orbit when closest to the sun, and slowest when it is farthest away. Thus t cannot represent time, or the speeds would be the same at the closest and farthest points.

The Circular Appearance of Planetary Orbits

Notice in Example 1 that the length of the major axis in Pluto's orbit is not much greater than the length of the minor axis, making its orbit in Figure 14.35 look circular. Since Pluto's orbit is the most "squashed" of all the planetary orbits, it is easy to understand why Kepler assumed the orbit of Mars to be circular.

Example 2 By finding a formula for c in terms of a and b, determine the focal points $(\pm c, 0)$ for the ellipse where a and b are positive and $a > b$:
$$\frac{x^2}{a^2} + \frac{y^2}{b^2} = 1.$$

Solution The graph of this ellipse is in Figure 14.36. From the geometric definition of an ellipse, the sum of the distances to the two focal points is the same at every point on the curve. Thus
$$\begin{array}{c} \text{Sum of distances to} \\ \text{focal points from } (a,0) \end{array} = \begin{array}{c} \text{Sum of distances to} \\ \text{focal points from } (0,b) \end{array}.$$

On the left side of this equation, the distance from $(a, 0)$ to $(c, 0)$ is $a - c$ and the distance from $(a, 0)$ to $(-c, 0)$ is $a + c$, so
$$\begin{array}{c} \text{Sum of distances to} \\ \text{focal points from } (a,0) \end{array} = (a - c) + (a + c) = 2a.$$

Notice that, as before, the sum of distances to the foci is the length of the major axis, $2a$.

Using the distance formula, we see that the distances from $(0, b)$ to $(c, 0)$ and from $(0, b)$ to $(-c, 0)$ are both $\sqrt{b^2 + c^2}$, so
$$\begin{array}{c} \text{Sum of distances to} \\ \text{focal points from } (0,b) \end{array} = 2\sqrt{b^2 + c^2}.$$

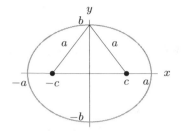

Figure 14.36: Locating the focal points

Putting this together and solving for c gives

$$2a = 2\sqrt{b^2 + c^2}$$
$$a = \sqrt{b^2 + c^2}$$
$$a^2 = b^2 + c^2$$
$$c^2 = a^2 - b^2$$
$$c = \sqrt{a^2 - b^2}.$$

Notice that applying the Pythagorean Theorem to the triangles in Figure 14.36 also gives $a = \sqrt{b^2 + c^2}$.

We have the following result:

Location of the Focal Points of an Ellipse
The focal points of the ellipse $x^2/a^2 + y^2/b^2 = 1$ with $a > b > 0$ are $(\pm c, 0)$ where

$$c = \sqrt{a^2 - b^2}.$$

The focal points lie on the major axis.
If $b > a$, the focal points are $(0, \pm c)$ with $c = \sqrt{b^2 - a^2}$.

Reflective Properties of Ellipses

The ellipse has a reflective property, which is used in applications involving light, sound, and shock waves. See Figure 14.37.

Reflective property of an ellipse
A ray that originates at one focus of an ellipse is reflected off the ellipse to the other focus.

Focus   Focus

Figure 14.37: Reflective property of an ellipse

This property of ellipses is used in lithotripsy, a medical procedure for treating kidney stones. The patient is placed in an elliptical tank of water with the kidney stone at one focus. High-energy shock waves generated at the other focus are concentrated on the stone, breaking it into small bits. The reflective property is also used in the construction of "whispering rooms." A person standing and whispering at one focus in an elliptical room can be heard at the other focus, but not at places in between. John Quincy Adams reportedly discovered this property while in the House of Representatives, and situated himself at a focal point in order to eavesdrop on other House members.

Example 3 An elliptical whispering gallery has a major axis of 100 m and minor axis of 40 m. Where should two speakers position themselves so as to hear each other most easily?

Solution Imagine the room centered at the origin with major axis on the x-axis. Then the positive x-intercept is $a = 50$ and the positive y-intercept is $b = 20$. The focal points are located at $c = \pm\sqrt{a^2 - b^2} = \pm\sqrt{50^2 - 20^2} = \pm 45.8$. The speakers should position themselves approximately 4.2 m in from the ends of the major axis.

Equivalence of the Algebraic and Geometric Definitions of the Ellipse

In Section 14.3, an ellipse was defined using rectangular coordinates as

$$\frac{x^2}{a^2} + \frac{y^2}{b^2} = 1.$$

In this section, we defined an ellipse is the set of points in the plane for which the sum of the distances to two focal points is constant. We now show that these two definitions are equivalent in the case in which the focal points are $(\pm c, 0)$ and the intercepts are $(\pm a, 0)$, with $0 < c < a$. Some of the details are omitted; see Problem 44.

Consider the set of points (x, y) such that the sum of the distances to two focal points $(\pm c, 0)$ is constant. We have

Sum of distances from (x, y) to focal points $=$ Sum of distances from $(a, 0)$ to focal points

$$\sqrt{(x - c)^2 + y^2} + \sqrt{(x + c)^2 + y^2} = 2a$$

$$\sqrt{(x - c)^2 + y^2} = 2a - \sqrt{(x + c)^2 + y^2}.$$

Square both sides and simplify to obtain:

$$-4cx = 4a^2 - 4a\sqrt{(x + c)^2 + y^2}.$$

Isolating the square root gives

$$a\sqrt{(x + c)^2 + y^2} = a^2 + cx.$$

We square both sides and simplify again to obtain:

$$a^2x^2 + a^2c^2 + a^2y^2 = a^4 + c^2x^2.$$

Let $b = \sqrt{a^2 - c^2}$. Then $b > 0$. Since $c^2 = a^2 - b^2$, simplifying again gives

$$-a^2b^2 + a^2y^2 = -b^2x^2$$

$$b^2x^2 + a^2y^2 = a^2b^2.$$

Dividing through by a^2b^2 gives the equation for an ellipse in rectangular coordinates

$$\frac{x^2}{a^2} + \frac{y^2}{b^2} = 1.$$

Hyperbolas

An ellipse is the set of points for which the sum of the distances to two points is constant. If the *difference* in the distances to two points is constant, we have a hyperbola. The two points are again called the focal points, or foci. See Figure 14.38.

A *hyperbola* is the set of points in the plane for which the difference of the distances to two points is constant.[8] Each of the two points is called a *focus* or *focal point* of the hyperbola.

Hyperbolic orbits describe two objects that pass by each other where neither object "captures" the other. Hyperbolas have two parts, or *branches*, as in Figure 14.38, but a hyperbolic orbit only uses one branch. In the hyperbolic orbit of a comet, for example, the comet comes in on almost a straight line, gets bent around the sun due to the gravitational pull, and goes out on almost a straight line. The straight lines that hyperbolas approach as the curve gets farther from the focus are the *asymptotes* of the hyperbola.

We saw in Section 14.4 that the equation for a hyperbola that opens left and right and is centered at the origin is

$$\frac{x^2}{a^2} - \frac{y^2}{b^2} = 1.$$

For this hyperbola, the asymptotes are

$$y = \pm \frac{b}{a} x,$$

and the focal points can be shown to be $(\pm c, 0)$ with

$$c = \sqrt{a^2 + b^2}.$$

Location of the Focal Points of a Hyperbola
The focal points of the hyperbola given by equation $x^2/a^2 - y^2/b^2 = 1$ are $(\pm c, 0)$ where

$$c = \sqrt{a^2 + b^2}.$$

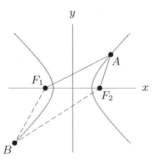

Figure 14.38: Difference between distances from any point on the curve, such as A or B, to the foci, F_1 and F_2, is constant

---

[8] We always subtract the shorter distance from the longer to get a positive constant. If the constant equals the distance between the two points, we have a degenerate hyperbola.

We have said that a hyperbola is the set of points for which the difference of the distances from two focal points is constant. Section 14.4 gave an equation for a hyperbola. The justification that these two definitions of a hyperbola are equivalent is similar to the justification for ellipses on page 593. See Problem 45.

Example 4   (a) Find the focal points and the asymptotes for the hyperbola given by

$$\frac{x^2}{9} - \frac{y^2}{16} = 1.$$

(b) Graph the hyperbola.
(c) For each of the two x-intercepts, find the difference of the distances to the two focal points.

Solution   (a) We have $a = 3$ and $b = 4$. Since $c = \sqrt{a^2 + b^2} = \sqrt{9 + 16} = 5$, the two focal points are $(\pm 5, 0)$. The asymptotes are the two lines $y = \pm(b/a)x = \pm(4/3)x$.
(b) See Figure 14.39.
(c) The intercept $(3, 0)$ is distance 2 from one focus and distance 8 from the other focus. The difference of the distance to the two focal points is 6. Similarly, the difference of the distances to the intercept $(-3, 0)$ is also $8 - 2 = 6$.

Application of Hyperbolas: Constant Time Difference

LORAN (LOng RAnge Navigation) is a navigational system that uses low-frequency radio transmitters to determine the location of a ship or aircraft. If two radio transmitters are transmitting signals, the time difference between the receipt of the signals by the ship or aircraft is measured. The ship or aircraft must be somewhere on the hyperbola with this constant difference. To determine the exact location, a third transmitter is needed. The constant time difference between this third transmitter and one of the first two gives a second hyperbola. The intersection of these two hyperbolas determines the location.

Sonic booms also involve hyperbolas. The cone created by the circular shock wave as its radius increases intersects the plane of the earth in a hyperbola.

Reflective Properties of Hyperbolas

Hyperbolas have a reflective property similar to that of ellipses. See Figure 14.40.

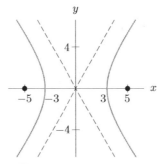

Figure 14.39: The hyperbola $x^2/9 - y^2/16 = 1$

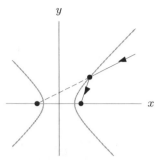

Figure 14.40: Reflective property
of a hyperbola

Reflective property of hyperbolas:
A beam aimed at the far focus behind the hyperbola is reflected off the curve to hit the focus in front of the hyperbola. Alternately, a beam originating from the focus in front of the hyperbola is reflected off the curve so that it appears to have originated from the focus behind the hyperbola.

Example 5 A hyperbolic mirror has equation

$$\frac{x^2}{16} - \frac{y^2}{9} = 1.$$

Find the equation of the line along which a beam of light could be sent out from point $A = (15, 50)$ to reflect off the hyperbola and arrive at the focus closest to point A.

Solution The focal points for this hyperbola are $(\pm c, 0)$ with $c = \sqrt{a^2 + b^2} = \sqrt{16 + 9} = 5$. The focal point closest to A is $(5, 0)$ and the focal point farthest away is $(-5, 0)$. Since we want the beam of light to reflect off the hyperbola and arrive at $(5, 0)$, we aim the beam at the other focal point, $(-5, 0)$. The line from point A to $(-5, 0)$ has slope

$$m = \frac{50 - 0}{15 - (-5)} = \frac{50}{20} = 2.5.$$

The equation of the line is

$$y = 2.5(x - (-5)) = 2.5x + 12.5.$$

A beam of light sent along the line $y = 2.5x + 12.5$ toward the point $(-5, 0)$ is reflected off the hyperbola to the point $(5, 0)$.

Parabolas

Similar to an ellipse and a hyperbola, a parabola can be defined in terms of the distance from a focal point. For a parabola, however, the definition involves one focal point, and a line called the *directrix*.

A *parabola* is the set of points in the plane for which the distance from a point is equal to the distance from a fixed line. The point is called the *focus* and the line is called the *directrix*.

The focus lies on the axis of symmetry of the parabola and the directrix is perpendicular to the axis of symmetry. See Figure 14.41. If the focus is on the positive y-axis at $(0, c)$ and the directrix is the horizontal line is $y = -c$, Example 6 shows that the geometric definition gives a parabola.

Figure 14.41: The focus and directrix of a parabola. Even though they may not look it, the two line segments are the same length

Example 6 For c a positive constant, find the equation for the set of points of equal distance from the point $(0, c)$ and a horizontal line $y = -c$..

Solution Let (x, y) be any point satisfying

$$\text{Distance from } (x,y) \text{ to the point } (0,c) = \text{Distance from } (x,y) \text{ to the line } y = -c$$

$$\sqrt{x^2 + (y-c)^2} = y + c$$
$$x^2 + (y-c)^2 = (y+c)^2$$
$$x^2 + y^2 - 2cy + c^2 = y^2 + 2cy + c^2$$
$$x^2 = 4cy$$
$$y = \frac{1}{4c}x^2.$$

Thus the set of points is a parabola through the origin.

Summarizing Example 6, we have the following result:

Location of the Focus and Directrix of a Parabola
The focus of the parabola $y = ax^2$ is the point $(0, c)$ where $c = 1/(4a)$.
The directrix is the line $y = -c$.

Example 7 (a) Find the focus and the directrix of the parabola $y = 3x^2$.
(b) Show that the point $(1, 3)$ on the parabola is equidistant from the focus and the directrix.

Solution (a) We have $a = 3$ so the focus is at the point $(0, 1/12)$ and the directrix is the line $y = -1/12$.
(b) We have

$$\text{Distance from } (1,3) \text{ to the focus } (0, 1/12) = \sqrt{1^2 + (3 - 1/12)^2}$$
$$= \sqrt{\frac{12^2 + 35^2}{12^2}}$$
$$= \frac{37}{12}.$$

The distance from $(1, 3)$ to the directrix $y = -1/12$ is the difference in the y-values, since the directrix is a horizontal line:

$$\text{Distance from } (1, 3) \text{ to directrix} \quad = 3 + \frac{1}{12}$$

$$= \frac{37}{12}.$$

Thus the distance from the point $(1, 3)$ to the focus equals the distance from the point $(1, 3)$ to the directrix. This property holds for all points (x, y) on the parabola.

Reflective Properties of Parabolas

Parabolas also have the reflective property illustrated in Figure 14.42.

> **Reflective property of parabolas**
> All beams parallel to the axis of symmetry reflect off the parabola to the focus.

Archimedes discovered this reflective property of parabolas in the third century BC, and legend has it that he constructed parabolic mirrors to concentrate the sun's rays at a single point and set fire to enemy targets.[9]

A solar furnace produces heat by focusing sunlight using parabolic mirrors. In fact, the word *focus* comes from Latin for "fireplace." Giant parabolic mirrors are used in telescopes to focus light and radio waves from outer space.

The reflective property of parabolas also works in reverse. A light placed at the focus of a parabolic mirror sends out light rays that are reflected out in a beam parallel to the axis of symmetry of the parabola. Car headlights have parabolic reflectors with the lightbulb at the focus.

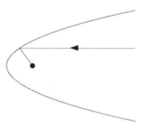

Figure 14.42: Reflective property of a parabola

Example 8 The parabolic reflector behind a car head light is 16 cm across and 3 cm deep. Where should the bulb be positioned?

Solution The shape of the parabolic reflector is made by rotating a parabola $y = ax^2$ about the y-axis; see Figure 14.43. Since the rim of the reflector lies on the parabola, the point $(8, 3)$ satisfies the equation $y = ax^2$ so $3 = a(8^2)$ and $a = 3/64$. The focus is located at:

$$c = \frac{1}{4a} = \frac{1}{4(3/64)} = \frac{16}{3}.$$

---

[9]The Discovery Channel's *Mythbusters* program has questioned the feasibility of such a strategy, though experiments conducted at MIT have demonstrated its potential (see http://web.mit.edu/2.009/www/lectures/10_ArchimedesResult.html, accessed February 27, 2006). However, the MIT experiments suggest that a number of carefully arranged small, flat mirrors might have been more practical than one large parabolic mirror.

Figure 14.43: Car headlight

The bulb should be placed $16/3$ cm from the vertex of the parabola along the axis of symmetry.

Exercises and Problems for Section 14.5

Exercises

In Exercises 1–5, identify the conic and identify the major axis if an ellipse or else the line of symmetry through the vertex or vertices.

1. $\dfrac{x^2}{5} + \dfrac{y^2}{3} = 1$

2. $\dfrac{x^2}{5} - \dfrac{y^2}{3} = 1$

3. $\dfrac{x^2}{2} - \dfrac{y^2}{3} = -1$

4. $\dfrac{x}{2} + \dfrac{y^2}{3} = 1$

5. $y^2 = 1 + \dfrac{x^2}{3}$

6. A circle is centered at the origin and includes the point $(-1, 3)$. Find the radius.

7. A circle is centered at the origin and includes the point $(1, 2)$. At what points does the circle intersect the vertical axis?

8. An ellipse with horizontal and vertical axes is centered at the origin and includes the point $(3, 2)$. Which of the following points are also on any such ellipse?

  (a) $(-3, 2)$ **(b)** $(3, -2)$

  (c) $(-3, -2)$ **(d)** $(2, 3)$

9. An ellipse is centered at the origin and has one focal point at $(0, 2)$. Find the other focal point and say whether the major axis is horizontal or vertical.

10. For the ellipse $\dfrac{x^2}{9} + \dfrac{y^2}{16} = 1$, find the focal points.

11. A hyperbola with foci on one of the axes is centered at the origin and includes the point $(1, 2)$. Which of the following points are also on any such hyperbola?

  (a) $(-1, 2)$ **(b)** $(1, -2)$

  (c) $(-1, -2)$ **(d)** $(2, 1)$

12. A hyperbola is centered at the origin and has one focal point at $(0, -3)$. Find the other focal point and the axis through the vertices.

13. For the hyperbola $x^2 - y^2 = 1$, find the focal points.

14. A parabola is centered at the origin, opens downward, and includes the point $(-1, -2)$. Which of the following points are also on any such parabola?

  (a) $(1, 2)$ **(b)** $(1, -2)$

  (c) $(-1, 2)$ **(d)** $(2, 1)$

15. Find the equation of a parabola centered at the origin and having a focal point at $(-1, 0)$.

16. Find the equation of a parabola centered at the origin and having a focal point at $(0, -3)$.

Problems

17. At a covert military operation camp, the operations sergeant suggests that a parabolic "mirror" be placed 200 meters from the communications transmitter, which sends signals to headquarters in a nearby city, to disguise its location. The mess sergeant objects that a hyperbolic mirror would be more effective, and the first platoon leader suggests that a series of elliptical mirrors would be best. As captain of the operation, which advice should you follow? Why?

For Problems 18–20, find the vertex and focal point of the parabola.

18. $(x + 2)^2 = 5(y - 1)$ **19.** $y^2 = \frac{1}{4}(x + 2)$

20. $y = x^2 - x + 1$

21. In Figure 14.44, where F is the focus, find the equation of the parabola and its directrix.

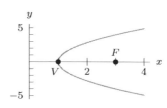

Figure 14.44

22. In Figure 14.45, find the equation of the parabola, its focus, and its directrix.

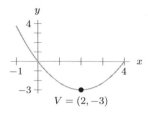

Figure 14.45

For Problems 23–25, find the center and focal points of the ellipse.

23. $\dfrac{x^2}{10} + \dfrac{y^2}{10} = 1$ **24.** $(y-3)^2 + 25x^2 = 25$

25. $x^2 + 2y^2 + 4x - 12y - 3 = 0$

26. In Figure 14.46, find the equation of the ellipse and give its focal points.

Figure 14.46

27. In Figure 14.47, find the equation of the ellipse. The foci are at $F_1 = (0, 1)$ and $F_2 = (0, 3)$.

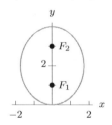

Figure 14.47

For Problems 28–30, find the vertices and focal points of the hyperbola.

28. $\dfrac{(y+2)^2}{25} - \dfrac{(x-2)^2}{4} = 1$

29. $x^2 - \dfrac{y^2}{2} = 8$

30. $4y^2 - x^2 + 56y - 8x + 100 = 0$

In Problems 31–32, find the equation and focal points of the hyperbola.

31.

32.

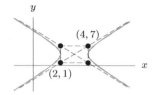

33. On an elliptical billiard table, a ball shot in any direction starting at a focal point and bouncing off a rail passes through the other focal point. What happens if the ball continues and bounces off a rail again?

34. Each end of a string is tacked to the points $(-2, 0)$ and $(2, 0)$ on centimeter grid paper. The string is $10\,\text{cm}$ long. A pencil pulls the string taut and rotates to sweep out an ellipse. Find the equation.

35. A laser beam is aimed straight down into an upward-facing hyperbolic mirror. If the beam is not aimed at the center then is it possible for a reflecting ray to pass through the near focal point?

36. A laser beam is aimed straight down into an upward-facing parabolic mirror. Is it possible for a reflecting ray to pass through the focal point?

37. Satellite television receivers use a dish with an arm extending over the center of the dish, as shown in Figure 14.48. The shape of the dish is made by rotating a parabola $y = ax^2$ about the y-axis. (This three-dimensional shape is called a paraboloid.) If a receiver dish is 24 inches across and 4 inches deep, how far above the center of the dish should the receiving end of the arm be positioned so that it is at the focus to receive the signal?

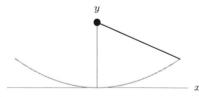

Figure 14.48

38. Satellite television receivers use a dish with a receiving arm extending over the center of the dish. The depth of modern dishes has decreased. If the depth of a dish with a given diameter is halved, what is the effect on the distance of the focal point from the center of the dish?

39. A searchlight in Los Angeles uses a 6-ft wide parabolic mirror that is 9 inches deep. Where should the lamp be positioned to create a 6-ft wide beam to the sky?

40. The earth moves in an elliptical orbit with the sun as a focus. The nearest it gets to the sun is 146 million km and the farthest is 152 million km.

    (a) The sun is at a focal point. Find the length of the major axis.

    (b) Find an equation for earth's orbit if the sun is at the origin, with the major axis on x-axis.

41. Halley's Comet moves in an elliptical orbit with the Sun at a focus. The nearest it gets to the sun is 88 million km and the farthest is 5250 million km.

    (a) Find the length of the major axis.

    (b) Find an equation for its orbit if the sun is at the origin, with the major axis on x-axis.

    (c) Give the parametric equations for the orbit of Halley's Comet.

42. A lamp with a shade casts a shadow described by a conic equation. With the bottom of the upright shade just touching the wall, consider an xy-axis on the wall, with the horizontal x-axis at the height of the lightbulb and the vertical y-axis touching the bottom of the shade. The equation for the shadow above the shade is

$$\frac{y^2}{(R_b A_t / R_t)^2} - \frac{x^2}{R_b^2} = 1$$

where R_b is the bottom radius of the shade, R_t is the top radius of the shade, and A_t is the vertical distance from the bulb to the level of the top rim. The equation for the shadow below the shade is

$$\frac{y^2}{A_b^2} - \frac{x^2}{R_b^2} = 1$$

where R_b is the bottom radius of the shade, and A_b is the vertical distance from the bulb to the level of the bottom rim.[10] See Figure 14.49.

    (a) Identify the conic from the equations.

    (b) Given that a specific lampshade is 8 inches across the top, 16 inches across the bottom and 14 inches high, find the two implicit equation for its upper and lower shadows if the bulb is centered in the lamp.

    (c) Solve each of the two equations for y and give an explicit equation in terms of x for each shadow.

----
[10]Adapted from *The Physics Teacher*, March 2001.

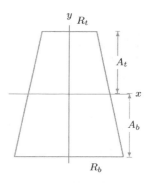

Figure 14.49

43. The use of the LORAN navigation system is currently diminished by the use of the GPS system, but LORAN continues being used as a backup system to GPS. The technique for finding your position is to measure the time for a wave to be sent and returned from three transmitters. Using a pair of transmitters as foci it is possible to find a hyperbolic curve on which your position coordinates lie. Using a second pair of foci, a second curve is found and your position is the intersection of the two hyperbolic curves.

    We use the property that the difference between the distance from two foci is constant for a hyperbola. However, for convenience in this exercise, we replace time measure with a distance measure. Suppose that you are at position P in Figure 14.50 and that the three transmitters lie along the vertical axis as shown.

    (a) Find the equation of a hyperbola that passes through P and has foci T_1 and T_2.

    (b) Find the equation of a hyperbola that passes through P and has foci T_1 and T_3.

    (c) Solve for y in the equations you found in parts (a) and (b). In each case choose the branch that passes through P.

    (d) Use a calculator or computer to graph the branches of the hyperbolas from part (c).

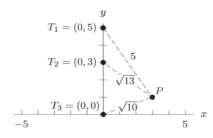

Figure 14.50

44. On page 593, we outline an argument to show that the set of points (x, y) satisfying the condition "the sum of the distances to two focal points $(\pm c, 0)$ is constant" is an ellipse. Fill in all the details of this argument. Assume that the x-intercepts are at $(\pm a, 0)$, where $a > c > 0$.

45. Show that the set of points (x, y) satisfying the condition that "the difference of the distances to two focal points $(\pm c, 0)$ is constant" is a hyperbola. Assume the intercepts are at $(\pm a, 0)$ with $0 < a < c$. [Hint: The justification in this problem is similar to the justification for ellipses on page 593.]

14.6 HYPERBOLIC FUNCTIONS

There are two combinations of the functions e^x and e^{-x} used so often in engineering that they are given their own names. They are the hyperbolic sine, abbreviated sinh (pronounced "cinch") and hyperbolic cosine, abbreviated cosh (rhymes with "gosh"). They are defined as follows:

Hyperbolic Sine and Hyperbolic Cosine

$$\cosh x = \frac{e^x + e^{-x}}{2} \qquad \sinh x = \frac{e^x - e^{-x}}{2}$$

Properties of Hyperbolic Functions

Figures 14.51 and 14.52 show graphs of $\cosh x$ and $\sinh x$ together with graphs of $\frac{1}{2}e^x$ and $\frac{1}{2}e^{-x}$.

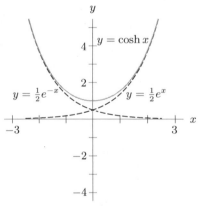

Figure 14.51: Graph of $y = \cosh x$ with multiples of e^x and e^{-x}

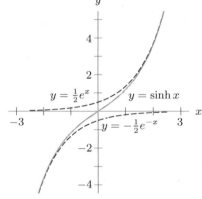

Figure 14.52: Graph of $y = \sinh x$ with multiples of e^x and e^{-x}

The graphs suggest that $\cosh x$ is even and $\sinh x$ is odd and that $\cosh x$ has a y-intercept of 1, whereas $\sinh x$ has a y-intercept of 0:

$\cosh 0 = 1 \qquad\qquad \sinh 0 = 0$

$\cosh(-x) = \cosh x \qquad \sinh(-x) = -\sinh x$

To show that the hyperbolic functions really do have these properties, we use their formulas.

Example 1   Confirm that   (a) $\cosh 0 = 1$ (b) $\cosh(-x) = \cosh x$.

Solution   (a) Substituting $x = 0$ into the formula for $\cosh x$ gives the y-intercept:

$$\cosh 0 = \frac{e^0 + e^{-0}}{2} = \frac{1 + 1}{2} = 1.$$

(b) Substituting $-x$ for x gives

$$\cosh(-x) = \frac{e^{-x} + e^{-(-x)}}{2} = \frac{e^{-x} + e^x}{2} = \cosh x.$$

Thus, $\cosh x$ is an even function.

Example 2   Describe and explain the behavior of $\cosh x$ as $x \to \infty$ and then as $x \to -\infty$.

Solution   From Figure 14.51, we see that as $x \to \infty$, the graph of $\cosh x$ resembles the graph of $\frac{1}{2}e^x$. Similarly, as $x \to -\infty$, the graph of $\cosh x$ resembles the graph of $\frac{1}{2}e^{-x}$. Since $e^{-x} \to 0$ as $x \to \infty$ and $e^x \to 0$ as $x \to -\infty$, we can predict these results algebraically:

$$\text{As } x \to \infty, \qquad \cosh x = \frac{e^x + e^{-x}}{2} \to \frac{1}{2}e^x.$$

$$\text{As } x \to -\infty, \qquad \cosh x = \frac{e^x + e^{-x}}{2} \to \frac{1}{2}e^{-x}.$$

Figures 14.51 and 14.52 suggest that the graph of $\cosh x$ is always above the graph of $\sinh x$. In the following example, we use the formulas to confirm this.

Example 3   Show that $\cosh x > \sinh x$ for all x.

Solution   The difference between $\cosh x$ and $\sinh x$ is given by

$$\cosh x - \sinh x = e^{-x}.$$

Since e^{-x} is positive for all x, we see that

$$\cosh x > \sinh x \quad \text{for all } x.$$

Identities Involving cosh x and sinh x

The hyperbolic functions have names that remind us of the trigonometric functions because they have some properties that are similar to those of the trigonometric functions. Consider the expression

$$(\cosh x)^2 - (\sinh x)^2.$$

This can be simplified using the fact that $e^x \cdot e^{-x} = 1$:

$$
\begin{aligned}
(\cosh x)^2 - (\sinh x)^2 &= \left(\frac{e^x + e^{-x}}{2}\right)^2 - \left(\frac{e^x - e^{-x}}{2}\right)^2 \\
&= \frac{e^{2x} + 2e^x \cdot e^{-x} + e^{-2x}}{4} - \frac{e^{2x} - 2e^x \cdot e^{-x} + e^{-2x}}{4} \\
&= \frac{e^{2x} + 2 + e^{-2x} - e^{2x} + 2 - e^{-2x}}{4} \\
&= 1.
\end{aligned}
$$

Thus, writing $\cosh^2 x$ for $(\cosh x)^2$ and $\sinh^2 x$ for $(\sinh x)^2$, we have the identity

$$\cosh^2 x - \sinh^2 x = 1.$$

This identity is reminiscent of the Pythagorean identity $\cos^2 x + \sin^2 x = 1$. Extending the analogy, we define

Hyperbolic Tangent

$$\tanh x = \frac{\sinh x}{\cosh x}.$$

Parameterizing the Hyperbola Using Hyperbolic Functions

Consider the curve parameterized by the equations

$$x = \cosh t, \quad y = \sinh t, \quad -\infty < t < \infty.$$

The parameter, t, can be eliminated using the identity $\cosh^2 t - \sinh^2 t = 1$. This gives

$$x^2 - y^2 = \underbrace{\cosh^2 t}_{x^2} - \underbrace{\sinh^2 t}_{y^2} = 1,$$

which is the implicit equation for the unit hyperbola in Figure 14.54:

$$x^2 - y^2 = 1.$$

Notice that since $\cosh t > 0$, we have $x > 0$, so the parameterization gives only the right branch of the hyperbola. At $t = 0$, we have $(x, y) = (\cosh 0, \sinh 0) = (1, 0)$, so the curve passes through the point $(1, 0)$. As $t \to \infty$, both $\cosh t$ and $\sinh t$ approach $\frac{1}{2}e^t$, so for large values of t we see that $\cosh t \approx \sinh t$. Thus, as t increases the curve draws close to the diagonal line $y = x$. Since $\sinh x < \cosh x$ for all x, we know that $y < x$, so the curve approaches this asymptote from below. See Figure 14.53.

Similarly, as $t \to -\infty$, we know that $x \to \frac{1}{2}e^{-t}$ and $y \to -\frac{1}{2}e^{-t}$, which means that $y \approx -x$. Thus, as $t \to -\infty$, the curve draws close to the asymptote $y = -x$. In this case, the curve approaches the asymptote from above, because the y-coordinate is slightly larger (less negative) than the x-coordinate.

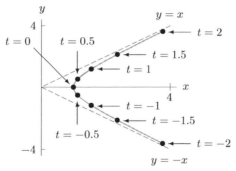

Figure 14.53: The hyperbola parameterized by $x = \cosh t$, $y = \sinh t$, $-\infty < t < \infty$

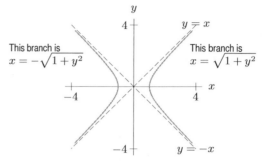

Figure 14.54: The hyperbola defined implicitly by $x^2 - y^2 = 1$

In addition to the parameterization, we can write an equation for each branch of the hyperbola. Solving the equation $x^2 - y^2 = 1$ for x, we obtain two values of x for every value of y:

$$x^2 - y^2 = 1$$
$$x^2 = 1 + y^2$$
$$x = \pm\sqrt{1 + y^2}.$$

The right branch has equation $x = \sqrt{1 + y^2}$; see Figure 14.54. The left branch is the graph of $x = -\sqrt{1 + y^2}$, which is a reflection across the y-axis of the graph of $x = \sqrt{1 + y^2}$. The two branches make up a single hyperbola.

Exercises and Problems for Section 14.6

Exercises

In Exercises 1–10, write a parameterization for one branch of the hyperbola using hyperbolic functions.

1. $y^2 - x^2 = 1$, $\quad y > 0$

2. $y^2 - x^2 = 1$, $\quad y < 0$

3. $x^2 - y^2 = 1$, $\quad x < 0$

4. $(x - 2)^2 - (y - 3)^2 = 1$, $\quad x > 2$

5. $\dfrac{(y + 1)^2}{9} - \dfrac{(x - 1)^2}{4} = 1$, $\quad y < -1$

6. $\dfrac{(x - 1)^2}{4} - \dfrac{(y + 1)^2}{9} = 1$, $\quad x > 1$

7. $9(y + 3)^2 - 4(x + 1)^2 = 1$, $\quad y < -3$

8. $4(x + 3)^2 - (y - 1)^2 = 1$, $\quad x > -3$

9. $9(y + 3)^2 - 4(x + 1)^2 = 36$, $\quad y > -3$

10. $12(x - 1)^2 - 3(y + 2)^2 = 6$, $\quad x > 1$

11. Show that $\sinh(-x) = -\sinh(x)$.

12. Show that $\sinh 0 = 0$.

13. Using the method of Example 2 on page 603, describe and explain the behavior of $\sinh x$ as $x \to \infty$ and as $x \to -\infty$.

Problems

In Problems 14–17, complete the square to write a parameterization for one branch of the hyperbola in terms of hyperbolic functions.

14. $x^2 - 2x = y^2 - 4y + 4, \quad x > 1$

15. $x^2 + 2x - 4y^2 + 8y = 7, \quad x < -1$

16. $y^2 - 4x^2 + 8x = 12, \quad y < 0$

17. $25 + 2x^2 - 12x = 4y^2 + 4y, \quad y > -\frac{1}{2}$

18. This problem concerns the parameterization of the unit hyperbola $x^2 - y^2 = 1$ given by

$$x = \sec t \quad \text{and} \quad y = \tan t \quad \text{for} \quad 0 \le t \le 2\pi.$$

Show on a graph of the hyperbola which section of the hyperbola is traced out and in which direction for

(a) $0 \le t < \pi/2$ **(b)** $\pi/2 < t \le \pi$

(c) $\pi \le t < 3\pi/2$ **(d)** $3\pi/2 < t \le 2\pi$

19. Show how to use hyperbolic functions to parameterize the hyperbola

$$\frac{(x-h)^2}{a^2} - \frac{(y-k)^2}{b^2} = 1.$$

20. Is there an identity analogous to $\sin 2x = 2 \sin x \cos x$ for the hyperbolic functions? Explain.

21. Is there an identity analogous to $\cos 2x = \cos^2 x - \sin^2 x$ for the hyperbolic functions? Explain.

22. Consider the family of functions $y = a \cosh(x/a)$ for $a > 0$. Sketch graphs for $a = 1, 2, 3$. Describe in words the effect of increasing a.

23. Show that $\sinh(ix) = i \sin x$.

24. Find an expression for $\cos(ix)$ in terms of $\cosh x$.

25. Find an expression for $\sin(ix)$ in terms of $\sinh x$.

CHAPTER SUMMARY

- **Parametric Equations**
  Describing motion; parameterizing curves.

- **Implicitly Defined Curves**
  Implicit and parametric equations.
  Circle: $(x - h)^2 + (y - k)^2 = r^2$

  $$x = h + r \cos t; y = k + r \sin t.$$

  Ellipse: $\dfrac{(x-h)^2}{a^2} + \dfrac{(y-k)^2}{b^2} = 1$

  $$x = h + a \cos t; y = k + b \sin t.$$

  Hyperbola: $\dfrac{(x-h)^2}{a^2} - \dfrac{(y-k)^2}{b^2} = 1$

  $$x = h + a \sec t; y = k + b \tan t.$$

- **Geometric and Reflective Properties of Conic Sections**
  Circle: Distance to a fixed point is constant
  Ellipse: Sum of distances to two fixed points is constant; ray from one focus reflects to the other.
  Hyperbola: Difference of distances to two fixed points is constant; ray aimed at one focus is reflected to the other.
  Parabola: Distance to a focus equals distance to the directrix line; ray from a focus reflects to a line parallel to the axis of symmetry.

- **Hyperbolic Functions**
  Formulas: $\cosh x = \dfrac{e^x + e^{-x}}{2}$; $\sinh x = \dfrac{e^x - e^{-x}}{2}$.
  Properties; identities: $\cosh^2 x - \sinh^2 x = 1$; parameterizing the hyperbola.

REVIEW EXERCISES AND PROBLEMS FOR CHAPTER FOURTEEN

Exercises

In Exercises 1–8, decide if the equation represents a circle, an ellipse, or a hyperbola. Give the center and the radius (for a circle) or the values of a and b (for an ellipse or hyperbola) and whether it opens left-right or up-down (for a hyperbola).

1. $x^2 + (y - 3)^2 = 5$

2. $7 - 2(x + 1)^2 = 2(y - 4)^2$

3. $\dfrac{x^2}{4} - \dfrac{(y-1)^2}{9} = 1$

4. $(x + 1)^2 = 1 - \dfrac{(y+2)^2}{8}$

5. $9(x - 5)^2 + 4y^2 = 36$

6. $63 + 9x^2 = 7(y - 1)^2$

7. $6 + 2(x + \frac{1}{3})^2 - 3(y - \frac{1}{2})^2 = 0$

8. $\dfrac{4 - 2(x - 1)^2}{(y + 2)^2} = 1$

Write a parameterization for the curves in Exercises 9–16.

9. A circle of radius 3 centered at the origin and traced clockwise.

10. A circle of radius 5 centered at the point $(2, 1)$ and traced counterclockwise.

11. A circle of radius 2 centered at the origin traced clockwise starting from $(-2, 0)$ when $t = 0$.

12. The circle of radius 4 centered at the point $(4, 4)$ starting on the x-axis when $t = 0$.

13. An ellipse centered at the origin and crossing the x-axis at ± 5 and the y-axis at ± 7.

14. A hyperbola crossing the x-axis at $x = \pm 1$ and with asymptotes $y = \pm 2x$.

15. An ellipse centered at the origin, crossing the x-axis at ± 3 and the y-axis at ± 7. Trace counterclockwise, starting from $(-3, 0)$.

16. A hyperbola crossing the y-axis at $(0, 7)$ and $(0, 3)$ and with asymptotes $y = \pm 4x + 5$.

17. For the ellipse $\dfrac{x^2}{25} + \dfrac{y^2}{4} = 1$, find the focal points.

18. For the hyperbola $y^2 - x^2 = 5$, find the focal points.

19. For the parabola $y = 5x^2$ find the focal point and directrix line.

Problems

Write a parameterization for the curves in Problems 20–22.

20. The horizontal line through the point $(0, 5)$.

21. The circle of radius 1 in the xy-plane centered at the origin and traversed counterclockwise.

22. The circle of radius 2 centered at the origin, starting at the point $(0, 2)$ when $t = 0$.

By completing the square, put the equations in Problems 23–26 into one of the following forms:

$$\frac{(x - h)^2}{a^2} + \frac{(y - k)^2}{b^2} = 1$$

or

$$\frac{(x - h)^2}{a^2} - \frac{(y - k)^2}{b^2} = 1$$

or

$$\frac{(y - k)^2}{b^2} - \frac{(x - h)^2}{a^2} = 1$$

and decide if it represents a circle, an ellipse, or a hyperbola. Give its center, radius (for a circle), or the values of a and b (for an ellipse or a hyperbola), and whether it opens left-right or up-down (for a hyperbola).

23. $x^2 + 2x + y^2 = 0$

24. $2x^2 + 2y = y^2 + 4x$

25. $6x^2 - 12x + 9y^2 + 6y + 1 = 0$

26. $\dfrac{x^2 - 4x}{2y - y^2} - 1 = 0$

27. On a graphing calculator or a computer, plot $x = 2t/(t^2 + 1)$, $y = (t^2 - 1)/(t^2 + 1)$, first for $-50 \leq t \leq 50$, and then for $-5 \leq t \leq 5$. Explain what you see. Is the curve really a circle?

28. Plot the Lissajous figure given by $x = \cos 2t$, $y = \sin t$ using a graphing calculator or computer. Explain why it looks like part of a parabola. [Hint: Use a double-angle identity.]

29. A planet P in the xy-plane orbits the star S counterclockwise in a circle of radius 10 units, completing one orbit in 2π units of time. A moon M orbits the planet P counterclockwise in a circle of radius 3 units, completing one orbit in $2\pi/8$ units of time. The star S is fixed at the origin $x = 0$, $y = 0$, and at time $t = 0$ the planet P is at the point $(10, 0)$ and the moon M is at the point $(13, 0)$.

   (a) Find parametric equations for the x- and y-coordinates of the planet at time t.

   (b) Find parametric equations for the x- and y-coordinates of the moon at time t. [Hint: For the moon's position at time t, take a vector from the sun to the planet at time t and add a vector from the planet to the moon].

   (c) Plot the path of the moon in the xy-plane, using a graphing calculator or computer.

30. A hyperbolic mirror is shown in Figure 14.55, and a beam needs to be directed from point P at $(8, 8)$ to point Q at $(0, 2)$. Because of the barrier shown in the figure, the direct path is obstructed. The hyperbola is defined by $3y^2 - x^2 = 3$.

   (a) Find the foci of the hyperbola.

   (b) Find the equation of the line through P along which a beam should be sent for it to be reflected to the point Q.

Figure 14.55

CHECK YOUR UNDERSTANDING

Are the statements in Problems 1–33 true or false? Give an explanation for your answer.

1. A moving particle with motion $x = 2t$, $y = 3t$, $0 \leq t \leq 100$ is moving in a straight line.

2. A moving particle with motion $x = 2t^2$, $y = 3t^2$, $0 \leq t \leq 100$ is moving in a straight line.

3. The motions $x = t$, $y = t$ and $x = t^3$, $y = t^3$ are on the same path.

4. If the motion of an object is described by $x = \sin(t/2)$ and $y = \cos(t/2)$, $0 \leq t \leq 4$, then when $t = \pi$ the object is located at the point $(1, 0)$.

5. If the motion of an object on the unit circle is described by $x = \sin(t/2)$ and $y = \cos(t/2)$, $0 \leq t \leq 4$, then the object is moving counterclockwise.

6. An object with motion $x = 2t$, $y = 3t+1$ passes through the point $(10, 16)$.

7. The graph of $x^2 - y^2 = 0$ is a circle.

8. The graph of $(x + 3)^2 + y^2 = 4$ is a circle of radius 4 centered at $(-3, 0)$.

9. The circle $x^2 + 8x + y^2 + 10y = 100$ has center $(4, 5)$.

10. The circle $x^2 + 8x + y^2 + 10y = 100$ has radius 10.

11. The parametric equations $x = t^3$, $y = t^6$ describe a parabola.

12. The graph of $y^2 - 4x^2 = 0$ is a hyperbola.

13. There is only one parameterization of the circle.

14. If the parameter t is eliminated from the parametric equations $x = 2t + 1$ and $y = t - 1$, the resulting equation can be written as $y = \frac{1}{2}(x - 3)$.

15. If a circle is centered at the point $(1, -1)$ and its radius is $\sqrt{5}$, then its equation is $(x - 1)^2 + (y + 1)^2 = 5$.

16. The equation $4x^2 + 9y^2 = 36$ represents a circle.

17. The equations $x = 2\cos t$, $y = \sin t$ parameterize an ellipse.

18. The horizontal axis of the ellipse $9x^2 + 4y^2 = 1$ is longer than its vertical axis.

19. The graph of $\dfrac{(y - k)^2}{b^2} - \dfrac{(x - h)^2}{a^2} = 1$ is a hyperbola that opens up and down.

20. The asymptotes of the hyperbola $x^2/4 - y^2/9 = 1$ are given by the equation $x^2/4 - y^2/9 = 0$.

21. The hyperbolic sine is defined as $\sinh x = \dfrac{e^x + e^{-x}}{2}$.

22. As x approaches infinity, $\cosh x$ approaches $\frac{1}{2}e^x$.

23. An identity that relates $\sinh x$ and $\cosh x$ is $\cosh^2 x + \sinh^2 x = 1$.

24. The function $\cosh t$ is periodic with period 2π.

25. The function $\cosh x$ is an even function of x.

26. The function $\cosh x$ grows faster than any power of x as $x \to \infty$.

27. $\cosh 0 = e$.

28. $\sinh x < \cosh x$ for all x.

29. $\sinh \pi = 0$.

30. $\cosh(\ln 2) = 5/4$.

31. If you know the lengths of the major and minor axes of an ellipse, then you can determine the distance between the two foci.

32. The distance between the vertex of a parabola and its focus is the same as the distance from the vertex to the directrix of the parabola.

33. Each asymptote of a hyperbola passes through one of its focal points.

Calculus
Early Transcendentals

Ninth Edition

14.7 CONIC SECTIONS

In this section* we will discuss some of the basic geometric properties of parabolas, ellipses, and hyperbolas. These curves play an important role in calculus and also arise naturally in a broad range of applications in such fields as planetary motion, design of telescopes and antennas, geodetic positioning, and medicine, to name a few.

■ CONIC SECTIONS

Circles, ellipses, parabolas, and hyperbolas are called *conic sections* or *conics* because they can be obtained as intersections of a plane with a double-napped circular cone (Figure 14.7.1). If the plane passes through the vertex of the double-napped cone, then the intersection is a point, a pair of intersecting lines, or a single line. These are called *degenerate conic sections*.

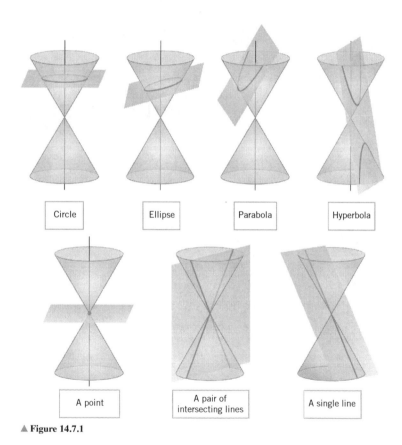

Circle   Ellipse   Parabola   Hyperbola

A point   A pair of intersecting lines   A single line

▲ Figure 14.7.1

---

*Some students may already be familiar with the material in this section, in which case it can be treated as a review. Instructors who want to spend some additional time on precalculus review may want to allocate more than one lecture on this material.

■ **DEFINITIONS OF THE CONIC SECTIONS**

Although we could derive properties of parabolas, ellipses, and hyperbolas by defining them as intersections with a double-napped cone, it will be better suited to calculus if we begin with equivalent definitions that are based on their geometric properties.

> **14.7.1 DEFINITION** A *parabola* is the set of all points in the plane that are equidistant from a fixed line and a fixed point not on the line.

The line is called the *directrix* of the parabola, and the point is called the *focus* (Figure 14.7.2). A parabola is symmetric about the line that passes through the focus at right angles to the directrix. This line, called the *axis* or the *axis of symmetry* of the parabola, intersects the parabola at a point called the *vertex*.

> **14.7.2 DEFINITION** An *ellipse* is the set of all points in the plane, the sum of whose distances from two fixed points is a given positive constant that is greater than the distance between the fixed points.

The two fixed points are called the *foci* (plural of "focus") of the ellipse, and the midpoint of the line segment joining the foci is called the *center* (Figure 14.7.3a). To help visualize Definition 14.7.2, imagine that two ends of a string are tacked to the foci and a pencil traces a curve as it is held tight against the string (Figure 14.7.3b). The resulting curve will be an ellipse since the sum of the distances to the foci is a constant, namely, the total length of the string. Note that if the foci coincide, the ellipse reduces to a circle. For ellipses other than circles, the line segment through the foci and across the ellipse is called the *major axis* (Figure 14.7.3c), and the line segment across the ellipse, through the center, and perpendicular to the major axis is called the *minor axis*. The endpoints of the major axis are called *vertices*.

All points on the parabola are equidistant from the focus and directrix.

▲ **Figure 14.7.2**

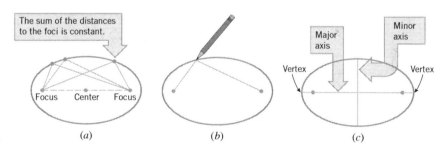

The sum of the distances to the foci is constant.

(a)   (b)   (c)

► **Figure 14.7.3**

> **14.7.3 DEFINITION** A *hyperbola* is the set of all points in the plane, the difference of whose distances from two fixed distinct points is a given positive constant that is less than the distance between the fixed points.

The two fixed points are called the *foci* of the hyperbola, and the term "difference" that is used in the definition is understood to mean the distance to the farther focus minus the distance to the closer focus. As a result, the points on the hyperbola form two *branches*, each "wrapping around" the closer focus (Figure 14.7.4*a*). The midpoint of the line segment joining the foci is called the ***center*** of the hyperbola, the line through the foci is called the ***focal axis***, and the line through the center that is perpendicular to the focal axis is called the ***conjugate axis***. The hyperbola intersects the focal axis at two points called the ***vertices***.

Associated with every hyperbola is a pair of lines, called the ***asymptotes*** of the hyperbola. These lines intersect at the center of the hyperbola and have the property that as a point P moves along the hyperbola away from the center, the vertical distance between P and one of the asymptotes approaches zero (Figure 14.7.4*b*).

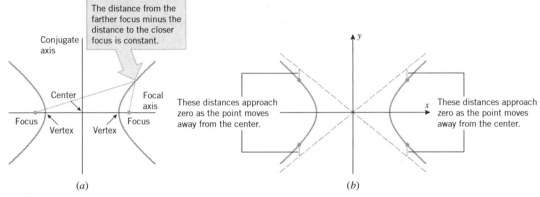

▲ **Figure 14.7.4**

EQUATIONS OF PARABOLAS IN STANDARD POSITION

It is traditional in the study of parabolas to denote the distance between the focus and the vertex by p. The vertex is equidistant from the focus and the directrix, so the distance between the vertex and the directrix is also p; consequently, the distance between the focus and the directrix is $2p$ (Figure 14.7.5). As illustrated in that figure, the parabola passes through two of the corners of a box that extends from the vertex to the focus along the axis of symmetry and extends $2p$ units above and $2p$ units below the axis of symmetry.

The equation of a parabola is simplest if the vertex is the origin and the axis of symmetry is along the x-axis or y-axis. The four possible such orientations are shown in Figure 14.7.6. These are called the ***standard positions*** of a parabola, and the resulting equations are called the ***standard equations*** of a parabola.

▲ **Figure 14.7.5**

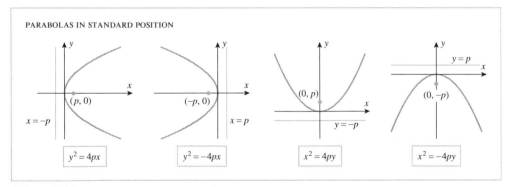

PARABOLAS IN STANDARD POSITION

▲ **Figure 14.7.6**

To illustrate how the equations in Figure 14.7.6 are obtained, we will derive the equation for the parabola with focus $(p, 0)$ and directrix $x = -p$. Let $P(x, y)$ be any point on the parabola. Since P is equidistant from the focus and directrix, the distances PF and PD in Figure 14.7.7 are equal; that is,

$$PF = PD \tag{1}$$

where $D(-p, y)$ is the foot of the perpendicular from P to the directrix. From the distance formula, the distances PF and PD are

$$PF = \sqrt{(x - p)^2 + y^2} \quad \text{and} \quad PD = \sqrt{(x + p)^2} \tag{2}$$

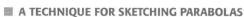

Substituting in (1) and squaring yields

$$(x - p)^2 + y^2 = (x + p)^2 \tag{3}$$

and after simplifying

$$y^2 = 4px \tag{4}$$

▲ **Figure 14.7.7**

The derivations of the other equations in Figure 14.7.6 are similar.

■ **A TECHNIQUE FOR SKETCHING PARABOLAS**

Parabolas can be sketched from their *standard equations* using four basic steps:

Sketching a Parabola from Its Standard Equation

Step 1. Determine whether the axis of symmetry is along the x-axis or the y-axis. Referring to Figure 14.7.6, the axis of symmetry is along the x-axis if the equation has a y^2-term, and it is along the y-axis if it has an x^2-term.

Step 2. Determine which way the parabola opens. If the axis of symmetry is along the x-axis, then the parabola opens to the right if the coefficient of x is positive, and it opens to the left if the coefficient is negative. If the axis of symmetry is along the y-axis, then the parabola opens up if the coefficient of y is positive, and it opens down if the coefficient is negative.

Step 3. Determine the value of p and draw a box extending p units from the origin along the axis of symmetry in the direction in which the parabola opens and extending $2p$ units on each side of the axis of symmetry.

Step 4. Using the box as a guide, sketch the parabola so that its vertex is at the origin and it passes through the corners of the box (Figure 14.7.8).

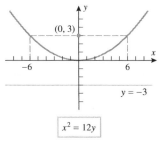

Rough sketch

▲ **Figure 14.7.8**

▶ **Example 1** Sketch the graphs of the parabolas

$$\text{(a) } x^2 = 12y \qquad \text{(b) } y^2 + 8x = 0$$

and show the focus and directrix of each.

Solution (a). This equation involves x^2, so the axis of symmetry is along the y-axis, and the coefficient of y is positive, so the parabola opens upward. From the coefficient of y, we obtain $4p = 12$ or $p = 3$. Drawing a box extending $p = 3$ units up from the origin and $2p = 6$ units to the left and $2p = 6$ units to the right of the y-axis, then using corners of the box as a guide, yields the graph in Figure 14.7.9.

The focus is $p = 3$ units from the vertex along the axis of symmetry in the direction in which the parabola opens, so its coordinates are $(0, 3)$. The directrix is perpendicular to the axis of symmetry at a distance of $p = 3$ units from the vertex on the opposite side from the focus, so its equation is $y = -3$.

▲ **Figure 14.7.9**

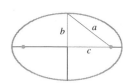

▲ Figure 14.7.10

Solution (b). We first rewrite the equation in the standard form

$$y^2 = -8x$$

This equation involves y^2, so the axis of symmetry is along the x-axis, and the coefficient of x is negative, so the parabola opens to the left. From the coefficient of x we obtain $4p = 8$, so $p = 2$. Drawing a box extending $p = 2$ units left from the origin and $2p = 4$ units above and $2p = 4$ units below the x-axis, then using corners of the box as a guide, yields the graph in Figure 14.7.10. ◄

▶ **Example 2** Find an equation of the parabola that is symmetric about the y-axis, has its vertex at the origin, and passes through the point $(5, 2)$.

Solution. Since the parabola is symmetric about the y-axis and has its vertex at the origin, the equation is of the form

$$x^2 = 4py \quad \text{or} \quad x^2 = -4py$$

where the sign depends on whether the parabola opens up or down. But the parabola must open up since it passes through the point $(5, 2)$, which lies in the first quadrant. Thus, the equation is of the form

$$x^2 = 4py \tag{5}$$

Since the parabola passes through $(5, 2)$, we must have $5^2 = 4p \cdot 2$ or $4p = \frac{25}{2}$. Therefore, (5) becomes

$$x^2 = \frac{25}{2}y \quad ◄$$

■ EQUATIONS OF ELLIPSES IN STANDARD POSITION

▲ Figure 14.7.11

It is traditional in the study of ellipses to denote the length of the major axis by $2a$, the length of the minor axis by $2b$, and the distance between the foci by $2c$ (Figure 14.7.11). The number a is called the ***semimajor axis*** and the number b the ***semiminor axis*** (standard but odd terminology, since a and b are numbers, not geometric axes).

There is a basic relationship between the numbers a, b, and c that can be obtained by examining the sum of the distances to the foci from a point P at the end of the major axis and from a point Q at the end of the minor axis (Figure 14.7.12). From Definition 14.7.2, these sums must be equal, so we obtain

$$2\sqrt{b^2 + c^2} = (a - c) + (a + c)$$

from which it follows that

$$a = \sqrt{b^2 + c^2} \tag{6}$$

or, equivalently,

$$c = \sqrt{a^2 - b^2} \tag{7}$$

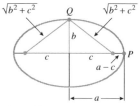

▲ Figure 14.7.12

From (6), the distance from a focus to an end of the minor axis is a (Figure 14.7.13), which implies that for *all* points on the ellipse the sum of the distances to the foci is $2a$.

It also follows from (6) that $a \geq b$ with the equality holding only when $c = 0$. Geometrically, this means that the major axis of an ellipse is at least as large as the minor axis and that the two axes have equal length only when the foci coincide, in which case the ellipse is a circle.

The equation of an ellipse is simplest if the center of the ellipse is at the origin and the foci are on the x-axis or y-axis. The two possible such orientations are shown in Figure 14.7.14.

▲ Figure 14.7.13

These are called the ***standard positions*** of an ellipse, and the resulting equations are called the ***standard equations*** of an ellipse.

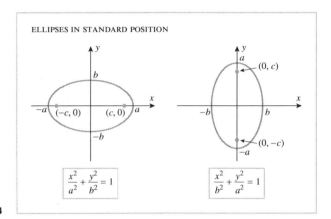

ELLIPSES IN STANDARD POSITION

$$\frac{x^2}{a^2} + \frac{y^2}{b^2} = 1$$

$$\frac{x^2}{b^2} + \frac{y^2}{a^2} = 1$$

▶ **Figure 14.7.14**

To illustrate how the equations in Figure 14.7.14 are obtained, we will derive the equation for the ellipse with foci on the x-axis. Let $P(x, y)$ be any point on that ellipse. Since the sum of the distances from P to the foci is $2a$, it follows (Figure 14.7.15) that

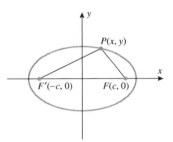

▲ **Figure 14.7.15**

$$PF' + PF = 2a$$

so

$$\sqrt{(x + c)^2 + y^2} + \sqrt{(x - c)^2 + y^2} = 2a$$

Transposing the second radical to the right side of the equation and squaring yields

$$(x + c)^2 + y^2 = 4a^2 - 4a\sqrt{(x - c)^2 + y^2} + (x - c)^2 + y^2$$

and, on simplifying,

$$\sqrt{(x - c)^2 + y^2} = a - \frac{c}{a}x \tag{8}$$

Squaring again and simplifying yields

$$\frac{x^2}{a^2} + \frac{y^2}{a^2 - c^2} = 1$$

which, by virtue of (6), can be written as

$$\frac{x^2}{a^2} + \frac{y^2}{b^2} = 1 \tag{9}$$

Conversely, it can be shown that any point whose coordinates satisfy (9) has $2a$ as the sum of its distances from the foci, so that such a point is on the ellipse.

A TECHNIQUE FOR SKETCHING ELLIPSES

Ellipses can be sketched from their *standard equations* using three basic steps:

Sketching an Ellipse from Its Standard Equation

Step 1. Determine whether the major axis is on the x-axis or the y-axis. This can be ascertained from the sizes of the denominators in the equation. Referring to Figure 14.7.14, and keeping in mind that $a^2 > b^2$ (since $a > b$), the major axis is along the x-axis if x^2 has the larger denominator, and it is along the y-axis if y^2 has the larger denominator. If the denominators are equal, the ellipse is a circle.

Step 2. Determine the values of a and b and draw a box extending a units on each side of the center along the major axis and b units on each side of the center along the minor axis.

Step 3. Using the box as a guide, sketch the ellipse so that its center is at the origin and it touches the sides of the box where the sides intersect the coordinate axes (Figure 14.7.16).

Rough sketch

▲ **Figure 14.7.16**

▶ **Example 3** Sketch the graphs of the ellipses

$$\text{(a)} \quad \frac{x^2}{9} + \frac{y^2}{16} = 1 \qquad \text{(b)} \quad x^2 + 2y^2 = 4$$

showing the foci of each.

Solution (*a*). Since y^2 has the larger denominator, the major axis is along the y-axis. Moreover, since $a^2 > b^2$, we must have $a^2 = 16$ and $b^2 = 9$, so

$$a = 4 \quad \text{and} \quad b = 3$$

Drawing a box extending 4 units on each side of the origin along the y-axis and 3 units on each side of the origin along the x-axis as a guide yields the graph in Figure 14.7.17.

The foci lie c units on each side of the center along the major axis, where c is given by (7). From the values of a^2 and b^2 above, we obtain

$$c = \sqrt{a^2 - b^2} = \sqrt{16 - 9} = \sqrt{7} \approx 2.6$$

Thus, the coordinates of the foci are $(0, \sqrt{7})$ and $(0, -\sqrt{7})$, since they lie on the y-axis.

Solution (*b*). We first rewrite the equation in the standard form

$$\frac{x^2}{4} + \frac{y^2}{2} = 1$$

Since x^2 has the larger denominator, the major axis lies along the x-axis, and we have $a^2 = 4$ and $b^2 = 2$. Drawing a box extending $a = 2$ units on each side of the origin along the x-axis and extending $b = \sqrt{2} \approx 1.4$ units on each side of the origin along the y-axis as a guide yields the graph in Figure 14.7.18.

From (7), we obtain

$$c = \sqrt{a^2 - b^2} = \sqrt{2} \approx 1.4$$

Thus, the coordinates of the foci are $(\sqrt{2}, 0)$ and $(-\sqrt{2}, 0)$, since they lie on the x-axis. ◀

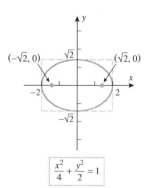

▲ **Figure 14.7.17**

$$\frac{x^2}{9} + \frac{y^2}{16} = 1$$

$$\frac{x^2}{4} + \frac{y^2}{2} = 1$$

▲ **Figure 14.7.18**

▶ **Example 4** Find an equation for the ellipse with foci $(0, \pm 2)$ and major axis with end-points $(0, \pm 4)$.

Solution. From Figure 14.7.14, the equation has the form

$$\frac{x^2}{b^2} + \frac{y^2}{a^2} = 1$$

and from the given information, $a = 4$ and $c = 2$. It follows from (6) that

$$b^2 = a^2 - c^2 = 16 - 4 = 12$$

so the equation of the ellipse is

$$\frac{x^2}{12} + \frac{y^2}{16} = 1 \quad \blacktriangleleft$$

▨ EQUATIONS OF HYPERBOLAS IN STANDARD POSITION

It is traditional in the study of hyperbolas to denote the distance between the vertices by $2a$, the distance between the foci by $2c$ (Figure 14.7.19), and to define the quantity b as

$$b = \sqrt{c^2 - a^2} \tag{10}$$

This relationship, which can also be expressed as

$$c = \sqrt{a^2 + b^2} \tag{11}$$

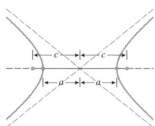

▲ **Figure 14.7.19**

is pictured geometrically in Figure 14.7.20. As illustrated in that figure, and as we will show later in this section, the asymptotes pass through the corners of a box extending b units on each side of the center along the conjugate axis and a units on each side of the center along the focal axis. The number a is called the **semifocal axis** of the hyperbola and the number b the **semiconjugate axis**. (As with the semimajor and semiminor axes of an ellipse, these are numbers, not geometric axes.)

If V is one vertex of a hyperbola, then, as illustrated in Figure 14.7.21, the distance from V to the farther focus minus the distance from V to the closer focus is

$$[(c - a) + 2a] - (c - a) = 2a$$

Thus, for *all* points on a hyperbola, the distance to the farther focus minus the distance to the closer focus is $2a$.

The equation of a hyperbola has an especially convenient form if the center of the hyperbola is at the origin and the foci are on the x-axis or y-axis. The two possible such orientations are shown in Figure 14.7.22. These are called the **standard positions** of a hyperbola, and the resulting equations are called the **standard equations** of a hyperbola.

The derivations of these equations are similar to those already given for parabolas and ellipses, so we will leave them as exercises. However, to illustrate how the equations of the asymptotes are derived, we will derive those equations for the hyperbola

$$\frac{x^2}{a^2} - \frac{y^2}{b^2} = 1$$

We can rewrite this equation as

$$y^2 = \frac{b^2}{a^2}(x^2 - a^2)$$

which is equivalent to the pair of equations

$$y = \frac{b}{a}\sqrt{x^2 - a^2} \quad \text{and} \quad y = -\frac{b}{a}\sqrt{x^2 - a^2}$$

▲ **Figure 14.7.20**

▲ **Figure 14.7.21**

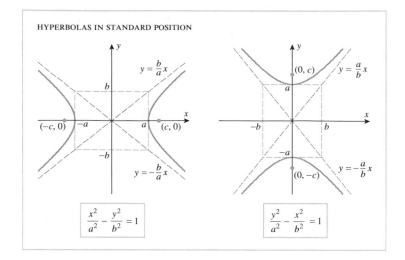

HYPERBOLAS IN STANDARD POSITION

▶ Figure 14.7.22

Thus, in the first quadrant, the vertical distance between the line $y = (b/a)x$ and the hyperbola can be written as

$$\frac{b}{a}x - \frac{b}{a}\sqrt{x^2 - a^2}$$

▲ Figure 14.7.23

(Figure 14.7.23). But this distance tends to zero as $x \to +\infty$ since

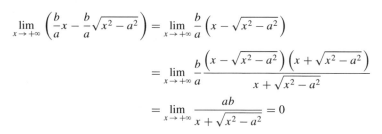

$$\lim_{x \to +\infty}\left(\frac{b}{a}x - \frac{b}{a}\sqrt{x^2 - a^2}\right) = \lim_{x \to +\infty}\frac{b}{a}\left(x - \sqrt{x^2 - a^2}\right)$$

$$= \lim_{x \to +\infty}\frac{b}{a}\frac{\left(x - \sqrt{x^2 - a^2}\right)\left(x + \sqrt{x^2 - a^2}\right)}{x + \sqrt{x^2 - a^2}}$$

$$= \lim_{x \to +\infty}\frac{ab}{x + \sqrt{x^2 - a^2}} = 0$$

The analysis in the remaining quadrants is similar.

■ A QUICK WAY TO FIND ASYMPTOTES

There is a trick that can be used to avoid memorizing the equations of the asymptotes of a hyperbola. They can be obtained, when needed, by replacing 1 by 0 on the right side of the hyperbola equation, and then solving for y in terms of x. For example, for the hyperbola

$$\frac{x^2}{a^2} - \frac{y^2}{b^2} = 1$$

we would write

$$\frac{x^2}{a^2} - \frac{y^2}{b^2} = 0 \quad \text{or} \quad y^2 = \frac{b^2}{a^2}x^2 \quad \text{or} \quad y = \pm\frac{b}{a}x$$

which are the equations for the asymptotes.

A TECHNIQUE FOR SKETCHING HYPERBOLAS

Hyperbolas can be sketched from their *standard equations* using four basic steps:

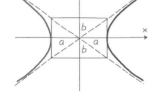

> #### Sketching a Hyperbola from Its Standard Equation
>
> **Step 1.** Determine whether the focal axis is on the x-axis or the y-axis. This can be ascertained from the location of the minus sign in the equation. Referring to Figure 14.4.22, the focal axis is along the x-axis when the minus sign precedes the y^2-term, and it is along the y-axis when the minus sign precedes the x^2-term.
>
> **Step 2.** Determine the values of a and b and draw a box extending a units on either side of the center along the focal axis and b units on either side of the center along the conjugate axis. (The squares of a and b can be read directly from the equation.)
>
> **Step 3.** Draw the asymptotes along the diagonals of the box.
>
> **Step 4.** Using the box and the asymptotes as a guide, sketch the graph of the hyperbola (Figure 14.7.24).

Rough sketch

▲ Figure 14.7.24

▶ **Example 5**   Sketch the graphs of the hyperbolas

$$\text{(a)} \ \frac{x^2}{4} - \frac{y^2}{9} = 1 \qquad \text{(b)} \ y^2 - x^2 = 1$$

showing their vertices, foci, and asymptotes.

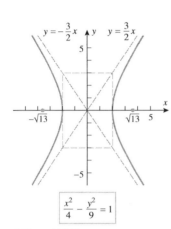

$$\frac{x^2}{4} - \frac{y^2}{9} = 1$$

▲ Figure 14.7.25

Solution (a).   The minus sign precedes the y^2-term, so the focal axis is along the x-axis. From the denominators in the equation we obtain

$$a^2 = 4 \quad \text{and} \quad b^2 = 9$$

Since a and b are positive, we must have $a = 2$ and $b = 3$. Recalling that the vertices lie a units on each side of the center on the focal axis, it follows that their coordinates in this case are $(2, 0)$ and $(-2, 0)$. Drawing a box extending $a = 2$ units along the x-axis on each side of the origin and $b = 3$ units on each side of the origin along the y-axis, then drawing the asymptotes along the diagonals of the box as a guide, yields the graph in Figure 14.7.25.

To obtain equations for the asymptotes, we replace 1 by 0 in the given equation; this yields

$$\frac{x^2}{4} - \frac{y^2}{9} = 0 \quad \text{or} \quad y = \pm\frac{3}{2}x$$

The foci lie c units on each side of the center along the focal axis, where c is given by (11). From the values of a^2 and b^2 above we obtain

$$c = \sqrt{a^2 + b^2} = \sqrt{4 + 9} = \sqrt{13} \approx 3.6$$

Since the foci lie on the x-axis in this case, their coordinates are $(\sqrt{13}, 0)$ and $(-\sqrt{13}, 0)$.

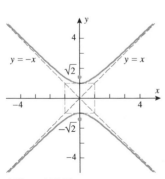

▲ Figure 14.7.26

Solution (b).   The minus sign precedes the x^2-term, so the focal axis is along the y-axis. From the denominators in the equation we obtain $a^2 = 1$ and $b^2 = 1$, from which it follows that

$$a = 1 \quad \text{and} \quad b = 1$$

Thus, the vertices are at $(0, -1)$ and $(0, 1)$. Drawing a box extending $a = 1$ unit on either side of the origin along the y-axis and $b = 1$ unit on either side of the origin along the x-axis, then drawing the asymptotes, yields the graph in Figure 14.7.26. Since the box is actually

A hyperbola in which $a = b$, as in part (b) of Example 5, is called an *equilateral hyperbola*. Such hyperbolas always have perpendicular asymptotes.

a square, the asymptotes are perpendicular and have equations $y = \pm x$. This can also be seen by replacing 1 by 0 in the given equation, which yields $y^2 - x^2 = 0$ or $y = \pm x$. Also,

$$c = \sqrt{a^2 + b^2} = \sqrt{1 + 1} = \sqrt{2}$$

so the foci, which lie on the y-axis, are $(0, -\sqrt{2})$ and $(0, \sqrt{2})$. ◄

▶ **Example 6** Find the equation of the hyperbola with vertices $(0, \pm 8)$ and asymptotes $y = \pm\frac{4}{3}x$.

Solution. Since the vertices are on the y-axis, the equation of the hyperbola has the form $(y^2/a^2) - (x^2/b^2) = 1$ and the asymptotes are

$$y = \pm\frac{a}{b}x$$

From the locations of the vertices we have $a = 8$, so the given equations of the asymptotes yield

$$y = \pm\frac{a}{b}x = \pm\frac{8}{b}x = \pm\frac{4}{3}x$$

from which it follows that $b = 6$. Thus, the hyperbola has the equation

$$\frac{y^2}{64} - \frac{x^2}{36} = 1 \quad ◄$$

■ **TRANSLATED CONICS**

Equations of conics that are translated from their standard positions can be obtained by replacing x by $x - h$ and y by $y - k$ in their standard equations. For a parabola, this translates the vertex from the origin to the point (h, k); and for ellipses and hyperbolas, this translates the center from the origin to the point (h, k).

Parabolas with vertex (h, k) and axis parallel to x-axis

$$(y - k)^2 = 4p(x - h) \quad \text{[Opens right]} \tag{12}$$
$$(y - k)^2 = -4p(x - h) \quad \text{[Opens left]} \tag{13}$$

Parabolas with vertex (h, k) and axis parallel to y-axis

$$(x - h)^2 = 4p(y - k) \quad \text{[Opens up]} \tag{14}$$
$$(x - h)^2 = -4p(y - k) \quad \text{[Opens down]} \tag{15}$$

Ellipse with center (h, k) and major axis parallel to x-axis

$$\frac{(x - h)^2}{a^2} + \frac{(y - k)^2}{b^2} = 1 \quad [b < a] \tag{16}$$

Ellipse with center (h, k) and major axis parallel to y-axis

$$\frac{(x - h)^2}{b^2} + \frac{(y - k)^2}{a^2} = 1 \quad [b < a] \tag{17}$$

Hyperbola with center (h, k) and focal axis parallel to x-axis

$$\frac{(x - h)^2}{a^2} - \frac{(y - k)^2}{b^2} = 1 \tag{18}$$

Hyperbola with center (h, k) and focal axis parallel to y-axis

$$\frac{(y - k)^2}{a^2} - \frac{(x - h)^2}{b^2} = 1 \tag{19}$$

▶ **Example 7**   Find an equation for the parabola that has its vertex at $(1, 2)$ and its focus at $(4, 2)$.

Solution.   Since the focus and vertex are on a horizontal line, and since the focus is to the right of the vertex, the parabola opens to the right and its equation has the form

$$(y - k)^2 = 4p(x - h)$$

Since the vertex and focus are 3 units apart, we have $p = 3$, and since the vertex is at $(h, k) = (1, 2)$, we obtain

$$(y - 2)^2 = 12(x - 1) \blacktriangleleft$$

Sometimes the equations of translated conics occur in expanded form, in which case we are faced with the problem of identifying the graph of a quadratic equation in x and y:

$$Ax^2 + Cy^2 + Dx + Ey + F = 0 \tag{20}$$

The basic procedure for determining the nature of such a graph is to complete the squares of the quadratic terms and then try to match up the resulting equation with one of the forms of a translated conic.

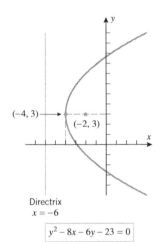

(−4, 3)

(−2, 3)

Directrix
$x = -6$

$y^2 - 8x - 6y - 23 = 0$

▲ **Figure 14.7.27**

▶ **Example 8**   Describe the graph of the equation

$$y^2 - 8x - 6y - 23 = 0$$

Solution.   The equation involves quadratic terms in y but none in x, so we first take all of the y-terms to one side:

$$y^2 - 6y = 8x + 23$$

Next, we complete the square on the y-terms by adding 9 to both sides:

$$(y - 3)^2 = 8x + 32$$

Finally, we factor out the coefficient of the x-term to obtain

$$(y - 3)^2 = 8(x + 4)$$

This equation is of form (12) with $h = -4$, $k = 3$, and $p = 2$, so the graph is a parabola with vertex $(-4, 3)$ opening to the right. Since $p = 2$, the focus is 2 units to the right of the vertex, which places it at the point $(-2, 3)$; and the directrix is 2 units to the left of the vertex, which means that its equation is $x = -6$. The parabola is shown in Figure 14.7.27. ◀

▶ **Example 9**   Describe the graph of the equation

$$16x^2 + 9y^2 - 64x - 54y + 1 = 0$$

Solution.   This equation involves quadratic terms in both x and y, so we will group the x-terms and the y-terms on one side and put the constant on the other:

$$(16x^2 - 64x) + (9y^2 - 54y) = -1$$

Next, factor out the coefficients of x^2 and y^2 and complete the squares:

$$16(x^2 - 4x + 4) + 9(y^2 - 6y + 9) = -1 + 64 + 81$$

or

$$16(x - 2)^2 + 9(y - 3)^2 = 144$$

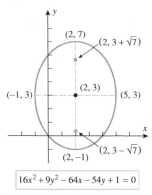

$16x^2 + 9y^2 - 64x - 54y + 1 = 0$

▲ Figure 14.7.28

Finally, divide through by 144 to introduce a 1 on the right side:

$$\frac{(x-2)^2}{9} + \frac{(y-3)^2}{16} = 1$$

This is an equation of form (17), with $h = 2$, $k = 3$, $a^2 = 16$, and $b^2 = 9$. Thus, the graph of the equation is an ellipse with center $(2, 3)$ and major axis parallel to the y-axis. Since $a = 4$, the major axis extends 4 units above and 4 units below the center, so its endpoints are $(2, 7)$ and $(2, -1)$ (Figure 14.7.28). Since $b = 3$, the minor axis extends 3 units to the left and 3 units to the right of the center, so its endpoints are $(-1, 3)$ and $(5, 3)$. Since

$$c = \sqrt{a^2 - b^2} = \sqrt{16 - 9} = \sqrt{7}$$

the foci lie $\sqrt{7}$ units above and below the center, placing them at the points $(2, 3 + \sqrt{7})$ and $(2, 3 - \sqrt{7})$. ◄

▶ **Example 10** Describe the graph of the equation

$$x^2 - y^2 - 4x + 8y - 21 = 0$$

Solution. This equation involves quadratic terms in both x and y, so we will group the x-terms and the y-terms on one side and put the constant on the other:

$$(x^2 - 4x) - (y^2 - 8y) = 21$$

We leave it for you to verify by completing the squares that this equation can be written as

$$\frac{(x-2)^2}{9} - \frac{(y-4)^2}{9} = 1 \qquad (21)$$

This is an equation of form (18) with $h = 2$, $k = 4$, $a^2 = 9$, and $b^2 = 9$. Thus, the equation represents a hyperbola with center $(2, 4)$ and focal axis parallel to the x-axis. Since $a = 3$, the vertices are located 3 units to the left and 3 units to the right of the center, or at the points $(-1, 4)$ and $(5, 4)$. From (11), $c = \sqrt{a^2 + b^2} = \sqrt{9 + 9} = 3\sqrt{2}$, so the foci are located $3\sqrt{2}$ units to the left and right of the center, or at the points $(2 - 3\sqrt{2}, 4)$ and $(2 + 3\sqrt{2}, 4)$.

The equations of the asymptotes may be found using the trick of replacing 1 by 0 in (21) to obtain

$$\frac{(x-2)^2}{9} - \frac{(y-4)^2}{9} = 0$$

This can be written as $y - 4 = \pm(x - 2)$, which yields the asymptotes

$$y = x + 2 \quad \text{and} \quad y = -x + 6$$

With the aid of a box extending $a = 3$ units left and right of the center and $b = 3$ units above and below the center, we obtain the sketch in Figure 14.7.29. ◄

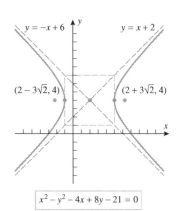

$x^2 - y^2 - 4x + 8y - 21 = 0$

▲ Figure 14.7.29

■ **REFLECTION PROPERTIES OF THE CONIC SECTIONS**

Parabolas, ellipses, and hyperbolas have certain reflection properties that make them extremely valuable in various applications. In the exercises we will ask you to prove the following results.

14.7.4 THEOREM (*Reflection Property of Parabolas*) *The tangent line at a point P on a parabola makes equal angles with the line through P parallel to the axis of symmetry and the line through P and the focus (Figure 14.7.30a).*

14.7.5 THEOREM (*Reflection Property of Ellipses*)   *A line tangent to an ellipse at a point P makes equal angles with the lines joining P to the foci (Figure 15.7.30b).*

14.7.6 THEOREM (*Reflection Property of Hyperbolas*)   *A line tangent to a hyperbola at a point P makes equal angles with the lines joining P to the foci (Figure 14.7.30c).*

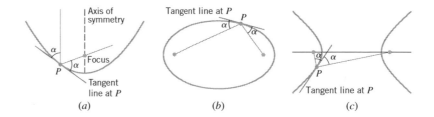

▶ **Figure 14.7.30**

(a)   (b)   (c)

John Mead/Science Photo Library/Photo Researchers
Incoming signals are reflected by the parabolic antenna to the receiver at the focus.

■ APPLICATIONS OF THE CONIC SECTIONS

Fermat's principle in optics implies that light reflects off of a surface at an angle equal to its angle of incidence. (See Exercise 62 in Section 4.5.) In particular, if a reflecting surface is generated by revolving a parabola about its axis of symmetry, it follows from Theorem 14.7.4 that all light rays entering parallel to the axis will be reflected to the focus (Figure 14.7.31*a*); conversely, if a light source is located at the focus, then the reflected rays will all be parallel to the axis (Figure 14.7.31*b*). This principle is used in certain telescopes to reflect the approximately parallel rays of light from the stars and planets off of a parabolic mirror to an eyepiece at the focus; and the parabolic reflectors in flashlights and automobile headlights utilize this principle to form a parallel beam of light rays from a bulb placed at the focus. The same optical principles apply to radar signals and sound waves, which explains the parabolic shape of many antennas.

▶ **Figure 14.7.31**   (a)   (b)

Visitors to various rooms in the United States Capitol Building and in St. Paul's Cathedral in London are often astonished by the "whispering gallery" effect in which two people at opposite ends of the room can hear one another's whispers very clearly. Such rooms have ceilings with elliptical cross sections and common foci. Thus, when the two people stand at the foci, their whispers are reflected directly to one another off of the elliptical ceiling.

Hyperbolic navigation systems, which were developed in World War II as navigational aids to ships, are based on the definition of a hyperbola. With these systems the ship receives synchronized radio signals from two widely spaced transmitters with known positions. The ship's electronic receiver measures the difference in reception times between the signals and then uses that difference to compute the difference $2a$ between its distances from the two transmitters. This information places the ship somewhere on the hyperbola whose foci are at the transmitters and whose points have $2a$ as the difference in their distances from the foci. By repeating the process with a second set of transmitters, the position of the ship can be approximated as the intersection of two hyperbolas (Figure 14.7.32). (The modern global positioning system (GPS) is based on the same principle.)

▲ Figure 14.7.32

✔ QUICK CHECK EXERCISES 14.7   (See page 748 for answers.)

1. Identify the conic.
   (a) The set of points in the plane, the sum of whose distances to two fixed points is a positive constant greater than the distance between the fixed points is _____.
   (b) The set of points in the plane, the difference of whose distances to two fixed points is a positive constant less than the distance between the fixed points is _____.
   (c) The set of points in the plane that are equidistant from a fixed line and a fixed point not on the line is _____.

2. (a) The equation of the parabola with focus $(p, 0)$ and directrix $x = -p$ is _____.
   (b) The equation of the parabola with focus $(0, p)$ and directrix $y = -p$ is _____.

3. (a) Suppose that an ellipse has semimajor axis a and semiminor axis b. Then for all points on the ellipse, the sum of the distances to the foci is equal to _____.
   (b) The two standard equations of an ellipse with semimajor axis a and semiminor axis b are _____ and _____.

   (c) Suppose that an ellipse has semimajor axis a, semiminor axis b, and foci $(\pm c, 0)$. Then c may be obtained from a and b by the equation $c =$ _____.

4. (a) Suppose that a hyperbola has semifocal axis a and semiconjugate axis b. Then for all points on the hyperbola, the difference of the distance to the farther focus minus the distance to the closer focus is equal to _____.
   (b) The two standard equations of a hyperbola with semifocal axis a and semiconjugate axis b are _____ and _____.
   (c) Suppose that a hyperbola in standard position has semifocal axis a, semiconjugate axis b, and foci $(\pm c, 0)$. Then c may be obtained from a and b by the equation $c =$ _____. The equations of the asymptotes of this hyperbola are $y = \pm$ _____.

EXERCISE SET 14.7   ▨ Graphing Utility

FOCUS ON CONCEPTS

1. In parts (a)–(f), find the equation of the conic.

(a)

(b)

(c)

(d)

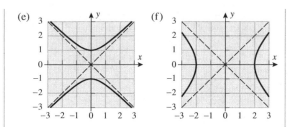

2. (a) Find the focus and directrix for each parabola in Exercise 1.

(b) Find the foci of the ellipses in Exercise 1.

(c) Find the foci and the equations of the asymptotes of the hyperbolas in Exercise 1.

3–6 Sketch the parabola, and label the focus, vertex, and directrix. ▪

3. (a) $y^2 = 4x$ (b) $x^2 = -8y$

4. (a) $y^2 = -10x$ (b) $x^2 = 4y$

5. (a) $(y - 1)^2 = -12(x + 4)$ (b) $(x - 1)^2 = 2\left(y - \frac{1}{2}\right)$

6. (a) $y^2 - 6y - 2x + 1 = 0$ (b) $y = 4x^2 + 8x + 5$

7–10 Sketch the ellipse, and label the foci, vertices, and ends of the minor axis. ▪

7. (a) $\dfrac{x^2}{16} + \dfrac{y^2}{9} = 1$ (b) $9x^2 + y^2 = 9$

8. (a) $\dfrac{x^2}{25} + \dfrac{y^2}{4} = 1$ (b) $4x^2 + y^2 = 36$

9. (a) $(x + 3)^2 + 4(y - 5)^2 = 16$

(b) $\frac{1}{4}x^2 + \frac{1}{9}(y + 2)^2 - 1 = 0$

10. (a) $9x^2 + 4y^2 - 18x + 24y + 9 = 0$

(b) $5x^2 + 9y^2 + 20x - 54y = -56$

11–14 Sketch the hyperbola, and label the vertices, foci, and asymptotes. ▪

11. (a) $\dfrac{x^2}{16} - \dfrac{y^2}{9} = 1$ (b) $9y^2 - x^2 = 36$

12. (a) $\dfrac{y^2}{9} - \dfrac{x^2}{25} = 1$ (b) $16x^2 - 25y^2 = 400$

13. (a) $\dfrac{(y + 4)^2}{3} - \dfrac{(x - 2)^2}{5} = 1$

(b) $16(x + 1)^2 - 8(y - 3)^2 = 16$

14. (a) $x^2 - 4y^2 + 2x + 8y - 7 = 0$

(b) $16x^2 - y^2 - 32x - 6y = 57$

15–18 Find an equation for the parabola that satisfies the given conditions. ▪

15. (a) Vertex $(0, 0)$; focus $(3, 0)$.

(b) Vertex $(0, 0)$; directrix $y = \frac{1}{4}$.

16. (a) Focus $(6, 0)$; directrix $x = -6$.

(b) Focus $(1, 1)$; directrix $y = -2$.

17. Axis $y = 0$; passes through $(3, 2)$ and $(2, -\sqrt{2})$.

18. Vertex $(5, -3)$; axis parallel to the y-axis; passes through $(9, 5)$.

19–22 Find an equation for the ellipse that satisfies the given conditions. ▪

19. (a) Ends of major axis $(\pm 3, 0)$; ends of minor axis $(0, \pm 2)$.

(b) Length of minor axis 8; foci $(0, \pm 3)$.

20. (a) Foci $(\pm 1, 0)$; $b = \sqrt{2}$.

(b) $c = 2\sqrt{3}$; $a = 4$; center at the origin; foci on a coordinate axis (two answers).

21. (a) Ends of major axis $(0, \pm 6)$; passes through $(-3, 2)$.

(b) Foci $(-1, 1)$ and $(-1, 3)$; minor axis of length 4.

22. (a) Center at $(0, 0)$; major and minor axes along the coordinate axes; passes through $(3, 2)$ and $(1, 6)$.

(b) Foci $(2, 1)$ and $(2, -3)$; major axis of length 6.

23–26 Find an equation for a hyperbola that satisfies the given conditions. [*Note:* In some cases there may be more than one hyperbola.] ▪

23. (a) Vertices $(\pm 2, 0)$; foci $(\pm 3, 0)$.

(b) Vertices $(0, \pm 2)$; asymptotes $y = \pm\frac{2}{3}x$.

24. (a) Asymptotes $y = \pm\frac{3}{2}x$; $b = 4$.

(b) Foci $(0, \pm 5)$; asymptotes $y = \pm 2x$.

25. (a) Asymptotes $y = \pm\frac{3}{4}x$; $c = 5$.

(b) Foci $(\pm 3, 0)$; asymptotes $y = \pm 2x$.

26. (a) Vertices $(0, 6)$ and $(6, 6)$; foci 10 units apart.

(b) Asymptotes $y = x - 2$ and $y = -x + 4$; passes through the origin.

27–30 True–False Determine whether the statement is true or false. Explain your answer. ▪

27. A hyperbola is the set of all points in the plane that are equidistant from a fixed line and a fixed point not on the line.

28. If an ellipse is not a circle, then the foci of an ellipse lie on the major axis of the ellipse.

29. If a parabola has equation $y^2 = 4px$, where p is a positive constant, then the perpendicular distance from the parabola's focus to its directrix is p.

30. The hyperbola $(y^2/a^2) - x^2 = 1$ has asymptotes the lines $y = \pm x/a$.

31. (a) As illustrated in the accompanying figure, a parabolic arch spans a road 40 ft wide. How high is the arch if a center section of the road 20 ft wide has a minimum clearance of 12 ft?

(b) How high would the center be if the arch were the upper half of an ellipse?

◀ **Figure Ex-31**

32. (a) Find an equation for the parabolic arch with base b and height h, shown in the accompanying figure.

(b) Find the area under the arch.

▲ **Figure Ex-32**

33. Show that the vertex is the closest point on a parabola to the focus. [*Suggestion:* Introduce a convenient coordinate system and use Definition 14.7.1.]

34. As illustrated in the accompanying figure, suppose that a comet moves in a parabolic orbit with the Sun at its focus and that the line from the Sun to the comet makes an angle of 60° with the axis of the parabola when the comet is 40 million miles from the center of the Sun. Use the result in Exercise 33 to determine how close the comet will come to the center of the Sun.

35. For the parabolic reflector in the accompanying figure, how far from the vertex should the light source be placed to produce a beam of parallel rays?

▲ **Figure Ex-34**

▲ **Figure Ex-35**

36. (a) Show that the right and left branches of the hyperbola

$$\frac{x^2}{a^2} - \frac{y^2}{b^2} = 1$$

can be represented parametrically as

$$x = a\cosh t, \quad y = b\sinh t \quad (-\infty < t < +\infty)$$
$$x = -a\cosh t, \quad y = b\sinh t \quad (-\infty < t < +\infty)$$

(b) Use a graphing utility to generate both branches of the hyperbola $x^2 - y^2 = 1$ on the same screen.

37. (a) Show that the right and left branches of the hyperbola

$$\frac{x^2}{a^2} - \frac{y^2}{b^2} = 1$$

can be represented parametrically as

$$x = a\sec t, \quad y = b\tan t \quad (-\pi/2 < t < \pi/2)$$
$$x = -a\sec t, \quad y = b\tan t \quad (-\pi/2 < t < \pi/2)$$

(b) Use a graphing utility to generate both branches of the hyperbola $x^2 - y^2 = 1$ on the same screen.

38. Find an equation of the parabola traced by a point that moves so that its distance from $(2, 4)$ is the same as its distance to the x-axis.

39. Find an equation of the ellipse traced by a point that moves so that the sum of its distances to $(4, 1)$ and $(4, 5)$ is 12.

40. Find the equation of the hyperbola traced by a point that moves so that the difference between its distances to $(0, 0)$ and $(1, 1)$ is 1.

41. Show that an ellipse with semimajor axis a and semiminor axis b has area $A = \pi ab$.

FOCUS ON CONCEPTS

42. Show that if a plane is not parallel to the axis of a right circular cylinder, then the intersection of the plane and cylinder is an ellipse (possibly a circle). [*Hint:* Let θ be the angle shown in the accompanying figure, introduce coordinate axes as shown, and express x' and y' in terms of x and y.]

◀ **Figure Ex-42**

43. As illustrated in the accompanying figure, a carpenter needs to cut an elliptical hole in a sloped roof through which a circular vent pipe of diameter D is to be inserted vertically. The carpenter wants to draw the outline of the hole on the roof using a pencil, two tacks, and a piece of string (as in Figure 14.7.3b). The center point of the ellipse is known, and common sense suggests that its major axis must be perpendicular to the drip line of the roof. The carpenter needs to determine the length L of the string and the distance T between a tack and the center point. The architect's plans show that the pitch of the roof is p (pitch = rise over run; see the accompanying figure). Find T and L in terms of D and p.

Source: This exercise is based on an article by William H. Enos, which appeared in the *Mathematics Teacher*, Feb. 1991, p. 148.

◀ **Figure Ex-43**

44. As illustrated in the accompanying figure on the next page, suppose that two observers are stationed at the points $F_1(c, 0)$ and $F_2(-c, 0)$ in an xy-coordinate system. Suppose also that the sound of an explosion in the xy-plane is heard by the F_1 observer t seconds before it is heard by the F_2 observer. Assuming that the speed of sound is a constant v, show that the explosion occurred somewhere on the hyperbola

$$\frac{x^2}{v^2t^2/4} - \frac{y^2}{c^2 - (v^2t^2/4)} = 1$$

$F_2(-c, 0)$ $F_1(c, 0)$ ◀ **Figure Ex-44**

45. As illustrated in the accompanying figure, suppose that two transmitting stations are positioned 100 km apart at points $F_1(50, 0)$ and $F_2(-50, 0)$ on a straight shoreline in an xy-coordinate system. Suppose also that a ship is traveling parallel to the shoreline but 200 km at sea. Find the coordinates of the ship if the stations transmit a pulse simultaneously, but the pulse from station F_1 is received by the ship 100 microseconds sooner than the pulse from station F_2. [*Hint:* Use the formula obtained in Exercise 44, assuming that the pulses travel at the speed of light (299,792,458 m/s).]

200 km

$F_2(-50, 0)$ $F_1(50, 0)$ ◀ **Figure Ex-45**

46. A nuclear cooling tower is to have a height of h feet and the shape of the solid that is generated by revolving the region R enclosed by the right branch of the hyperbola $1521x^2 - 225y^2 = 342,225$ and the lines $x = 0$, $y = -h/2$, and $y = h/2$ about the y-axis.
(a) Find the volume of the tower.
(b) Find the lateral surface area of the tower.

47. Let R be the region that is above the x-axis and enclosed between the curve $b^2x^2 - a^2y^2 = a^2b^2$ and the line $x = \sqrt{a^2 + b^2}$.
(a) Sketch the solid generated by revolving R about the x-axis, and find its volume.
(b) Sketch the solid generated by revolving R about the y-axis, and find its volume.

48. Prove: The line tangent to the parabola $x^2 = 4py$ at the point (x_0, y_0) is $x_0x = 2p(y + y_0)$.

49. Prove: The line tangent to the ellipse

$$\frac{x^2}{a^2} + \frac{y^2}{b^2} = 1$$

at the point (x_0, y_0) has the equation

$$\frac{xx_0}{a^2} + \frac{yy_0}{b^2} = 1$$

50. Prove: The line tangent to the hyperbola

$$\frac{x^2}{a^2} - \frac{y^2}{b^2} = 1$$

at the point (x_0, y_0) has the equation

$$\frac{xx_0}{a^2} - \frac{yy_0}{b^2} = 1$$

51. Use the results in Exercises 49 and 50 to show that if an ellipse and a hyperbola have the same foci, then at each point of intersection their tangent lines are perpendicular.

52. Consider the second-degree equation

$$Ax^2 + Cy^2 + Dx + Ey + F = 0$$

where A and C are not both 0. Show by completing the square:
(a) If $AC > 0$, then the equation represents an ellipse, a circle, a point, or has no graph.
(b) If $AC < 0$, then the equation represents a hyperbola or a pair of intersecting lines.
(c) If $AC = 0$, then the equation represents a parabola, a pair of parallel lines, or has no graph.

53. In each part, use the result in Exercise 52 to make a statement about the graph of the equation, and then check your conclusion by completing the square and identifying the graph.
(a) $x^2 - 5y^2 - 2x - 10y - 9 = 0$
(b) $x^2 - 3y^2 - 6y - 3 = 0$
(c) $4x^2 + 8y^2 + 16x + 16y + 20 = 0$
(d) $3x^2 + y^2 + 12x + 2y + 13 = 0$
(e) $x^2 + 8x + 2y + 14 = 0$
(f) $5x^2 + 40x + 2y + 94 = 0$

54. Derive the equation $x^2 = 4py$ in Figure 17.4.6.

55. Derive the equation $(x^2/b^2) + (y^2/a^2) = 1$ given in Figure 14.7.14.

56. Derive the equation $(x^2/a^2) - (y^2/b^2) = 1$ given in Figure 14.7.22.

57. Prove Theorem 14.7.4. [*Hint:* Choose coordinate axes so that the parabola has the equation $x^2 = 4py$. Show that the tangent line at $P(x_0, y_0)$ intersects the y-axis at $Q(0, -y_0)$ and that the triangle whose three vertices are at P, Q, and the focus is isosceles.]

58. Given two intersecting lines, let L_2 be the line with the larger angle of inclination ϕ_2, and let L_1 be the line with the smaller angle of inclination ϕ_1. We define the **angle θ between L_1 and L_2** by $\theta = \phi_2 - \phi_1$. (See the accompanying figure on the next page.)
(a) Prove: If L_1 and L_2 are not perpendicular, then

$$\tan \theta = \frac{m_2 - m_1}{1 + m_1m_2}$$

where L_1 and L_2 have slopes m_1 and m_2.
(b) Prove Theorem 14.7.5. [*Hint:* Introduce coordinates so that the equation $(x^2/a^2) + (y^2/b^2) = 1$ describes the ellipse, and use part (a).] (*cont.*)

(c) Prove Theorem 14.7.6. [*Hint:* Introduce coordinates so that the equation $(x^2/a^2) - (y^2/b^2) = 1$ describes the hyperbola, and use part (a).]

◄ **Figure Ex-58**

59. Writing Suppose that you want to draw an ellipse that has given values for the lengths of the major and minor axes by using the method shown in Figure 14.7.3*b*. Assuming that the axes are drawn, explain how a compass can be used to locate the positions for the tacks.

60. Writing List the forms for standard equations of parabolas, ellipses, and hyperbolas, and write a summary of techniques for sketching conic sections from their standard equations.

✔**QUICK CHECK ANSWERS 14.7**

1. (a) an ellipse (b) a hyperbola (c) a parabola 2. (a) $y^2 = 4px$ (b) $x^2 = 4py$
3. (a) $2a$ (b) $\dfrac{x^2}{a^2} + \dfrac{y^2}{b^2} = 1$; $\dfrac{x^2}{b^2} + \dfrac{y^2}{a^2} = 1$ (c) $\sqrt{a^2 - b^2}$ 4. (a) $2a$ (b) $\dfrac{x^2}{a^2} - \dfrac{y^2}{b^2} = 1$; $\dfrac{y^2}{a^2} - \dfrac{x^2}{b^2} = 1$ (c) $\sqrt{a^2 + b^2}$; $\dfrac{b}{a}x$

ANSWERS TO ODD-NUMBERED EXERCISES

63. (a) **(b)**

67. (a) $r = 1 + \dfrac{\sqrt{2}}{2}(\cos\theta + \sin\theta)$ **(b)** $r = 1 + \sin\theta$

(c) $r = 1 - \cos\theta$ **(d)** $r = 1 - \dfrac{\sqrt{2}}{2}(\cos\theta + \sin\theta)$

69. $(3/2, \pi/3)$ **73.** $\sqrt{2}$

▶ **Exercise Set 15.3**

1. $\sqrt{3}$ **3.** $\dfrac{\tan 2 - 2}{2\tan 2 + 1}$ **5.** $1/2$ **7.** $1, 0, -1$

9. horizontal: $(3a/2, \pi/3), (0, \pi), (3a/2, 5\pi/3)$;
vertical: $(2a, 0), (a/2, 2\pi/3), (a/2, 4\pi/3)$

11. $(0, 0), (\sqrt{2}/4, \pi/4), (\sqrt{2}/4, 3\pi/4)$

13. **15.**

$\theta = \pi/2, \pm\pi/6$ $\theta = \pm\pi/4$

17.

$\theta = \pm\pi/3$

19. $L = 2\pi a$ **21.** $L = 8a$

23. (b) ≈ 2.42

(c)

n	2	3	4	5	6	7
L	2.42211	2.22748	2.14461	2.10100	2.07501	2.05816

n	8	9	10	11	12	13	14
L	2.04656	2.03821	2.03199	2.02721	2.02346	2.02046	2.01802

n	15	16	17	18	19	20
L	2.01600	2.01431	2.01288	2.01167	2.01062	2.00971

25. (a) $\displaystyle\int_{\pi/2}^{\pi} \tfrac{1}{2}(1 - \cos\theta)^2 d\theta$ **(b)** $\displaystyle\int_{0}^{\pi/2} 2\cos^2\theta\, d\theta$

(c) $\displaystyle\int_{0}^{\pi/2} \tfrac{1}{2}\sin^2 2\theta\, d\theta$ **(d)** $\displaystyle\int_{0}^{2\pi} \tfrac{1}{2}\theta^2\, d\theta$

(e) $\displaystyle\int_{-\pi/2}^{\pi/2} \tfrac{1}{2}(1 - \sin\theta)^2 d\theta$ **(f)** $\displaystyle\int_{0}^{\pi/4} \cos^2 2\theta\, d\theta$

27. (a) πa^2 **(b)** πa^2 **29.** 6π **31.** 4π **33.** $\pi - 3\sqrt{3}/2$

35. $\pi/2 - \tfrac{1}{4}$ **37.** $10\pi/3 - 4\sqrt{3}$ **39.** π **41.** $9\sqrt{3}/2 - \pi$

43. $(\pi + 3\sqrt{3})/4$ **45.** $\pi - 2$

Responses to True–False questions may be abridged to save space.

47. True; apply Theorem 10.3.1: $\cos\dfrac{\theta}{2}\Big|_{\theta=3\pi} = 0$ and $\dfrac{dr}{d\theta}\Big|_{\theta=3\pi} = \dfrac{1}{2} \neq 0$, so the line $\theta = 3\pi$ (the x-axis) is tangent to the curve at the origin.

49. False; the area of the sector is $\dfrac{\theta}{2\pi} \cdot \pi r^2 = \dfrac{1}{2}\theta r^2$.

51. (b) a^2 **(c)** $2\sqrt{3} - \dfrac{2\pi}{3}$ **53.** $8\pi^3 a^2$

59. $\pi/16$ **65.** π^2

67. $32\pi/5$

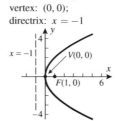

▶ **Exercise Set 14.7**

1. (a) $x = y^2$ **(b)** $-3y = x^2$ **(c)** $\dfrac{x^2}{9} + \dfrac{y^2}{4} = 1$ **(d)** $\dfrac{x^2}{4} + \dfrac{y^2}{9} = 1$

(e) $y^2 - x^2 = 1$ **(f)** $\dfrac{x^2}{4} - \dfrac{y^2}{4} = 1$

3. (a) focus: $(1, 0)$; **(b)** focus: $(0, -2)$;
vertex: $(0, 0)$; vertex: $(0, 0)$;
directrix: $x = -1$ directrix: $y = 2$

5. (a) **(b)**

7. (a) **(b)**

9. **(a)** $\dfrac{(x+3)^2}{16} + \dfrac{(y-5)^2}{4} = 1$

$c^2 = 16 - 4 = 12, c = 2\sqrt{3}$

(b) $\dfrac{x^2}{4} + \dfrac{(y+2)^2}{9} = 1$

$c^2 = 9 - 4 = 5, c = 2\sqrt{5}$

11. **(a)** vertices: $(\pm 4, 0)$;   **(b)** vertices: $(0, \pm 2)$;
foci: $(\pm 5, 0)$;   foci: $(0, \pm 2\sqrt{10})$;
asymptotes: $y = \pm 3x/4$ asymptotes: $y = \pm x/3$

13. **(a)** $c^2 = 3 + 5 = 8, c = 2\sqrt{2}$

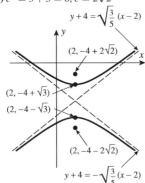

(b) $\dfrac{(x+1)^2}{1} - \dfrac{(y-3)^2}{2} = 1$

$c^2 = 1 + 2 = 3, c = \sqrt{3}$

15. **(a)** $y^2 = 12x$ **(b)** $x^2 = -y$ 17. $y^2 = 2(x-1)$

19. **(a)** $\dfrac{x^2}{9} + \dfrac{y^2}{4} = 1$ **(b)** $\dfrac{x^2}{16} + \dfrac{y^2}{25} = 1$

21. **(a)** $\dfrac{x^2}{81/8} + \dfrac{y^2}{36} = 1$ **(b)** $\dfrac{(x+1)^2}{4} + \dfrac{(y-2)^2}{5} = 1$

23. **(a)** $\dfrac{x^2}{4} - \dfrac{y^2}{5} = 1$ **(b)** $\dfrac{y^2}{4} - \dfrac{x^2}{9} = 1$

25. **(a)** $\dfrac{y^2}{9} - \dfrac{x^2}{16} = 1, \dfrac{x^2}{16} - \dfrac{y^2}{9} = 1$ **(b)** $\dfrac{x^2}{9/5} - \dfrac{y^2}{36/5} = 1$

Responses to True–False questions may be abridged to save space.

27. False; the description matches a parabola.

29. False; the distance from the parabola's focus to its directrix is $2p$; see Figure 17.4.6.

31. **(a)** 16 ft **(b)** $8\sqrt{3}$ ft   35. $\frac{1}{16}$ ft

39. $\frac{1}{32}(x-4)^2 + \frac{1}{36}(y-3)^2 = 1$

43. $L = D\sqrt{1 + p^2}, T = \frac{1}{2}pD$ 45. $(64.612, 200)$

47. **(a)** $V = \dfrac{\pi b^2}{3a^2}(b^2 - 2a^2)\sqrt{a^2 + b^2} + \dfrac{2}{3}ab^2\pi$

(b) $V = \dfrac{2b^4}{3a}\pi$

53. **(a)** $(x-1)^2 - 5(y+1)^2 = 5$, hyperbola
(b) $x^2 - 3(y+1)^2 = 0, x = \pm\sqrt{3}(y+1)$, two lines
(c) $4(x+2)^2 + 8(y+1)^2 = 4$, ellipse
(d) $3(x+2)^2 + (y+1)^2 = 0$, the point $(-2, -1)$ (degenerate case)
(e) $(x+4)^2 + 2y = 2$, parabola
(f) $5(x+4)^2 + 2y = -14$, parabola

Section 1.1

S1 $(2/3)c$

S3 $6\pi r^2$

S5 $51/2$

S7 $3/2$

S9 $A = (-2, 8)$

1 (a) 2
(b) 2
(c) About 12 hours

3 $w = f(c)$

5

Cost ($)

q (items)

7

D

y

9 (a) 4
(b) 3
(c) 2
(d) 2 and 4

11 2.9

13 $0, 4, 8$

15 (a) w
(b) $(-4, 10)$
(c) $(6, 1)$

17 (a) Yes
(b) No

19
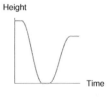
Height

Time

21 (a) 100.3 m. own phones in 2000
(b) 20 m. own phones a years after 1990
(c) b m. own phones in 2010
(d) n m. own phones t years after 1990

23 (a) Most: Hannah; least: Madison
(b) Most: Madison; least: Alexis

25 (a) 10.71 gallons
(b) 0.25 gallons
(c) 55 mph

27 (a) 72π ft^3
(b) 45π ft^3
(c) $V(h) = 9\pi h$

29 (a) 69°F
(b) July 17 and 20
(c) Yes

(d) No

31 (a) No
(b) Yes
(c) In 1981, record was 3 min 47.33 sec
(d) 1967, record of 3 min 51.1 sec

33 (a) $x + y$
(b) $0.15x + 0.18y$
(c) $(15x + 18y)/(x + y)$

35 $A(r) = \pi r^2$
21%

37 (b) $C = 2 + (0.5)l$

Section 1.2

S1 -2

S3 -2

S5 -1

S7 $-3x^2 - 4ax - a^2$

S9 $x + y$

1 (a) 80/3 CDs per year
(b) -20 CDs per year
(c) 0 CDs per year

3 Decreasing

5 0.513

7 0.513

9 (a) Negative
(b) Positive

11 $F(-2) > F(2)$

13 (a) $A = (10, 30)$
$B = (30, 40)$
$C = (50, 90)$
$D = (60, 40)$
$E = (90, 40)$

(b) Point F is on the graph.
(c) Increasing: 6–21,
36–51, 66–81
(d) Decreasing: 22–35,
52–65, 82–96

15 (a) 2
(b) Increasing
(c) Increasing everywhere

17 (a) Town B
(b) Town A

19 24.5 degrees/minute

21 (a) 162 calories
(b) Swimmer
(c) Increases

23 (a) 9
(b) $\dfrac{n - k}{m - j}$
(c) $6x + 3h$

25 (a) 10, 10, 10, 10, 7, 1
(b) 30, 30.5, 53.6, 33.9, 15.5, -5
(c) No; $\Delta G/\Delta t$ not constant
(d) Recycling and composting program in US

Section 1.3

S1 $f(0) = 5, f(3) = 7$

S3 5

S5 $y = 3; x = 3/4$

S7 $7/2, -2$

S9 $-ab + a + 3, a - 3$

1 Not linear

3 No

5 Yes

7 (a) $y = 7 + 2x$
(b) $y = 8 - 15x$

9 Vert int: 54.25 thousand; Slope: $-2/7$ thousand/yr

11 Vert int: $-\$3000$; Slope: $\$0.98$/item

13 (a) $r = f(v)$ could be linear
(b) \$5 increase/mph
(c)

r (dollars)

$r = f(v)$

v (mph)

15 $V = 21{,}500 - 3200t$

17 (b)

Cost (dollars)

x (cups)

(c) 0.25
(d) Start-up cost

19 $\pi(n) = -10{,}000 + 127n$

21 $c = 4000 + 80r$

23 (a) Radius and circumference
(c) 2π

25 (a) No
(b) Looks linear

(c) $\Delta T/\Delta d = 0.01^\circ$C/meter

27 (a) $T = \$1900$
   (b) $C = 7$
   (d) Twelve credits
   (e) Fixed costs that do not depend on the number of credits taken

29 (a) $r = 5/2, s = 16$
   (b) $k = 0.2, j = -3$

33 No

Section 1.4

S1 $y = 26$

S3 $x = 2$

S5 $y = -17/16$

S7 $F = (9/5)C + 32$

S9 $x = (c - ab)/(2a)$

1 $y = 4/5 - x$

3 $y = 180 - 10x$

5 $y = -0.3 + 5x$

7 $y = -40/3 - 2/3x$

9 $y = 21 - x$

11 Yes; $F(P) = 13 + (-1/8)P$

13 Yes; $C(r) = 0 + 2\pi r$

15 Yes; $f(x) = n^2 + m^2x$

17 $y = 8 + 3x$

19 $y = (11 + 2x)/3$

21 $y = 0.03 + 0.1x$

23 $f(x) = 3 - 2x$

25 $q = 2500 - 2000p$

27 $459.7 + 1x$

29 $u = (1/12)n$

31 $f(x) = -12.5 - 1.5x$

33 $h(t) = 12,000 + 225t$

35 (a) $\$11,375$
   (b) $\$125$
   (c) $\$5$

37 $C(n) = 10,500 + 5n$

39 (b) $v = 40 - 32t$

41 (a) $q = 210 - 50p$

43 $y = -4 + 4x$

45 $y = \frac{16+5\sqrt{7}}{2+\sqrt{7}} - \frac{3}{2+\sqrt{7}}x$ or
   $y = (1 + 2\sqrt{7}) + (2 - \sqrt{7})x$

47 (a) $p = 0.1t - 1$, and $t \geq 10$
   (b) 11
   (d) $t = 10p + 10$
   (e) 2 hours 40 minutes

49 (a) $i(x) = 2.5x$
   (b) $i(0) = 0$

51 $w(r) = \pi x^2 - s\sqrt{x} + (-3x - 4s)r$;
   $b = \pi x^2 - s\sqrt{x}; m = -3x - 4s$

53 (a) $r = 0.005H - 0.03$
   (b) $S = 200$

Section 1.5

S1 $x = -2, y = 5$

S3 No solution

S5 $x = 7, y = 4$

S7 $x = 3/2, y = 3/2$

1 (a) (V)
  (b) (VI)
  (c) (I)
  (d) (IV)
  (e) (III)
  (f) (II)

5 (a)

(b) Yes ($y = 3 + 0x$), No

7 Perpendicular

9 Neither

11 Parallel

13 $y = 6 - (3/5)x$

15 Parallel line:
   $y = -4x + 9$
   Perpendicular line:
   $y = 0.25x + 4.75$

17 $(1, 0)$

19 (a) 5 years

21 (a) $y = 9 - \frac{2}{3}x$
   (b) $y = -4 + \frac{3}{2}x$
   (c)

23 (a) $P = (a, 0)$
   (b) $A = (0, b), B = (-c, 0)$
       $C = (a + c, b), D = (a, 0)$

27 $3 < \beta < 6$

29 (a) $y = -\sqrt{3}x$
   (b) $y = (1/\sqrt{3})x + 4/\sqrt{3}$

31 $y = x/3 + 2/3$.

Section 1.6

1 $r = 0.93$ is reasonable.

3 $r = 1$ is not reasonable.

5 $r = 1$ is not reasonable.

7 (a) $r = 1$
  (b) $r = 0.7$

(c) $r = 0$
(d) $r = -0.98$
(e) $r = -0.25$
(f) $r = -0.5$

9 (a) and (b)

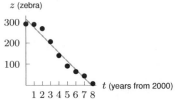

(c) $z = -40t + 314$
(e) Strong negative correlation ($r = -0.983$)

11 (a) nonpreferred hand strength (kg)

(c) $y = 3.623 + 0.825x$
(d) ≈ 34
(e) ≈ 40

Chapter 1 Review

1 Neither

3 Both

5 Neither

7 (a)

x	0	1	2	3
$f(x)$	10	5	2	1

(b) $x = 0$; smallest x-value

9 (a) #2
  (b) #1, #3
  (c) #3

11 (a) Owens: 12 yards/sec horse: 20 yards/sec
   (b) 6 seconds

13 Yes

15 $f(t) = 2.2 - 1.22t$

17 (a) (ii)
   (b) (iii)
   (c) (i)

19 (a) $y = 3 + 4x$
   (b) $y = 5 - 2x$

21 Neither

23 Perpendicular

25 120

27 500 m

29

distance of bug from light
time

31

temperature
time

33 $T(d) = d/5 + (10 - d)/8$

35 $s = 1440 - w$

37 (a) (i) $1/2$
    (ii) $1/2$
    (iii) $1/2$
   (b) Always $1/2$

39 (a) $0°C/meter$
   (b) $-0.008°C/meter$
   (c) $0.009°C/meter.$

41 (a) $5350, $5700, $6750,
       $8500, $12,000

C, total cost ($1000s)
$C = 5000 + 350n$
n, number of horses

(b) $C = 5000 + 350n$
(c) $350/horse

43 $h(t) = 254 - 248t$

45 (a) 1000, 990.2, 980.4, 970.6, 960.8
   (b) v decreasing at constant rate
   (c) Slope: -9.8 meter/sec^2
       v-intercept: 1000meters/sec
       t-intercept: 102.04 sec

49 (a) $S = -100 + 100p$
   (c) Yes, $1
   (d) $4

51 $g(x) = -2 - 2x$

53 $y = 2.8 - 0.1x$

55 $d = 60 + 50t$

57 $g(x) = 32 - (3/5)x$

59 (a) $Y_A = 0.37x$
       $Y_B = 13.95 + 0.22x$
       $Y_C = 50$
   (c) $93 < x \leq 163$

61 (a)

hours of TV
IQ

(b) $r \approx -1/2$
(c) $y = 27.5139 - 0.1674x$
    $r = -0.5389$

63 (a)

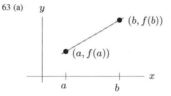
y
$(b, f(b))$
$(a, f(a))$
a b x

(b) $(f(b) - f(a))/(b - a)$

65 $y = 0.75/(0.75 - 1) - (\sqrt{0.5})^2 x; p = 0.75, r = \sqrt{0.5}$

67 (a) y-intercept: c/q
       x-intercept: c/p
   (b) $-(p/q)$

69

hair length
maximum length
t (years)
1 2 3 4 5

71 $g(x) = 17/5 + 6/(5\pi) \cdot x$

73 $g(54) = 8^{1/5} = \sqrt[5]{8}$

Ch. 1 Understanding

1 False
3 True
5 True
7 True
9 True
11 True
13 True
15 True
17 False
19 False
21 False
23 True
25 True
27 False
29 True
31 False
33 False

35 True
37 False
39 False
41 True
43 False
45 True
47 True
49 False
51 True
53 True

Ch. 1 Skills: Linear Equations

1 $x = 5$
3 $z = 11/2$
5 $w = -11$
7 $t = 45/13$
9 $t = 10/7$
11 $B = -2$
13 $l = A/w$
15 $a = 2(h - v_0 t)/t^2$
17 $v = (3w - 2u - z)/(u + w - z)$
19 $x = -a(b+1)/(ad - c)$
21 $y' = 4/(y + 2x)$
23 $x = 4, y = 3$
25 $x = -55, y = 39$
27 $x = 1, y = a$
29 $x = 3, y = 6$
31 $A = (-4, 7)$
33 $A = (2, 9), B = (10, 1)$
35 $A = (-7, 8), B = (-3, 4)$

Section 2.1

S1 $5x - 15$
S3 $4m^2 - 38m + 90$
S5 $(3x + 3)/3$
S7 $x = \pm 3$
S9 $(18 \pm \sqrt{285})/3$

1 (a) -4
  (b) ± 2
3 (a) $-1/2$
  (b) -1
5 $3/2$
7 54
9 $(0, 2)$

$(0, 2)$ y $g(x)$ $f(x)$
x

11 Intersect at $x = 2$

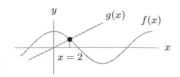

13 100

15 $f(1/3) = 3.222$; $f(1)/f(3) = 0.238$; Not equal

17 (a)   (i) $1/(1-t)$
          (ii) $-1/t$
   (b) $x = 3/2$

19 (a) 48 feet for both
   (b) 4 sec, 64 ft

21 (a) $s(2) = 146$
   (b) Solve $v(t) = 65$
   (c) At 3 hours

23 (a) \$4261
   (b) $T(x) = 0.8x$
   (c) $L(x) = 0.0548x - 397$
   (d) \$4261

27 (a) $h(1) = b + c + 1$
   (b) $h(b+1) = 2b^2 + 3b + c + 1$

29 $a/2$

31 $a/(a - a^2 + 1)$

33 (a)   (i) 6
          (ii) 5
          (iii) Not defined
   (b)   (i) $50 \leq s \leq 75$
          (ii) $76 \leq s \leq 125$

35 (a) 7000
   (b) 8500; 4 weeks after the beginning of the epidemic
   (c) $w = 1, w = 10$
   (d) $1.5 \leq w \leq 8$

Section 2.2

S1 $x = 3$

S3 $x < 15$

S5 $x > 8$

S7 $n < 0$

S9 $x > 5$ or $x < -5$.

1 $f(x) \leq -(1/2)$ or $f(x) \geq (1/2)$

3 $-4 \leq f(x) \leq 5$

5 D: all real numbers $\neq -3$

7 D: all real numbers $\neq -3$

9 Domain: $x > 4$
   Range: $y > 0$

11 D: $x \geq 2$ or $x \leq -2$

13 D: all real numbers

15 D: all real numbers
    R: all real numbers

17 $a = 3$

19 $a = -3$

21 D: $1 \leq x \leq 7$; R: $2 \leq f(x) \leq 18$

23 $y = 1/((x+5)\sqrt{-x})$

25 D: $0 \leq t \leq 12$
    R: $0 \leq f(t) \leq 200$

27 Domain: integers $0 \leq n \leq 200$
    Range: $0, 4, 8, \ldots, 800$

29 (a) 162 calories
   (c)   (i) Calories $=$
              $0.025 \times$ weight

   (ii) (0,0) is the number of calories burned by a weightless runner
   (iii) Domain $0 < w$; range $0 < c$
   (iv) 3.6

31 D: all real numbers;
    R: $h(x) \geq 6$

33 (a) $p(0) = 50$
        $p(10) \approx 131$
        $p(50) \approx 911$
   (c) $50 \leq p(t) < 1000$

35 (a) 800; 200; -200
   (b)

   (c) $t = 20$; $t = 0$
   (d) Domain: $0 \leq t \leq 30$
        Range: $-400 \leq r(t) \leq 800$

Section 2.3

S1 $x > 0$

S3 $2 \leq x \leq 3$

S5 $x \leq -1$ or $x \geq 2$

S7 Domain: $2 \leq x < 6$
    Range: $3 \leq x < 5$

S9 Domain: $-2 \leq x \leq 3$
    Range: $-2 \leq x \leq 3$

1

3

5 Domain: all reals;
   Range: $G(x) < 0$ and $G(x) \geq 3$

7 $y = \begin{cases} 5 - x & \text{for } x < 3 \\ -1 + (1/2)x & \text{for } x \geq 3 \end{cases}$

9 $y = \begin{cases} 4 - \frac{1}{2}x & \text{for } 1 \leq x \leq 3 \\ -9 + 2x & \text{for } 5 \leq x \leq 8 \end{cases}$

11 (a) Yes
   (b) No
   (c) $y = 1, 2, 3, 4$

13 (c) Domain: all x, $x \neq 0$
        Range: -1 and 1
   (d) False, $u(0)$ is undefined

15 (a)

   (b) Integers from 1 to 50
        Even integers from 40 to 120

17 (a) \$1.01
   (b) $y = \begin{cases} 1 + x & \text{for } 0 < x < 0.1 \\ 10x + x & \text{for } 0.1 \leq x \leq 0.5 \\ 5 + x & \text{for } x > 0.5 \end{cases}$
   (c) \$4
   (d)

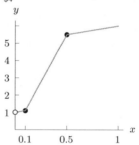

19 (b) 13-69

21 (a) $f(x) = \begin{cases} 2x - 6 & \text{for } x \geq 3 \\ 6 - 2x & \text{for } x < 3 \end{cases}$
   (b)

23 (a) $f(0) = 0, f(3) = 1$
   (b) Domain: $-1 \leq x \leq 5$;
        Range: $-3 \leq f(x) \leq 3$.

25 $y = \begin{cases} x^2 & \text{for } x < 0 \\ x - 1 & \text{for } x \geq 0 \end{cases}$

Section 2.4

S1 $y = (x + 4)/3$

S3 $y = (2x + 1)/(x - 2)$

S5 $y = \sqrt[3]{x + 4}$

S7 x

S9 $3y^2 - 12y + 5$

1 Area in sq cm at time t

3 Price for diameter d

5 0

7 -10

9 $9x - 4$

11 Year pop is P; years

13 Days for N inches snow; days

15 Diameter in inches of pizza costing c dollars

17 $f^{-1}(Q) = (Q - 3)^{1/3}$

19 $g^{-1}(y) = 1/(y - 1)$

21 (a) b
   (b) a
   (c) a
   (d) b

23 $n = f(100) = 0.4$ gal
   $A = f^{-1}(100) = 25,000$ ft^2

25 (a)   (i) 2
      (ii) 1
      (iii) 1
      (iv) 2
   (b) $f(0) = 2$ means $f^{-1}(2) = 0$
   (c) $f(1) = 0$ means $f^{-1}(0) = 1$

27 (a) 5000 loaves cost $653
   (b) 620 loaves $80
   (c) $790 for 6300 loaves
   (d) 1200 loaves for $150

29 (a) 12, perimeter for $s = 3$
   (b) 5; side for $P = 20$
   (c) $f^{-1}(P) = P/4$

31 $t = f^{-1}(H) = \frac{9}{5}H + 32 = t$

33 $20 + (50/9)2^{-n}$;
   $H = f(g(n))$ is temperature in $^\circ$C at time n

35 (a) $A = f(r) = \pi r^2$
   (b) $f(0) = 0$
   (c) $f(r + 1) = \pi(r + 1)^2$
   (d) $f(r) + 1 = \pi r^2 + 1$
   (e) Centimeters

37 $f(t) = 4\pi(50 - 2.5t)^3/3$

39 $f(t) = \pi(2t - 0.1t^2)^2$

41 (a) 2 lbs cost $2.80
   (b) 0.5 lb costs $0.70
   (c) $0.35 buys 1/4 lb
   (d) $7 buys 5 lb

43 $23/4$; -2

45 $f^{-1}(y) = (y - 1)^{1/3}$

47 D: all real numbers
   R: all real numbers

49 D: all real numbers < 3
   R: all real numbers > 0

Section 2.5

1 Concave down

3 Concave up

5 Concave up

7 Concave up

9 Rates of change: 2.889, 1.417, 1.167; Concave down

11 Possible graph:

13 Increasing;
   concave up

15 Increasing;
   concave up then down

17 Increasing;
   concave up then down

19 (a) E, III
   (b) G, I
   (c) F, II

21 No

23 (a) Larger swims twice as fast
   (b) Increasing, concave down

   (c) $\sqrt{l}$ increasing
   (d) $\sqrt{l}$ concave down;
      greater

Chapter 2 Review

1 $f(-7) = -9/2$

3 $-3/31$; 1

5 32; $\sqrt[3]{9/4}$

7 (a) 1
   (b) $-1/2$

9 -8

11 (a) $2, 0, -2$
   (b) $x = -1$

13 Domain: $x \geq 3$ or $x \leq -3$
   Range: $q(x) \geq 0$

15 Domain: all real numbers
   Range: all real numbers

17 D: all real numbers
   R: all real numbers

21 (a) $2(1 - x)$
   (b) $2 - x$
   (c) x
   (d) $(1 - x)^2$
   (e) 0

(f) $\sqrt{1 - x}$

23 $(3x - 7)^3 + 1$

25 Period in sec at time t

27 26

29 7

31 $2x^2 + 5$

33 $4x + 9$

35 Interest rate for I interest; %/year

37 D: all real numbers $\geq b$;
   R: all real numbers ≥ 6

39 $f^{-1}(P) = (P + 2)/14$.

41 Time, yrs, at which pop is P mil

43 Rates of change: 4.35, 4.10, 3.80; Concave down

45 8; 81

47

49 (a) -22
   (b) $3 - a^2$
   (c) $-a^2 + 10a - 22$
   (d) $-a^2 - 2$
   (e) $-a^2 + 25$

51 (a) $t = 6$
   (b) $t = 1, t = 2$

53 (a) -1
   (b) $x = \pm 3$
   (c) 0
   (d) -1
   (e) $3, -3$

55 $g^{-1}(7) = 1, g^{-1}(12) = 2, g^{-1}(13) = 3,$
   $g^{-1}(19) = 4, g^{-1}(22) = 5$

57 (a) $s = f(A) = +\sqrt{\frac{A}{6}}$
   (b) $V = g(f(A)) = \left(\sqrt{A/6}\right)^3$.

59 (a) $C(3.5) = \$6.25$
   (b) $C^{-1}(\$3.5) \approx 1.67$

61 (a) $d/\sqrt{2}$
   (b) s^2
   (c) $d^2/2$
   (d) $h(d) = g(f(d))$

63 (a) $(-2, 2)$
   (b) $(-2\sqrt{2}, -2), (2\sqrt{2}, -2)$
   (c)

   (d) -3

65 (a) $t(400) = 272$
 (d) $t(2x) = t(x)/2$

69 $y = \sqrt{x-4} + 1/(x-8)$

71 (a) Increasing until year 60, then decreasing
 (c) Appears concave up
 (d) Greatest between 40 and 60; smallest between 60 and 70
 (f) 1840; potato famine

Ch. 2 Understanding

1 False

3 False

5 False

7 False

9 True

11 True

13 False

15 False

17 True

19 True

21 True

23 False

25 True

27 True

29 True

31 True

33 False

35 True

37 True

39 True

41 True

Section 3.1

S1 $-200t$

S3 $u(u-2)$

S5 $(3x-4)(x+1)$

S7 $(4x-1)(4x+1)$

S9 $x = -6$ or $x = -1$

1 Yes; $f(x) = 2x^2 - 28x + 99$

3 Yes; $g(m) = -2m^2 + \sqrt{3}m + 42$

5 Not quadratic

7 Yes; $T(n) = (\sqrt{3} - 1/2)n^2 + \sqrt{5}$

9 $x \approx -0.541$ and $x \approx 5.541$

11 $x = 2, 3/2$

13 $x = 2, x = -1$

15 $x = (-1 \pm \sqrt{6})/5$

17 No zeros

19 $y = (7/4)(x-1)(x-4)$

21 3 sec

23 $f(x) = a(x-1)(x-2)$ for any constant a

25 For example $y = (x+2)(x-3)$

27

29 $y = -(5/12)x^2 - (5/3)x + 5$

31 $k = -30, r = 8, s = 0.2$

33 (a) 4 meters per second
 (b) 2 seconds
 (c) Concave up

35 -2.4% in 2004

37 (a) 5 km
 (b) 4430 m
 (c) $h \approx -0.000000255d^2 + 5$

Section 3.2

S1 $(y-6)^2 - 36$

S3 $(c+3/2)^2 - 37/4$

S5 $r = 4, 2$

S7 $q = 1/5 \pm \sqrt{41}/5$

S9 $n = -5, 1$

1 $(1, 2)$; $x = 1$; opens upward

3 Vertex: $(-11/2, -137/4)$
 Axis of symmetry: $t = -11/2$

5 (a) $a = 1, b = 0, c = 3$
 Axis of symmetry: y-axis
 Vertex: $(0, 3)$
 No zeros
 y-intercept: $y = 3$

 (b) $a = -2, b = 4, c = 16$
 Axis of symmetry: $x = 1$
 Vertex: $(1, 18)$
 Zeros: $x = -2, 4$
 y-intercept: $y = 16$

7 $k = 4$

9 $y = -(3/16)(x-4)^2 + 7$

11 $y = \frac{7}{9}(x-3)^2 - 5$

13 $f(x) = (x+4)^2 - 13$;
 Vertex: $(-4, -13)$; axis: $x = -4$

15 $p(t) = 2(t - 0.03)^2 + 0.0982$, vertex $(0.03, 0.0982)$, axis of symmetry $t = 0.03$

17 $(1/2)x^2 - (1/2)x - 6$;
 $(1/2)(x - 1/2)^2 - (49/8)$;
 $(1/2)(x-4)(x+3)$

19 $2s^2 - 7s - 15$;
 $2(s - 7/4)^2 - (169/8)$;
 $2(s-5)(s+3/2)$

21 $y = (1/4)(x-4)^2 + 2$

23 $y = (-2/49)(x-4)^2 + 2$

25 (a)

 (b) $y = (x-1)^2 - 1$ or $y = x^2 - 2x$
 (c) Range: $y \geq -1$
 (d) The other zero is $(2, 0)$

27 Vertex: $(20, 30)$

29 12.5 cm by 12.5 cm; $k/4$ by $k/4$

31 (b) Maximum height: $t = T/2$

Chapter 3 Review

1 $f(x) = -2x^2 + 13x - 15$; $a = -2, b = 13, c = -15$

3 $w(n) = 3n^2 + 6n + 0$; $a = 3, b = 6, c = 0$

5 $x = -1/3$

7 No zeros

9 2 and 5

11 There are no real zeros

13 $y = -3(x-1)^2 - 2$

15 $(1/4)(x-7)^2 + 3$

17 $y = 4(x+1)(x-2)$

19 $y = (x+1)(x-3)$

21 $y = -(x-2)^2$

23 Vertex is $(3/4, -2/3)$, axis of symmetry is $x = 3/4$, y-intercept $y = 11/24$, concave up

25 Vertex is $(0.6, 0)$, axis of symmetry is $x = 0.6$, y-intercept is $y = 0.36$, concave up

27 $y = 0.3(x-6)(x+4)$, zeros at $x = 6$ and $x = -4$, vertex at $(1, -7.5)$

29 $y = -3(x-6)(x-2)$, vertex is $(4, 12)$, zeros at $x = 6$ and $x = 2$

31 Rates of change: $-4, 0, 4$; Concave up

33 1/2 second

Ch. 3 Understanding

1 True

3 False

5 False

7 False

9 False

11 True

13 False

15 True

Ch. 3 Skills: Factoring

1 $6x - 14$

3 $12x + 12y$

5 $2x^2 + 5x$

7 $-50r^2 - 60r^2 s$

9 $5xz - 10z - 3x + 6$

11 $x^2 + 4x - 12$

13 $yz + 3y + z + 3$

15 $5xz - 10z - 3x + 6$

17 $x - 25$

19 $Pp^2 - 6Ppq + 9Pq^2$

21 $-2x - 2\sqrt{2x} - 1$

23 $2(x+3)$

25 $5(z-6)$

27 $5(2w-5)$

29 $3u^2(u^5 + 4)$

31 $7rs(2r^3 s - 3t)$

33 $(x-2)(x-1)$

35 Cannot be factored

37 Cannot be factored

39 $(2x+1)(x+2)$

41 $(x+7)(x-4)$

43 $x(x+3)(x-1)$

45 $(x+2y)(x+3z)$

47 $(ax-b)(ax+b)$

49 $(B-6)(B-4)$

51 Cannot be factored.

53 $(t-1)(t+7)$

55 $(a-2)(a^2+3)$

57 $(d+5)(d-5)(c+3)(c-3)$

59 $(r+2)(r-s)$

61 $xe^{-3x}(x+2)$

63 $P(1+r)^3$

65 $(k+2m)(d-3e)$

67 $(2g-3h)(4s+5m)$

69 $x = (-3 \pm \sqrt{249})/8$

71 $x = 7/4$

73 $t = 3 \pm \sqrt{6}$

75 $x = 2, x = -4/3$

77 $N = 3, N = 1$

79 $x = 1 \pm \sqrt{2}$

81 $t = 3 \pm \sqrt{6}$

83 $a = -10, \pm 2\sqrt{5}/5$

85 $z = -7/2$

87 $L = \pm 1/2$

89 $r = \pm 5$

91 $x = 0, x = 36$

93 $x = -4/3, x = 2$

95 $b = \sqrt[5]{C/A}$

97 $x = 4m$

99 $x = 1/2$ and $y = 2$, or $x = -1/2$ and $y = -2$

101 $x = -3$ and $y = -5$, or $x = 1$ and $y = 3$

103 $(0,0)$ and $(3,9)$

105 $(-5, 25), (3, 9)$

Ch. 3: Completing Square

1 $(x+4)^2 - 16$

3 $2(r+5)^2 - 50$

5 $(a-1)^2 - 5$

7 $3(r+3/2)^2 - 43/4$

9 $(x-1)^2 - 4$

11 $-(x-3)^2 + 7$

13 $(-3, -6)$

15 $(-4, 18)$

17 $(1/2, -23/4)$

19 $(1, -2)$

21 $(7/4, -25/8)$

23 $g = 6, -4$

25 $d = 2, -1$

27 $s = -5/2 \pm \sqrt{27}/2$

29 $p = -9/10 \pm \sqrt{101}/10$

31 $y = -1/2, -2$

33 $w = (-1 \pm \sqrt{17})/2$

35 $q = (-3 \pm \sqrt{15})/2$

37 $s = \left(-3 \pm \sqrt{13}\right)/2$

39 $u = (3 \pm \sqrt{5})/5$

41 $y = 1 \pm \sqrt{7}$

43 $w = 3, 2, -2$

45 $m = (-5 \pm \sqrt{3})/7$

Section 4.1

S1 0.06

S3 0.12%

1 Yes; $g(w) = 2(1/2)^w$

3 Yes; $f(x) = (1/4)9^x$

5 Yes; $q(r) = -4(1/3)^r$

7 Yes; $Q(t) = 2^t$

9 Not exponential

11 1.28 (per decade)

13 0.20 (per century)

15 $a = 34.3; b = 0.788; r = -21.2\%$

17 $a = 0.0022; b = 0.0811; r = -91.89\%$

19 \$109,272.70

21 (a) (ii)
   (b) (i)
   (c) (iv)
   (d) (ii)
   (e) (iii)
   (f) (i)

23 (a) $Q = 35(0.92)^t$
   (b) 15.204

25 (a) $Q = 5.35(1.008)^t$
   (b) 5.794

27 (a) $Q = 0.2(0.995)^t$
   (b) 0.190

29 $P = 70(1.019)^t$

31 $f(n) = P_0(0.8)^n$

33 (a) $P = 7.50(1.035)^t$
   (b) $\approx \$14.92$

35 (a) $C = 100(0.84)^t$
   (b) 41.821 mg

37 (a) 14.026 m; 19.371 m
   (b) 2030-55 larger; graph concave up

39 (a) $P = 1.15(1.0135)^t$
   (b) 1.230 billion; 1.315 billion
   (c) 15.525 million people per year
   (d) About 29 people per minute

41 (a) 31,532 megawatts; 62.3 megawatts
   (b) 8.1%; 0.2%

43 $5 \cdot 4^{-\frac{1}{6} \cdot t}; a = 5, k = -1/6$

45 (a) $N = 13.4(1.05)^t$
   (b) 17.957 million; 11.024 million

47 (a) $N(r) = 64(1/2)^r$

(b) 6

49 9.712%

51 (a) \$444 per month
(b) \$286.20 per month
(c) \$506.40 per month
(d) \$11,232
(e) \$23,112

53 366.875 miles

55 0.5

57 b_0

59 t_0 decreases

61 (a) $R = Nr$
(b) $A = R/P = Nr/P$
(c) $N_{\text{new}} = 1.02N$
$r_{\text{new}} = 1.03r$
(d) $R_{\text{new}} = 1.0506R$; 5.06%
(e) $A_{\text{new}} = (0.9728)A$; average revenue falls by 2.7%

Section 4.2

S1 b^{10}

S3 $6a^7b^{10}$

S5 5.6; 6.354

S7 $x = 1.710$

S9 $x = 1.393$

1 (a) $p = 2.50 + 0.03t$
(b) $p = 2.50 - 0.07t$
(c) $p = 2.50(1.02)^t$
(d) $p = 2.50(0.96)^t$

3 B, C, D exponential

5 $Q = 70.711(0.966)^t$

7 $f(x) = 2(1/3)^x$

9 $Q = 0.7746 \cdot (0.3873)^t$

11 $y = 50(0.833)^x$

13 $y = 2(3/2)^x$

15 $y = 160(0.983)^x$

17 Not exponential

19 $g(t) = 5.7(0.315)^t$

21 f is exponential, h is linear, g is neither

23 (a) $g(x)$ is linear
(b) $g(x) = 2x$

25 (a) $i(x)$ is linear
(b) $i(x) = 18 - 4x$

27 $x < -1.69$ and $x > 2$

29 $p = 20(1.0718)^x$; $q = 160(0.8706)^x$

31 Exponential,
$R(t) = 2.001(1.030)^t$

33 (a) $P = 1154.160(1.20112)^t$
(b) \$1154.16
(c) 20.112%

35 $P = 1046(0.798)^t$; decreasing by 20.2%/yr

37 (a) $W = 43.45 - 0.126t$; 40.43 seconds
(b) $W = 43.45(0.997057)^t$; 40.48 seconds

39 (a) $P = 3500 - 180t$; -180 fish/year
(b) $P = 3500(0.93)^t$; -7%/year
(c)

41 (a) Linear
(b) $L = 0.25t + 75.85$
(c) 88.35 years

43 (a) $N = 84 + 11.3684t$;
increasing by 11.3684 million people per year
(b) $N = 84(1.0693)^t$;
increasing by 6.93% per year
(c) Linear: 425.0520 million; Exponential: 626.9982 million

45 (a) Neither
(b) Not possible

Section 4.3

1 (b)

3 $h(x)$ top; $g(x)$ middle; $f(x)$ bottom

5 Yes

7 No

9 No

11 D

13 D

15 (a) 13 ft^3
(b) 3.2 weeks

17 $q = 5.662$

19 $t = 2.452$

21 Zero

23

25

27

29 (a) $-\infty$
(b) $-\infty$

31 (a) All
(b) b
(c) b, a, c, p
(d) $a = c$
(e) d and q

33 Increasing: $b > 1$, $a > 0$ or $0 < b < 1$, $a < 0$;
Decreasing: $0 < b < 1$, $a > 0$ or $b > 1$, $a < 0$;
Concave up: $a > 0$, $0 < b < 0$ or $b > 1$.

35 y_0 decreases, $y_0 > b$

37 (a) $P = 651(0.9925)^t$
(b) 603,790
(c) $t = 22.39$

41 (a) $P \approx 0.538$ millibars
(b) $h \approx 0.784$ km

43 (a)

(b) $f(x) < 1$
(c) $(0,0)$ $(2,0)$
(d) As $x \to +\infty$, $f(x) \to -\infty$
As $x \to -\infty$, $f(x) \to 0$
(e) Increasing for $x < 0$, decreasing for $x > 0$

45 (a)

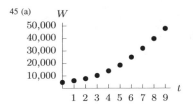

(b) $W = 4710(1.306)^t$; answers may vary
(c) 30.6%/yr

Section 4.4

1 (a) 8.300%
(b) 8.322%
(c) 8.328%

3 165.3%

5 (a) $1270.24
(b) $1271.01
(c) $1271.22

7 (a) $505
(b) $505.02
(c) $505.03

9 (a) $525
(b) $525.62
(c) $525.64

11 (a) Nom: 1% Eff: 1%
(b) Nom: 1% Eff: 1.004%
(c) Nom: 1% Eff: 1.005%

13 (a) Nom: 3% Eff: 3%
(b) Nom: 3% Eff: 3.034%
(c) Nom: 3% Eff: 3.045%

15 34.392%

17 7.352%

19 1.628%

21 (i) (b)
(ii) (a)
(iii) (c)
(iv) (b), (c) and (d)
(v) (a) and (e)

Section 4.5

S1 1.073

S3 1.433

S5 2.3; 7.636

S7 161.6; 202.027

S9 $f(t) = 27e^{0.12t}$

S11 $Q = 1,096.633e^{-3t}$

S13 $m(x) = \frac{7}{\sqrt{3}}e^{-0.3x}$

S15 $H(r) = \frac{1}{6}e^{0.65r}$

1 Bottom to top:
$y = e^x, y = 2e^x, y = 3e^x$

3 (a)=(II); (b)=(III); (c)=(IV); (d)=(I)

5 $f(x) = e^{-x}$
$g(x) = e^x$
$h(x) = -e^x$

7 (a)=(I); (b)=(II); (c)=(III); (d)=(IV)

9 0

11 2

13 $a > 0, k > 0$

15 (a) $Q_0 = 2.7$
(b) Decreasing
(c) −88%
(d) Not continuous

17 (a) $Q_0 = 0.01$
(b) Decreasing
(c) −20%
(d) Continuous

19 (a) $Q_0 = 1$
(b) Increasing
(c) 100%
(d) Not continuous

21 (a) $Q = 8(1.12)^t$; 24.847
(b) $Q = 8e^{0.12t}$; 26.561

23 (a) (i) 23.183
(ii) 23.645
(b) Continuous growth faster

25 (a) $P = 3000 + 200t$
(b) $P = 3000(1.06)^t$
(c) $P = 3000e^{0.06t}$
(d) $P = 3000 - 50t$
(e) $P = 3000(0.96)^t$
(f) $P = 3000e^{-0.04t}$

27 (a) $P(t) = 22,000e^{0.071t}$
(b) $\approx 7.358\%$

31 54.931 years

33 (a) $24,102.64
(b) 124.323 years

35 Eff. yield: 20.925%
Cont. rate: 19%

37 5.127%

39 (a) (i) 6.14%
(ii) 6.17%
(iii) 6.18%
(iv) 6.18%
(b) 1.0618
The highest possible APR is 6.18%.

41 From best to worst: B, C, A

43 (a) $G = 145.8e^{0.051t}$
(b) 5.23%
(c) $G = 145.8(1.0523)^t$
(d) The two formulas have the same graph

45 $143.70

47 $a = b > 1$
$0 < k < 1$
$l < 0$

49 (a) $A = 50e^{-0.14t}$
(b) 12.330 mg
(c) 2025

51 $27,399.14

53 (a) 2.708333333
(b) 2.718055556
(c) 2.718281828; thus (a) is correct to 2 correct digits, while (b) is correct to 4 digits
(d) 13 terms

Chapter 4 Review

1 550

3 495

5 411.8

7 $P = 2200(0.968)^t$

9 20%; 2%.

11 Linear: $p(r) = 10 + 3r$

13 Neither

15

Yr	2010	2011	2012	2013	2014
$	95	101.65	108.77	116.38	124.53

17 (a) 4.2%
(b) $\approx 4.28\%$
(c) $\approx 4.29\%$

19 $h(x) = 3(5)^x$

21 $g(x) = 2(4)^x$

23 $g(x) = 14.20(0.6024)^x$

25 (a) $f(x) = \frac{31}{8}x + \frac{49}{4}$
(b) $f(x) = 5(2)^x$

27 $y = (1/2)^x$

29 $y = \frac{1}{5}(3)^x$

31 $y = 2(0.8)^x$

33 (a) $P(t) = 2.58 + 0.09t$,
increases by 90,000 people per year
(b) $P(t) = 2.68(1.026)^t$,
increases by 2.6% per year

35 0

37 15

39 $-\infty$

41 $N = 10(1.13)^t$; 13%/yr

43 (a) $S = 128.4(1.13)^t$
(b) Increasing by 13%/yr
(c) No

45

47

49 f

51 $y = 2$

55 (a) Initial balance = $1100
Effective yield = 5%
(b) Initial balance = $1500
Effective yield $\approx 5.13\%$

57 $p(x) = 7e^x\sqrt{e}/20$

59 $s(w) = (v - 4t + kv)j^w$
$a = v - 4t + kv, b = j$

61 $g(n) = 1000(0.7071)^n$

65 $d > b$

67 f matches (ii) and (iv); g matches (i) and (iii)

69 (a)
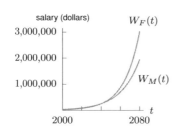

(b) 0.69
(c) 1.10
(d) $e \approx 2.72$

71 $V = 12{,}000e^{0.042t}$

73 $y = -13.1x + 2090$

75 $a = 12{,}000;\ k = -12.2\%;\ b = 0.8851;$ $r = -11.49\%$

77 (a) $15.269(1.122)^t$
(b) 108,066
(c) Not useful

79 t_0 decreases

81 (a) salary (dollars)

(b) $W_F(t) = 953e^{0.062(t-1950)}$ (women)
$W_M(t) = 2570e^{0.051(t-1950)}$ (men)

(c) salary (dollars)

salary (dollars)

(d) Yes, in about 2060
(e) Not reliable

83 50.7%

Ch. 4 Understanding

1 True

3 True

5 False

7 True

9 True

11 False

13 False

15 True

17 True

19 False

21 True

23 False

25 True

27 False

29 True

31 False

Ch. 4 Tools: Exponents

1 25

3 10,000

5 5

7 1

9 4

11 4

13 16

15 -121

17 2100

19 2

21 32

23 100,000

25 -6

27 4

29 $1/(3\sqrt{3})$

31 $1/625$

33 0.5

35 y^4

37 $x^{5/2}y^2$

39 $5x^{3/2}z^2$

41 $r^{3/2}$

43 $8s^{7/2}$

45 $4\sqrt{3}u^5v^6y^{5/2}$

47 $16S^2xt^2$

49 $A^3/\left(3B^3\right)$

51 $(M+2)^2$

53 $3a$

55 $25(2b+1)^{20}$

57 -8

59 Not a real number

61 $1/512$

63 Not a real number

65 $x = \pm 1.690$

67 $(2.5, 31.25)$

69 False

71 True

73 True

75 $x = r + s$

77 $x = 5/a$

79 $x = 3/a$

81 $x = b/a$

Section 5.1

S1 $x = 6$

S3 $z = 3/2$

S5 No solution

S7 $t = 14/9$

S9 $t = -1/8$

1 $19 = 10^{1.279}$

3 $26 = e^{3.258}$

5 $P = 10^t$

7 $8 = \log 100{,}000{,}000$

9 $v = \log \alpha$

11 (a) 3
(b) 1.5
(c) 0
(d) 1/2
(e) 5
(f) 2
(g) $-1/2$
(h) 100
(i) 1
(j) 0.01

13 $(\log 11)/(\log 2) = 3.459$

15 $(\ln 100)/(0.12) = 38.376$

17 $(\log(48/17))/(\log(2.3)) = 1.246$

19 (a) $2x$
(b) x^3
(c) $-3x$

21 (a) 3, 3
(b) 5, 5
(c) $-1, -1$
(d) $-1, -1$
(e) 2, 2
(f) 3, 3
Both answers equal

23 (a) True
(b) False
(c) False
(d) True
(e) True
(f) False

25 $x = 57.002$

27 $x = (a - \log M)/(\log N)$

29 $x = 2.714$

31 (a) 10; 15%
(b) $t \approx 10.5$
(c) $t = (\ln 0.2)/(-0.15) = 10.730$

33 (a) $\log 15 - \log 5$
(b) $2 \log 5$
(c) $\log 15 + \log 5$

35 $(\log(91/46))/(\log(1.1))$

37 $(\ln 6/0.044)$

39 $x = \ln 10 - 4$

41 $\log(35/2)/\log(2/27)$

43 $t = \ln(500/400)/0.02$

45 $\ln 10 - 4$

47 $(\ln Q - \ln P)/k$

49 $x = -2, \frac{1}{3},$ or $-\frac{1}{3}$

51 $-2, 1/3, -1/3$

53 The log increases by 0.3010

55 $\log \sqrt{vw} = (\log v + \log w)/2$

57 $B > A$

Section 5.2

S1 $(5x)^{-1}$

S3 $t^2/2$

S5 $x = (\log 9)/(\log 4) = 1.585$

S7 $x = \ln(13/2) = 1.872$

S9 $x = 93/2$

1 $y = 25(1.0544)^t$,
5.44%/yr, 5.3%/yr

3 $y = 6000e^{-0.1625t}$,
-15%/yr, -16.25%/yr

5 $Q = 4 \cdot 1096.633^t$

7 $Q = (14/5)1.030^t$

9 $Q = 12e^{-0.105t}$

11 $Q = 14e^{-0.208t}$

13 $a = 230, r = 18.2\%, k = 16.72\%$

15 $a = 0.81, r = 100\%,$ and $k = 69.31\%$

17 $a = 12.1, r = -22.38\%, k = -25.32\%$

19 $a = 5.4366, b = 0.4724, r = -52.76\%, k = -3/4$

21 $t \approx 3.466$

23 About 26 years

25 About 12.3 years

27 6.301 minutes

29 (a) 7.70%
(b) 6.18%

31 27.756 years

33 (a) 4.729%
(b) 4.621%

35 -34.7% per hour

37 23.1%/yr; $W = 90e^{0.231t}$

39 (a) 10; 30; and 70 yrs
(b) 14.207; 28.413; and 42.620 yrs

41 (a) 4 hours
(b) -17.3% per hour; $Q = 150e^{-0.173t}$

45 (a) 300; 600
(b) 34.739 years

47 (a) 27.465 years
(b) 28.011 years

49 (a) $R(t) \approx 200(0.8909)^t$
(b) ≈ 4.422 hours
(c) concave up

51 5092.013 years ago

53 (a) $f(x) = \frac{1}{2}(4)^x$
$g(x) = 4\left(\frac{1}{3}\right)^x$
$h(x) = x + 2$
(b) $x = \log 8/\log 12$
(c) $x = 1.378$ or $x = -1.967$

57 (a) $20, 395, 954$
(b) 5.615 years, 7.2 years

(c) 1000 toads

59 $t = -10\ln(-2\ln 0.5) = -3.266$

61 (a) $v = \log 1.12, w = \log 6.3$
(b) $t = w/v; t = 16.241$

Section 5.3

S1 -4

S3 $\log 100,000 = 5$

S5 $x = e^{-12}$

S7 $\ln x + 3\ln(7 - x)$

S9 $\ln x^5$

1 $y = 0, y = 0, x = 0$

3 $A: y = 10^x, B: y = e^x$
$C: y = \ln x, D: y = \log x$

5

(a)

7

(c)

9 Vertical asymptote at 3,
Domain $(3, \infty)$

11 (a) 0
(b) $-\infty$

13 (a) $-\infty$
(b) $-\infty$

15 0.1 moles/l

17 3.162×10^{-5} moles/l

21 (a) $t(x)$
(b) $r(x)$
(c) $s(x)$

23 100 watts/cm^2

25 37

27 79,432,823

29 $M_2 - M_1 = \log(W_2/W_1)$

31 (a) $10^{-2}, 10^{-4}, 10^{-7}$

(b) Less

33 (a) 0.005 moles/liter
(b) 3.3×10^{-4} moles H$^+$ ions
1.987×10^{20} ions

35 $y = b^x, 0 < b < 1$

37 $y = \ln x$

39 $y = -b^x, b > 1$

Section 5.4

S1 1.455×10^6

S3 6.47×10^4

S5 3.6×10^{-4}

S7 $10^4 < \log 12,500 < 10^5$

S9 $10^{-1} < 1/3 < 10^0$

1 Log

3 Linear

7 (a) $y = -3582.145 + 236.314x; r \approx 0.7946$
(b) $y = 4.797(1.221)^x; r \approx 0.9998$
(c) Exponential is better fit

9 $10^{-3.65}$ million years ago

11 A: \$1.58
B: \$6.31
C: \$31.62
D: \$630.96
E: \$10,000.00
F: \$125,892.54
G: \$6,309,573.45
Answers are approximate.

17 (a)

(b) Exponential
(c) Linear

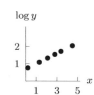

19 Yes

21 (a) $a \approx -7.787, b \approx 86.283$
(b)

(c) $69,918.342$ minutes ≈ 45 days
0.172 minutes ≈ 10 seconds

(d) P (%)

23 (a) W

(b) $W = 3.06L - 4.54$
(c) $w = 0.011\ell^{3.06}$

Chapter 5 Review

1 $Q = 7(0.0000454)^t$

3 $Q = 4e^{1.946t}$

5 $Q = 4e^{2.703t}$

7 $(\log 3)/(\log 1.04)$

9 $(\log(14/3))/(\log 1.081)$

11 $(\log(12/5))/(3\log 1.014)$

13 $(\log 1.6)/(\log 1.031)$

15 47

17 2.324

19 $(1/0.049) \cdot \ln(25/13) \approx 13.345$

21 $x = 1000$

23 $2(x + 1)$

25 $\ln(AB)$

27 Domain: $x > 20$; Asymptote: $x = 20$

29 Domain: $x < 300$; Asymptote: $x = 300$

31 Domain: $x > -15$; Asymptote: $x = -15$

33 3.7

35 2.2

37 0.6

39 (a) $q + 4p$
(b) $-q$
(c) p/q
(d) $3q$

41 (a) $\ln 8 - 3 \approx -0.9206$
(b) $\log 1.25/ \log 1.12 \approx 1.9690$
(c) $-\dfrac{\ln 4}{0.13} \approx -10.6638$
(d) 10^5
(e) $\frac{1}{3}e^{3/2} \approx 1.4939$
(f) $e^{1/2}/(e^{1/2} - 1) \approx 2.5415$
(g) -1.599 or 2.534
(h) 2.478 or 3
(i) 0.653

43 158.5 times larger

45 15.85 times larger

47 (a) Initial balance: $1100
Effective yield: 5%
(b) Initial balance: $1500
Effective rate: 5.127%/yr
(c) Continuous rate: 4.879%/yr

49 (a) 1412 bacteria
(b) 10.011 hours
(c) 1.005 hours

51 (a) 7 years
(b) 10.4%

53 $\ln(1.5)/0.2 = 2.027$

55 $t = (\ln 2)/0.22$

57 (a) Domain: all x
Range: $y > 0$
Asymptote: $y = 0$
(b) Domain: all $x > 0$
Range: all y
Asymptote: $x = 0$

59 (a) Log function

(b)

(c) Linear; $y = 4 + 9.9z$
(d) $y = 4 + 9.9\ln x$
(e) $x = 0.67e^{0.1y}$;
Exponential function of y

61 (a) $Q(t) = 2e^{-0.04t}$
(b) 3.921%
(c) After 51.986 hours
(d) 54.931 hrs after second injection

63 (a) $\approx 33.517\%$
(b) $k \approx 4.082\%$, continuous hourly decay rate

65 (a) 10
(b) 50
(c) 10^{50}

67 $\sqrt[8]{k}$

Ch. 5: Understanding

1 False

3 True

5 True

7 True

9 True

11 False

13 False

15 False

17 True

19 False

21 False

23 True

25 True

27 True

29 True

31 True

33 False

35 False

37 False

Ch. 5 Skills: Logs

1 0

3 8

5 0

7 2

9 $\log 0.0001 = -4$

11 $\ln 0.135 = -2$

13 $10^{-2} = 0.01$

15 $e^{x^2} = 4$

17 Cannot be rewritten

19 $\log(x^2 + 1) - 3\log x$

21 Cannot be rewritten

23 Cannot be rewritten

25 $\log 12x$

27 $\log(\sqrt{x}y^4)$

29 $\log\left((x + 1)^3(x + 4)^2\right)$

31 $\log(9 - x^2)$

33 Cannot be simplified

35 0

37 $4z$

39 $-\ln(e^x + 1)$

41 $x = (\log 3)/(\log 5) \approx 0.683$

43 $x = -(\ln 9)/5 \approx -0.439$

45 $x = (\log 77)/(6\log 19 - 4\log 7) \approx 0.440$

47 $x = (10^{3/2} - 17)/9 \approx 1.625$

49 $x = (e + 1)/6 \approx 0.620$

Section 6.1

S1 2

S3 -1

S5 $x = 0$

S7 $x = -8$

S9 (a) Shift right 4 units
(b) Shift down 7 units
(c) Shift left $\sqrt{2}$ units
(d) Shift right 3 units and up 5 units

1 (a) $-3, 0, 2, 1, -1$
One unit right

(b) $-3, 0, 2, 1, -1$
One unit left
(c) $0, 3, 5, 4, 2$
Up three units
(d) $0, 3, 5, 4, 2$
One right and three up

3 (a) $(3, 1)$
(b) $(-2, -4)$
(c) $(6, -6)$

5

7

11 $-50 \leq R(s) - 150 \leq 50$

13 $(1/2)n^2 + 1$

15 $(1/2)n^2 - 3.7$

17 $(1/2)n^2 + \sqrt{13}$

19 $(1/2)n^2 + 3n + 23/2$

21 $3^w - 3$

23 $3^w + 1.8$

25 $3^{w+2.1} - 1.3$

27 (a) (i) 248

    (ii) 142

    (iii) 4

    (iv) 12

    (v) 378

    (vi) -18

    (vii) 248

    (viii) 570

    (ix) 13
(b) (i) $x = 2$

    (ii) $x = 8$

    (iii) $x = 7$
(c) $x = 1, 4$

29 $y = f(x - 2) - 6$

31 (a) $g(x) + 3$
(b) $g(x - 2)$

33 (a) Population 100 people larger than original
(b) Population same as 100 years earlier

35 Average for 7 mos, 10 mos
Above average

37 Up 1, right 3

39 Vertical shifts

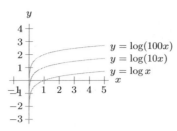

41 Shift $y = x^2$ right by 5 units to get $y = (x - 5)^2 = x^2 - 10x + 25$

43 Shift up 3

45 Shift left 4

47 Shift left b, down a

49 (a) $T(d) = S(d) + 1$
(b) $P(d) = S(d - 1)$

51 $w(x) = v(x - 5) - 7; h = 5, k = -7$

53 (a) $t(x) = 20 + 7x$ for $x \geq 0$
(b) $n(x) = t(x) + 5$
(c) $p(x) = t(x - 2) + 10$ for $x \geq 2$

55 (a)

Temperature, °F

57 $H(t) - 37$

Section 6.2

S1 20.086

S3 0.050

S5 (a) $f(-x) = 2x^2$
(b) $-f(x) = -2x^2$

S7 (a) $f(-x) = -2x^3 - 3$
(b) $-f(x) = -2x^3 + 3$

S9 (a) $f(-x) = 3x^4 + 2x$
(b) $-f(x) = -3x^4 + 2x$

1 (a) $(-2, -3)$
(b) $(2, 3)$

3 -7

5 Domain: $t < 0$
Range: $-4 \leq Q(-t) \leq 7$

7 Domain: $t < 0$
Range: $-7 \leq -Q(-t) \leq 4$

9 $y = -e^x$

13 Reflected across x-axis;
$-g(x) = -(1/3)^x$

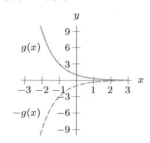

15 $-m(n) = -(n)^2 + 4n - 5$

17 $m(-n) + 3 = n^2 + 4n + 8$

19 $-k(w) = -3^w$

21 $-k(w - 2) = -3^{w-2}$

577

23 Odd

25 Neither

27 (a) $y = 2^{-x} - 3$

(b) $y = 2^{-x} - 3$

(c) Yes

29 (a) $g(-x) = -\sqrt[3]{x}$
   (c) Odd

31 Reflections across x-axis

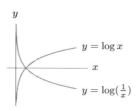

33 (i) b
   (ii) c
   (iii) d
   (iv) e
   (v) a

35 (a)

(b)

(c)

37 (a) Odd
   (b) Unless $f(x) = 0$ or $g(x) = 0$, $k(x)$ is neither.
   (c) Even

39 $y = x$. $y = -x + b$, where b is an arbitrary constant

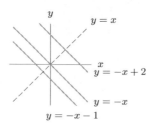

43 No

45 If $f(x)$ is odd, then $f(0) = 0$

49 Yes, $f(x) = 0$

Section 6.3

S1 (a) 72
   (b) -18
   (c) 177
   (d) 25/4

S3 (a) $-(1/3)f(x) = -(1/3)\sqrt{x}$
   (b) $5f(-x) = 5\sqrt{-x}$
   (c) $6f(x - 8) = 6\sqrt{x - 8}$
   (d) $(1/4)f(2 - x) = (1/4)\sqrt{2 - x}$

1 $y = 10f(x - 2)$

3 $-0.25 \le 0.25C(x) \le 0.25$

5 $R(n) = -5P(n)$

7 $T(n) = 1/4P(n + 7)$

9

11

13 (d) All three

15

17

19

21 Stretch vertically by a factor of 2, Shift left 1 unit

23

25

27

578

29 I is (b)
    II is (d)
    III is (c)
    IV is (h)
31 $1.3C(t)$

33

35

37 (a) $h(x) = 1/2 f(x)$
   (b) $k(x) = f(-x)$
   (c) $m(x) = f(x) - 4$
39 (a) $y = -2f(x)$
   (b) $y = f(x) + 2$
   (c) $y = 3f(x - 2)$
43 -7

Section 6.4

S1 $8x^3 - 5$
S3 $(-x^3)/27 - 5$
S5 $4e^{2t}$
S7 $4e^{12t} + 11$
 1 $(1, 3)$
 3 Same function values for
    $x = -6, -4, -2, 0, 2, 4, 6$
 5

 7

 9

11 (a) -0.33

   (b)

   (c)

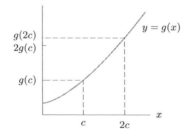

13 (a) Domain: $-6 \le x \le 6$;
         Range: $0 \le l(2x) \le 3$
   (b) Domain: $-24 \le x \le 24$;
         Range: $0 \le l((1/2)x) \le 3$
15

17 $T(1000x)$
19 (a) $A(s/60)$
   (b) $A(60\,h)$
21 $r(t)$: half the level
    $s(t)$: half the rate
23 (a) III
   (b) II
   (c) I
   (d) IV
25 $y = -f(-\frac{1}{2}x)$
27

29 (a) $-24 \le x \le 8$
   (b) $-3/4$
31 (a) $-2 \le x \le 6$
   (b) 3

Section 6.5

S1 -3
S3 $10/3$
S5 (a) -1
   (b) $8\sqrt[3]{-2}$
   (c) 5
   (d) -16
   (e) $-2\sqrt[3]{2}$
   (f) $\sqrt[3]{5}$
S7 $A = 1, B = -2, h = 0, k = 9$
S9 $A = 6, B = -1/3, h = -27, k = 0$
 1 A horizontal compression by a factor of $1/3$ and
    then a horizontal shift right by $2/3$ units.
 3 (a) $(3, -14)$
   (b) $(6, -26)$
   (c) $(18, 17)$
   (d) $(-33, -25/2)$
 7 (a)

 (b)

 (c)

 (d)

9

11

13 $t = -2.5, y = 5$

15

17 (a)

(b)

(c) The graphs are not the same.

19 No; down 10 units

21 $g(x) = -3f(x+4) + 6$

23 $h(x) = -2f(-x+3) - 4$

25 $(-9, 7), (3, 0), (39, -4)$

27

29 All four transformations are equivalent.

31 (a) $+1$

(b) $\log(10x) = 1 + \log x$

(c) $k = \log a$

33 A vertical compression by a factor of e^{-k}.

35 (a) Vertical; stretch by 2, shift by 8

(b) Vertical; shift by 4, stretch by 2

37 (b) $d(t)$ reflected about the t-axis and then raised 142

39 (a)

(b)

41 (a) $y = mx, m > 1$

(b) $y = mx + b$, $m > 1$ and b an arbitrary constant

43 Yes; $g(x) = (rb + j) + (rms) \cdot x, B = rb + j, M = rms$

45 Yes; $g(x) = (ras^2) \cdot (x - h/s)^2 + (rk + j), A = ras^2, H = h/s, K = rk + j$

Chapter 6 Review

1 (a) 4

(b) 1

(c) 5

(d) -2

3 (a) $(6, 5)$

(b) $(2, 1)$

(c) $(1/2, 5)$

(d) $(2, 20)$

5 Odd

7 Neither

9 Even

11 (a) $f(2x) = 1 - 2x$

(b) $f(x + 1) = -x$

(c) $f(1 - x) = x$

(d) $f(x^2) = 1 - x^2$

(e) $f(1/x) = (x - 1)/x$

(f) $f(\sqrt{x}) = 1 - \sqrt{x}$

13

15 $y = f(t + 4) - 8$

17 (a) A horizontal reflection about the y-axis.

(b) A horizontal shift 6 units to the right.

19 (a) VI

(b) V

(c) III

(d) IV

(e) I

(f) II

21 (a) $-16t^2 + 23$

$-16t^2 + 48t + 2$

(b)

(d) 1.541 secs

1.199 secs

(e) 3.041 secs

23 $y = -(x + 1)^3 + 1$

25 $y = (1/2)h(x + 6) + 1$

27 $p \approx 15, q \approx 7190$

31

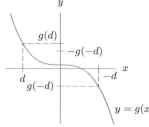

33 $y = 3h(x)$

35 $y = -h(2 - 2x)$

37 $y = 2f(x/2) + 3$

41

d	20	45	70	95
$h(d)$	5.5	5.2	5.1	5.1
d	120	145	170	195
$h(d)$	5.3	5.5	5.75	6

43

d	25	50	75	100
$n(d)$	8.25	7.8	7.65	7.65
d	125	150	175	200
$n(d)$	7.95	8.25	8.63	9

45

d	25	50	75	100
$q(d)$	10.25	9.8	9.65	9.65
d	125	150	175	200
$q(d)$	9.95	10.25	10.63	11

Ch. 6: Understanding

1 True

3 True

5 True

7 False

9 True

11 False

13 False

15 True

17 True

19 False

21 False

23 True

Section 7.1

1 (I), (II), (IV)

3 90 m

5 90 m

7 b

9 41

11 12 o'clock position; 165 m

13 6 o'clock position; 15 m

15

17

19

21 12 o'clock; descending; 4 minutes;
30 meters; 5 meters; 10 minutes

23 3 (or 9) o'clock; descending;
5 minutes; 40 meters; 0 meters;
11.25 minutes

27 (a) Weight B
   (b) Weight A
   (c) Weight A

29 Midline: $y = 5.55$;
Amplitude: 5.15 WBC $\times 10^4$/mL;
Period: 72 days

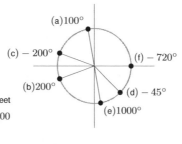

Section 7.2

1 (a) $(-0.174, 0.985)$
  (b) $(-0.940, -0.342)$
  (c) $(-0.940, 0.342)$
  (d) $(0.707, -0.707)$
  (e) $(0.174, -0.985)$
  (f) $(1, 0)$

3 $-720°$

5 $D = (0, -1)$, $E = (-0.707, -0.707)$,
$F = (-0.707, 0.707)$

7 (a) 0.923
  (b) 0.385

9 (a) 0.447
  (b) 0.894

13 (a) 307°
   (b) 127°

15 (a)

(b) $180 - \phi$

(c)

(d)

19 (a) $72°$
   (b) $180°$
   (c) $216°$

21 (a) All are equal
   (b) $KP = 1/2$
   (c) $OP = \sqrt{3}/2$
   (d) $(\sqrt{3}/2, 1/2)$
   (e) $\cos 30° = \sqrt{3}/2$;
       $\sin 30° = 1/2$
   (f) $\cos 60° = 1/2$;
       $\sin 60° = \sqrt{3}/2$

23 $d = 3\cos\alpha$ meters

Section 7.3

1 Mid: $y = 2$; Amp: 1

3 Mid: $y = -3$; Amp: 7

5 Mid: $i(t) = 223$ cm; Amp: 20 cm

7 $(0, 3.8)$

9 $(-3.8, 0)$

11 $(0, 3.8)$

13 $(3.687, -0.919)$

15 $(3.8\sqrt{2}/2, 3.8\sqrt{2}/2)$ or $(2.687, 2.687)$

17 $(-3.8\sqrt{2}/2, -3.8\sqrt{2}/2)$
   $(-2.687, -2.687)$

19 $(3.742, -0.660)$

21 $(-5\sqrt{3}, -5)$

23 period 50, midline $y = 12$, amplitude 5

25 period 24, midline $y = -500$, amplitude 2000

27 period 25, midline $y = 30$, amplitude 25

29 $g(x) = \cos x$, $a = 90°$, $b = 1$

33 $f(x) = \sin(x + 90°)$
   $g(x) = \sin(x - 90°)$

35 $(60, 0)$, $(7.5, 0)$
   $(60\cos\theta, 60\sin\theta)$
   $(7.5\cos\theta, 7.5\sin\theta)$

37 $h(\theta) = 2.5 + 2.5\sin\theta$.

Section 7.4

1 $0, 1, 0$

3 (a) $\tan\theta = 2$
   (b) $\sin\theta = 2/\sqrt{5}$
   (c) $\cos\theta = 1/\sqrt{5}$

5 (a) $\sqrt{45}/7$
   (b) $2/7$
   (c) $\sqrt{45}/2$

7 (a) $8/12$
   (b) $\sqrt{80}/12$
   (c) $8/\sqrt{80}$

9 (a) $\sqrt{117}/11$
   (b) $2/11$

   (c) $\sqrt{117}/2$

11 $r = 7\sin 17°$; $q = 7\cos 17°$

13 $r = 6/\cos 37°$; $q = 6\tan 37°$

15 $r = 9/\tan 77°$; $q = 9/\sin 77°$

17 0

19 Undefined

21 1

23 0

25 $h = 400$ feet; $x = 346.410$ feet

27 $d = 35000/\tan\theta$ feet

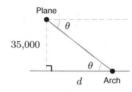

29 $d \approx 15.877$ feet

Section 7.5

1 $61.164°$

3 $7.012°$

5 no solution

7 $89.190°$

9 $\theta = 60°$

11 $\theta = 60°$

13 $\theta = 45°$

15 $c = 34.409$; $A = 35.538°$, $B = 54.462°$

17 $B = 62°$; $a = 9.389$; $b = 17.659$

19 The angle is k; a represents the value

21 The angle is c; the value is $1/d$

23 The angle is n; the value is p

25 (a) 0.009
   (b) $30°$
   (c) 114.593

27 (a) $\sqrt{2} + 1$
   (b) $2\sqrt{2} + 1$
   (c) $90.008°$

29 $\theta = 33.557°$

31 No solution

33 $9°$

35 $30°$

37 $15.859°$

39 $39.806°$

41 $\approx 39.806°$

43 (a) $a = 4$; $c = 2$; $B = 60°$
   (b) $A \approx 73.740°$; $B \approx 16.260°$; $b = 7$

Section 7.6

1 $x \approx 19.121$

3 $b \approx 5.120$, $c \approx 6.497$; $\beta = 52°$

5 $a \approx 11.818$, $b \approx 2.084$; $\theta = 80°$

7 $a = 10.450$; $\theta = 16.560°$, $\psi = 143.440°$

9 $A = 25.922°$, $B = 37.735°$, $C = 116.343°$

11 $b = 31.762$, $A = 38.458°$, $C = 60.542°$

13 $c = 10.954$, $A = 54.010°$, $B = 45.990°$

15 $c = 7.2605$; $A = 21.4035°$; $B = 126.597°$

17 $a = 15.860$, $b = 2.569$, $C = 66°$

19 $a = 10.026$, $b = 6.885$, $C = 61°$

21 $a = 2.079$, $b = 3.090$, $B = 18°$

23 $a = 1.671$, $b = 4.639$, $B = 166°$

25 $a = 13.667$, $A = 90.984°$, $C = 17.016°$

27 $a = 12.070$, $A = 135.109°$, $C = 27.891°$
   or
   $a = 3.231$, $A = 10.891°$, $C = 152.109°$

29 $b = 0.837$ m, $c = 2.720$ m; $\gamma = 143.7°$

31 $\alpha \approx 41.410°$, $\beta \approx 82.819°$, $\gamma \approx 55.771°$

33 (a) $\sin\theta = 0.282$
   (b) $\theta \approx 16.374°$
   (c) 12.077 cm^2

35 B closer by 2.387 miles

37 396.004 miles

39 $(18.876, 10.071)$

43 (a) First: 3.062 feet closer
   (b) 157.279 feet to home
       113.218 feet to third

45 158.926 feet

47 4 rolls

Chapter 7 Review

1 Yes

3 No

5 No

7 Yes

9 $S = (-0.707, -0.707)$, $T = (0, -1)$, $U = (0.866, -0.5)$

270°

T

330°

U

11   $S = (-3.536, -3.536)$
     $T = (0, -5)$
     $U = (4.330, -2.5)$

13   $(4.944, -15.217)$

15   $44.971°$

17   $59.036°$

19   $\theta = 30°$

21   $\theta = 45°$

23   Angle is y; value is x

25   Angle is d; value is $1/c$

27 (a) $30°$
  (b) $-30°$
  (c) $150°$

29   (i) is B; (ii) is C; (iii) is A

31   Period: 6; Amp: 5; Mid: $y = 0$

33   Midline: $h = 2$;
     Amplitude: 1;
     Period: 1

35   419.856 feet

37   $\phi = 53.130°; \theta = 36.870°$

39   $5; 67.380°, 22.620°$

41   $\theta \approx 22.620°$

43   Approximately 80 meters

45   $h = 200 \tan \theta$

Ch. 7: Understanding

1   True

3   True

5   True

7   True

9   False

11   False

13   False

15   True

17   False

19   False

21   True

23   False

25   True

27   True

Ch. 7 Skills: Special Angles

1   $1/2$

3   $-\sqrt{3}/2$

5   $1/2$

7   $\sqrt{3}/2$

9   $1/\sqrt{2}$

11   $-\sqrt{3}/2$

13   $1/\sqrt{2}$

15   $-1/\sqrt{2}$

17   $-\sqrt{3}/2$

19   They are equal

21   5

23   $20/\sqrt{3}$

25   $5, 5, 5\sqrt{2}$

27   $7/\sqrt{2}, 7/\sqrt{2}, 7$

29   $45°\text{-}45°\text{-}90°, 4\sqrt{2}$

31   $(3\sqrt{2}, -3\sqrt{2})$

Section 8.1

1   $\pi/3$

3   1.7453 radians

5   $5\pi/6$

7   $-3\pi/2$

9   $630°$

11   $16,200/\pi \approx 5156.620°$

13   $8100/\pi \approx 2578.310°$

15 (a)   I
  (b)   II
  (c)   II
  (d)   III
  (e)   IV
  (f)   IV
  (g)   I
  (h)   II
  (i)   II
  (j)   III

17   -4π

19   8.54π

21   $6.2\pi/4 \approx 4.869$

23   $6.2a\pi/180$

25 (a) $\sqrt{3}/2$
  (b) $-1/\sqrt{2}$
  (c) 1
  (d) $\sqrt{3}/2$

27   5π feet

29   $\pi/9$ radians or $20°$

31   $r = \sqrt{65}; \theta = 0.5191$ rad $= 29.7449°$;
     $s = 4.185; P = (7, 4)$

33   $r = 12; \theta = 1.3$ rad $= 74.485°$;
     $s = 15.6; P = (3.2100, 11.5627)$

35   $\theta = 0.4$ rad $= 22.918°; P = (0.9211r, 0.3894r)$

37 (a)   Negative
  (b)   Negative
  (c)   Positive
  (d)   Positive

39   $\sin \theta = 0.6$;

$\cos \theta = -0.8$

41   $(-0.99, 0.14)$

43   $m = 5 \cos(4/5)$
     $n = 5 \sin(4/5)$
     $p = 5\sqrt{2(1 - \cos(4/5))}$

45 (a) $1718.873°$
  (b)   0.00914 radians

47   7π inches

49   t

Section 8.2

1   Mid: $y = 0$; Amp: 6; Per: 2π

3   Mid: $y = 1$; Amp: $1/2$; Per: $\pi/4$

5   Hor: $-4/3$; Phs: -4

7   Both f and g have periods of 1, amplitudes of 1, and midlines $y = 0$

9   $h(t) = 4 \sin(2\pi t)$

11   $g(t) = -2 \cos(t/2) + 2$

13   $y = 4000 + 4000 \sin((2\pi/60)x)$

15   $y = -2 \sin(\pi\theta/6) + 2$

17

19

21   $f(x) = \sin x, a = \pi/2, b = \pi,$
     $c = 3\pi/2, d = 2\pi, e = 1$

23   Amplitude: 20
     Period: $3/4$ seconds

25   $3/10, g(x) = 10 \sin((\pi/5)x - 3\pi/5)$

27 $f(t) = 14 + 10\sin(\pi t + \pi/2)$

29 $f(t) = 20 + 15\sin((\pi/2)t + \pi/2)$

31 (a) $12°/\text{min}$
   (b) $\theta = (12t - 90)°$
   (c) $f(t) =$
       $225 + 225\sin(12t - 90)°$
   (d) Amp = Midline = 225 feet
       Period = 30 min

33 (a) $P = f(t) =$
       $-450\cos(\pi t/6) + 1750$
   (c) $t_1 \approx 1.9; t_2 \approx 10.1$

35 $y = 3f(x)$

37 $y = -f(2x)$

39 Amplitude: 41.5;
   Period: 12 months

blanket sales (thousands)

41 $f(t) =$
   $-100\cos(\pi t) + 100$ (for $0 \le t \le 1$)
   $10\cos(4\pi t) + 190$ (for $1 < t \le 2$)

43 (a) $T(°F)$

   (b) 23.2°; 12 months
   (c) $T = f(t) =$
       $-23.2\cos((\pi/6)t) + 58.6$
   (d) $T = f(9) \approx 58.6°$

45 (a) Not exactly regular
   (b) Usage repeats each week
   (c) $n = 45,000\cos(2\pi(t - 2)/7) +$
       $100,000.$

Section 8.3

1 1

---

3 $-\sqrt{3}$

5 $-1/\sqrt{3}$

7 $-1/\sqrt{3}$

9 $2/\sqrt{3}$

11 $(\cos(2\theta))^2 + (\sin(2\theta))^2 = 1$

13 1

15 $\cos t$

17 1

19 (a) $(-x, -y)$

21 $\sec\theta = 2$
    $\tan\theta = \sqrt{3}$

23 $\sec\theta = 3/\sqrt{8}$
    $\tan\theta = 1/\sqrt{8}$

25 $f(\theta) = (1/2)\tan\theta$

27 $\cos\theta = \sqrt{1 - y^2}$

29 (a) $\sin\phi = -0.8866$, $\tan\phi = -1.9166$
   (b) $\cos\theta = -0.8062$, $\tan\theta = 0.7339$

31 $\cos\theta = \sqrt{9 - x^2}/3$,
    $\tan\theta = x/\sqrt{9 - x^2}$

33 $\sin\theta = \sqrt{4 - x^2}/2$,
    $\tan\theta = \sqrt{4 - x^2}/x$

35 (a)   (i) Is identity

         (ii) Not identity
   (b) Three

37 (a) $\ldots, -3\pi/2, -\pi/2, \pi/2, 3\pi/2, \ldots$;
        It has t-intercepts.
   (b) $\ldots, -2\pi, -\pi, 0, \pi, 2\pi, \ldots$;
        It has t-intercepts.

Section 8.4

1 1.570

3 1.330

5 -1.447

7 $\theta = 0.708, 2.434$

9 $t = 1.813, 4.473$

11 (a) 1.88, 4.41
   (b) 1.88, 4.41

13 $\pm 1.159, \pm 5.124, \pm 7.442, 11.407, 13.725$

15 $\pi/6, 5\pi/6$

17 $\pi/3, 5\pi/3$

19 $3\pi/4, 7\pi/4$

21 $0, \pi, 2\pi$

23 0.340, 2.802

25 0.152, 1.418, 3.294, 4.560

27 1.914, 4.653

29 (a) $65°, 295°$
   (b) $65°, 245°, 425°, 605°$

31 0.305, 2.837

33 4.069, 5.356, 10.352, 11.639

35 $\theta = \pi/6 + 2\pi k, 11\pi/6 + 2\pi k$, k an integer

37 $\theta \approx 1.893$

39 $t = \pi/6, 5\pi/6$,
    $7\pi/6$, or $11\pi/6$

41 $t = \pi/2, 3\pi/2$,
    $\pi/6$, or $5\pi/6$

---

43 (a) $f(t) = 40,000\cos\left(\frac{\pi}{6}t + \frac{\pi}{6}\right) + 60,000$
   (b) $f(3) = \$40,000$
   (c) Mid-March and mid-September

45 $P: x \approx 0.819$;
    $Q: x \approx 3.181$

47 (a) $\pi/3$
   (b) π
   (c) ≈ 0.1

49 (a) $t_1 \approx 0.161$ and $t_2 \approx 0.625$.
   (b) $t_1 = \arcsin(3/5)/4$ and
        $t_2 = \pi/4 - \arcsin(3/5)/4$

51 (a) $\pi/3$
   (b) $2\pi/3$
   (c) $1/2$
   (d) $\pi/3$

53 (b) $t^2 = 2\sin t$ for $t = 0$ and $t \approx 1.40$
   (d) $k \approx 20$

55 $\theta = \arctan(m_1) - \arctan(m_2)$

Section 8.5

1 IV

3 II

5 III

7 I

9 IV

11 $90°$ to $180°$

13 $180°$ to $270°$

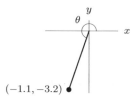

15 $(1, \pi)$

17 $(2, 5\pi/6)$

19 $(-\sqrt{6}/2, -\sqrt{6}/2)$

21 $(-\sqrt{3}, 1)$

23 $x^2 + y^2 = 6x$

25 $y = x^2 - 2x$

27 $r = \sqrt{5}$

29 $r = 1/\sqrt{2\cos\theta\sin\theta}$

31 $H : x = 3, y = 0; r = 3, \theta = 0$
    $M : x = 0, y = 4; r = 4, \theta = \pi/2$

33 $H : x = 3/2, y = 3\sqrt{3}/2; r = 3, \theta = \pi/3$
    $M : x = 0, y = 4; r = 4, \theta = \pi/2$

35 $H : x = -1.5, y = -3\sqrt{3}/2; r = 3,$
$\theta = 4\pi/3$
$M : x = 0, y = 4; r = 4, \theta = \pi/2$

37 $H : x \approx -2.974, y \approx 0.392; r = 3,$
$\theta = 172.5\pi/180$
$M : x = 4, y = 0; r = 4, \theta = 0$

39 $0 \le r \le 2$ and $-\pi/6 \le \theta \le \pi/6$

41 (b)

(c) Cartesian:
$(\sqrt{3}/4, 1/4);$
$(-\sqrt{3}/4, 1/4)$ or polar:
$r = 1/2, \theta = \pi/6$ or $5\pi/6$
(d)

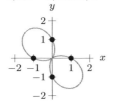

43 Looks the same

45 Rotated by $90°$ clockwise

47 $\pi/4 \le \theta \le 5\pi/4;$
$0 \le \theta \le \pi/4$ and $5\pi/4 \le \theta \le 2\pi$

Section 8.6

1 $5e^{i\pi}$

3 $0e^{i\theta}$, for any θ.

5 $5e^{i4.069}$

7 $-5 + 12i$

9 $-3 - 4i$

11 $-\frac{1}{2} + i\frac{\sqrt{3}}{2}$

13 $\frac{\sqrt{3}}{2} + \frac{i}{2}$

15 $\sqrt{2} + i\sqrt{2}$

17 $\frac{\sqrt{3}}{2} + \frac{i}{2}$

19 $\sqrt{2}/2 + i\sqrt{2}/2$

21 $\sqrt{2}\cos\frac{\pi}{12} + i\sqrt{2}\sin\frac{\pi}{12}$

23 $2.426 + 4.062i$

25 $A_1 = 2 - i$
$A_2 = -2 + 2i$

27 (a) $e^{i\pi/2}$

33 $2e^{\pi i/3} = 1 + 1.732i, 2e^{\pi i} = -2,$
$2e^{5\pi i/3} = 1 - 1.732i$

35 $2^{1/6}e^{\pi i/12} = 1.084 + 0.291i,$
$2^{1/6}e^{3\pi i/4} = -0.794 + 0.794i,$
$2^{1/6}e^{17\pi i/12} = -0.291 - 1.084i$

37 1

39 $(\sqrt{2})/2 + i(\sqrt{2})/2$

Chapter 8 Review

1 $11\pi/6$

3 $-5\pi/4$

5 $270°$

7 $900/\pi = 286.479$

9 -12π

11 (a) II
(b) III
(c) IV
(d) I
(e) III

13 $3\cos 2A$

15 $6.2 \cdot 13\pi/4 \approx 63.303$

17 (a) $C(t)$
(b) $D(t)$
(c) $A(t)$
(d) $B(t)$

19 Mid: $y = 7$; Amp: 1; Per: 2π

21 I

23 I

25 $(1.571, 0)$

27 $(0, 0)$

29 Amplitude: 4
Period: 2π
Phase shift: 0
Horizontal shift: 0

31 Amplitude: 1
Period: π
Phase shift: $-\pi/2$
Horizontal shift: $-\pi/4$ (left)

33 Amp: 30; mid: $y = 60$; per: 4

35 Amp: 40; mid: $y = 50$; per: 16

37 $y = \sin x$ for $f(x), k(x); y = \cos x$ for $g(x), h(x)$

39

41

43 Appear to be same

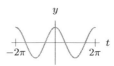

45 (a) OE
(b) OA
(c) DB
(d) OF
(e) OC
(f) GH

47 $-1/2$

49 $\tan\theta = -3/4$

51 1.168

53 (a) $y = (-1/\sqrt{3})x + 2$
(b) $2\sqrt{3}$

55 (a) $z = -2 + 3i$

57 (a) $y = 600 - 300\cos(2\pi x/80)$
(b) $x = 14.5279, 65.4721, 94.5279$

59 $f_1(x) = 6\cos((1/2)(x - 3\pi)) + 2,$
$f_2(x) = -6\cos((1/2)(x - \pi)) + 2,$
$f_3(x) = 6\sin((1/2)(x - 2\pi)) + 2,$
$f_4(x) = -6\sin((1/2)x) + 2;$
answers may vary

61 $f_1(x) = 5\cos((\pi/6)(x + 2)) + 3,$
$f_2(x) = -5\cos((\pi/6)(x - 4)) + 3,$
$f_3(x) = 5\sin((\pi/6)(x - 7)) + 3,$
$f_4(x) = -5\sin((\pi/6)(x - 1)) + 3;$
answers may vary

63 $\pi/6, 7\pi/6$

65 0.616, 2.526, 3.757, 5.668

67 69.115 miles

69 $0.516°$

71 0.1345 radians

73 $f(t) = -900\cos((\pi/4)t) + 2100$

75 $y = 30\sin(10.5t - \pi/2) + 150$

Ch. 8 Understanding

1 False
3 False
5 False
7 True
9 False
11 True
13 False
15 True
17 False
19 True
21 True
23 True
25 False
27 False
29 False
31 False
33 True
35 True
37 True
39 True
41 True
43 False
45 True
47 False
49 True
51 False
53 True
55 False
57 True
59 False
61 True
63 False
65 False
67 False
69 True
71 True
73 False
75 True
77 True
79 True

Section 9.1

1 $\sin t - \cos t$
3 $\cos t + 3\sin t$
5 $2\sin\alpha$
7 $\cos t - \sin t$
9 0
11 $\tan\sqrt{\theta}$
13 $(3/4)\tan(\phi + 1)$
15 $(10/3)\tan\left(\dfrac{2}{k+3}\right)$

---

17 $\cos^2\theta + \sin^2\theta = 1$;
$\cos 2\theta = \cos^2\theta - \sin^2\theta$
$\quad = 2\cos^2\theta - 1 = 1 - 2\sin^2\theta$
27 $\pi/6, 5\pi/6, \pi/2, 3\pi/2$
29 $0, \pi/3, 2\pi/3, \pi, 4\pi/3, 5\pi/3, 2\pi$
31 Not an identity
33 Not an identity
35 Not an identity
37 Identity
39 Identity
41 Identity
43 Not an identity
45 Not an identity
47 (a) $\theta = 60°, 180°,$ and $300°$
   (b) $\theta = \frac{7\pi}{6}, \frac{3\pi}{2}, \frac{11\pi}{6}$
49 (a) $\sqrt{1 - y^2}$
   (b) $y/\left(\sqrt{1 - y^2}\right)$
   (c) $1 - 2y^2$
   (d) y
   (e) $1 - y^2$
51 $\sin 2\theta = \frac{2x}{9}\sqrt{9 - x^2}$
53 (a) $2x\sqrt{1 - x^2}/(2x^2 - 1)$
   (b) $2x/(1 + x^2)$
55 $\sin 4\theta = 4(\sin\theta\cos\theta)(2\cos^2\theta - 1)$
61 $\cos\left(\cos^{-1}\left(\frac{1}{2}\right)\right) = \frac{1}{2}$;
   $\cos^{-1}\left(\cos\left(\frac{5\pi}{3}\right)\right) = \frac{\pi}{3}$

Section 9.2

1 $10\sin(t - 0.644)$
3 $\sqrt{2}\sin(t + 3\pi/4)$
5 $\sin 15° = \cos 75° = (\sqrt{6} - \sqrt{2})/4$
   $\cos 15° = \sin 75° = (\sqrt{6} + \sqrt{2})/4$
7 $\sqrt{6}/2$
9 $(\sqrt{6} + \sqrt{2})/4$
11 (a) 1.585
   (b) 0.053
   (c) 1.216
   (d) -0.069
19 $x = 2\pi/5, 4\pi/5, 6\pi/5,$
   $8\pi/5, \pi/3, \pi, 5\pi/3$

Section 9.3

1 All integral multiples of π

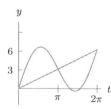

3 (a) $P = 5000 + 300t$
   (b) $P = 3200(1.04)^t$

(c) $P(t) = -900\cos(2\pi t/5) + 2100$
5 (a) $m = 2.5; b = 20; A = 10$
   (b) Roughly in January and December
   (c) Roughly between May and September
7 (a) $y = 1$
   (b) f oscillates faster and faster between -1 and
      1 as t increases.
   (c) ≈ 0.540
   (d) $t_1 = \ln(\pi/2)$
   (e) $t_2 = \ln(3\pi/2)$
11 (a) $h = f(t)$
      $\quad = 25 + 15\sin(\pi t/3) + 10\sin(\pi t/2)$
   (b) $f(t)$ is periodic with period 12

   (c) $h = f(1.2) = 48.776$ m

Chapter 9 Review

1 $1 - \cos t - \sin t$
3 $4\tan t$
5 $\tan t$
7 $\cos t - \sin t$
9 $\sin\theta$
11 $2\cos\phi$
13 Both are right
15 (a) y
   (b) $y/\sqrt{1 + y^2}$
   (c) $\tan^{-1}y$
      Other answers possible
   (d) $2y/(1 + y^2)$
17 $\cos\theta = \sqrt{8835}/94$
   $\tan\theta = 1/\sqrt{8835}$
19 No; the ratio is $3/4$
21 $\theta = \pi/6, 5\pi/6,$ and $3\pi/2$
23 $120/169$
29 $1.231, 5.052, \pi$
31 $\cos 3\theta = 4\cos^3\theta - 3\cos\theta$
33 $\sin(\ln(xy)) \approx 0.515$
35 (a) P_2
   (b) P_2
   (c) P_1
   (d) P_2

Ch. 9 Understanding

1 True
3 True
5 True
7 True
9 True
11 False
13 True

15 True

17 True

19 False

21 True

23 False

25 True

27 False

29 True

Section 10.1

1 $2^{x/(x+1)}$

3 $\sin(4\sqrt{x})$; $\sqrt{\sin 4x}$

5 $w(x) = 4x + 3$

7 $s(0) = 2, s(1) = 5, s(2) = 8$,
$s(3) = 3, s(4) = 1, s(5) = 4$

9 $9x$

11 $27x^2 - 2$

13 $3888x^2 - 1728x + 192$

15 $\ln(x^2 + 4)$

17 $\cos 2x$

19 Area in terms of time

21 Revenue in terms of fertilizer

23 $u(x) = 1/(x-1)$,
$v(x) = x^2$

25 $g(x) = \sqrt{x}, h(x) = 1 + \sqrt{x}$

27 $g(x) = 1/x^2, h(x) = x + 4$

29

x	$f(x)$	$g(x)$	$h(x)$
0	2	1	3
1	1	0	0
2	4	3	2
3	0	4	1
4	3	2	4

31 $f(x) = 2x$

33 $f(x) = \ln x$

35 $(\sqrt{x+h} - \sqrt{x})/h$

37 $(2^{x+h} - 2^x)/h$

39 (a) 4
(b) 1
(c) 4
(d) 0

41 (a)

(b) $0 < x < 2$
(c) $2 < x < 4$

43

45

47 $v(x) = x + 1/x$

49 (a) $u(x) = (1+x)/(2+x)$
(b) $u(x) = x/(1+x)$

51 (a) $v(x) = -x$
(b) $u(x) = \sqrt{1-x}$

53 (a) $v(x) = \sin x$
(b) $u(x) = \sin^2(\sqrt{x})$

55 (a) (i) 3
(ii) 4
(iii) 3
(iv) 4
(b) 5

57 $1/2$

59 All real numbers;
All real numbers greater than or equal to zero

61 $q(x) = 2^x$

63 $g(x) = -1$, provided $x \neq -3$

65 (a) and (e)

Section 10.2

1 Not invertible

3 Not invertible

5 Not invertible

11 Yes, $f(f^{-1}(x)) = f^{-1}(f(x)) = x$

13 Yes, $f(f^{-1}(x)) = f^{-1}(f(x)) = x$

15 $f^{-1} = x - 5$

17 $h^{-1} = x^2$

19 $f^{-1}(x) = (x+7)/3$

21 $l^{-1} = \sqrt{(1-x^2)/2}$

23 $n^{-1} = \sqrt{\sqrt{x} - 1}$

25 $j^{-1}(x) = (x^2 - 1)^2$

27 $k^{-1}(x) = (3 - 2x)^2/(x+1)^2$

29 $h^{-1}(x) = (5 + 4 \cdot 10^x)/(10^x - 1)$

31 $g^{-1}(x) = \arcsin(\ln x / \ln 2)$

33 Time at which pop is P; years

35 (a) $f^{-1}(R) = (1/5)R - 30$

37 (a) $f(3) = 5^3 = 125$; $f^{-1}(\frac{1}{25}) = -2$

(b) $f^{-1}(10) \approx 1.43086$

39 $f^{-1}(3) < f(3) < 0 < f(0) < f^{-1}(0) < 3$

41 $f^{-1}(P) = 50 \ln(P/10)$

43 (a) $f(t) = 800 - 14t$ gals
(b) (i) 800 gals
(ii) 57.143 days
(iii) 28.571 days
(iv) $14t$

45 (a) $f(g(x)) = g(f(x)) = x$; inverses
(b) Line $y = x$

47 (a) $P(t) = 150(1.1)^t$
(b) $P^{-1}(N) = (\log(N) - \log(150))/(\log(1.1))$
(c) 10.3 years

49 (a) $H(t) = 200e^{-1.15129t}$
(b) Dropped 50.021°C in the first 15 mins, 37.532°C in the next 15 mins
(c) $H^{-1}(y) = -\ln(y/200)/1.15129$
(d) About 3 hours and 12 minutes
(e) Brick's temperature approaches room temperature

51 $f^{-1}(x) = \left(0.5x^{-1} - A^{-1}\right)^{-1}$

53 $W(-1/e) = -1, W(0) = 0, W(e) = 1$

55 (a) $f(t) = 7.112(1.08998)^t$
(b) $f^{-1}(P) = (\log(P/7.112))/(\log 1.08998)$
(c) $f(25) = 61.299$
$f^{-1}(25) = 14.590$

57 (a) $C(0) = 99\%$
(b) $C(x) = (99 - x)/(100 - x)$
(c) $C^{-1}(y) = (99 - 100y)/(1 - y)$

Section 10.3

1 (a) $f(x) + g(x) = 3x^2 + x + 1$
(b) $f(x) - g(x) = -3x^2 + x + 1$
(c) $f(x)g(x) = 3x^3 + 3x^2$
(d) $f(x)/g(x) = (x+1)/(3x^2)$

3 (a) $f(x) + g(x) = 2x$
(b) $f(x) - g(x) = 10$
(c) $f(x)g(x) = x^2 - 25$
(d) $f(x)/g(x) = (x+5)/(x-5)$

5 (a) $f(x) + g(x) = x^3 + x^2$
(b) $f(x) - g(x) = x^3 - x^2$
(c) $f(x)g(x) = x^5$
(d) $f(x)/g(x) = x$

7 $f(x) = x$

9 $h(x) = 7x - 5$

11 $k(x) = 1 - 2x + x^2$

13 $f(x) = e^x(2x + 1) = 2xe^x + e^x$

15 $h(x) = 4e^{2x} + 4e^x + 1$

17 $\sin x + x^2$

19 $(\sin x)/x^2$

21 $\sin^2 x$

25 (a) $p(t) = f(t) + g(t)$
   (b) $m(t) = g(t) \cdot h(t)$

27 4550

31

35 $17.50

37

39 (a) Yes

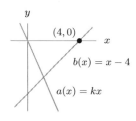

(b) The function has no zeros

41 $H(x) = (e^{-x^2})/(x^4)$,
   $h(x) = (-2x^5 e^{-x^2} - 4x^3 e^{-x^2})/(x^8)$

43 (b) $p(t) = (f_{CA}(t) \cdot g_{CA}(t) + f_{FL}(t) \cdot g_{FL}(t))/(f_{US}(t) \cdot g_{US}(t))$

45 40

47 $g(2000) = 100$, the dollar cost per square foot for building 2000 square feet of office space

49 $g(q) < g(p) < f(p) < f(q)$

51 $j(x) = x/h(x)$

Chapter 10 Review

1 $2^{x^2}; 4^x$

3 $1/(x^2 - 2)$

5 $\sqrt{x^2 + 1}$

7 $1/(x - 2)$

9 (a) Not invertible
   (b) Not invertible
   (c) Invertible

11 $h^{-1}(x) = x/(1 - 2x)$

13 $g^{-1}(x) = \frac{1}{3}\ln(x - 1)$

15 $h^{-1}(x) = \frac{1}{2}(1 - e^x)$

17 $g^{-1}(x) = (3x + 2)/(1 - 2x)$

19 $f^{-1}(x) = (11x - 3)^2/(1 + x)^2$

21 $s^{-1}(x) = 10^{(3/x)-2}$

23 Not invertible

25 Not invertible

27 $r^{-1}(y) = \ln(y + 7)$

31 $2e^x - 1$

33 $4x - 3$

35 $\sqrt{x}e^{2x-1}$

37 (a) $f(2x) = 4x^2 + 2x$
   (b) $g(x^2) = 2x^2 - 3$
   (c) $h(1 - x) = (1 - x)/x$
   (d) $(f(x))^2 = (x^2 + x)^2$
   (e) $g^{-1}(x) = (x + 3)/2$
   (f) $(h(x))^{-1} = (1 - x)/x$
   (g) $f(x)g(x) = (x^2 + x)(2x - 3)$
   (h) $h(f(x)) = (x^2 + x)/(1 - x^2 - x)$

39 $x/(1 + e^{2x})$

41 $3x^2 + x$

43 $2x\sqrt{x + 2}$

45 $3x/2 - 1/2$

47 $x^{3/2}\tan 2x$

49 $\tan((3x - 1)^2/2) - 27x^{3/2}$

51

t	$p(t)$	$q(t)$	$r(t)$
0	4	3	5
1	5	2	1
2	3	4	0
3	2	0	4
4	1	5	2
5	0	1	3

53 $u(x) = \sqrt{x}, v(x) = 3 - 5x$

55 $u(x) = x^2$, $v(x) = \sin x$

57 $u(x) = x^3, v(x) = 2x + 5$

59 $u(x) = 3^x, v(x) = 2x - 1$

63 (a) $r(x) = (x - 1)/(x - 2)$
   (b) $s(x) = x + 1$ and $t(x) = 1/x$
   (c) $p(p(a)) = (2a + 1)/(a + 1)$

65

x	$f(x)$	$g(x)$	$h(x)$
0	9	1	0
1	0	2	1
2	1	0	9

67 (a) $f^{-1}(P) = 2.5P - 50$
   (b)

t	$P = f(t)$
0	20
5	22
10	24
15	26
20	28

P	$t = f^{-1}(P)$
20	0
22	5
24	10
26	15
28	20

69 Velocity for time t; mph

71 $1 - t^2$

73 $x = (\ln 3/\ln 2) - 5$

75 $x = e^{1.8} - 3$

77 $x = (19 - \sqrt{37})/2$

79 (a) $A = \pi r^2$
   (b)

   (c) $r \geq 0$

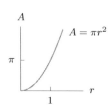

   (d) $f^{-1}(A) = \sqrt{A/\pi}$
   (e)

(f) Yes

81 (a) $f(g(a)) = a$
(b) $g(f(c)) = b$
(c) $f^{-1}(b) - g^{-1}(b) = -c$
(d) $0 < x \leq a$

83 $2\sqrt{x} - 9$

85 $(3 \pm \sqrt{17})/4$

87
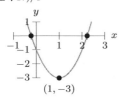
$(1, -3)$

89 (a) Only to $(u(x))^2$.
(b) $u((v(x))^2)$ and $u(w(v(x)))$
(c) (i) $1 + \sin 2x$
(ii) 1
(iii) $\cos(x^2) + \sin(x^2)$

91 $y = f(g(x))$

93 $y = g(f(x - 2))$

95 (a)

(c)

(f) $f(x) = x^2 - 8x + 14$;
$g(x) = -x^2 + 4x + 4$;
$f(x) - g(x) = 2x^2 - 12x + 10$
(g) Yes

97 (a) $f(x) = 2x + 4, g(x) = \frac{1}{3}x - 1$
(b)

99 (a)

(b)

101 False

103 $g(x) = (x + 2)/2 = 0.5x + 1$

105 (a) $f(x) = e^x, g(x) = 6x, G(x) = 3x^2$
(b) $f(x) = \sin x, g(x) = -1/(2\sqrt{x})$,
$G(x) = \sqrt{x}$

107 (a) True
(b) False
(c) False
(d) True

109 Increasing

111 Can't tell

113 (a) $f(8) = 2, f(17) = 2$,
$f(29) = 2, f(99) = 0$
(b) $f(3x) = 0$

(c) No
(d) $f(f(x)) = f(x)$
(e) No

115 $f^{-1}(L) = -\frac{1}{k}\ln(1 - L/L_\infty)$
$f^{-1}(L) = $ Age of fish of length L
Domain: $0 \leq L \leq L_\infty$

Ch. 10 Understanding

1 False
3 True
5 True
7 True
9 True
11 False
13 False
15 True
17 False
19 False
21 False
23 False
25 True
27 True
29 True
31 False
33 True
35 True
37 True

Section 11.1

S1 $6|t|$
S3 $0.16x^2y^4$
S5 $x = 0.585$
S7 False
S9 False

1 Yes; $g(x) = (-1/6)x^9$
3 No
5 Not a power function
7 $y = \frac{48}{30625} \cdot x^{-2}, a = \frac{48}{30625}, p = -2$
9 Even
11 Fractional
13 $y = 3x^{1.058}$
15 $f(x) = (3/2) \cdot x^{-2}$
17 $k = 5; c = 5d^2; c = 125$
19 $k = 3/2; y = (3x)/2; x = 5.33$
21 $f(x) = 3x^2$
23 $j(x) = 2x^3$
25 (a) 0
(b) 0
29 (a) $x^{-3} \to +\infty, x^{1/3} \to 0$
(b) $x^{-3} \to 0, x^{1/3} \to \infty$
31 Formula not unique
33 v, w, f, g
35 $f(x) = -1/(3\sqrt[3]{7}) \cdot x^{-4/3}$
37 (a) $C(x) = kx$
(b) $k = 9.5; C(x) = 9.5x$

(c)

cost ($)
$C(x) = 9.5x$
50
5
x (yards)

(d) $52.25

39 (b) 16 times greater

41 $P = k/\sqrt{\rho}$

43 $h = 192.5/v$; 64.167 mph

45 (a) $d = 1.7, 3.4, 20.4, 102$
$d = 0.34t$
(b) 9.8 mins
(c) $A = 9.1, 36.3, 1307, 32685$
$A = 0.363t^2$
(d) $P = 11.25t^2$
(e) 298 sec, or approx 5 min

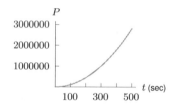

P
3000000
2000000
1000000
100   300   500
t (sec)

47 (a) $t = 4875/w$
(b) $19.5, 16.25, 9.75, 7.5$ mins
(c) t (mins)

20
10
500   1000
w (watts)

(d) 1 min

49 (a) p even: all positive real numbers
p odd: all nonzero real numbers
(b) p even: symmetric about the y-axis
p odd: symmetric about the origin.
(c) p even: $y \to \infty$ as $x \to 0^-$ or $x \to 0^+$
p odd: $y \to -\infty$ as $x \to 0^-$ and $y \to \infty$
as $x \to 0^+$
(d) $y \to 0$ as $x \to \pm\infty$

51 (a) $p < 0, x \neq 0$
(b) $p > 0, y \geq 0$;
$p < 0, y > 0$;
$p > 0, y$ is any real;
$p < 0, y \neq 0$
(c) p even: y-axis symmetry;
p odd: origin symmetry

Section 11.2

1 No

3 Yes, 2

5 No

---

7 Degree: 3; Terms: 3;
$x \to -\infty: y \to -\infty$;
$x \to +\infty: y \to +\infty$

9 Degree: 3; Terms: 4;
$x \to -\infty: y \to +\infty$;
$x \to +\infty: y \to -\infty$

11 $x \approx 0.718, x \approx 1.702$.

15 $y = \frac{1}{2}x - 1$

17 (a) $-3 \leq x \leq -1, -5 \leq y \leq 5$
(b) $-3 \leq x \leq 4, -35 \leq y \leq 15$
(c) $1.25 \leq x \leq 2.35, -0 \leq y \leq 6$
(d) $-8 \leq x \leq 8, -50 \leq y \leq 2000$

19 $-1.1 \leq x \leq -0.9, -0.121 \leq y \leq 0.081$

21 $-20 \leq x \leq 20, -7600 \leq y \leq 8400$

23 $-1.764 < x < 0.875$, or $x > 3.889$

25 (a)

y
10
8
6
4
2
-2
2   4   6   8
t

(b) 100 people
(c) July of 1897
(d) 1010; February of 1893
(e) -115.7; not reasonable

27 (a)

Volume
1
0.8
0.6
0.4
0.2
$V(t)$
1   2   3   4   5
t (sec)

(b) $V \approx .886$ at $t \approx 3.195$
(c) $(0, 0)$ and $(5, 0)$;
Lungs empty at beginning and end

29 Yes

31 (a) False
(b) False
(c) False
(d) True

33 (a) $p(0.5) \approx 0.65625$; 2 dec pl
(b) $p(1) = 0, f(1) = 0.5$; poor approx
(c)

y
6
4
2
-1   1
x

Section 11.3

1 $0, -4, -3$

3 $-3, 2, -7$

5 $h(x) = x(x + 2)^2(x - 3)$

7 $f(x) = (x + 2)(x - 2)^3$

9 $y = (-1/8)(x + 2)(x - 2)^2(x - 5)$;
$y = (-1/20)(x + 2)(x - 2)(x - 5)^2$

11

500
-5   4 5

13 (a) $f(x) = (x + 5)(x + 1)(2x - 1)(x - 1)$
(b) $-7 \leq x \leq 2, -150 \leq y \leq 10$

15 C

17 $f(x) = 1$

19 $f(x) = -\frac{1}{2}(x + 3)(x - 1)(x - 4)$

21 $p(x) = x^2 + 2x - 3$

23 $f(x) = -(x + 1)(x - 1)^2$

25 $f(x) = kx^3(x + 1)(x - 2)$ for $k > 0$

27 $f(x) = 3x(x + 1)(x - 1)^2$

29 $h(x) = (x + 2)(x + 1)^2(x - 1)$

31 $g(x) = -\frac{1}{3}(x^2)(x + 2)(x - 2)$

33 $x = \pm\frac{1}{2}$

35 $6, 2, 3$

37 None

39 $r = -1, s = 2, g(x) = k(x + 5)^2$ or
$r = -5, s = 2, g(x) = k(x + 5)(x + 1)$,
$k \neq 0$

41 (a) $V(x) = x(6 - 2x)(8 - 2x)$
(b) $0 < x < 3$
(c)

y
25
20
15
10
5
$V(x) = x(6 - 2x)(8 - 2x)$
1   2   3
x

(d) ≈ 24.26 in^3

43 7.83 by 5.33 by 1.585 inches

45 $x \geq c$ and $a \leq x \leq b$

47 (a) $f(x) = \frac{2}{15}(x + 2)(x - 3)(x - 5)$
(b) $f(x) = -\frac{2}{75}(x + 2)(x - 3)(x - 5)^2$
(c) $f(x) = \frac{1}{15}(x + 2)^2(x - 3)(x - 5)$

Section 11.4

S1 $(6y^2 + 7)/y^3$

S3 $x^3/2$

S5 $(-18x^2 + 18x + 41)/((x - 2)^2(x + 1))$

S7 $1/2$

S9 $1/(x - 1)$

1 Rational; $(x + 2)/(x^2 - 1)$

3 Rational; $(x^3 + 2)/(2x)$

5 Not rational

7 Not rational

9 ∞

11 0

13 $y = 1$

15 As $x \to \pm\infty, f(x) \to 1, g(x) \to x$, and
$h(x) \to 0$

19 (a)

(c) Approaches 1
(d) About 3.73 weeks
21 (a) $f(x) = (3 + x)/(12 + x)$
   (b)   (i) 28%
         (ii) 25%
         (iii) $\approx 18.2\%$
         (iv) 6
         (v) -3
   (c)

   (d)

23 2011; Never
25 (a) $f(x) = x/(x + 5)$
   (b) $f(7) = 7/12 \approx 58.333\%$
   (c) $x = 0$
   (d) $y = 1$
27 (a) $C(n_0)/n_0$
   (b) Slope is average cost for n_0 units
29 (a) $C(x) = 30000 + 3x$
   (b) $a(x) = 3 + 30000/x$
   (c)

   (f) $a^{-1}(y) = 30000/(y - 3)$
   (g) 15,000

Section 11.5

1 Zeros: $x = 4$;
   Asymptote: $x = \pm 3$;
   $y \to 0$ as $x \to \pm\infty$

3 Zero: $x = -3$;
   Asymptote: $x = -5$;
   $y \to 1$ as $x \to \pm\infty$

$y = \frac{x+3}{x+5}$

5 x-int: $x = \pm 2$
   y-int: None
   Horiz asy: $y = 0$
   Vert asy: $x = 0, x = -4$
7 x-int: $x = 2$
   y-int: $y = 1/2$
   Horiz asy: $y = 1$
   Vert asy: $x = 4$
9 (c) Horizontal: $y = 2$
      Vertical: $x = -4$

$G(x) = \frac{2x}{x+4}$

11

$y = 2 + 1/x$

13 (a) $-\infty$
   (b) $+\infty$
15 (a) (iii)
   (b) (i)
   (c) (ii)
   (d) (iv)
   (e) (vi)
   (f) (v)
17 (a) 0, 0
   (b) $\lim_{x \to -2+} f(x) = \infty$;
       $\lim_{x \to -2-} f(x) = \infty$
19 (a) Small
   (b) Large
   (c) Undefined
   (d) Positive
   (e) Negative
21 (a)

(b)

23 (a) $y = -1/(x + 2)$
   (b) $y = -1/(x + 2)$
   (c) $(0, -1/2)$
25 $p = 1, (0, 11/3), (11/4, 0)$
    $x = 3, y = 4$

27 $p = 1, (0, 3), (3/2, 0)$
    $x = 1, y = 2$

29 (a) $y = 1/x$
   (b) $y = x/(2x - 4)$
31 (a) $1/x$
   (b) $y = (1/x) + 2$
33 $y = -(x + 1)/(x - 2)$
35 $y = -(x - 3)(x + 2)/((x + 1)(x - 2))$
37 $y = (x - 2)/((x + 1)(x - 1))$
39 $y = x - 9; (2, -7)$
41 $h(x) = (x^4 - 2x^3)/(x - 2)$
43 $g(x) = (x - 5)/((x + 2)(x - 3))$

Section 11.6

1 $p(x) = 25^x$

3 Neither

5 $r(x) = 2(\frac{1}{9})^x$

7 A - (i)
B - (iv)
C - (ii)
D - (iii)

11 $y = 6x^{35}$

13 $y = 50x^{1.1}$

15 $y = e^{-x}$

17 (a) $f(x) = 720x - 702$
(b) $f(x) = 2(9)^x$
(c) $f(x) = 18x^4$

19 (a) $f(x) = y = \frac{63}{4}x + \frac{33}{2}$
(b) $f(x) = 3 \cdot 4^x$
(c) $f(x) = \frac{3}{4}x^6$

21 A: $kx^{5/7}$; B: $kx^{9/16}$;
C: $kx^{3/8}$; D: $kx^{3/11}$

23 $m = 2, t = 4, k = \frac{1}{4}$

25 $y \to 0$ as $x \to \pm\infty$

27 $y \to 0$ as $t \to \infty$
$y \to 7/9$ as $t \to -\infty$

29 $y \to \infty$ as $x \to \infty$
$y \to -\infty$ as $x \to -\infty$

31 $y \to 0$ as $x \to \infty$

33 $y \to \infty$ as $x \to \infty$
$y \to -\infty$ as $x \to -\infty$

35 $y \to \infty$ as $x \to \infty$
$y \to 0$ as $x \to \infty$

37 $f(x) = 2\sin(\frac{\pi}{2}x) + 4$ (trigonometric);
$g(x) = -\frac{5}{2}x^3$ (power function);
$h(x) = \frac{1}{3}(\frac{1}{2})^x$ (exponential)

39 (a) $p_5(r) = 1000[(1 + r)^5 + (1 + r)^4 + (1 + r)^3 + (1 + r)^2 + (1 + r) + 1]$;
$p_{10}(r) = 1000[(1 + r)^{10} + (1 + r)^9 + (1 + r)^8 + (1 + r)^7 + (1 + r)^6 + (1 + r)^5 + (1 + r)^4 + (1 + r)^3 + (1 + r)^2 + (1 + r) + 1]$
(b) 20.279%

Section 11.7

1 $f(x) = x^{\ln c / \ln 2}$

3 $g(x) = 2x^{1.2}$

5 (a) $f(x) = 201.353x^{2.111}$
(b) $f(20) = 112,313.62$ gm
(c) $x = 18.930$ cm

7 $y = x^{3/2}$

9 $y = (3/2)x$

11 $y = e^{0.4x}$

13 (a) $y = -83.039 + 61.514x$; superb fit
(b) Good only for close values

15 $a \approx 3.49$

17 (b) $R(p) = -0.0565p^2 + 72.9981p + 4749.85$
(c) $p = \$646, R = \$28,349$

19 (a) $C(t) = 841.368(1.333)^t$
(b) 33.3% per year
(c) Slower growth; concave down

21 (a)
Population (thousands)

(b) $P(t) = 56.108(1.031)^t$, answers may vary
(c) 56.108 is 1650 population, 1.031 means 3.1% annual growth
(d) $P(100) = 1194.308$, slightly higher
(e) $P(150) = 5510.118$, higher

23 (a) $N = 1148.55e^{0.3617t}$

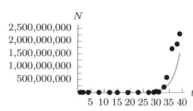

(b) About 1.92 years

25 (a) $y = 0.310t^2 - 12.177t + 144.517$
(b) $y = 3.01t^2 - 348.43t + 10,955.75$

27 (b) Points lie on a line

29 (a) Quadratic
(b) $y = -34.136x^2 + 3497.733x - 39,949.714$; answers may vary
(c) $\$42,734$; answers may vary
(d) Age 10, $-\$8386$, not reasonable; answers may vary

31 (a) $t = 8966.1H^{-2.3}$

(b) $r = 0.0124H - 0.1248$

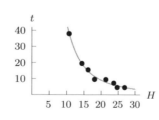

(c) $H = 0°C$; $H = 10.1°C$; model (b)

33 Yes; $k \approx 0.2$; $P = 0.2D^{3/2}$

Chapter 11 Review

1 Yes; $k = 1/6$ and $p = -7$

3 No

5 No

7 Yes; $y = x^2$

9 Even

11 Odd

13 Odd

15 $k = 2\sqrt[3]{7}, p = 11/15$

17 4th degree

19 $y \to \infty$; like $4x^4$

21 $y \to \infty$; like $2x^9$

23 $x = (3 \pm \sqrt{33})/4$

25 Not rational

27 $y = 4/e^{-x}$

29 (a) 2
(b) 5/6

31 Not a power function

33 Graph (i): J;
Graph (ii): L;
Graph (iii): O;
Graph (iv): H

35 $y = -\frac{3}{2}(x + 4)(x + 2)(x - 2)$

37 $y = \frac{1}{2}(x + \frac{1}{2})(x - 3)(x - 4)$

39 $y = -x(x + 3)(x - 2)$

41 $y = (x + 3)x^2$

43 $y = (x + 3)(x + 2)(x + 1) + 4$

45 (a) $y = 1/(x - 2)^2 - 1$
(b) $y = (-x^2 + 4x - 3)/(x^2 - 4x + 4)$
(c) $(0, -3/4), (1, 0)$ and $(3, 0)$

47 (a) $y = -1/(x - 3)^2$
(b) $y = -1/(x^2 - 6x + 9)$
(c) $(0, -1/9)$

49 (a) $-2, -3$; None
(b) $-2, -3$; No; $r(x) \to 1$ as $x \to \pm\infty$
(c) No; Yes at $x = -2$ and $x = 3$;
$s(x) \to 1$ as $x \to \pm\infty$

51 (a) False
(b) False
(c) True
(d) False

53 $f(x) = (x + 3)(x - 2)/((x + 5)(x - 7))$

55 $f(x) = (x + 1)/(x - 1)$

57 $f(x) = (-1/5)(x + 3)(x - 2)(x - 5)$

59 $h(x) = (1/5)(x + 5)(x + 1)(x - 4) + 7$

61 $d = 0.1x$; 32.5 miles

63 (a) 20 lbs; 1620 lbs
(b) 3/10

65 (a) 500 people
(b) May of 1908
(c) 790; February of 1907

67 (b) $k \approx 0.0087$
(c) Yes

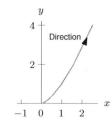

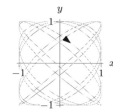

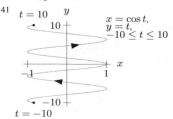

69 (c)

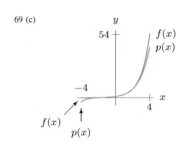

Ch. 11 Understanding

1 False
3 True
5 True
7 False
9 True
11 True
13 False
15 True
17 False
19 False
21 True
23 False
25 True
27 True
29 True
31 True
33 True
35 False
37 False
39 True
41 True
43 False
45 False
47 False

Ch. 11 Skills: Fractions

1 $41/35$
3 $(3 - 4x)/6x$
5 $-2(1 - 2y)/yz$
7 $(2 - 3x)/x^2$
9 $1/18$
11 $x/2$
13 $(4y^3z - 3wx)/(x^2y^4)$
15 $(8(y + 4))/(y - 4)$
17 $(-27x + 44)/((x + 1)(3x - 4))$
19 $(x + 20)/(x^2 - 16)$
21 $1/2r$
23 $(x - 1)/(\sqrt{x})^3 = x\sqrt{x} - \sqrt{x}/x^2$
25 $(4x + 1)/(b - a)$
27 $(r_2r_3 + r_1r_3 + r_1r_2)/(r_1r_2r_3)$
29 $(2a + 3)/((a + 3)(a - 3))$

31 $(-2x - h)/\left(x^2(x + h)^2\right)$
33 $-2x - h$
35 $1 - (1/a)$
37 $x^2y/(2x + 1)$
39 $(2x - 4x^4)/(x^3 + 1)^3$
41 $13/x^2 + 1/(2x^3)$
43 $(2/l^2) + (1/l^3) - 4/(3l^4)$
45 $1/6 - 1/(4x)$
47 $1 - 7/(x + 5)$
49 $1 + 1/R$
51 $1 + \sin x/\cos x$
53 False
55 False
57 True

Section 12.1

1 Scalar
3 Vector
5 Scalar
7 Vector
9

11

13

15 $\vec{p} = 2\vec{w}$
$\vec{q} = -\vec{u}$
$\vec{r} = \vec{u} + \vec{w}$
$\vec{s} = 2\vec{w} - \vec{u}$
$\vec{t} = \vec{u} - \vec{w}$

17 (a) 1.710 miles
(b) 5.848 miles
19 5.116 miles; 14.639° east of north
21 14,705 meters;
angle of 17.819° from horizontal
23 (a) 14.3373
(b) Veers right
(c) Not possible

Section 12.2

1 $-3\vec{i} - 4\vec{j}$
3 $\vec{w} \approx -0.725\vec{i} - 0.95\vec{j}$
5 $\vec{i} + 3\vec{j}$
7 $0.3\vec{i} - 1.8\vec{j} + 0.03\vec{k}$
9 $\sqrt{11} \approx 3.317$
11 7.649
13 $-5\vec{i} + 10\vec{j}$ knots
15 45° or $\pi/4$
17 90° or $\pi/2$
19 $-140.847\vec{i} + 140.847\vec{j} + 18\vec{k}$
21 $21\vec{j} + 35\vec{k}$
23 (a) 50 km/hr
(b) Horizontal: 43.301; vertical: 25
25 (a) $3.536(\vec{i} + \vec{j})$.
(b) $3.536\vec{i} + 4.736\vec{j}$
27 (a) (i) $\vec{m} = 3\vec{j}, \vec{h} = 2\vec{j}$

(i)

(ii) $\vec{m} = 3\vec{j}, \vec{h} = 2\vec{i}$

(ii)

(iii) $\vec{m} = 3\vec{j}, \vec{h} = \vec{i} + \sqrt{3}\vec{j}$

(iii)

(iv) $\vec{m} = -3\vec{j}, \vec{h} = \sqrt{2}\vec{i} + \sqrt{2}\vec{j}$

(iv)

(b) $3\vec{j} - 2\vec{i}$

(c) $\sqrt{2}\vec{i} + (\sqrt{2}-3)\vec{j}$

$$\vec{h} = \sqrt{2}\vec{i} + \sqrt{2}\vec{j}$$
$$\vec{S}$$
$$\vec{m} = -3\vec{i}$$

29 $\vec{k}$

31 $\vec{i} + \vec{k}$

Section 12.3

1 $(2, 2, 4, 6, 10, 16)$

3 $(-4, -5, -5, -5, -4, -2)$

5 $(5, 6, 7, 8, 9, 10)$

7 $(13/6, 5/2, 10/3, 25/6, 11/2, 22/3)$

9 $(3.63, 1.44, 6.52, 1.43, 1.20, 0.74)$

11 $(3.467, 1.277, 6.357, 1.267, 1.037, 0.577)$

13 $(79.000, 79.333, 89.000, 68.333, 89.333)$

15 $3.378°$ north of east

17 (a) $\vec{v} = 4.330\vec{i} + 2.500\vec{j}$
    For the second leg of his journey, $\vec{w} = x\vec{i}$

$\vec{w}$ finish
start $\vec{v}$ $30°$ $10°$

(b) $x = 9.848$

(c) 14.397

19 (a) $\vec{F}_{\text{net}} = (8, 7)$

(b) $\vec{F}_4 = (-8, -7)$

21 $\vec{q}_a = 1.065\vec{i} + 1.966\vec{j}$; $(1.065, 1.966)$
    $\vec{q}_b = 2.703\vec{i} + 3.113\vec{j}$; $(2.703, 3.113)$
    $\vec{q}_c = 2.129\vec{i} + 3.933\vec{j}$; $(2.129, 3.933)$
    $\vec{q}_d = 0.491\vec{i} + 2.785\vec{j}$; $(0.491, 2.785)$

Section 12.4

1 -7

3 -38

5 14

7 -2

9 $28\vec{j} + 14\vec{k}$

11 238

13 $108.435°$

15 2100 ft-lbs

17 1.911 radians $(109.471°)$

19 For both, max $= 11$, min $= 3$

21 No

25 (a) $\vec{a} = (3, 2, 4)$; $\vec{c} = (c_b, c_e, c_m)$
    $3c_b + c_e + 4c_m = 40$,   or $\vec{a} \cdot \vec{c} = 40$

(b) The "freshness-adjusted" cost is cheaper at Beta

27 $43.297°$

29 (a) Width

(b) Height

(c) Perimeter

Section 12.5

1 (a) $\begin{pmatrix} 15 & 35 \\ 10 & -5 \end{pmatrix}$

(b) $\begin{pmatrix} -2 & 10 \\ 0 & -16 \end{pmatrix}$

(c) $\begin{pmatrix} 4 & 2 \\ 2 & 7 \end{pmatrix}$

(d) $\begin{pmatrix} -8 & -26 \\ -6 & 11 \end{pmatrix}$

(e) $\begin{pmatrix} 13 & 45 \\ 10 & -21 \end{pmatrix}$

(f) $\begin{pmatrix} k & -5k \\ 0 & 8k \end{pmatrix}$

3 (a) $\begin{pmatrix} 12 & 8 & 20 & 4 \\ 16 & 24 & 28 & 12 \\ 4 & 36 & 20 & 32 \\ 0 & -8 & 16 & 24 \end{pmatrix}$

(b) $\begin{pmatrix} -2 & -12 & -8 & -4 \\ -6 & -10 & 2 & -14 \\ -18 & -8 & -14 & -6 \\ -4 & -16 & -8 & -10 \end{pmatrix}$

(c) $\begin{pmatrix} 2 & -4 & 1 & -1 \\ 1 & 1 & 8 & -4 \\ -8 & 5 & -2 & 5 \\ -2 & -10 & 0 & 1 \end{pmatrix}$

(d) $\begin{pmatrix} 6 & -12 & 3 & -3 \\ 3 & 3 & 24 & -12 \\ -24 & 15 & -6 & 15 \\ -6 & -30 & 0 & 3 \end{pmatrix}$

(e) $\begin{pmatrix} 4 & 8 & 9 & 3 \\ 7 & 11 & 6 & 10 \\ 10 & 13 & 12 & 11 \\ 2 & 6 & 8 & 11 \end{pmatrix}$

(f) $\begin{pmatrix} 10 & -4 & 12 & 0 \\ 10 & 14 & 30 & -2 \\ -14 & 28 & 6 & 26 \\ -4 & -24 & 8 & 14 \end{pmatrix}$

5 (a) $(51, 15, 38)$

(b) $(-8, -11, 33)$

(c) $(70, 20, 22)$

(d) $(11, -6, 17)$

(e) 681

(f) $\begin{pmatrix} 24 & 60 & 84 \\ 48 & -72 & 36 \\ 192 & -60 & 0 \end{pmatrix}$

7 (a) Defined

(b) Not defined

(c) Not defined

(d) Not defined

(e) Defined

(f) Not defined

9 (a) $\mathbf{T} = \begin{pmatrix} 0.90 & 0 & 0 \\ 0.10 & 0.50 & 0.02 \\ 0 & 0.50 & 0.98 \end{pmatrix}$

(b) $\vec{p_1} = (1.8, 0.2, 0)$,
    $\vec{p_2} = (1.62, 0.28, 0.1)$,
    $\vec{p_3} = (1.458, 0.304, 0.238)$

11 (a) $\mathbf{T} = \begin{pmatrix} 0.97 & 0.05 \\ 0.03 & 0.95 \end{pmatrix}$

(b) $\vec{p}\ 2006 = (214, 386)$,
    $\vec{p}\ 2007 = (226.88, 373.12)$.

13 (a) $\vec{v} = \begin{pmatrix} 11 \\ 19 \end{pmatrix}$

(b) $\vec{v} = \begin{pmatrix} 5 \\ 11 \end{pmatrix}$

(c) $\vec{v} = \begin{pmatrix} 2a + b \\ 3a + 2b \end{pmatrix}$

15 (a) $\lambda_2 = -1$

(b) $\lambda_3 = -1$

(c) $\mathbf{A}\vec{v} = \lambda\vec{v}$, and $\mathbf{A}\vec{v}$ is parallel to $\vec{v}$

17 (a) $\begin{pmatrix} 3 & 5 \\ 2 & 4 \end{pmatrix} \begin{pmatrix} a \\ b \end{pmatrix} = a\begin{pmatrix} 3 \\ 2 \end{pmatrix} + b\begin{pmatrix} 5 \\ 4 \end{pmatrix}$

(b) $\vec{v} = \begin{pmatrix} -8.5 \\ 5.5 \end{pmatrix}$

(c) $\vec{v} = -8.5\vec{c_1} + 5.5\vec{c_2}$

Chapter 12 Review

1 $(3, 3, 6)$

3 $(-3, -2, 9)$

5 $(7, 8, -21)$

7 $(4, -2, 18)$

9 $-4.5\vec{i} + 8\vec{j} + 0.5\vec{k}$

11 13

13 6

15 $6\vec{i} + 6\vec{j} + 6\vec{k}$

17 $\vec{a} = \vec{b} = \vec{c} = 3\vec{k}$
    $\vec{d} = 2\vec{i} + 3\vec{k}$
    $\vec{e} = \vec{j}$
    $\vec{f} = -2\vec{i}$

19 $\|\vec{u}\| = \sqrt{6}$
    $\|\vec{v}\| = \sqrt{5}$

21 (a) Yes

(b) No

23 (a) $\vec{L} = (11, 7, 11, 7, 13)$

(b) $\vec{F} = (32, 36, 21, 8, 4)$,
    $\vec{G} = (3, 3, 2, 0, 7)$

25 $F = g \sin\theta$

29 $0.4v\vec{i} + 0.693v\vec{j}$

31 (a) $\overrightarrow{AB} = 2\vec{i} - 2\vec{j} - 7\vec{k}$
    $\overrightarrow{AC} = -2\vec{i} + 2\vec{j} - 7\vec{k}$

(b) $\theta = 44.003°$

35 $\overrightarrow{AB} = -\vec{u}$; $\overrightarrow{BC} = 3\vec{v}$;
    $\overrightarrow{AC} = \overrightarrow{AB} + \overrightarrow{BC} = -\vec{u} + 3\vec{v}$; $\overrightarrow{AD} = 3\vec{v}$

594

37 $3\vec{n} - 3\vec{m}$;
$3\vec{m} + \vec{n}$;
$4\vec{m} - \vec{n}$;
$\vec{m} - 2\vec{n}$

Ch. 12 Understanding

1 False

3 False

5 False

7 False

9 True

11 True

13 False

15 True

17 True

19 False

21 True

23 False

25 True

Section 15.1

1 Not arithmetic

3 Arithmetic

5 Arithmetic, $a_n = 3 + 3n$

7 Arithmetic, $a_n = -0.9 - 0.1n$

9 Not geometric

11 Geometric

13 Not geometric

15 Geometric; $4(1/2)^{n-1}$

17 Geometric; $1/(1.2)^{n-1}$

19 $1, 5/4, 7/5, 3/2$; not geometric

21 $-1, 1, -1, 1$; geometric

23 $1, 1/\sqrt{2}, 1/\sqrt{3}, 1/2$; not geometric

25 $n \geq 101$

27 $10.8, 64.8, 4.8 + 1.2n$

29 $7.9, 57.4, 2.4 + 1.1n$

31 $1.661, 7(0.75)^{n-1}$

33 $486, 2 \cdot 3^{n-1}$

35 (a) $646.7, 650.580, 654.484, 658.411$
   (b) $367.7, 396.748, 428.091, 461.911$
   (c) 2012

37 (a) $17.960, 18.314, 18.675$
   (b) $17.960(1.0197)^n$
   (c) 36.5 years

39 Arithmetic, $d > 0$

41 Arithmetic, $d < 0$

43 $2, 7, 12, 17$; $a_n = -3 + 5n$

45 $3, 7, 15, 31$;
   $a_n = 2^{n-1} \cdot 3 + 2^{n-2} + 2^{n-3} + \cdots + 1$

47 (a) $150, 187.5, 199.219, 199.997, 200, 200$; converging

49 (a) \$256
   (b) $d_n = 4^n$

Section 15.2

1 Not arithmetic

3 Not arithmetic

5 $(-1)^2 + 0^2 + 1^2 + 2^2 + 3^2 + 4^2 + 5^2$

7 $1 + 3 + 5 + 7 + 9 + 11$

9 $(-1)^2 + (-1)^3 + (-1)^4 + \cdots + (-1)^{10}$

11 $\sum_{n=1}^{7} 3n$

13 $\sum_{n=1}^{8} (1/2)n$

15 (a) $\sum_{i=1}^{10} 2i$
   (b) 110

17 $a_1 = 3, d = 4$

19 $a_1 = 2, d = 9$

21 500,500

23 2625

25 -132

27 -561

29 -111.3

31 $150; 2325$

33 (a) (i) $226.6, 248.7, 281.4$; population at census time
   (ii) $28.6, 22.1, 32.7$; change in population over the decade.
   (iii) 3.27; average yearly population growth over the decade.

35 612

37 9

39 (a) 256 feet, 400 feet, 576 feet
   (b) 744 feet, 600 feet, 424 feet

41 7.906 sec

43 Last row: 106
   Auditorium: 1360

45 (a) 297

Section 15.3

1 1,572,768

3 5.997

5 781.248

7 7.199

9 Yes, $a = 1$, ratio $= -1/2$

11 Yes, $a = 5$, ratio $= -2$

13 $\sum_{n=1}^{6} (-1)^{n+1}(3^n)$

15 $\sum_{n=0}^{5} (-1)^n 32(\frac{1}{2})^n$

17 189/32

19 1 if N is even and 0 is N is odd.

21 (a) $\sum_{n=1}^{25} 81(1.012)^{n-1}$
   (b) 2345.291 bn barrels

23 (a) \$64,735.69
   (b) \$65,358.46

25 (a) Doubles
   (b) Less than doubles
   (c) More than doubles

27 (a) \$59,159.48
   (b) \$5927.45

Section 15.4

1 Yes, $a = 1$, ratio $= -x$

3 No. Ratio between successive terms is not constant

5 Yes, $a = e^x$, ratio $= e^x$

7 Yes, $a = 1$, ratio $= \sqrt{2}$

9 $1/(1 + x), |x| < 1$

11 10

13 1/54

15 4

17 $x^2/(1 - x^2)$

19 235/999

21 11/90

23 3781/4950

25 (a) $P_n = 250(0.04) + 250(0.04)^2 + \cdots + 250(0.04)^{n-1}$
   (b) $P_n = 10(1 - (0.04)^{n-1})/(1 - 0.04)$
   (c) $P_n = 10.417$

27 22.3 million dollars

29 \$1081.11

Chapter 15 Review

1 $603; 59$

3 (a) $1 + 5 + 9 + 13 + 17$
   (b) 45

5 No

7 $1/(1 - 2z), |z| < 1/2$

9 315

11 $n(n + 1)/2$

13 24 cans at bottom
   3 less per row
   8 rows

15 435

17 \$25,503.33

19 (a) $300, 350, 400, 450, 500, 550, 600$.
   (b) 950 yards
   (c) 31st day and after

21 (a) $h_n = 10(3/4)^n$
   (b) $D_1 = 10$ feet
   $D_2 = h_0 + 2h_1 = 25$ feet
   $D_3 = h_0 + 2h_1 + 2h_2 = 36.25$ feet
   $D_4 = h_0 + 2h_1 + 2h_2 + 2h_3 \approx 44.688$ feet
   (c) $D_n = 10 + 60\left(1 - (3/4)^{n-1}\right)$

23 (a) \$1250
   (b) 12.50

Ch. 15 Understanding

1 True

3 True

5 True

7 True

9 True

11 False

13 True

15 False

17 False

19 False

21 True

23 False

25 False

27 True

29 False

31 False

33 False

Section 16.1

1 $x = 1 + 2t, y = 3 + t, 0 \le t \le 1$

3 $x = t, y = t, 0 \le t \le 1, x = t, y = 2 - t,$ for $1 \le t \le 2.$

5 True

7 False

9 $y = 11 - 2x$

11 $y = 2x^2 + 1$

13 $y = (x + 4)^2$

15 $y = x^{3/2}$

17 $y = (2/3) \ln x, x > 0$

19 $(x^2/4) + (y^2/9) = 1$

21 Lines from $(0, 0)$ to $(2, 0)$ to $(2, 1)$ to $(0, 1)$ to $(0, 0)$

23 Lines from $(2, 0)$ to $(1.5, 1)$ to $(0.5, -1)$ to $(0, 0)$ to $(0.5, 1)$ to $(1.5, -1)$ to $(2, 0)$

25 Clockwise for all t.

27 Clockwise: $t < 0,$ Counter-clockwise: $t > 0.$

31 (a) $x = t, y = t^2$
      $x = t + 1, y = (t + 1)^2$
   (b) $x = t, y = (t + 2)^2 + 1$
      $x = t + 1, y = (t + 3)^2 + 1$

33

35

37 (a) Line $y = x$
   (b) Circle, with starting point $(1, 0)$ and period 2π
   (c) Ellipse, with starting point $(1, 0)$ and period 2π

39 $x = t, y = -4t + 7$

41

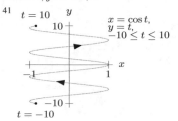

43 (a) $x = t, y = -16t^2 + 48t + 6$
   (b)

   (c) 6 feet
   (d) 3 seconds
   (e) 42 feet

Section 16.2

1 Explicit

3 Implicit

5 Implicit

7 $(0, 0)$; $\sqrt{10/3}$

9 $(4, 4)$; 2

11 $x = 4 \cos t, y = -4 \sin t, 0 \le t \le 2\pi$

13 $x = 5 \sin t, y = -5 \cos t, 0 \le t \le 2\pi$

15 $x = 3 + 5 \cos t, y = 4 + 5 \sin t, 0 \le t \le 2\pi$

17 $x = -2 - \sqrt{5} \sin t, y = 1 + \sqrt{5} \cos t, 0 \le t \le 2\pi$

19 True

21 (a) Center $(2, -4)$, radius $\sqrt{20}$
   (b) Center $(-1, 2)$, radius $\sqrt{11}$

23 Parabola:
   $y = (x - 2)^2, 1 \le x \le 3$

25 $x = 4(y - 3)^2, 2 \le y \le 4.$

27 Implicit: $xy = 1, x > 0$
   Explicit: $y = 1/x, x > 0$
   Parametric: $x = t, y = 1/t, t > 0$

29 Explicit: $y = \sqrt{4 - x^2}$
   Implicit: $y^2 = 4 - x^2$ or $x^2 + y^2 = 4, y > 0$
   Parametric: $x = 4 \cos t, y = 4 \sin t,$ with $0 \le t \le \pi$

31 (a) $x = t, y = 1$
   (b) $x = t + \cos t, y = 1 - \sin t$